# Catalog

## OF THE

## Schmulowitz Collection
## of Wit and Humor

## (SCOWAH)

## San Francisco Public Library

San Francisco

June 1962

# INTRODUCTION

Mᴏʀᴇ ᴛʜᴀɴ ᴀɴʏ other time in history, this age of ours is fraught with tensions and threats of peril, but there is still one human characteristic that continues to stabilize our emotions and lessen our fears. That precious quality is our sense of humor, and one could cite many instances in our history where the humorous comment has cut deep into a serious moment and brought some welcome release. Once, during the dark days of the Civil War, Secretary of War Stanton called Lincoln "a damned fool" in the presence of Mr. Lovejoy of Illinois. When the enraged Lovejoy reported this to the President, Lincoln said, "Did Stanton call me a damn fool?" and was thoughful for a moment. "Well, I guess I had better step over and see Stanton about this. Stanton is usually right." In this way, Lincoln eased a delicate situation. It was a good example of what Lin Yutang has said about men and ideas, stating that only he who handles his ideas lightly is master of his ideas, and only he who is master of ideas is not enslaved by them.

We do not mean to imply that we should make humor a serious subject, but we do believe it to be a vital area of Literature that deserves recognition and preservation. The founder of this collection on Wit and Humor—Mr. Nat Schmulowitz, a prominent San Francisco attorney—has had this idea for a long time. In building the collection, which is called SCOWAH for purposes of brief identification, Mr. Schmulowitz has shown himself to be a collector of catholic tastes. Not content with the finding of such rarities as the Joe Miller books and other publications of the eighteenth century, he has also assembled a very sound, practical collection of books, pamphlets, and magazines published in almost every language over the past three hundred and fifty years.

The donor made his initial contribution in 1947 with 93 volumes. During the interim he has assiduously built the collection until today it consists of more than 11,200 volumes, published in a variety of more than 35 languages and dialects. The accompanying catalog is a record of the collection as of October 10, 1961. The collection is continuing to grow and it is expected that subsequent catalogs will be published in due course.

For the past several years, the donor has also edited and published an "American Journal of World's Folklore," under the title ANEC-DOTA SCOWAH, which have included: ANECDOTA SCOWAH Number One, Epitaphia, and a Precursory Apologia with an Apologue, by Nat Schmulowitz; ANECDOTA SCOWAH Number Two, The Legend of Joe Miller, by Evan Esar, with a Prefatory Fragment by Nat Schmulowitz; ANECDOTA SCOWAH Number Three, The Ancient Greeks and Joe Miller, by Albert Rapp, and a Prolegomenon by Nat Schmulowitz; ANECDOTA SCOWAH Number Four, The Joe Miller of the Near East (Nasreddin Hojah), by Albert Rapp, and an Onsoz and Bibliography by Nat Schmulowitz; ANECDOTA SCOWAH Number Five, The Facetiæ of Poggio, by Albert Rapp, and a Præfatio and Bibliography by Nat Schmulowitz.

This first catalog was prepared by Miss Frances Langpaap who served as Head of the Catalog Department of the San Francisco Public Library for more than twenty years. During the later years of this service, she was the proud and efficient custodian of SCOWAH.

The preparation and publication of the catalog was made possible by still another grant from Mr. Schmulowitz. We are deeply grateful for Mr. Schmulowitz's continual devotion and interest in the Library's development.

WILLIAM R. HOLMAN

*City Librarian*

# A

ABBEHUSEN, C. H. The first story book. *boards. 12mo. Berlin, Simion, 1919.*

ABBOTT, E. A. A Shakespearian grammar. *buckram. 16mo. Lond., Macmillan, 1886.*

ABDULLA, A. 50 enthralling stories of the mysterious East. *buckram, 8vo. Lond., Odhams, n.d.*

A BECKETT, A. W. The A Becketts of Punch. *buckram, 8vo. Westminster, Constable, 1903.*

————— The comic history of England. *buckram, 12mo. Lond., Punch, 1864.*

————— Green-room recollections. *buckram, 12mo. Bristol, Arrowsmith, 1895-6.*

————— Recollections of a humourist. *buckram, 8vo. Lond., Pitman, 1907.*

A BECKETT, G. A. The comic Blackstone. *8vo. Lond., Bradbury, Agnew, 1887. New and rev. ed.*

————— Comic history of England. *buckram, 8vo. Lond., Routledge, n.d. New ed.*

————— Comic history of Rome. *buckram, 12mo. Lond., Bradbury, Agnew, 1852.*

ABEL, ALAN. Crazy ads. *paper, 24mo. N. Y., Citadel, n.d.*

ABHEDANANDA, *swami.* The sayings of Ramakrishna. *buckram, 16mo. Calcutta, Ramakrishna Vedanta Math, 1946. 2d. ed.*

ABINGDON, A. Bigger and better boners. *buckram, 8vo. N.Y., Viking, 1952.*

————— Boners, being a collection of schoolboy wisdom. *buckram, 12mo. N.Y., Blue Ribbon, 1931.*

————— More boners. *buckram, 16mo. N.Y., Viking, 1931.*

————— Second boners omnibus. *buckram, 8vo. N.Y., Blue Ribbon, 1938.*

————— Still more boners. *buckram, 16mo. N.Y., Viking, 1931.*

ADAMS, J. DONALD, *ed.* The new treasure chest. *buckram, 12mo. N.Y., Dutton, 1953.*

————— Triumph over odds. *buckram, 8vo. N.Y., Duell, 1957.*

ADAMS, JOEY. Joey Adams' joke book, a mad merry mixture. *buckram, 12mo. N.Y., Fell, 1952.*

————— The curtain never falls. *buckram, 8vo. N.Y., Fell, 1949.*

————— From gags to riches. *buckram, 8vo. N.Y., Fell, 1946.*

————— Strictly for laughs. *buckram, 8vo. N.Y., Fell, 1955.*

ADAMS, JOHN. Anecdotes, bons-mots and characteristic traits of the greatest princes, politicians . *calf, 12mo. Dublin, Chamberlaine, Byrne, Wogan, et. al. 1789.*

————— Same. *Lond., Kearsley, 1789.*

————— Elegant anecdotes and bon-mots. *calf, 24mo. Lond., Kearsley, 1794.*

ADAMS, SAMUEL HOPKINS. Alexander Woollcott. *buckram, 8vo. Lond., Hamilton, 1946.*

_____ Grandfather stories. *buckram, 8vo. N.Y., Random, 1955.*

**ADAMS, WILLIAM DAVENPORT.** A book of burlesque. *buckram, 12mo. Lond., Henry, 1891.*

_____ The comic poets of the 19th century. *buckram, 12mo. Lond., Routledge, n.d.*

_____ English epigrams. *buckram, 12mo. Lond., Routledge, n.d.*

_____ Modern anecdotes; a treasury of wise and witty sayings. *buckram, 12mo. Lond., Hamilton, Adams, 1886.*

_____ Quips and quiddities. *buckram, 16mo. Lond., Chatto & Windus, 1881.*

_____ Treasury of modern anecdote. *buckram, 12mo. Edinburgh, Edinburgh Pub. Co., 1881.*

**ABERDEEN AND TEMAIRE, GEORGE GORDON,** 2d. *marquess of.* Tell me another. *buckram, 12mo. Lond., Arnold, 1925.*

**AN ACCOUNT OF THE LIFE OF THAT CELEBRATED ACTRESS, MRS. SUSANNAH MARIA CIBBER.** *buckram, 8vo. Lond., Reader, 1887.*

**ACE, GOODMAN.** The book of little knowledge; more than you want to know about television. *boards, 8vo. N.Y., Simon & Schuster, 1955.*

**ACTORS' MONOLOGUES AND JOKES.** *paper, 12mo. Chic., Rossiter, 1902.*

**ADAMIC, LOUIS.** Yugoslav proverbs. *paper, 32mo. Girard, Kan., Haldeman-Julius, n.d. (Little Blue Books)*

**ADAMS, CHARLES FOLLEN.** Dialect ballads. *buckram, 12mo. N.Y., Harper, 1888.*

_____ Leedle Jawcob Strauss. *buckram, 12mo. Bost., Lee & Shepard, 1878.*

**ADAMS, DOROTHY.** My mother told me. *boards, 12mo. Bost., Houghton, Mifflin, 1917.*

**ADAMS, FRANKLIN P.** Among us mortals. *boards, 12mo. Bost., Houghton, Mifflin, 1917.*

_____ The book of diversion. *buckram, 12mo. N.Y., Greenberg, 1925.*

_____ Innocent merriment. *buckram, 8vo. N.Y., Garden City, 1945.*

_____ Nods and becks. *buckram, 8vo. N.Y., Whittlesey, 1944.*

_____ Overset. *boards, 12mo. N.Y., Garden City, 1922.*

**ADAMS, H. C.** Traveller's tales; a book of marvels. *buckram, 8vo. N.Y., Boni & Liveright, 1927.*

**ADAMSON, WILLIAM.** The religious anecdotes of Scotland. *buckram, 8vo. Lond., Hamilton, Adams, 1885.*

**ADDAMS, CHARLES.** Black Maria. *buckram, 4to. Lond., Hamilton, 1960.*

_____ Dear dead days. *buckram, 4to. Lond., Hamlyn, 1959.*

_____ Drawn and quartered. *boards, folio. N.Y., Random House, 1942.*

_____ Homebodies. *boards, 4to. N.Y., Simon & Schuster, 1954.*

_____ Monster rally. *boards, 4to. N.Y., Simon & Schuster, 1950.*

_____ Nightcrawlers.
*boards, 4to. Lond., H. Hamilton,
1957.*

ADDISON, _____, comp.
Interesting anecdotes, memoirs,
allegories, essays and political.
*fragments. 2v. half morocco,
8vo. Lond., Author, 1795, 1797.*

ADDISON, JOSEPH. Maxims,
observations and reflections,
moral, political and divine.
*calf., 12mo. Lond., Curll, 1719.*

ADDISON, WILLIAM. Worthy Dr.
Fuller. *buckram, 8vo. Lond.,
Dent, 1951.*

ADE, GEORGE. Breaking into
society. *buckram, 12mo. N.Y.,
Harper, 1904.*

_____ Fables in slang.
*buckram, 16mo. Chic., Stone,
1899.*

_____ Same. *Lond.,
Pearson, 1902.*

_____ Fables in slang, and
More fables in slang. *paper, 8vo.
N.Y., Dover, 1960.*

_____ Forty modern
fables. *boards, 12mo. N.Y.,
Russell, 1901.*

_____ Hand-made fables.
*buckram, 12mo. Lond., Pearson,
1921.*

_____ In Babel; stories of
Chicago. *buckram, 12mo. N.Y.,
McClure, Phillips, 1903.*

_____ In pastures new.
*buckram, 12mo. N.Y., McClure,
Phillips, 1906.*

_____ Knocking the
neighbors. *buckram, 12mo. N.Y.,
Doubleday, Page, 1912.*

_____ More fables. *buckram,
16mo. Chic., Stone, 1900.*

_____ The old-time saloon.
*buckram, 12mo. N.Y., Long &
Smith, 1931.*

_____ People you know.
*buckram, 12mo. N.Y., Harper,
1904.*

_____ Single blessedness.
*paper, 12mo. N.Y., Doubleday,
Doran, 1933.*

ADELER, MAX. Elbow-room.
*buckram, 12mo. Phila., Stoddart,
1876.*

_____ Out of the hurly-
burly. *buckram, 12mo. Phila.,
McLean, 1874.*

ADMIRAL'S THOUSAND AND
ONE TALES. *limp leather, 8vo.
n.p. n.d.*

ADRIAN, JACK. The comedian; a
very personal interview with
Jerry Lester. *paper, 8vo. Bost.,
Wilson-Hall, 1951.*

ADVENTURES OF JERRY LAST,
the fortunate cobler. *paper, 16mo.
Lond., Maiden, 1800.*

ADVICE TO THE OFFICERS of
the British Army. *quarter-calf.,
16mo. Lond., Richardson, 1783.*

AESOP, G. WASHINGTON. *see*
LANIGAN, G. T.

AESOPUS. Fables of Aesop; a
new translation by S. A. Handford.
*paper, 12mo. Lond., Penguin,
1954.*

_____ Fables of Aesop and
others. Translated into English..
by Samuel Croxall. *quarter-calf.,
16mo. Lond., J. F. and C. Rivington, (et.al.) n.d. 13th ed.*

_____ Fables of Aesop, as
first published by William Caxton
in 1484, with those of Avia,
Alfonso and Poggio, ed. by
Joseph Jacobs. *2v. paper, 12mo.
Lond., D. Nutt, 1889.*

——————— Fables, selected, told anew and their history traced by Joseph Jacobs. *half-calf, 12mo. Lond., Macmillan, 1910.*

——————— Select fables of Esop, and other fabulists in three books. *calf., 12mo. Birmingham, Baskerville, 1764.*

AFLALO, F. G. The salt of my life. *buckram, 8vo. Lond., Pitman, 1905.*

AFTER DINNER SCRAPS, NO. 2. *paper, 8vo. Bloomfield, Iowa, Bloomfield Pub. Co., 1924.*

AFTER DINNER STORIES BY FAMOUS MEN. *buckram, 16mo. N.Y., Hearst, 1914.*

ALAIN. Steeplechase. *boards, 4to. N.Y., Simon & Schuster, 1957.*

ALBATROSS BOOK OF ENGLISH HUMOUR. *paper, 12mo. Leipzig, Albatross, 1938.*

ALDEN, JOHN CARVER. Chuckles. *boards, 12mo. Bost., Marshall Jones, 1920.*

ALDERSON, W.A. Here's to you. *buckram, 12mo. N.Y., Dodge, 1907.*

ALDIN, CECIL. Sleeping partners. *buckram, folio. Lond., Eyre & Spottiswoode, n.d.*

ALDRICH, R.S. Gertrude Lawrence as Mrs. A. *boards, 8vo. N.Y., Greystone, 1954.*

ALDRICH, THOMAS BAILEY. Poems. *buckram, 24mo. N.Y., Carleton, 1863.*

ALFORD, VIOLET. Introduction to English folklore. *buckram, 12mo. Lond., Beli, 1952.*

ALI, A. YUSUF. The message of Islam. *buckram, 12mo. Lond., Murray, 1956.*

ALINGTON, C.A. King Harrison and others. *boards, 8vo. Lond., Ingleby, 1923.*

——————— Shrewsbury fables. *buckram, 12mo. Lond., Longmans, Green, 1917.*

ALL ABOUT AMOS 'N ANDY and their creators, Correll and Godsen. *buckram, 12mo. N.Y., Rand McNally, 1920.*

ALL IN FUN; a collection of 309 cartoons from the pages of the Stamp wholesaler. *paper, 8vo. Burlington, Vt., Jackson, 1951.*

ALLARDICE, JAMES B. At war with the army. *paper, 12mo. Lond., French, 1944.*

ALLEN, SIR CARLETON KEMP. Law and disorders; legal indiscretions. *buckram, 16mo. Lond., Stevens, 1954.*

ALLEN, EDWARD F., *ed.* Modern humor for effective speaking. *buckram, 8vo. N.Y., Citadel, 1945.*

ALLEN, FRED. Much ado about me. *buckram, 8vo. Bost., Little, Brown, 1956.*

——————— Treadmill to oblivion. *buckram, 8vo. Bost., Little, Brown, 1954.*

ALLEN, GEORGE E. Presidents who have known me. *buckram, 8vo. N.Y., Simon & Sch ter, 1950.*

ALLEN, GEORGE HOYT. It tickled him. *buckram, 12mo. Clinton, N.Y., Occidental and Oriental Pub. Co., 1910.*

ALLEN, GRACIE. How to become president. *buckram, 12mo. N.Y., Duell, Sloan and Pearce, 1940.*

ALLEN, GRANT. Post-prandial philosophy. *cloth, 12mo. Lond., Chatto & Windus, 1894.*

ALLEN, JOHN. One hundred great lives. *buckram, 8vo. N.Y., Journal of Living, 1944.*

ALLEN, HERVEY. Israfel; the life and times of Edgar Allan Poe. *buckram, 8vo. N.Y., Farrar & Rinehart, 1934.*

ALLEN, IDA BAILEY. When you entertain; what to do and how. *boards, 16mo. Atlanta, Ga., Coca Cola Co., 1932.*

ALLEN, LEWIS. Around the clock with the rounder. *boards 12mo. Bost., Luce, 1910.*

ALLEN, STEVE. The question man. *paper, 4to. N.Y., Bellmeadows Press, 1959.*

──────────── The funny men. *boards, 8vo. N.Y., Simon & Schuster, 1956.*

──────────── Wry on the rocks. *buckram, 8vo. N.Y., Holt, 1956.*

ALMOND, KERNEL *see* THOMES, CHARLES J.

AMALIE PENNSYLVANIA MOTOR OIL CO. Hints; (a collection of advise to motorists of 1909.) *paper, 16mo. N.Y., Sonneborn, 1956.*

AN AMATEUR SPORTSMAN, *pseud.* Sporting anecdotes, original and select. *half-calf, 12mo. Lond., Albion, 1807.*

AN AMERICAN, *pseud.* American anecdotes; original and select. *2v. half-morocco, 12mo. Bost., Putnam & Hunt, 1830.*

AMERICAN ANECDOTES. *leather 24mo. Edinburgh, Symon, n.d.*

AMERICAN CIVIL LIBERTIES UNION. Censorship of comic books; a statement on civil liberties grounds. *paper, 8vo. N.Y., American Civil Liberties Union, 1955.*

AMERICAN COMIC ALMANAC, 1835. with whims, scraps and oddities. *paper, 8vo. Bost., Ellms, 1835.*

THE AMERICAN GIRL. Lots of laughs; jokes selected. *boards, 24mo. N.Y., Oxford Univ. Press, 1942.*

AMERICAN JEST BOOK, being a chaste collection of anecdotes, bon-mots, and epigrams. *buckram, 24mo. Phila, Hogan & Thompson, 1833.*

AMERICAN JEST BOOK, containing a choice selection of jests, anecdotes, bon-mots and stories. *calf, 16mo. Wilmington, Bonsal & Niles, 1800.*

AMERICAN JESTS AND ANECDOTES. *buckram, 24mo. Lond., Dent, n.d.*

AMERICAN LEGION MAGAZINE. American Legion Reader, fiction, articles, humor and cartoons. *buckram, 8vo. N.Y., Hawthorne, 1933.*

AMERICAN TRADITION IN 1957. *paper, narrow 8vo. N.Y., Fund for the Republic, 1957.*

AMERICAN WIT AND HUMOR. *buckram, 24mo. Phila., Jacobs, 1900.*

AMERICAN WIT AND HUMOR; choice selections from the boundless humor of America's favorite humorists; George W. Peck, Bill Nye, M.Quad. *buckram, 12mo. Chic., Homewood, 1883.*

AMERICAN WIT AND HUMOR, by 100 of America's leading humorists. Introduction by Joel Chandler Harris. *buckram, 16mo. N.Y., Review of Reviews, 1907.*

AMERICANA ESOTERICA. By
various American authors. *buckram, 4to. Priv. Print., 1927.*

AMES, V. B. Matrimonial primer.
*buckram, 12mo. San Francisco,
Elder, 1905.*

AMICUS *see* FERRIS,
BENJAMIN.

L'AMOUR: epigrams and witticisms
on love. *boards, 12mo. Mount
Vernon, N.Y., Peter Pauper,
1957.*

AMSTERDAM, MOREY. Keep
laughing. *boards, 16mo. Lond.,
Hammond, 1960.*

AMUSEMENTS SERIOUS AND
COMICAL, or, a new collection of bon-mots, keen-jests,
ingenious thoughts . . . *full
calf, large 16mo. The Hague,
I. Vaillant, 1719. English and
French on opposite pages.*

AMUSING AND POPULAR
RIDDLES. *paper, 3mo. Girard,
Kan., Haldeman-Julius, n.d.
(Little Blue Books)*

ANCELET-HUSTACHE, JEANNE.
Master Eckhart and the Rhine-
land mystics. *paper, 12mo. N.Y.,
Harper, 1957.*

ANCIENT CHINESE FABLES,
translated by Yang Hsien-Yi
and Gladys Yang. *boards, 4to.
Peking, Foreign Languages
Press, 1957.*

ANDERSEN, HANS CHRISTIAN.
Fairy tales. *buckram, 12mo.
Lond., Dent, 1955.*

—————— Hans Andersen's
fairy tales. *buckram, 8vo. Lond.,
Dakers, n.d.*

ANDERSON, BRAD and LEEM-
INC, PHIL. Marmaduke rides
again. *paper, 12mo. Derby,
Conn., Monarch, 1959.*

ANDERSON, C.J.J. Forbidden
limericks. *paper, 4to. n.p., n.d.*

ANDRE, H. Colonel Bogey's
sketch book. *boards, 8vo.
Lond., Longmans, Green, 1897.*

ANDREEV, LEONID. The dear
departing. *paper, 12mo. Lond.,
Henderson, n.d.*

ANDREWS, JAMES PETITT.
Anecdotes, etc., antient and
modern, with observations.
*calf., 8vo. Lond., Stockdale,
1790. New ed. corrected and
much enlarged.*

ANDREWS, WILLIAM. At the sign
of the barber's pole. *buckram,
12mo. Cottingham, Yorkshire.
Tutin, 1904.*

—————— Curious epitaphs.
*buckram, 8vo. Lond., Andrews,
1899.*

—————— Ecclesiastical curiosities. *buckram, 8vo. Lond.,
Andrews, 1899.*

—————— The lawyer in his-
tory, literature and humour.
*buckram, 8vo. Lond., Andrews,
1897.*

—————— Legal lore; curiosities of law and lawyers. *buckram, 8vo. Lond., Andrews, 1897.*

ANDREWS, WILLIAM ELLIOTT.
Imagine my surprise! *buckram,
12mo. N.Y., Stokes, 1928.*

ANECDOTA AMERICANA; 500
stories for the amusement of
the 500 nations that comprise
America. *buckram, 8vo. N.Y.,
Faro, 1933.*
*see also* NEW ANECDOTA
AMERICANA.

ANECDOTA, SCOWAH.
 I: Epitaphia, by Nat
    Schmulowitz
 II: The legend of Joe Miller, by
     Evan Esar.
 III: The ancient Greeks & Joe
      Miller, by Albert Rapp.
 IV: The Joe Miller of the Near
     East, by Albert Miller.

ANECDOTE LIBRARY, being the
largest collection of anecdotes
ever assembled in a single
volume. By the editor of The
Vocal Library. *leather, 24mo.
Lond., Whittaker, 1822.*

ANECDOTES FOR THE FAMILY
AND THE SOCIAL CIRCLE,
selected for the American Tract
Society. *calf., 24mo. N.Y.,
American Tract Soc., n.d.*

ANECDOTES, HISTORICAL AND
LITERARY: or, A miscel-
laneous selection of curious
and striking passages from
eminent modern authors. *calf,
8vo. Lond., Vernor & Hood,
1796.*

ANECDOTES OF AURANGZIB
(English translation of AKHAM-
I-ALAMGIRI, ascribed to
Hamid-ud-din Khan Bahadur)
*boards, 12mo. Calcutta,
Sarkar, 1949.*

ANECDOTES OF IMPUDENCE,
being a collection of entertaining facts relating to extraordinary men. *quarter-boards,
24mo. Lond., Tilt, 1827.*

ANECDOTES OF NAPOLEON
BONAPARTE. *buckram, 32mo.
Manchester, S. Johnson, 1845.*

ANECDOTES OF OLIVE THE
BLACK, KING OF MAN and the
Hebridian princes of the Somer-
led family . . . *paper, 8vo.
Author, 1780.*

ANECDOTES OF POPULAR
AUTHORS. *half-calf, 24mo.
Lond., Bogue, n.d.*

ANECDOTES OF SOME DIS-
TINGUISHED PERSONS, chiefly
of the present and two preceding centuries. *2v. calf, 12mo.
Lond., Cadell & Davies, 1795.
2d. ed.*

ANECDOTES OF THE CELE-
BRATED WILLIAM HOGARTH.
*boards, 24mo. Lond., Thomas
Davison for John Stockdale,
1811.*

ANECDOTES OF THE HOUR BY
FAMOUS MEN. *buckram, 16mo.
N.Y., Hearst's, 1914.*

ANECDOTES OF THE LEARNED
PIG. *paper, 4to. Lond., Hook-
man, 1786.*

ANECDOTES OF THE PURITANS.
*buckram, 16mo. N.Y., Dodd,
1849.*

ANGELO, EMIDIO. Just be
patient. *paper, 8vo. Phila.,
Toronto, 1957.*

——————— Oh, baby! *buckram,
8vo. Phila., Winston, 1958.*

——————— The time of your life.
*paper, 8vo. Phila., Winston,
1957.*

ANGLY, EDWARD, *comp.* Oh
yeah? *buckram, 12mo. N.Y.,
Viking, 1931.*

ANGRAVE, BRUCE. The new
English fictionary. *buckram,
8vo. Lond., Weidenfeld &
Nicholson, 1953.*

ANNARINO, JOHN *and* HUME,
BILL. Anchors are heavy. *paper
12mo. Tokyo, Tuttle, 1955.*

ANNUAL GLEANINGS OF WIT AND HUMOUR IN PROSE AND VERSE, by a celebrated Wit of the Age. *2v. in 1. boards, 16 mo. Lond., Keys, 1816.*

ANNUAL SCRAP-BOOK AND ENCYCLOPEDIA OF ANEC-DOTES. *buckram, 16mo. Lond., Smith, 1841.*

ANSTEY, F. Baboo Hurry Bungsho Jabberjee, B.A. *buckram, 12mo. N.Y., Appleton, 1897.*

——————— The brass bottle. *paper, 12mo. Harmondsworth, Middlesex, Penguin, 1946.*

——————— Humour & fantasy. *buckram, 12mo. Lond., Murray, 1931.*

——————— Voces populi (re-printed from Punch) *boards, 8vo. Lond., Longmans, Green, 1890.*

ANTHOLOGIA, a collection of epigrams, ludicrous epitaphs, sonnets, tales, miscellaneous anecdotes. *boards, 12mo. Lond., Spilsbury, 1807.*

ANTHONY, EDWARD. How to get rid of a woman. *buckram, 12mo. Indianapolis, Bobbs-Merrill, 1928.*

ANTHONY, NORMAN, *and* SOGLOW, O. The drunk's blue book. *buckram, 12mo. N.Y., Stokes, 1939. Rev. ed.*

ANTRIM, MINNA THOMAS. At the sign of the Golden Calf. *buckram, 16mo. Phila., Altemus, 1905.*

——————— A book of toasts. *buckram, 24mo. Phila., Altemus, 1902.*

——————— Don'ts for girls; a manual of mistakes. *cloth, 24mo. Phila., Altemus, 1902.*

——————— Knocks witty wise and . . . *boards, 16mo. Phila., Jacobs, 1905.*

——————— Naked truths and veiled illusions. *buckram, 24mo. Phila., Altemus, 1901.*

APOLOGY ADDRESSED TO THE TRAVELLERS CLUB, or, Anec-dotes of monkeys. *half-calf, 12mo. Lond., Murray, 1824.*

APPLEBY, BARRY. The Gambols. Daily Express cartoons, no. 4. *paper, 24mo. Lond., Daily Express, n.d.*

——————— The Gambols, book no. 9. *paper, wide 16mo. Lond., Daily Express, n.d.*

APULEIUS MADAURENSIS, LUCIUS. The golden asse. *buckram, 8vo. Lond., Abbey Library, n.d.*

——————— The transformations of Lucius, otherwise known as The Golden Ass. *paper, 16mo. Harmondsworth, Middlesex, Penguin, 1956.*

ARABIAN NIGHTS. The Arabian nights, their best known tales retold by Kate Douglas Wiggin and Nora Smith. *buckram, 8vo. Lond., Laurie, 1909.*

——————— Arabian tales; or. A continuation of the Arabian Nights Entertainments. *4v. tree-calf, 12mo. Edinburgh, Bell & Bardfute, 1792.*

——————— Fairy tales from the Arabian nights, edited by E. Dixon. *buckram, 4to. Lond., Dent, 1893.*

——————— Portable Arabian Nights, edited by Joseph Campbell. *buckram, 16mo. N.Y., Viking, 1952.*

——————— Selections from the Arabian Nights, with new illustrations and decorations by Steele Savage. *buckram, 8vo. Garden City, De Luxe Editions Club, n.d.*

——————— Stories from the Arabian Nights, retold by Laurence Housman. *buckram, 4to. Lond., Hodder & Stoughton, 1907.*

A'RABBIT, SHAMUS, *pseud.* Ballads of the East. *boards, 4to. Shanghai, Hager, 1937.*

——————— China coast ballads. *buckram, 8vo. Shanghai, Hager, 1938.*

ARBERRY, A.J. A Maltese anthology. *buckram, 16mo. Oxford, Clarendon, 1960.*

ARBO, SEBASTIAN JUAN. Cervantes, adventurer, idealist and destiny's fool. *buckram, 8vo. Lond., Thames & Hudson, 1955.*

ARGOSY. The best cartoons from Argosy, edited by 3 crazy people. *paper, 16mo. Rockville Center, N.Y., Zenith, 1958.*

ARIOSTO, LUDOVICO. Tales from Ariosto, by J. Shield Nicholson. *buckram, 8vo. Lond., Macmillan 1913.*

THE ARKANSAW TRAVELER. *see* Jokes, monologues . . . from The Arkansaw Traveler.

ARKELL, REGINALD. Bridge without sighs. *buckram, 8vo. Lond., Jenkins, n.d.*

——————— Green fingers. *boards, 12mo. Lond., Jenkins, 1935.*

——————— Green fingers again. *buckram, 12mo. Lond., Jenkins, 1942.*

——————— Meet these people. *boards, 12mo. Lond., Jenkins, 1930. Rev. and enl. ed.*

——————— More green fingers. *boards, 8vo. Lond., Jenkins, 1938.*

——————— Playing the game. *cloth, 12mo. Lond., Jenkins, 1935.*

ARKELL, ROD. *comp.* Cream of wit. *buckram, 8vo. Sebring, Fla., Author, 1953.*

AN ARM-CHAIR IN THE SMOKING ROOM, or, Fiction, anecdote, humour and fancy for dreamy half-hours. With notes on cigars, meer-schaums, and smoking. *buckram, 12mo. Lond., Rivers, n.d.*

ARMIN, ROBERT. Fools and jesters, by J.P.C. with a reprint of Robert Armin's Nest of Ninnies, 1608. *cloth, 8vo. Lond., Shakespeare Soc., 1842.*

ARMITAGE, G.T. How's our Hawaiian? *paper, 8vo. Honolulu, Hawaiian Service, 1956.*

ARMOUR, RICHARD. It all started with Columbus. *boards, 12mo. N.Y., McGraw-Hill, 1953.*

——————— It all started with Europa. *buckram, 12mo. N.Y., McGraw-Hill, 1955.*

——————— It all started with Eve. *buckram, 8vo. Lond., Hammond, 1957.*

——————— Leading with my left. *buckram, 8vo. N.Y., Beechhurst, 1946.*

——————— Light armour; playful poems. *boards, 12mo. N.Y., McGraw-Hill, 1954.*

_____ Pills, potions and Granny. *buckram, 8vo. Lond., Hammond, 1959.*

_____ Twisted tales from Shakespeare. *buckram, 8vo. Lond., Hammond, 1958.*

ARMSTRONG, ANTHONY. The after-breakfast book. *buckram, 12mo. Lond., Hodge, 1937.*

_____ Laughter parade. *cloth, 12mo. Lond., Faber, 1940.*

_____ Anthony Armstrong "A. A." Methuen's Library of Humour. *cloth, 16mo. Lond., Methuen, 1934.*

_____ Nothing to do with the war. *buckram, 16mo. Lond., Methuen, 1940.*

_____ Nice types. *buckram, 12mo. Lond., Methuen, 1944. 2d. ed.*

_____ Pack of pieces. *buckram, 12mo. Lond., Joseph, 1942.*

_____ The prince who hiccupped. *buckram, 12mo. Lond., Benn, 1932.*

_____ Prune's progress. *buckram, 12mo. Lond., Jenkins, n.d.*

_____ Yesterdailies. *buckram, 12mo. Lond., Methuen, 1933. 4th ed.*

ARMSTRONG, ARCHIE. A banquet of jests and merry tales by Archie Armstrong, court jester to King James I and King Charles II. *buckram, 12mo. Lond., Hamilton, Adams, 1889.*

_____ Banquest of jests, reprinted from the original editions. Together with Archie's Dream, printed in the yeare 1641. *buckram, 8vo. Edinburgh. Paterson, 1872.*

ARMSTRONG, MARTIN. 54 conceits; a collection of epigrams and epitaphs serious and comic. *boards, 16mo. Lond., Secker, 1933.*

_____ Laughing, an essay. *boards, 16mo. N.Y., Harper, 1928.*

_____ Same. *Lond., Jarrolds, 1928.*

_____ The major pleasures of life. *buckram, 12mo. Lond., Gollancz, 1936.*

ARNO, PETER. Hell of a way to run a railroad. *buckram, 4to. N.Y., Simon & Schuster, 1956.*

_____ The man in the shower. *boards, folio. N.Y., Simon & Schuster, 1944.*

_____ New Peter Arno pocket book. *paper, 16mo. N.Y., Pocket Books, 1955.*

_____ Penguin Peter Arno. *paper, 16mo. Harmondsworth, Middlesex, Penguin, 1957.*

_____ Peter Arno's circus. *buckram, folio. N.Y., Liveright, 1931.*

_____ Peter Arno's ladies and gentlemen. *buckram, 4to. N.Y., Simon & Schuster, 1951.*

_____ Sizzling platter. *buckram, 4to. N.Y., Simon & Schuster, 1949.*

_____ Whoops dearie! *buckram, 12mo. N.Y., Simon & Schuster, 1927.*

ARNOLD, ALFRED C. The Englishman in anecdote and story. *buckram, 12mo. Stirling, Mackay, 1906.*

ARNOLD, OREN. Wild West joke book. *buckram, 8vo. N.Y., Fell, 1956.*

ARNOLD, PAUL. Humor and wisdom from the pages of Legal Chatter. *paper, 12mo. Baltimore, Legal Chatter, 1939.*

ARQUETTE, CLIFF. Charley Weaver's letters from Mama. *buckram, 8vo. Phila., Winston, 1959.*

ARTHUR, ELLA B. My husband keeps telling me to go to hell. *boards, 8vo. N.Y., Hanover, 1954.*

ASBURY, HERBERT. Carry Nation. *buckram, 12mo. N.Y., Knopf, 1929.*

ASHBEE, C.R. The kings of Min Zaman. *boards, 4to. Lond., Oxford Univ. Press, 1938.*

ASHBY, LYLE W. Our faith in education. *paper, 24mo. (Personal Growth Leaflets)*

ASHMORE, MARION. Lost, stolen or strayed; the adventures of an Aberdeen terrier. *buckram, 8vo. Lond., Eyre & Spottiswoode, 1931.*

ASHTON, ALGERNON. Truth, wit and wisdom; a mine of information. 525 letters to the press, 1887-1903. *buckram, 12mo. Lond., Chapman & Hall, 1905.*

ASHTON, JOHN. Chap-books of the 18th century. *buckram, 12mo. Lond., Chatto & Windus, 1882.*

———————— English caricature and satire on Napoleon I. *buckram, 12mo. Lond., Chatto & Windus, 1888.*

———————— Humour, wit & satire of the 17th century. *buckram, 12mo. Lond., Chatto & Windus, 1883.*

"ASK MAMMA", or, The richest commoner in England. By the author of: "Sponge's sporting tour". *buckram, 8vo. Lond., Bradbury, Agnew, 1892.*

ASQUITH, CYNTHIA, *Lady, ed.* New tales of humour. *buckram, 8vo. Lond., Jarrolds, n.d.* First published as "The Funnybone"

THE ASS RACE, or, The secret history of Archy Armstrong, fool to King Charles I. *paper, rebound, 16mo. Lond., n.p., 1711.*

ASWELL, JAMES R. Native American humor. *buckram, 8vo. N.Y., Garden City, 1949.*

ATHENAEUS. The Deipnosophists, or Banquet of the learned. *3v. buckram, 12mo. Lond., Bohn, 1854.*

ATHENIAN SOCIETY, THE. The Athenian oracle. *4v. calf., 12mo. Lond., Bell, 1793.*

———————— Athenian sport, or 2,000 paradoxes merrily argued. *calf., 12mo. Lond., Bragg, 1707.*

ATHERTON, GERTRUDE. The splendid idle forties. *buckram, 12mo. N.Y., Macmillan, 1902.*

ATKIN, G. DUCKWORTH. House scraps. With illus. by George Cruikshank. *buckram, 8vo. Lond., 1887.*

ATKINSON, ALEX *and* SEARLE, RONALD. The big city, or, The new Mayhew. *buckram, 4to. Lond., Perpetua, 1958.*

———————— Russia for beginners; by rocking chair across Russia. *buckram, small 4to. Lond., Perpetua, 1960.*

AUGIER, EMILE. The post-
scriptum. *paper, 12mo. N.Y.,
French, 1915.*

AULTON, MARGARET. Fair
Touraine; legends and stories
of the Loire. *buckram, folio.
Lond., Lane, 1925.*

AUMONIER, STACY *and* BELCHER,
GEORGE. Odd fish, being a
casual selection of London residents. *buckram, 8vo. Lond.,
Heinemann, 1923.*

AURAND, A. MONROE. Wit and
humor of the Pennsylvania Ger-
mans. *paper, 8vo. Harrisburg,
Pa., Aurand press, 1946.*

AURELIUS ANTONINUS, MARCUS.
The Emperour Marcus Antoninus, his conversation with
himself. *calf., 8vo. Lond., Sare,
1726. 3d ed. corrected.*

_____ Meditations. *paper,
24mo. Girard, Kan., Haldeman-
Julius, 1924. (Little Blue
Books)*

AUTHUR, ROBERT ALAN. The
glorification of Al Toolum.
*buckram, 8vo. N.Y., Rinehart,
1953.*

AUSTIN, EBENEZER. Anecdotage;
or, Stray leaves from the note
books of a provincial reporter.
*buckram, 12mo. Lond., Pitman,
1872.*

AUSTIN, YOUNG. Amusing stories
for speakers. *buckram, 12mo.
Lond., Routledge, n.d.*

AUSUBEL, NATHAN. Treasury of
Jewish folklore. *buckram, 8vo.
N.Y., Crown, 1948.*

AVERY, RUTH *and* HAMMACK,
LEWIS. Jest for laughs. *buckram, 8vo. N.Y., Exposition
press, 1954.*

AVERY, SAMUEL. The book of
1000 comical stories, an endless repast of fun, by the
author of "Mrs. Partington's
Carpet-bag of fun." *buckram,
12mo. N.Y., Dick & Fitz-
gerald, 1859.*

_____ Mrs. Partington's
Carpet-bag of fun. *buckram,
12mo. N.Y., Dick & Fitz-
gerald, 1854.*

AYE, JOHN. Clerical chuckles.
*buckram, 12mo. Lond., Univer-
sal, 1934.*

_____ Humour among the
clergy. *buckram, 12mo. Lond.,
Universal, 1931.*

_____ Humour among the
doctors. *buckram, 12mo. Lond.,
Universal, 1931.*

_____ Humour among the
lawyers. *buckram, 12mo. Lond.,
Universal, 1931.*

_____ Humour in our streets.
*buckram, 12mo. Lond., Univer-
sal, 1933.*

_____ Humour in sports.
*buckram, 12mo. Lond., Univer-
sal, 1932.*

_____ Humour in the army.
*buckram, 12mo. Lond., Univer-
sal, 1931.*

_____ Humour in the civil
service. *boards, 12mo. Lond.,
Palmer, 1928.*

_____ Humour in the
theatre. *buckram, 12mo. Lond.,
Universal, n.d.*

_____ Humour of drinking.
*buckram, 12mo. Lond., Univer-
sal, 1934.*

_____ Humour of parliament.
*buckram, 12mo. Lond., Univer-
sal, 1931.*

# A-B

———— Humour on the rail. *buckram, 12mo. Lond., Universal, 1933.*

———— I am the joker. *buckram, 12mo. Lond., Universal, 1933.*

———— Love and laughter. *buckram, 12mo. Lond., Universal, 1933.*

AYRTON, MICHAEL. Tittivulus; or, The verbiage collector. *buckram, 8vo. Lond., Reinhardt, 1953.*

B., J.J. *see* Bell, John Joy.

B., T. *and* C., T. The new pun book. *buckram, 12mo. N.Y., Carey-Stafford, 1906.*

BABSON, ROGER W. Cheer up! better times ahead! *boards, 16mo. N.Y., Revell, 1932.*

BACHELOR BIGOTRIES. compiled by an Old Maid and approved by a Young Bachelor. *buckram, 24mo. San Francisco, Commercial Pub. Co., 1903. 2d. ed.*

BACON, FRANCIS. A collection of apothegms. *paper, 32mo. Girard, Kan., Haldeman-Julius, n.d. (Little Blue Books)*

———— Of the proficience and advancement of learning. Edited by B. Montagu. *calf, 16mo. Lond., Pickering, 1838.*

———— Truth and seventeen other essays. *paper, 32mo. Girard, Kan., Haldeman-Julius, n.d. (Little Blue Books)*

BACON, THOMAS. The Oriental annual. *buckram, 12mo. Lond., Tilt, 1839.*

———— The Orientalist. First series. *buckram, 12mo. Lond., Arnold, 1842.*

BAER, ARTHUR "BUGS". The family album. *buckram, 12mo. N.Y., Boni, 1925.*

BAERLEIN, HENRY. The Diwan of Abu'l-ala. *buckram, 16mo. Lond., Murray, 1908.*

BAILEY, JOHN. Mr. Webster's bloomers, or, English bashed and unabashed. *boards, 12mo. N.Y., Morrow, 1956.*

BAILY, LESLIE, *ed.* Travellers' tales, a series of BBC programmes broadcast throughout the world. *buckram, 8vo. Lond., Allen & Unwin, 1947.*

BAIN, GEORGE W. Wit, humor, reason, rhetoric, prose, poetry and story. *buckram, 12mo. Louisville, Pentecostal Pub. Co., 1915.*

BAIRNSFATHER, BRUCE. Fragments from France. *paper, folio. Lond., "The Bystander" 1918.*

———— Jeeps and jests. *buckram, 8vo. N.Y., Putnam's, 1943.*

———— Laughing through the Orient, with "Old Bill". *buckram, 8vo. N.Y., Viking, 1932.*

———— No diddin! *buckram, 8vo. N.Y., Putnam's, 1945.*

BAIRNSFATHER, a few fragments from his life, collected by a friend. *buckram, small 4to. N.Y., Putnam's, n.d.*

BAKER, GEORGE. The sad sack. *boards, 8vo. N.Y., Simon & Schuster, 1944.*

BAKER, GEORGE M. Mrs. Walthrop's bachelors. *paper, 12mo. Bost., Baker, n.d.*

BAKER, GEORGE P. Modern American plays. *buckram, 12mo. N.Y., Harcourt, Brace, 1920.*

# B

BAKER, HETTIE GRAY. 195 cat
tales. *boards, 8vo. N.Y.,
Farrar, Straus, 1953.*

BAKER, ROBERT. Witticisms and
strokes of humour. *half-calf.,
12mo. Lond., Bathoe, 1766.*

BALCHIN, NIGEL. How to run a
bassoon factory, by Mark
Spade, *pseud. buckram, 12mo.
Lond., Hamilton, 1950.*

BALDWIN, BILL. Willie goes to
New York. *pamphlet. N.Y.,
American news co., 1953.
2d. ed.*

BALDWIN, EDWARD, *ed.* The
book of fables. Selections from
Aesop, and other authors. *buckram, 12mo. N.Y., Collins, 1856.*

BALLADS OF THE BENCH AND
BAR, or, Idle lays of the
Parliament house. *4to. buckram,
Edinburgh, Priv. printed, 1882.*
(Contains MS. "Lines after
Cooper suggested by a recent
"Judicial scandal" Nov. 1867.
by Alexander Nicolson.)

BALLOWE, HEWITT. Creole folk
tales; stories of the Louisiana
marsh country. *buckram, 8vo.
Baton Rouge, Lousiana State
Univ. Press, 1948.*

BALZAC, HONORE DE. Ten droll
tales. *buckram, 8vo. Lond.,
Abbey Library, n.d.*

BANCROFT, GEORGE. Memorial
address on the life and character of Abraham Lincoln, delivered . . . in the House of Repre-
sentatives . . . on the 12th of
February, 1866. *buckram, 8vo.
Washington, Govt. Print Office,
1866.*

BANDINI, ARTURO. Navidad; a
Christmas day with early Cali-
fornians. *buckram, 8vo. San
Francisco, California Historical
Society, 1958.* (Bound with:
"Pastorela, a shepherd's play"
translated by Gwladys Louise
Williams)

BANGS, FRANCIS HYDE. John
Kendrick Bangs, humorist of
the nineties. *buckram, 8vo.
N.Y., Knopf, 1941.*

BANGS, JOHN KENDRICK. Alice
in Blunderland. *buckram, 12mo.
N.Y., Doubleday, Page, 1907.*

——————— Cobwebs from a
library corner. *buckram, 16mo.
N.Y., Harper, 1899.*

——————— Coffee and repartee.
*buckram, 24mo. N.Y., Harper,
1893.*

——————— The enchanted type-
writer. *buckram, 12mo. N.Y.,
Harper, 1899.*

——————— The genial idiot.
*buckram, 16mo. N.Y., Harper,
1908.*

——————— A houseboat on the
Styx. *buckram, 16mo. N.Y.,
Harper, 1895.*

——————— Mr. Munchausen. *buckram, 12mo. Bost., Noyes, Platt,
1901.*

——————— Over the plum-pudding.
*buckram, 12mo. N.Y., Harper,
1899.*

——————— Peeps at people.
*buckram, 16mo. N.Y., Harper,
1899.*

_____ The pursuit of the house-boat. *buckram, 16mo. N.Y., Harper, 1897.*

BANIER, ANTOINE. The mythology and fables of the ancients. *4v. calf, 12mo. Lond., Miller, 1739.*

BANKHEAD, TALLULAH. Tallulah, my autobiography. *buckram, 8vo. N.Y., Harper, 1952.*

BANKS, LOUIS ALBERT. Anecdotes and morals. *buckram, 12mo. N.Y., Funk & Wagnalls, 1898.*

BANKS, MURRAY. How to live with yourself. *paper, 8vo. Brooklyn, Institute Press, 1949.*

_____ How to stay normal and enjoy life. *paper, 8vo. Brooklyn, Institute Press, 1952.*

BANNISTER, CONNIE. "Senator, I'm glad you asked me that!" *paper, 8vo. N.Y., American Binder Co., 1952.*

BANVARD, JOSEPH. Wisdom, wit and whims of the distinguished ancient philosophers. *buckram, 12mo. N.Y., Sheldon, Lamport & Blakeman, 1855.*

BARBEE, LINDSEY. After the game. *paper, 12mo. Chic., Denison, 1907.*

BARBER, JOHN W. Hand book of illustrated proverbs. *leather, 12mo. N.Y., Tuttle, 1858.*

BARD, MARY. The doctor has three faces. *buckram, 8vo. Phila., Lippincott, 1949.*

BARHAM, ROBERT HARRIS. The Ingoldsby legends, or, Mirth and marvel, by Thomas Ingoldsby, esquire. *2v. buckram, 16mo. Lond., Methuen, 1903.*

BAR-HEBRAEUS, GREGORY JOHN. Oriental wit and wisdom or The "Laughable stories." Translated from the Syriac by E. A. Wallis Budge. *buckram, 8vo. Lond., Luzac, 1899.*

BARING-GOULD, SABINE. Curious myths of the middle ages. *calf., 12mo. Lond., Rivingtons, 1872.*

_____ Historic oddities and strange events. *buckram, 8vo. Lond., Methuen, 1889. First series.*

_____ Legends of Old Testament characters, from the Talmud and other sources. *buckram, 12mo. Lond., Macmillan, 1871.*

BARKER, DUDLEY. Laughter in court. *buckram, 16mo. Lond., Methuen, 1935.*

BARKER, GEORGE C., *ed. and trans.* The shepherd's play of the Prodigal Son (Coloquio de pastores del hijo prodigo) A folk drama of Old Mexico. *paper, 4to. Berkeley, Univ. of Calif. Press, 1953. (Folklore Studies, no. 2)*

BARKER, H. M. The old sailor's jolly boat. *buckram, 8vo. Lond., Willougby, n.d.*

BARKER, HENRY J. Merry moments with scholars. *paper, 12mo. Lond., Harper, 1909.*

_____ Original English as written by our little ones at school. *paper, 16mo. Lond., Jarrold, 1889.*

BARKER, WILLIAM J. The wayward west. *buckram, 8vo. N.Y., Doubleday, 1959.*

BARKLEY, ALBEN W. That reminds me . . . *buckram, 8vo. N.Y., Doubleday, 1954.*

BARLOW, BILL. Sagebrush
philosophy. June 1907, November 1907, July 1908. *paper,
16mo. Douglas, Wyo., Budget
Printshop.*

BARLOW, WILLIAM P. Collected
works. *boards, 12mo. Pasadena,
Coterie des Epicuriens, 1954.*

BARNARD, FRANCIS PIERREPONT. A fardel of epigrams.
*buckram, 16mo. Lond., Milford,
1922.*

BARNES, CLARE. Home sweet
zoo. *paper, 8vo. N.Y., Doubleday, 1950.*

_____ White collar zoo.
*paper, 12mo. Lond., Methuen,
n.d.*

BARNHAM, HENRY D., *tr.* The
Khoja; tales of Nasr-ed-din.
*buckram, 8vo. N.Y., Appleton,
1924.*

BARNUM, PHINEAS T. Funny
stories. *buckram, 12mo. Lond.,
Routledge, 1890.*

_____ Humbugs of the
world. *buckram, 12mo. Lond.,
John Camden Hotten, 1866.*

_____ Struggles and
triumphs. *buckram, 12mo.
Buffalo, Warren, Johnson, 1873.*

BARR, JAMES, *ed.* American
humorous verse. *buckram, 24mo.
Lond., W. Scott, 1891. 5th ed.*

_____ The humour of
America. *buckram, 12mo.
Lond., Scott, 1894.*

BARRANGON, ELOISE. How to
travel with parents. *boards,
8vo. N.Y., Dial, 1956.*

BARRIE, *Sir* JAMES MATTHEW.
Half hours. *buckram, 12mo.
N.Y., Scribner's, 1914.*

BARRON, E. J. Joke upon joke.
*half-calf., 12mo. Lond.,
Symonds, 1800.*

BARROWS, R. M., *comp.* Heading
for a wedding, *paper, 8vo.
Chic., Consolidated Book Pub.,
1944.*

_____ Kitbook for soldiers,
sailors and marines. *boards,
16mo. Chic., Consolidated
book pub., 1943.*

BARRYMORE, LIONEL. We
Barrymores. *buckram, 12mo.
Lond., Davies, 1951.*

BARSIS, MAX. Bottoms up; an
unreliable handbook for skiers.
*boards, 8vo. Brattleboro, Vt.
Daye, 1939.*

_____ They're all yours,
Uncle Sam! *buckram, 8vo. N.Y.,
Daye, 1943.*

BARSLEY, MICHAEL. The intimate papers of Colonel Bogus.
*buckram, 12mo. Lond., Pilot
press, 1943.*

_____ Modern American
humour. *buckram, 12mo. Lond.,
Pilot press, 1946.*

_____ The Phoenix book of
modern American humour.
*boards, 8vo. Lond., Phoenix,
1956.*

_____ The Phoenix book of
wit and humour. *buckram, 8vo.
Lond., Phoenix, 1949.*

BARTLETT, VERNON. Topsyturvy. *buckram, 12mo. Lond.,
Constable, 1927.*

BARTON, LEWIS. Considered
trifles. *buckram, 8vo. Lond.,
W. Laurie, 1955.*

BARTON, WILLIAM E. The
paternity of Abraham Lincoln;
was he the son of Thomas
Lincoln? *buckram, 8vo. N.Y.,
Doran, 1920.*

_____ The wit and wisdom
of Safed the sage. *boards, 12mo.
Bost., Pilgrim, 1919.*

BASON, FRED. Fred Bason goes
fishing. *paper, 24mo. Lond.,
n.p., n.d.*

_____ Fred Bason has a
picnic. *North Shields, England,
Tyne Brand Products, 1961.*

_____ Fred Bason's diary.
*buckram, 12mo. Lond., Wingate,
1951.*

_____ Fred Bason's 2d.
diary. *buckram, 12mo. Lond.,
Wingate, 1952.*

_____ Fred Bason's 3d.
diary. *buckram, 12mo. Lond.,
Deutsch, 1955.*

_____ The last bassoon.
*buckram, 8vo. Lond., Parrish,
1960.*

BASS, EDUARD. The Chatter-
tooth eleven; a tale of a Czech
football team. *boards, 8vo.
Lond., "The Czechoslovak"
1943.*

BASSOMPIERRE, FRANCOIS DE.
Memoirs of the embassy of the
Marshal de Bassompierre to the
court of England, in 1626.
*morocco, 8vo. Lond., Murray,
1819.*

BATCHELOR, JOHN. The Ainu
and their folk lore. *buckram,
8vo. Lond., Religious Tract
Society, 1901.*

BATCHELOR, JULIE FORSYTH
*and* DE LYS, CLAUDIA.
Superstitious? Here's why!
*buckram, 12mo. N.Y., Harcourt,
Brace, 1954.*

BATEMAN, H.M. A book of
drawings. *boards, folio. Lond.,
Methuen, 1922. 5th ed.*

_____ Burlesques. *boards,
4to. Lond., Duckworth, 1916.*

_____ More drawings.
*boards, folio. Lond., Methuen,
1922.*

_____ Suburbia. *boards, 4to.
Lond., Methuen, 1922.*

BATES "BRAINLESS" The life
and death of the Kaiser in six
chapters and a headache.
*paper, narrow 8vo. Bost.,
Davis, 1917.*

"BATHROOM PHILOSOPHY"
Laughin tissue. (A roll of toilet
tissue imprinted with gags or
jokes) *Asbury Park, N.J.,
Adams, n.d.*

BATHROOM READER. *buckram,
8vo. Wm. Penn, 1946.*

BATTLE OF THE SEXES. *paper,
16mo. N.Y., Avon, 1955.*

BAUM, LYMAN FRANK. Rinkitink
in Oz. *boards, 16mo. Chic.,
Rand McNally, 1926. Abridged
ed.*

_____ Wizard of Oz. *buckram, 8vo. N.Y., Grosset & Dunlap, 1956.*

BAXENDALE, WALTER. Dictionary of anecdote, incident,
illustrative fact .. *simulated
leather, 8vo. Lond., Dickinson,
1903. 6th ed.*

BAXTER, JOHN E. Locker room
ballads. *buckram, 12mo. N.Y.,
Appleton, 1923.*

BAXTER, W.G. Fifty more Sloper cartoons. *buckram, wide 4to.* *Lond., Dalziel, 1888.*

BAXTER, WILLIAM J. How to make money . . . that you can keep. *paper, 4to. N.Y., International Economic Research Bureau, 1961.*

BAYER, ELEANOR *and* BAYER, LEO. Dirty hands across the sea. *buckram, 8vo. Cleveland, World, 1952.*

BAYLEY, F.W.N. The exhibition. *buckram, 12mo. Lond., Darton, 1861.*

BAYLEY, HAROLD. Lost language of symbolism. *2v. buckram, 8vo. Lond., Williams & Norgate, 1951.*

BEABLE, W.H., *comp.* Epitaphs; graveyard humour and eulogy. *boards, 12mo. N.Y., Crowell, 1925.*

BEACH, REX. Too fat to fight. *boards, 12mo. N.Y., Harper, 1919.*

"BEACHCOMBER" *see* MORTON, JOHN BINGHAM.

BEARD, W.H. Humor in animals. *buckram, 4to. N.Y., Putnams', 1885.*

BEARDSLEY, AUBREY. The best of Beardsley, collected and edited by R. A. Walker. *buckram, 4to. Lond., Spring Books, n.d.*

BEATON, CECIL. I take great pleasure. *buckram, 8vo. N.Y., Day, 1956.*

BEATTIE, JAMES. The minstrel, or, The progress of genius. *calf, 16mo. Alnwick, Cainach & Davison, 1898.*

BEATTY, JEROME, *jr.* Sex rears its lovely head. *paper, 12mo. N.Y., Bantam Books, 1956.*

BEAUMONT, EDOUARD *de.* The sword and womankind, being an informative history of indiscreet revelations. *buckram, 8vo. N.Y., Panurge, 1930.*

BEGGINGTON, W.G., *ed.* A tale told. *buckram, 12mo. Lond., Allen & Unwin, 1952.*

BECHTEL, JOHN H. Proverbs. *buckram, 16mo. Phila., Penn, 1911.*

BECK, FRED. Second carrot from the end. *buckram, 8vo. N.Y., Morrow, 1946.*

──────── 73 years in a sand trap. *buckram, 8vo. N.Y., Wyn, 1949.*

BECK, THOMAS. The age of frivolity, by Timothy Touch'em, *pseud. paper, 16mo. Lond., Author, 1807. 2d. ed., rev. and enl.*

BECKER, MAY LAMBERTON. Home book of laughter. *buckram, 12mo. N.Y., Dodd, Mead, 1948.*

BEDE, CUTHBERT. Little Mr. Bouncer and his friend, Verdant Green. *buckram, 12mo. Bost., Little, Brown, 1893.*

BEDROOM COMPANION, or, A cold night's entertainment. *buckram, 8vo. N.Y., Arden, 1943.*

BEDSIDE TALES: a gay collection. *buckram, 8vo. N.Y., Penn, 1945.*

BEEBE, LUCIUS. Snoot if you must. *buckram, 8vo. N.Y., Appleton-Century, 1943.*

BEECHER, HENRY WARD.
Beecher as a humorist. Comp.
by Eleanor Kirk. *buckram, 12mo.*
*N.Y., Fords, Howard & Hulbert,*
*1887.*

——————— Metaphors, similes
and other characteristic sayings. *buckram, 12mo. N.Y.,*
*Graham, 1895.*

BEERBOHM, MAX. Fifty caricatures. *buckram, 8vo. Lond.,*
*Heinemann, 1923.*

——————— Max's Nineties; drawings, 1892-1899. *boards, 4to.*
*Lond., Hart-Davis, 1958.*

——————— Seven men, and two
others. *paper, 16mo. Harmonds-*
*worth, Middlesex, Penguin,*
*1954.*

BEETON'S BOOK OF ANEC-
DOTE, JOKES AND JESTS.
*half-calf, 8vo. Lond., Beeton,*
*n.d.*

BEETON'S BOOK OF JOKES
AND JESTS, or, Good things
said and sung. *paper, 8vo.*
*Lond., Ward, Lock & Tyler, n.d.*

BEETON'S CHRISTMAS ANNUAL.
14th season. The siliad, or,
The siege of the seats. *buck-*
*ram, 8vo. Lond., Ward, Lock &*
*Tyler, n.d.*

BEETON'S CHRISTMAS ANNUAL.
19th season. D's diary. *paper,*
*8vo. Lond., Ward, Lock & Co.,*
*n.d.*

BEITH, JOHN HAY. The queen of
hearts, by Ian Hay. *paper, 12mo.*
*Phila., Penn, 1912.*

——————— The right stuff. *buck-*
*ram, 16mo. Edinburgh, Black-*
*wood, 1910.*

BELFOUR, JOHN. Fables on subjects connected with literature.
*calf., 16mo. Lond., Whitting-*
*ham, 1804.*

BELL, EDWARD A. These meddle-
some attorneys. *buckram, 8vo.*
*Lond., Secker, 1939.*

BELL, HORACE. Reminiscences
of a ranger. *buckram, 12mo.*
*Santa Barbara, Hebberd, 1927.*

BELL, JOHN JOY. Wee Macgregor
again; a sequel. *paper, 16mo.*
*Glasgow, Scotts Pictorial Pub.*
*Co., n.d.*

BELL, JUNE. It's a joke. *buck-*
*ram, 12mo. N.Y., Pageant*
*Press, 1955.*

BELL, SAM HANNA. Erin's
orange lily. *buckram, 12mo.*
*Lond., Dobson, 1956.*

BELLEW, FRANK. The art of
amusing. *buckram, 12mo. N.Y.,*
*Carleton, 1867.*

——————— Chip's unnatural
history. *boards, 16mo. N.Y.,*
*Stokes, 1888.*

——————— That comic primer.
*buckram, 16mo. N.Y., Carlton,*
*1877.*

BELLOC, HILAIRE. Cautionary
verses. *cloth, 12mo. Lond.,*
*Duckworth, 1939.*

——————— Methuen's library of
humour: Hilaire Belloc. *buck-*
*ram, 16mo. Lond., Methuen,*
*1935.*

BELL'S BRITISH THEATRE.
*24v. half-calf, 24mo. Lond.,*
*Bell's Library, 1795.*

BELLUS, JEAN. Clementine
cherie; the rage of Paris. *buck-*
*ram, 4to. N.Y., Grayson, 1955.*

BELSON, WALTER. Who me? *buck-ram, 8vo. Drexel Hill, Bell, 1951.*

BEMELMANS, LUDWIG. Hotel Bemelmans. *buckram, 8vo. N.Y., Viking, 1946.*

——————— How to travel incognito. *buckram, 12mo. Lond., Hamilton, 1952.*

——————— Life class. *paper, 12mo. West Drayton, Penguin, 1948.*

——————— My war with the United States. *buckram, 12mo. N.Y., Modern Library, 1941.*

BEN-GAVRIEL, M.Y. Mahaschavi in peace and war. *buckram, 8vo. N.Y., Citadel, 1960.*

BENCHLEY, ROBERT. Benchley beside himself. *buckram, 8vo. N.Y., Harper, 1943.*

——————— Benchley — or else! *buckram, 12mo. Lond., Dobson, 1948.*

——————— Benchley roundup. *buckram, 8vo. Lond., Cassell, 1956.*

——————— Chips off the old Benchley. *buckram, 8vo. N.Y., Harper, 1949.*

——————— The early worm. *buckram, 12mo. Garden City, Blue Ribbon, 1946.*

——————— Love conquers all. *buckram, 12mo. N.Y., Holt, 1922.*

——————— My ten years in a quandary and how they grew. *buckram, 8vo. N.Y., Blue Ribbon, 1936.*

——————— Of all things. *buck-ram, 12mo. N.Y., Holt, 1921.*

——————— Pluck and luck. *buck-ram, 8vo. N.Y., Blue Ribbon, 1925.*

——————— 20,000 leagues under the sea, or, David Copperfield. *buckram, 8vo. N.Y., Blue Ribbon, 1946.*

BENDER, C.J. African jungle tales. *paper, 24mo. Girard, Kan., Haldeman-Julius, n.d. (Little Blue Books.)*

——————— Proverbs of West Africa. *paper, 32mo. Girard, Kan., Haldeman-Julius, n.d. (Little Blue Books.)*

BENECKE, ELSE C.M., tr. Selected Polish tales. *buckram, 16mo. Lond., Milford, 1921.*

BENHAM, FREDDIE. Laugh, you sinners. *buckram, 8vo. N.Y., Fell, 1955.*

BENNET, H. The treasury of wit. *2v. in 1. half calf, 12mo. Lond., Dilly, 1786.*

BENNETT, ARNOLD. Polite farces for the drawing-room. *boards, 12mo. N.Y., Doran, n.d.*

BENNETT, CHARLES H. Proverbs with pictures. *boards, small 4to. Lond., Tegg, 1877.*

BENNETT, EDNA. The best cartoons from France. *buckram, 4to. N.Y., Simon & Schuster, 1953.*

BENNETT, F.W. Tiddyoody pie. *paper, 8vo. n.p., n.d.*

BENNETT, J.A.W. The parlement of foules; an interpretation. *buckram, 8vo. Oxford, Clarendon, 1957.*

BENNETT, JAMES O'DONNELL. When good fellows get together. *boards, 12mo. Chic., Reilly & Britton, 1908.*

BENSON, E.F. *and* MILES, E.H.
The mad annual. *paper, 8vo.
Lond., Richards, 1903.*

———— Spook stories. *buckram, 8vo. Lond., Hutchinson,
n.d.*

BENSTEAD, C.R. Alma mater; a
profound study of a great
university. *buckram, 12mo.
Lond., Muller, 1944.*

———— Hic, haec, hock! A
low fellow's grammar and guide
to drinking. *buckram, 12mo.
Lond., Muller, 1934.*

———— Steady, boys, steady!
A profound study of the royal*
navy. *buckram, 12mo. Lond.,
Muller, 1943.*

BENTLEY, EDMUND C. Base-
less biography. *buckram, 12mo.
Lond., Constable, 1939.*

BENTLEY, NICOLAS. Animal,
vegetable and South Kensing-
ton. *boards, 4to. Lond.,
Methuen, 1940.*

———— Die? I thought I'd
laugh! *boards, 4to. Lond.,
Methuen, 1936. 2d. ed.*

———— Gammon and espio-
nage. *cloth, 8vo. Lond.,
Cresset, 1938.*

———— How can you bear
to be human? *boards, 4to.
Lond., Deutsch, 1957.*

———— Ready refusal, or,
The white liars engagement
book. *boards, 12mo. Lond.,
Methuen, 1935.*

BENTLEY'S MISCELLANY. *5v.
half-calf, 8vo. Lond., Bentley,
1837-1839.*

BENTON, ROBERT *and* SCHMIDT,
HARVEY. The in and out book.
*boards, wide 12mo. N.Y., Vik-
ing, 1959.*

BENTZ, FELIX. Oil talk. *paper,
12mo. San Antonio, Texas,
Oliver, 1952.*

BERENSTAIN, STANLEY *and*
BERENSTAIN, JANICE. And
baby makes four. *boards, 8vo.
N.Y., Macmillan, 1956.*

———— Have a baby, my wife
just had a cigar. *paper, 16mo.
N.Y., Dell, 1960.*

———— It's all in the family.
*boards, 4to. N.Y., Dutton,
1958.*

———— Lover boy; the last
word in animal husbandry.
*boards, 8vo. N.Y., Macmillan,
1958.*

———— Tax-wise; a pic-
torial romp through the tax
form. *paper, 8vo. N.Y., Schuman, 1952.*

BERESFORD, JAMES. The
miseries of human life; or,
The groans of Timothy Testy
and Samuel Sensitive. *2v. quarter-calf, 12mo. Lond., Wright,
1826.*

BERGER, OSCAR. Aesop's
foibles. *buckram, 4to. N.Y.,
Day, 1947.*

———— A la carte ... the
gourmet's phantasmagoria in
fifty cartoons. *buckram, 4to.
Lond., Hutchinson, 1951.*

BERGMANN, FRANZ. Uriel for
president. Text by M. Peake.
*buckram, 8vo. Bost., Hale,
Cushman and Flint, 1938.*

BERGSON, HENRI. Laughter; an essay on the meaning of the comic. Translation by Cloudesley Brereton and Fred Rothwell. *buckram, 12mo. Lond., Macmillan, 1921.*

BERKELEY, GRANTLEY F. Anecdotes of the upper ten thousand. *2v. buckram, 8vo. Lond., R. Bentley, 1867. 2d ed.*

BERLE, MILTON. Milton Berle's fabulous fun-tasy. Out of my trunk. *paper, 4to. N.Y., Grayson, 1945.*

BERNARD OF CLAIRVAUX, Saint. The proverbs of Saynt Bernarde. *boards, 16mo. Chiswick, Caradoc, 1934.*

BERNHARDT, SARAH. Sarah Bernhardt's philosophy of love. *paper, 32mo. Girard, Kan., Haldeman-Julius, n.d. (Little Blue Books)*

BERRY, BREWTON. You and your superstitions. *buckram, 8vo. Columbia, Mo., Lucas, 1940.*

BERTHOLDE, or Wonderful sallies of wit. *buckram, 16mo. Bombay, Sagoon, 1887.*

BEST, SIGNE ELLISON. Whys and otherwise. *buckram, 8vo. Santa Ana, Calif., Golden Press, 1929.*

BEST ARTICLES AND STORIES FROM SELECT CURRENT MAGAZINES. November 1957- October 1959. *binder.*

BESTLAFFS OF THE YEAR. *buckram, 12mo. N.Y., Harper, 1927.*

BETJEMAN, JOHN. What's the use? *boards, 8vo. Lond., Mowbray, 1955.*

BETTS, ERNEST. Heraclitus, or, The future of films. *buckram, 16mo. Lond., Kegan Paul, Trench, Trubner, 1928.*

BEVAN, J.O. Wits and their humours. *buckram, 16mo. Lond., Allen. 1911.*

BEYLE, MARIE. Maxims of love, by Stendhal, *pseud. paper, 32mo. Girard, Kan., Haldeman-Julius, n.d. (Little Blue Books)*

BIBLE. Self-contradictions of the Bible. *paper, 32mo. Girard, Kan., Haldeman-Julius, n.d. (Little Blue Books)*

BIBLE. O.T. ECCLESIASTIS. The wisdom of Koheleth; a new translation by Robert Gordis. *buckram, 12mo. Lond., East & West Library, 1950.*

BIBLE. O.T. PROVERBS. The proverbs, translated out the original Hebrew. *buckram, 48mo. Lond., Eyre & Spottiswoode, 1846.*

_____ Proverbs, with commentary by Julius H. Greenstone. *buckram, 8vo. Phila., Jewish Pub. Soc., 1950.*

BIBLE FOLK-LORE. *buckram, 8vo. N.Y., Bouton, 1884.*

BICKERSTAFF, ISAAC. The tatler. *4v. calf, 12mo. Lond., Tonson, 1764.*

BIERCE, AMBROSE. Extraordinary opinions on commonplace subjects. *paper, 32mo. Girard, Kan., Haldeman-Julius. n.d. (Little Blue Books)*

_____ Fantastic debunking fables. *paper, 32mo. Girard, Kan., Haldeman-Julius, n.d. (Little Blue Books)*

BIGELOW, L.J. Bench and bar, a complete digest of the wit, humor, asperities and amenities of the law. *buckram, 12mo. N.Y., Harper, 1867.*

———— *Same. New edition, 1871.*

BILDERSEE, ADELE, comp. The hidden books. *buckram, 8vo. Lond., Abelard-Schuman, 1957.*

"BILL" Rice-paddy daddy; the adventures of G. I. "Bill" in Japan. *paper, 12mo. Rutland, Vt., Tuttle, 1956.*

BILL, ALFRED H. Alas, poor Yorick. *buckram, 8vo. Bost., Little, Brown, 1927.*

BILLINGS, JOSH *see* SHAW, HENRY WHEELER.

BIOGRAPHICAL ANECDOTES OF THE FOUNDERS OF THE FRENCH REPUBLIC . . . *paper, 16mo. Phila., Carey, 1808.*

———— *Same. 2v. boards, 12mo. Lond., Phillips, 1799.*

BIOGRAPHICAL ANECDOTES OF WILLIAM HOGARTH. *calf., 8vo. Lond., Nichols, 1784.*

BIRD, ARTHUR. Just a few lines. *buckram, 12mo. Lond., Methuen, 1944. 3d. ed.*

BIRD, KENNETH. Between the lines, by Fougasse, *pseud. buckram, 12mo. Lond., Methuen, 1958.*

———— The changing face of Britain. *buckram, wide 24mo. Lond., Methuen, 1940.*

———— Fun fair. *quarter-calf., folio. Lond., Hutchinson, 1934.*

———— The good-tempered pencil. *buckram, 8vo. Lond., Reinhardt, 1956.*

———— The home circle. *buckram, 12mo. Lond., Methuen, 1945.*

———— The luck of the draw. *buckram, 12mo. Lond., Methuen, 1942.*

———— The neighbours; an animal anthology. *buckram, 12mo. Lond., Methuen, 1954.*

———— P.T.O. a book of drawings. *boards, folio. Lond., Methuen, 1926.*

———— Second century of humour. *buckram, 8vo. Lond., Hutchinson, n.d.*

———— Stop or go; a diary for 1939. *buckram, 12mo. Lond., Methuen, 1938.*

———— You have been warned. *buckram, 12mo. Lond., Methuen, 1937. 9th ed.*

BIRMINGHAM, GEORGE A. The lighter side of Irish life. *buckram, 8vo. Lond., Foulis, 1912.*

BIRRELL, AUGUSTINE. Obiter dicta. *2v. buckram, 16mo. Lond., E. Stock, 1896. First and second series.*

BIRTHDAY GREETING CARD. "A Gibson smile card" leaflet. *Gibson, Cinn., n.d.*

BISHOP, JOSEPH B. Early political caricature in America. *pamphlet. Century magazine, 1892.*

BISHOP, MORRIS. A bowl of Bishop. *buckram, 8vo. N.Y., Dial, 1954.*

———— A treasury of British humor. *buckram, 8vo. N.Y., Coward-McCann, 1942.*

BISWAS, NALINI MOHAN.
Anecdotes of ancient history.
*boards, 12mo. Calcutta,
Biswas, n.d.*

BITNEY, MAYME RIDDLE.
Humorous monologues. *paper,
12mo. Minneapolis, Denison,
n.d.*
—————— Monologues, grave
and gay. *paper, 12mo. Minneapolis, Denison, 1911.*

BLACK JOKES AND BROWN FOR
COUNTRY OR TOWN. *paper,
8vo. Lond., Dean, n.d.*

BLACKHAM, ROBERT J. Woman,
in honour and dishonour. *buckram,
8vo. Lond., Low, Marston, 1936.*

BLACKMANTEL, BERNARD. The
punster's pocket-book, or, The
art of punning. . . . Illus. by
Robert Cruikshank. *half-calf.,
12mo. Lond., Sherwood, Gilbert
& Piper, 1826.*

BLACKMORE, R. D. Tales from the
telling-house. *buckram, 12mo.
Lond., Low, Marston, 1896.*

"BLACKWOOD" Humorous tales.
*buckram, 12mo. Edinburgh,
Blackwood, 1935.*
—————— More humorous tales
from Blackwood. *buckram, 12mo.
Edinburgh, Blackwood, 1954.*
—————— Tales from the Out-
posts. In Lighter vein. *buckram,
12mo. Edinburgh, Blackwood,
1942.*

BLAIR, ALAN. More bright
brevities. *buckram, 12mo. Lond.,
Muller, 1945. 2d.ed.*

BLAIR, WALTER and MEINE,
FRANKLIN J. Half horse, half
alligator, the growth of the
Mike Fink legend. *buckram, 8vo.
Chic., Univ. of Chic. Press,
1956.*

—————— Horse sense in
American humor, from Benjamin
Franklin to Ogden Nash. *buckram,
12mo. Chic., Univ. of Chic.
Press, 1942.*

BLAKE, RODNEY, *comp. and ed.*
After dinner verse. *buckram, 12
mo. N.Y., Burt, n.d.*

BLATT, W. M. Inklings; one man's
observations. *paper, 8vo.
Girard, Kan., Haldeman-Julius,
1948.*

BLIGHTY LAUGHS ITS WAY TO
VICTORY. June 6, 1942-Feb.
28, 1942. *Lond., Ludgate,
1942. Newspapers mounted in
folder.*

BLOCK, HERBERT. The Herblock
book. *buckram, 8vo. Bost.,
Beacon, 1952.*
—————— Herblock's here and
now. *buckram, 8vo. N.Y., Simon
& Schuster, 1955.*

BLOSSOMS OF ANECDOTE AND
WIT, or, Mirth for the parlour.
*half-calf., 16mo. Lond., Baldwin,
Cradock and Joy, 1823.*

BLOUET, PAUL. A Frenchman in
America (The Anglo-Saxon race
revisited) by Max O'Rell, *pseud.
buckram, 12mo. Bristol, Arrowsmith, 1891.*
—————— Friend MacDonald.
*buckram, 16mo. Bristol, Arrow-
smith, 1887.*
—————— John Bull, junior,
or, French as she is traduced.
*paper, 16mo. N.Y., Cassell,
1888.*
—————— Jonathan and his
continent. (Rambles through
American society) *buckram,
12mo. N.Y., Cassell, 1889.*

BLUMENTHAL, WALTER HART.
Formats and foibles; a few
books which be called curious.
*48mo. morocco. Worcester, St.
Onge, 1956.*

BLUNDEN, GEOFFREY. The
looking-glass conference.
*buckram, 8vo. N.Y.,
Vanguard, 1956.*

BLUNT, ARTHUR A. At retreat.
*paper, 12mo. Bost., Baker,
1901.*

BLUNT, J. J. Undesigned coincidences in the writings of
the Old and New Testaments.
*buckram, 12mo. Lond., Murray,
1876. 13th ed.*

BLUSHING DEEP AND PALING.
*paper, 8vo. Stanford, Drofnats,
1947.*

BLYTH, HARRY, *comp.* Eat, drink
and be merry; or, Dainty bits
from many tables. Amusing
anecdotes, anecdotal customs
interesting facts and food.
*folk-lore. paper, 12mo. Lond.,
Brook, n.d.*

BLYTH, R. H. Humour in English
literature. *paper. 12mo. Tokyo,
Hokuseido, 1959.*

——————— Japanese humour.
*buckram, 12mo. Tokyo. Japan
Travel Bureau, 1957.*

——————— Oriental humour.
*buckram, 8vo. Tokyo,
Hokuseido, 1959.*

——————— Senryu; Japanese
satirical verses. *buckram, 8vo.
Tokyo, Hokuseido, 1949.*

BLYTHE, SAMUEL G. The
fakers. *buckram, 12mo. N.Y.,
Doran, 1914.*

BOAS, GUY. An anthology of wit.
*buckram, 12mo. Lond.,
Macmillan, 1934.*

——————— Humorous narratives.
*buckram, 12mo. Lond., Arnold,
n.d.*

——————— Lays of learning.
*buckram, 12mo. Lond., Jenkins,
1926.*

——————— Traffic and theatre
rhymes. *boards, 8vo. Lond.,
Methuen, 1925.*

BOATRIGHT, MODY C. Folk
laughter on the American
frontier. *buckram, 12mo. N.Y.,
Macmillan, 1949.*

——————— Tall tales from
Texas. *paper, 8vo. Girard, Kan.
Haldeman-Julius, 1946.*

BOBBIN, TIM. Miscellaneous
works. *half-calf, 16mo. Manchester, Hopper, n.d.*

BOBBY AND BEAK. Cutchery
chips. *paper, 8vo. Lahore,
Civil and Military Gazette,
1918.*

BODENHAM, JOHN. Politeuphuia.
Wits commonwealth. Newly
corrected and amended. *calf.,
16mo. Lond., Flesher, 1674.*

BODENHEIM, MAXWELL.
Introducing irony. *boards, 8vo.
N.Y., Boni & Liveright, 1922.*

BODMER, FREDERICK. The loom
of language. *buckram, 8vo.
N.Y., Norton, 1944.*

BOHN, HENRY G. A hand-book of
proverbs . . . *buckram, 12mo.
Lond., Bell & Daldy, 1870.*

——————— A polyglot of foreign
proverbs. *buckram, 12mo. Lond.,
Bell, 1893.*

BOKSER, BEN ZION. The wisdom of the Talmud; a thousand years of Jewish thought. *boards, 12 mo. N.Y., Philosophical Library, 1951.*

BOLTIN, LEE. Jail keys made here, and other signs. *paper, 4to. N.Y., Meridian, 1959.*

BOLTINOFF, HENRY. The howls of ivy. *paper, 12mo. N.Y., Bantam books, 1955.*

BOMBAUGH, C.C. Gleanings from the harvest-fields of literature. *buckram, 12mo. Baltimore, Kurtz, 1869.*

BONERS OF HAWAII, an anthology of magnificent mistakes. *paper, 12mo. Honolulu, White Knight Press, 1951.*

BONES, HIS GAGS AND STUMP SPEECHES. *paper, 12mo. N.Y., Weyman, 1879.*

THE BOOK-FOOL; bibliophily in caricatures. Supplement to the American book-collector. *paper, 4to. Metuchen, N.H., 1934.*

BOOK OF AMERICAN HUMOR IN PROSE AND VERSE. *buckram, 12mo. N.Y., Duffield, 1925.*

BOOK OF ANECDOTES AND BUDGET OF FUN. *buckram, 12mo. Phila., Evans, 1859.*

A BOOK OF "CHARACTERS" FROM THEOPHRASTUS, JOSEPH HALL, SIR THOMAS OVERBURY, & C. *buckram, 8vo. Lond., Routledge, 1924.*

BOOK OF ENTERTAINMENT, OF CURIOSITIES AND WONDERS IN NATURE, ART, AND MIND. *buckram, 16mo. N.Y., Francis, 1847.*

BOOK OF FORD JOKES. *paper, 24mo. Bost., Standard Thermometer Co., n.d.*

BOOK OF FUN. First and second series. *2v. buckram, 16mo. Lond., Gilbert, n.d.*

BOOK OF FUN. Hundreds of jokes and riddles. *buckram, 12mo. Lond., Hamilton, n.d.*

BOOK OF HUMOROUS ANECDOTES. *paper, 32mo. Girard, Kan., Haldeman-Julius, n.d. (Little Blue Books)*

BOOK OF HUMOROUS POETRY. *buckram, 12mo. Edinburgh, Nimmo, 1881.*

BOOK OF HUMOUR, WIT AND WISDOM; a manual of table-talk. *half-boards, 24mo. Lond., Routledge, 1887.*

BOOK OF JESTS. *simulated leather, 32mo. Lond., Hill, n.d.*

BOOK OF LAUGHTER, *quarter-buckram, 8vo. Manchester, Allied Newspapers, ltd. n.d.*

BOOK OF MYSTIC-HUMOROUS STORIES, by Algernon Blackwood, Theophile Gautier, Guy de Maupassant. *paper, 32 mo. Girard, Kan., Haldeman-Julius, n.d. (Little Blue Books)*

BOOK OF SCOTISH PASQUILS, 1568-1715. *quarter-calf., 8vo. Edinburgh, Paterson, 1868.*

BOOK OF TABLE-TALK. *2v. half-calf, 16mo. Lond., Knight, 1836.*

BOOKS AND AUTHORS: curious facts and characteristic sketches. *boards, 16mo. Brooklyn, Swayne, n.d.*

BOONZAEIR, D. C. Rand faces. *buckram, folio. Cape Town, Argus, 19_ _.*

BOORDE, ANDREW. The wisdom of Andrew Boorde. *boards, 8 vo. Leicester, Backus, 1936.*

BOOSEY, THOMAS. Anecdotes of fish and fishing. *buckram, 8vo. Lond., Hamilton, Adams, 1887.*

BOOTH, HILLIARD. His majesty, the queen. *paper, 12mo. N.Y., French, 1927.*

BOOTH, J. B. Pink parade. *buckram, 8vo. N.Y., Dutton, 1933.*

BOOTH, JOHN. Epigrams, ancient and modern. *buckram, 12mo. Lond., Longman, Green, Longman, Roberts, 1863.*

——————— Metrical epitaphs, ancie and modern. *buckram, 16mo. Lond., Bickers, 1868.*

BOOTHBY, *Sir* BROOKE. Fables and satires, with an essay on the Esopean fable. *2v. half-calf., 12mo. Edinburgh, G. Ramsay, 1809.*

BOOTHROYD, J.B. Motor if you must. *buckram, 12mo. Lond., Allen & Unwin, 1960.*

BORDEN, RAYMOND D. Maggie of the suicide fleet. *buckram, 8vo. N.Y., Doubleday, Doran, 1930.*

BORROW, GEORGE, *tr.* The Turkish jester, or, The pleasantries of Cogia Nasr Eddin effendi. *boards, 8vo. Ipswich, Webber, 1884.*

BOSTWICK, MARY E. Last page lyrics. *boards, 12mo. Indianapolis, Pratt Poster, n.d.*

BOSWELL, RICHARD. Dr. Johnson's table-talk, containing aphorisms on literature life and manners. *calf, 12mo. Lond., Dilly, 1789.*

BOSWORTH, ALLAN R. Ginza Go, papa-san. *buckram, 12mo. Tokyo, Tuttle, 1955.*

BOTKIN, B. A. The American people in their stories, legends, tall tales, traditions, ballads and songs. *buckram, 8vo. Lond., Pilot Press, 1946.*

——————— The lore of the Lizzie label. *pamphlet. Reprint from American Speech, Dec. 1930.*

——————— Sidewalks of America. *buckram, 8vo. Indianapolis, Bobbs-Merrill, 1954.*

——————— Treasury of American anecdotes. *buckram, 8vo. N.Y., Random House, 1857.*

——————— Treasury of American folklore. *buckram, 8vo. N.Y., Crown, 1944.*

——————— Treasury of Mississippi folk-lore. *buckram, 8vo. N.Y., Crown, 1955.*

——————— Treasury of Southern folklore. *buckram, 8vo. N.Y., Crown, 1949.*

BOUCICAULT, DION L. London assurance. *paper, 12mo. N.Y., Dick & Fitzgerald, 1889.*

BOURDEILLE, PETER *de.* Collection of Spanish rhodomontades, witty conceits, devices, tales, fights, jests, news . . . *quarter-morocco, 8vo. Lond., 1741.*

BOWEN, CATHERINE DRINKER. Yankee from Olympus. *buckram, 8vo. Bost., Little, Brown, 1944.*

BOWEN-ROWLANDS, ERNEST. 72 years at the bar. *buckram, 8 vo. Lond., Macmillan, 1924.*

BOWER, EDWARD W. *de. comp. and ed.* The business man's book of proverbs. *limp leather, 12mo. Chic., Blackstone, 1920.*

BOWES, EDWARD, comp. Verse I like. buckram, 8vo. N.Y., Garden City, 1939.

BOWMAN, R. C. Freckles and tan. paper, 16mo. Minneapolis, Priv. Print., 1900.

BOYCE, ANNIE M. Tall tales from a ranch. boards, 8vo. San Antonio, Naylor, 1957.

BOYKIN, ELEANOR. Famous quotations. paper, 8vo. Home Institute, 1940.

BOYLE, MARY. Aesop redivivus. buckram, 12mo. Lond., Field & Tuer, 1890.

BRADBURY, CHARLES, Cabinet of jewels opened to the curious by a key of real knowledge. buckram, 12mo. Berwick, Phorson, Law & Matthews, 1785.

BRADBURY, MALCOLM. Phogey! or, How to have class in a classless society. buckram, 12mo. Lond., Parrish, 1960.

BRADSHAW, PERCY V. They make us smile. buckram, 12mo. Lond., Chapman and Hall, 1942.

BRALEY, BERTON. Songs of the workaday world. buckram, 8vo. N.Y., Doran, 1915.

BRANDEIS, LOUIS D. True Americanism. paper, 24mo. (Personal growth Leaflets)

BRANDON-THOMAS, JEVAN. Charley's Aunt's father; a life of Brandon Thomas. buckram, 8vo. Lond., Saunders, MacGibbon & Kee, 1955.

BRANT, SEBASTIAN. Stultifera navis; the modern ship of fools. calf., 16mo. Lond., W. Miller, 1807.

BRAUN, WILBUR. Youth and Uncle Sam. paper, 12mo. N.Y., French, 1941.

BRAVE CRACK! An anthology of Ulster wit and humor. buckram, 8vo. Belfast, Carter, n.d.

BREDESON, LENORE and NELSON, DICK, comps. Space jokes, cosmic cartoons and Martian laughs. paper, 8vo. N.Y., Citadel press, 1959.

BREEZY JOKES. paper, 24mo. Baltimore, Ottenheimer, 1915.

BREGER, DAVE, ed. But that's unprintable. paper, 16mo. N.Y., Bantam, 1954.

_____ "G.I. Joe" from the pages of Yank and Stars and Stripes. buckram, 8vo. Garden City, Blue Ribbon, 1945.

_____ Private Breger in Britain. buckram, 12mo. Lond., Pilot, 1944.

BRENDLE, THOMAS and TROXWELL, WILLIAM S., comps. Pennsylvania German folk tales, legends, once-upon-a-time stories, maxims and sayings, spoken in the dialect popularly known as Pennsylvania Dutch. boards, 4to. Norristown, Pa., Pennsylvania German Society, 1944.

BRENNAN, IGNATIUS. Humorous poems. buckram, 12mo. Bost., Badger, 1916.

BRESLER, FENTON. Strictly legal. buckram, 12mo. Lond, Wingate, 1958.

BRETON, NICHOLAS. Cornvcopiae. Pasquil's night-cap, or Antidot for the head-ache. half-calf, 12mo. Lond., T. Thorpe, 1612. Reprinted by C. Whittingham at the Chiswick Press, 1819.

BREWER, R. F. Orthometry; the
art of versification. *buckram,
8vo. Edinburgh, Grant, 1937.*

BREWER, THOMAS. The life and
death of the Merry Deuill of
Edmonton. *boards, 8vo. Lond.,
Printed in the black letter, by
T.P. 1631. Reprinted by J.
Nichols, 1819.*

BRICKMAN, MORRIS. Do it yourself; or, My neighbor is an
idiot. *paper, 12mo. N.Y., Permabooks, 1955.*

_____ Don't do it yourself.
*paper, 16mo. N.Y., Permabooks,
1957.*

_____ Sure you can "Do it
yourself" *buckram, 4to. N.Y.,
Arlich, 1955.*

BRICKTOP *see* SMALL, GEORGE
G.

BRIDGES, CONSTANCE, *comp.*
Great thoughts of great
Americans. *buckram, 12mo. N.Y.
Crowell, 1951.*

BRIDGEWATER, DONALD. Author!
Author! *buckram, 8vo. Lond.,
Westhouse, 1945.*

BRIGGS, CLARE. How to start
the day wrong. Aint it a grand
and glorious feelin'. *buckram,
wide 12mo. N.Y., Wise, 1930.
(v.1 of Selected drawings)*

_____ Kelly pool. Tedious
pastimes. Golf. *buckram, wide
12mo. N.Y., Wise, 1930. (v.2 of
Selected drawings)*

_____ Selected drawings;
memorial edition. *4v. buckram,
wide 12mo. N.Y., Wise, 1930.*

_____ That guiltiest
feeling. Oh, man. Old songs.
*buckram, wide 12mo. N.Y., Wise
1930. (v.3 of selected drawings)*

_____ When a feller needs a
friend. *buckram, wide 12mo. N.Y.,
Wise, 1930. (v.4 of Selected
drawings.)*

BRIGHOUSE, HAROLD. Lonesome
like. *paper, 24mo. Lond.,
Gowans & Gray, 1914.*

_____ The price of coal.
*paper, 24mo. Lond., Gowans &
Gray, 1911.*

BRIGHTE, JOHN, *pseud.* The book
to keep the spirits up in dull
and gloomy hours. *buckram, 16
mo. Lond., Ewins, 1868.*

_____ Same. *Halifax,
Nicholson, 1865.*

_____ Same. *Wakefield,
Nicholson, n.d.*

A BRIGHTER-SIDE ANTHOLOGY:
the third pocket-trivet. *boards,
24mo. Lond., Morning Post,
1934.*

BRINGS, LAWRENCE M. Clever
introductions for chairmen.
*buckram, 8vo. Minneapolis,
Denison, 1954.*

_____ Humorous intro-
ductions for emcees. *buckram,
8vo, Minneapolis, Denison,
1955.*

BRINISTOOL, E. A. Trail dust of
a maverick. *buckram, 12mo.
N.Y., Dodd, Mead, 1914.*

BRINTON, SELWYN. The 18th
century in English caricature.
*leather, 16mo. Lond., Siegle,
1904.*

BRISCOE, ROBERT *and* HATCH,
ALDEN. For the life of me.
*buckram, 8vo. Bost., Little,
Brown, 1958.*

BRISK, RICHARD. The railway
book of fun. *buckram, 16mo.
Lond., Nicholson, n.d.*

BRISSETTE, HENRY J. Humour through history. *buckram, 12 mo. Paris, Les editions de L'Impremerie Industrielle et Artistique, 1938.*

BRISTOL, RICHARD R. *comp.* The wisdom of India, *paper, 8 vo. Girard, Kan., Haldeman-Julius, 1949.*

——————— The wisdom of the Chinese. *paper, 8vo. Girard, Kan., Haldeman-Julius, 1948.*

THE BRITISH APOLLO, containing two thousand answers to curious questions in most arts and sciences, serious, comical and humorous ... Performed by a Society of Gentlemen. *3v. calf., 16mo. Lond., T. Sanders, 1726.*

THE BRITISH DRAMA. *2v. calf., 8vo. Phila., Woodward, 1832.*

THE BRITISH MARTIAL; or, An anthology of English epigrams. *2v. in 1. half-calf., 16mo. Lond., Phillips, 1806.*

THE BRITISH THEATRE. *10v. half-calf., 32mo. Lond., Hughes, Whittingham, various dates, ca. 1800.*

BROAD GRINS, or, A cure for the horrors. *paper, 16mo. Lond., Evans, 1810.*

BROAD GRINS, or, Fun for the New Year. *paper, 8vo. Bost., Ainsworth, 1832.*

BROAD GRINS FROM CHINA. *buckram, 24mo. Lond., Bentley, 1852.*

BROCK, H. I. The little book of limericks. *buckram, 16mo. N.Y., Duell, Sloan & Pearce, 1947.*

BROCKBANK, RUSSELL. The Brockbank omnibus. *buckram, 4to. Lond., Perpetua, 1957.*

——————— *Same, N.Y., Putnam's 1959.*

——————— Manifold pressures; motoring misadventures of Major Upsett. *boards, wide 24 mo. Lond., Temple, 1958.*

——————— Up the straight. *buckram, 4to. Lond., Temple, n.d.*

BROMLEY, ALBERT J. The return uv Snowshoe Al. *buckram, 8vo. N.Y., Minton, Balch, 1927.*

——————— Snowshoe Al's bed time stories. *buckram, 8vo. N.Y. Minton, Balch, 1926.*

BROOK, ROGER. Really nurse! *buckram, 12mo. Lond., Souvenir, 1960.*

BROOKS, ELBRIDGE S. The true story of Abraham Lincoln, the American. *buckram, 8vo. Bost., Lothrop, 1896.*

BROOKS, FRED EMERSON. Cream toasts. *boards, 16mo. Chic., Forbes, 1915.*

BROOKS, SHIRLEY, *ed.* Amusing poetry. *paper, 16mo. Lond., Diprose & Bates, n.d. New ed.*

——————— Wit and humour (from Punch) *buckram, 16mo. Lond., Bradbury, Agnew, 1883.*

BROOKS, WILLIAM ALLAN. Fishin' fun; a treasury of fishing humor. *buckram, 8vo. N.Y., Derby, 1954.*

——————— Keep'em laughing; a fun manual for men in the military service. *N.Y., Knickerbocker, 1942.*

BROOKS, WILLIAM ALLAN. *ed.* The playboy's handbook; in defense of the bachelor. *paper, 8vo. N.Y., Knickerbocker, 1942.*

—————— The playboy's handbook; the delight of the bachelor. *paper, 12mo. N.Y., Knickerbocker, 1946.*

—————— The sexpert's travel guide. *buckram, 8vo. N.Y., Derby, 1956.*

BROOME, J.E. and ROSS, JOHN ADRIAN. Keep your eye on the ball. *buckram, 4to. Lond., Collins, 1936.*

BROTHER CHOLERIC *see* VAN ZELLER, HUBERT.

BROTHER JONATHAN'S JOKES, FUNNY STORIES AND LAUGHABLE SKETCHES. *paper, 8vo. N.Y., Excelsior, 1885.*

BROUGHAM AND VAUX, HENRY PETER BROUGHAM, *baron.* Brougham and his early friends. Letters to James Loch, 1798-1809. *3v. quarter-vellum, 4to. Lond., Priv. Printed, 1908.*

BROWER, BILL. The complete barbershop joke book. *buckram, 8vo. N.Y., Stravon, 1952.*

—————— The complete army-navy joke book. *buckram, 8vo. N.Y., Stravon, 1952.*

—————— The complete traveling salesman's joke book. *buckram, 8vo. N.Y., Stravon, 1952.*

BROWN, A.E. *and* JEFFCOTT, H.A. Beware of imitations! Compiled from the records of the U.S. Patent Office. *buckram 8vo. N.Y., Viking, 1932.*

BROWN, ALEX J. Popular recitations, humorous readings and laughable stories. *paper, 16mo. N.Y., Excelsior, 1891.*

BROWN, BETSEY. Foaks an' people; or, Three years in Millbrook. *buckram, 12mo. Chic., Donohue & Hennebery, 1888.*

BROWN, BRIAN, *comp.* Chinese nights entertainments. *buckram, 8vo. N.Y., Brentano's, 1922.*

—————— The wisdom of the Chinese; their philosophy in sayings and proverbs. *buckram, 8vo. N.Y., Garden City Pub. Co., 1938.*

BROWN, C.C. Malay sayings. *buckram, 8vo. Lond., Routledge & Kegan Paul, 1959.*

BROWN, CHARLES WALTER, *comp.* Comic recitations and readings. *paper, 16mo. Chic., Drake, 1903.*

BROWN, ELIJAH P. Ciderville folks as seen by Silas Ganderfoot. *buckram, 4to. Chic, Date. 1898.*

BROWN, FRANCIS. Political parables. *buckram, 8vo. Lond., T. Fisher Unwin, 1906.*

BROWN, HARRY. Artie Greengroin, pfc. *buckram, 12mo. N.Y., Knopf, 1945.*

BROWN, JAMES. Bible truths, with Shakspearian parallels. *buckram, 12mo. Lond., Whittaker, 1864. 2d.ed.*

BROWN, JOE E. Laughter is a wonderful thing. *buckram, 8vo. N.Y. Barnes, 1956.*

BROWN, JOHN. Essays on the characteristics. *calf., 8vo. Lond., Davis, 1751.*

BROWN, JOHN MASON. Accustomed as I am. *buckram, 8vo. N.Y., Norton, 1942.*

BROWN, MARSHALL, ed. Bulls and blunders. buckram, 12mo. Chic., Griggs, 1894. 2d ed.

_____ Humour of bulls and blunders. paper, 16mo. Lond., Gay & Hancock, 1925.

_____ Same. Lond., Gay and Bird, n.d.

_____ Sayings that never grow old; wit and humor of well-known quotations. buckram, 12 mo. Bost., Small, Maynard, 1918.

_____ Wit and humor. buckram, 12mo. Chic., Griggs, 1882.

_____ Wit and humor of bench and bar. buckram, 8vo. Chic., Flood, 1899.

_____ Wit and humor of familiar sayings. buckram, 16mo. Chic., Griggs, 1895.

BROWN, T. The polite modern jester: or, Wit-a-la mode. paper, 16mo. Newcastle, G. Robinson, 1775.

BROWN, THOMAS, the younger. Intercepted letters; or, The two-penny post-bag, to which are added, Trifles reprinted. half-calf, 16mo. Lond., Carr, 1813.

BROWN, THOMAS C., comp. Colorful California names; their history and meaning. pamphlet. San Francisco, American Trust co., 1957.

BROWN, TOM. Celebrated dunces. buckram, 12mo. Lond., Sunday School Union, n.d.

BROWN, WILL H. Illustrative incidents for public speakers. buckram, 12mo. Cincinnati, Standard Pub. Co., 1915. 5th ed.

_____ Patriotic illustrations for public speakers. buckram, 12mo. Cincinnati, Standard Pub. Co., 1919.

_____ Stories of the great war for public speakers. buckram, 12mo. Cincinnati, Standard Pub. Co., 1919.

_____ Wit and humor for public speakers. buckram, 12 mo. Cincinnati, Standard Pub. Co., 1916.

BROWN, WILLIAM F. The abominable showmen. paper, 12mo. N.Y., Signet, 1960.

_____ Beat, beat, beat. paper, 12mo. N.Y., Signet, 1959.

_____ The girl in the Freudian slip. paper, 12mo. Signet, 1959.

BROWNE, CHARLES FARRAR. Artemas Ward, his book. buckram, 16mo. Lond., John Camden Hotten, 1865.

_____ Same. N.Y., Carleton, 1862.

_____ Same. Girard, Kan., Haldeman-Julius, n.d. (Little Blue Books.)

_____ Artemas Ward, his travels. buckram, 12mo. N.Y., Carleton, 1865.

_____ Artemas Ward in London. buckram, 12mo. N.Y., Harper, 1912.

_____ Artemas Ward's best stories. buckram, 12mo. N.Y., Harper, 1912.

_____ Artemas Ward's lecture as delivered at the Egyptian Hall, London. buckram, 16mo. Lond., John Camden Hotten, 1869.

———————— Artemas Ward's travels. *paper, 32mo. Girard, Kan., Haldeman-Julius, n.d. (Little Blue Books)*

———————— Betsey Jane Ward, better-half to Artemas, hur book of goaks. *buckram, 12mo. N.Y., O'Kane, 1866.*

———————— Comic journey to California and back. *paper, 32mo. Girard, Kan., Haldeman-Julius, n.d. (Little Blue Books)*

———————— Complete works of Artemas Ward, with a biographical sketch by Melville D. Landon. *buckram, 12mo. N.Y., Dillingham, 1898. Rev.ed.*

———————— Letters to Punch and practical jokes, by Artemas Ward and Mark Twain. *buckram, 16mo. Lond., Ward, Lock and Tyler, n.d.*

BROWNE, GORDON. Proverbial sayings, being some old friends in new dresses. *boards, wide 8vo. Lond., Wells, Gardner, Darton, n.d.*

BROWNE, IRVING. Humorous phases of the law. *buckram, 16 mo. San Francisco, Whitney, 1876.*

BROWNE, WILLIAM H. Witty sayings of witty people. *buckram, 12mo. Phila., McKay, 1888.*

BROWNELL, WILLIAM L. Horse and buggy philosopher. *buckram, 12mo. Kalamazoo, Kalamazoo Vegetable Parchment Co., 1939.*

BROWNING, ROBERT. Jocoseria. *buckram, 16mo. Lond., Smith, Elder, 1883.*

BROWNLOW, LOUIS. The anatomy of the anecdote. *buckram, 8vo. Chic., Univ. of Chic. Press, 1960.*

BRUDDER GARDNERS' STUMP SPEECHES AND COMIC LECTURES *paper, 12mo. n.p. n.d.*

BRUERE, MARTHA BENSLEY and BEARD, MARY RITTER. Laughing their way; women's humor in America. *buckram, 8vo. N.Y., Macmillan, 1934.*

BRULLER, JEAN. 21 delightful ways of committing suicide. *boards, small 4to. N.Y., Covici, Friede, 1930.*

BUBER, MARTIN. Tales of the Hasidim. The early masters. *buckram, 8vo. N.Y., Schocken, 1947.*

———————— Tales of the Hasidim. The later masters. *buckram, 8vo. N.Y., Schocken, 1948.*

BUCHANAN-TAYLOR, W. Shake it again. *buckram, 8vo. Lond., Heath Cranton, 1944.*

BUCHWALD, ART. The brave coward. *buckram, 8vo. N.Y., Harper, 1957.*

———————— I chose caviar. *buckram, 12mo. Lond., Gollancz, 1957.*

———————— More caviar. *buckram, 8vo. Lond., Gollancz, 1958.*

BUCK, CHARLES. Anecdotes, religious, moral and entertaining. *calf., 12mo. Lond., Chapman, 1799. 2d.ed.*

———————— *Same. 3v. half-calf. Lond., Compton, 1811. 5th ed.*

———————— *Same. N.Y., Sheldon, Blakeman, 1856.*

BUCKLE, THOMAS. Wisdom of Thomas Buckle. *paper, 8vo. Girard, Kan., Haldeman-Julius, 1947.*

BUCKMINSTER, THOMAS. An almanack and prognostication for the year 1598. *boards, 8vo. Lond., H.Milford for the Shakespeare Association, 1935. (Shakespeare Association facsimiles, no. 8)*

BUCKSTONE, JOHN BALDWIN. The dead shot. *paper, 12mo. Chic., Dramatic Pub. Co., n.d.*

——————— Married life, a comedy. *paper, 12mo. N.Y., French, n.d.*

BUDDHA *see* SUTTAPITAKA. VAJRACHCHEDIKA.

BUDGET OF DUTCH JOKES, containing the gleanings from the whole field of German dialectic wit and humor. *paper, 16mo. N.Y., Wehman, n.d.*

BUERGER, GOTTFRIED AUGUST. Baron Munchausen's miraculous adventures on land. *buckram, 12mo. Los Angeles, U.S. Library Association, 1933.*

BULL, JOHN, *pseud. see* LAUGHING PHILOSOPHER.

BULLIANA; a selection of the jeux d'esprits, facetiae anecdotes of the John Bull. Part I: Mrs. Ramsbottom's tour from England to France. *boards, 16 mo. Lond., Hodgson, 1824.*

BULLIET, C. J. Venus Castina, famous female impersonators, celestial and human. *buckram, 8vo. N.Y., Bonanza, 1956.*

BULOSAN, CARLOS. The laughter of my father. *buckram, 12mo. Lond., Joseph. 1945.*

BUNCE, JOHN THACKRAY. Fairy tales; their origin and meaning with some account of dwellers in Fairyland. *buckram, 12mo. Lond., Macmillan, 1878.*

BUNCLE, JOHN, *jnr.* Of wives and wiving; a manual of instruction, exhortation & admonition. *buckram, 12mo. Lond., J. Lehmann, 1947.*

BUNGAY, GEORGE W. Temperance anecdotes. *buckram, 16mo. N.Y., National Temperance Society, 1870.*

BURDETTE, ROBERT J. Chimes from a jester's bells. *buckram, 12mo. Indianapolis, Bobbs-Merrill, 1897.*

——————— Hawkeyes. *buckram, 12mo. N.Y., Carleton, 1879.*

———————Masterpieces of wit and humor. *half-morocco, 4to. N.Y., Modern Popular Library, 1903.*

——————— Smiles yoked with sighs. *buckram, 12mo. Indianapolis, Bowen-Merrill, 1900.*

——————— The rise and fall of the mustache, and other "Hawkeyetems" *buckram, 12mo. Burlington, Iowa. Burlington Pub. Co., 1877.*

BURDETT'S BOOK OF COMIC PARODIES. *paper, 12mo. N.Y., Hurst, 1883.*

BURGESS, GELETT. The goop encyclopedia. *buckram, 12mo. N.Y., Stokes, 1916.*

——————— The maxims of Methuselah. *boards, 12mo. N.Y., Stokes, 1913.*

——————— Are you a bromide, or, The sulphitic theory. *boards, 12mo. N.Y., Huebsch, 1909.*

——————— The maxims of Noah. *boards, 12mo. N.Y., Stokes, 1913.*

———— Why be a goop?
*buckram, 8vo. N.Y., Stokes,
1924.*

———— Why men hate
women. *boards, 12mo. N.Y.,
Payson & Clarke, 1927.*

BURGESS, J. HARVEY. "The
folks that I have knowed".
*paper, 16mo. Harrington, Del.,
Author, n.d.*

———— Hosses ... Hosses ..
Hosses! and A tale of two
dogs, by "The gentleman from
Sussex" *paper, 12mo.
Harrington, Del., Harrington
Journal, 1950.*

BURGH, A. Anecdotes of music.
*3v. half-calf, 12mo. Lond.,
Longman, Hurst, Rees, Orme &
Brown, 1814.*

BURGUNDY, BILLY. Toothsome
tales told in slang. *buckram,
16mo. N.Y., Street & Smith,
1901.*

BURKE, BILLY. With powder on
my nose. *buckram, 8vo. N.Y.,
Coward-McCann, 1959.*

BURKE, EDMUND. On the sublime and beautiful. *paper,
16mo. N.Y., Alden, 1855.*

BURKE, OLIVER J. Anecdotes of
the Connaught Circuit. *half-
russia, 8vo. Dublin, Hodges,
Figgis, 1885.*

BURLESK HANDBOOK. *paper, 12
mo. Toronto, Burlesk Handbook,
n.d.*

BURLESQUE JOKE BOOK. *paper,
32mo. Baltimore, Ottenheimer,
1916.*

BURNAND, F.C. Happy thoughts.
*buckram, 8vo. Lond., Nevill,
1954.*

———— More happy thoughts
& c. & c. *buckram, 16mo. Bost.,
Roberts, 1871.*

———— Some old friends.
*buckram, small 8vo. Lond.,
Bradbury, Agnew, 1892.*

BURNETT, W. B. Scotland laughing; the humour of the Scot.
*buckram, 12mo. Edinburgh,
Albyn, 1955.*

BURNETT, WHIT, ed. This is my
best humor. *buckram, 8vo.
N.Y., Dial, 1955.*

BURNS, GEORGE. I love her,
that's why! *boards, 8vo. N.Y.,
Simon & Schuster, 1955.*

BURNS, ROBERT. Guid bits frae
Robert Burns. *calf., 16mo.
Glasgow, Bryce, n.d.*

———— The merry muses.
*leather, 8vo. (Made in fac-
simile of original edition)*

BURRITT, ELIHU. Chips from
many blocks. *buckram, 12mo.
Toronto, Rose-Belford, 1878.*

BURROWS, ABE. The Abe Burrows
songbook. *buckram, 4to. N.Y.,
Doubleday, 1955.*

BURRUSS, WILLIAM B. Shakespeare the salesman. *cloth, 8vo.
Chic., Dartnell, 1942.*

BURTON, ROBERT. The anatomy
of melancholy, by Democritus,
junior. *buckram, 8vo. Lond.,
Tegg, 1849.*

BURTON, WILLIAM E. Cyclopedia
of wit and humor. *buckram, 4to.
N.Y., Appleton, 1858.*

BUTLER, CHARLES HENRY. A
century at the bar of the Supreme
Court. *buckram, 8vo. N.Y., Putnam's 1942.*

# B-C

BUTLER, ELLIS PARKER. The confessions of a daddy. *buckram, 12mo. N.Y., Century, 1907.*

—————— Dollarature, or The drug-store book. *boards, 12mo. Bost., Houghton, Mifflin, 1930.*

—————— The great American pie company. *buckram, 12mo. N.Y., McClure, Phillips, 1907.*

—————— Mike Flannery on duty and off. *buckram, 12mo. N.Y., Doubleday, Page 1909.*

—————— Philo Gubb, correspondence-school detective. *buckram, 12mo. Bost., Houghton, Mifflin, 1918.*

—————— Pigs is pigs. *buckram, 12mo. N.Y., Burt, 1906.*

—————— That pup. *buckram, 12mo. N.Y., Doubleday, 1905.*

—————— The thin Santa Claus. *buckram, 16mo. N.Y., Doubleday, 1906.*

—————— The water goats, and other troubles. *buckram, 12 mo. N.Y., Doubleday, Page, 1910.*

BUTLER, SAMUEL. The humour of Homer, and other essays. *buckram, 12mo. N.Y., Kennerley, 1914.*

BUTTON BUSTERS JOLLY JOKES; laugh and be happy. *paper, 32mo. Baltimore, Ottenheimer, 1915.*

BYERLY, THOMAS, *and* ROBERTSON, JOSEPH CLINTON. The Percy anecdotes, original and select, by Sholto and Reuben Percy, brothers of the Benedictine Monastery, Mont Benger. *20v. half-calf. 24mo. Lond., Boys, 1821-1823.*

—————— Same. *20v. Lond., Berger, n.d.*

—————— Same. *2v. in 1. calf., 8vo. N.Y., Harper, 1843.*

—————— Same. *3v. cloth, Lond., Warne, 1868.*

BYRN, M.LAFAYETTE. The repository of wit and humor. *buckram, 12mo. Lond., Jewett, 1856.*

BYRNES, GENE. Reg'lar fellers. *boards, 8vo. N.Y., Cupples & Leon, 1929.*

BYRNES, JAMES F. Speaking frankly. *buckram, 8vo. N.Y., Harper, 1947.*

BYRON, H.J. "Our boys" *paper, 12mo. N.Y., French, 1875.*

BYRON, HENRY J. Mirth. A miscellany of wit and humour. *Lond., Tinsley, 1878.*

THE CABINET OF ENTERTAINMENT: a new and select collection of aenigmas, charades, rebuses, &c. *half-calf, 24mo. Lond., Richard Taylor, 1811.*

THE CABINET OF MIRTH, or, Comic medley. *boards, 16mo. Lond., Kaygill, n.d.*

CADWALADER *and* NUDNICK *see* NERNEY, PATRICK W. *and* CLEMENS, PAUL.

CAEN, HERBERT EUGENE. Baghdad-by-the-bay. *buckram, 8vo. N.Y., Doubleday, 1949.*

—————— Baghdad: 1951. *buckram, 8vo. N.Y., Doubleday, 1950.*

—————— Don't call it Frisco. *buckram, 8vo. N.Y., Doubleday, 1950.*

# C

CAHILL, F.J., *comp.* A bunch of yarns and rare bits of humor. *buckram, 12mo. N.Y., Carey-Stafford, 1906.*

—————— Rare bits of humor; after-dinner stories, convivial toasts and humorous anecdotes. *buckram, 12mo. N.Y., Sully, 1906.*

CAHN, WILLIAM. The laugh makers; a pictorial history of American comedians. *buckram, 4to. N.Y., Putnams, 1957.*

CAINE, RALPH H. Humorous poems of the century. *buckram, 24mo. Lond., Scott, n.d.*

CAINE, WILLIAM. The glutton's mirror. *buckram, 4to. Lond., T. Fisher Unwin, 1925.*

CALAMANDREI, PIERO. Eulogy of judges. *boards, 8vo. Princeton, N.Y., Princeton Univ. Press, 1942.*

CALDECOTT, RANDOLPH. The complete collection of Randolph Caldecott's contributions to the "Graphic". *buckram, folio. Lond., Routledge, 1888.*

CALDERON, GEORGE. The fountain. *paper, 24mo. Lond., Gowans & Gray, 1914.*

CALEDONIAN BEE; or, A select collection of interesting extracts, from modern publications. *leather, 16mo. Perth, Morison, 1795.*

CALEDONIAN JEST-BOOK; being a new and extensive collection of anecdotes, bon-mots & witticisms... *boards, small 16mo. Edinburgh, Brown, 1803.*

CALEDONIAN JESTER: being a choice selection of repartees, puns and bon mots... *paper, 16 mo. Lond., Hughes, 1806.*

CALTHROP, DION. Punch and Judy, a corner in the history of entertainment. With an essay on the pleasant art of keeping people amused. *boards, 12mo. Lond., Dulau, 1926.*

CALVINO, ITALO. Italian fables. *buckram, 8vo. N.Y., Orion Press, 1959.*

CAMBRIDGE SCRAP-BOOK...by A Special Commissioner. *boards, wide 12mo. Cambridge, Macmillan, 1859.*

CAMBRIDGE TART; epigrammatic and satiric-poetical effusions .. *boards, 16mo. Lond., J. Smith, 1823.*

CAMERER, DAVE. Pounditout. *boards, 8vo. N.Y., Barnes, 1954.*

CAMERON—————and HANNEN —————— Where do we go from here? *paper, 12mo. Lond., Bladford, 1952.*

CAMERON, NIGEL. The Chinese smile. *buckram, 8vo. Lond., Hutchinson, 1958.*

CAMPBELL, C.G. From town and tribe. *buckram, 12mo. Lond., Benn, 1952.*

CAMPBELL, COLIN. The miraculous birth of King Amonhotep III, and other Egyptian studies. *buckram, 8vo. Edinburgh, Oliver & Boyd, 1912.*

CAMPBELL, E. SIMMS. More cuties in arms. *boards, 12mo. Phila., McKay, 1943.*

CAMPBELL, JOHN CAMPBELL,
*1st baron.* The lives of the chief
justices of England from the
Norman conquest till the death
of Lord Tenterden. *4v. tree
calf., 16mo. Lond., Murray,
1874. 3d.ed.*

CAMPBELL, PATRICK. Come
here till I tell you. *buckram,
8vo. Lond., Hutchinson, 1960.*

_____ Life in thin slices.
*buckram, 12mo. Lond., Falcon,
1951.*

_____ Long drink of cold
water. *buckram, 12mo. Lond.,
Falcon, 1949.*

_____ Short trot with a
cultured mind. *buckram, 12mo.
Lond., Falcon, 1950.*

THE CANDIDATE; a photograph
interview with the Honorable
James Durante. *paper, 4to.
N.Y., Simon & Schuster, 1952.*

CANOPY, WILLIARD B. Burlesque
debates for high schools,
clubs, colleges, or what have
you? *paper, 12mo. Chic.,
Denison, 1932.*

CANSICK, FREDERICK TEAGUE.
A collection of curious and
interesting epitaphs ... *2v.
buckram, 12mo. Lond., J.
Russell Smith, 1869, 1872.*

CANTOR, EDDIE. Between the
acts. *buckram, 16mo. N.Y.,
Simon & Schuster, 1930.*

_____ Caught short! a saga
of wailing Wall Street. *buckram,
16mo. N.Y., Simon & Schuster,
1929.*

_____ World's book of
best jokes. *boards, 8vo.
Cleveland, World, 1943.*

_____ Yoo-hoo, prosperity!
the Eddie Cantor five-year plan.
*buckram, 16mo. N.Y., Simon &
Schuster, 1941.*

CAPOTE, TRUMAN. Breakfast at
Tiffany's. *paper, 12mo. N.Y.,
Signet, 1959.*

CAPP, AL. The world of Li'l
Abner. *boards, 12mo. N.Y.,
Farrar, Straus & Young, 1953.*

CAPTAIN KID BOOK AND JUDGE
ANNUAL. *buckram, 4to, N.Y.,
Leslie-Judge, 1922.*

CAPWELL, IRENE STODDARD.
Mrs. Alderman Casey. *buckram,
12mo. N.Y., Fenno, 1905.*

CARB, ALFRED B. Bar, bench and
table. *buckram, 8vo. N.Y.,
American Arbitration Assoc.,
1957.*

CAREY, THOMAS J. The comic
reciter, a burlesque and dialect
book of oratory, by T.J. See,
*pseud. buckram, 12mo. N.Y.,
Hurst, n.d.*

_____ The drummers'
latest. *paper, 8vo. N.Y.,
Popular, 1902.*

_____ Popular recitations.
*paper, 8vo. N.Y., Excelsior,
1888.*

CARICATURE. Wit and humor of a
nation in picture, song and
story, *buckram, 4to. N.Y.,
Leslie-Judge, n.d.*

_____ *Same. 8th ed.*

_____ *Same. 11th ed.*

_____ *Same. 13th ed.*

CARICATURISTS SCRAP BOOK,
THE. *buckram, wide 4to. n.p.,
n.d.*

CARLETON, WILL. Farm ballads. *buckram, 8vo. N.Y., Harper, 1873.*

CARPENTER, F.B. Six months at the White House with Abraham Lincoln. *buckram, 16mo. N.Y., Hurd & Houghton, 1867.*

CARPENTER, RHYS. Folk tale, fiction and saga in the Homeric epics. *paper, 12mo. Berkeley, Univ. of Calif. Press, 1958.*

CARRICK, JOHN DONALD. The laird of Logan, being anecdotes and tales illustrative of the wit and humour of Scotland. *buckram, 12mo. Lond., Hamilton, Adams, 1888.*

CARRINGTON, DOROTHY. The traveller's eye. *buckram, 8vo. N.Y., Pilot, 1947.*

CARROLL, LEWIS. Alice's adventures in Wonderland. *paper, 12mo. Lond., Penguin, 1946.*

——————— Alice in Wonderland, and Through the looking glass. *buckram, 8vo. Lond., Dakers, n.d.*

——————— Complete works. *buckram, 12mo. Lond., Nonesuch, 1939.*

——————— Humorous verse. *paper, 8vo. N.Y., Dover, 1933.*

——————— Logical nonsense. *buckram, small 4to. N.Y., Putnam, 1934.*

CARRYL, GUY WETMORE. Fables for the frivolous (with apologies to La Fontaine) *buckram, 8vo. N.Y., Harper, 1898.*

CARSWELL, JOHN. The romantic rogue; the singular life and adventures of Rudolf Erich Raspe, creator of Baron Munchausen. *buckram, 8vo. N.Y., Dutton, 1950.*

CARTER, BOB. Little things that linger. *cloth, 8vo. N.Y., Orlin Tremaine, 1940.*

CARTER, EDWARD FOUNTAIN. The toastmaster. *buckram, 12 mo. Keokuk, Iowa, Author, 1914.*

CARTER, JOHN HENTON. Duck Creek ballads. *buckram, 12mo. N.Y., Nixon, 1894.*

CARTER, SIMEON. Poems and aphorisms; a woodman's musings. *buckram, 12mo. Baldwinville, Mass., 1893.*

CARY, JOYCE. The horse's mouth. *paper, 8vo. N.Y., Universal, 1957.*

CASANOVA DE SEINGALT, GIACOMO GIROLAMO. The memoirs of Casanova. *2v. buckram, 8vo. Lond., Navarre Society, n.d.*

CASE, CARLETON B. The big joke-book. *paper, 12mo. Chic., Stein, 1943. New ed.*

——————— The big toast-book. *paper, 12mo. Chic., Shrewsbury, 1931.*

——————— Comic declamations and readings. *paper, 12mo. Chic., Shrewsbury, 1929.*

——————— Comic dialogues for boys and girls. *paper, 12mo. Chic., Shrewsbury, 1929.*

_____ Ford smiles; all the current jokes about a rattling good car. *paper, 12mo. Chic., Shrewsbury, 1917.*

_____ The sunny side of life. *paper, 12mo. Chic., Shrewsbury, 1916.*

CASE, FRANK. Tales of a wayward inn. *buckram, 8vo. N.Y., Garden City, 1938.*

THE CASQUET OF GEMS; choice selections from the poets. *leather, 12mo. Edinburgh, Nimmo, Hay & Mitchell, n.d.*

CASWELL, EDWARD. A new art, teaching how to be plucked, by Scriblerus Redivivus, *pseud. half-calf, 16mo. Oxford, Vincent, 1837. 7th ed.*

CATHER, THOMAS. Thomas Cather's Journal of a voyage to America in 1836. *boards, 8vo. Emmaus, Pa., Rodale, 1955.*

CATHERINE II, EMPRESS OF RUSSIA. Memoirs. *buckram, 8vo. N.Y., Macmillan, 1955.*

CATS, JACOB. Moral emblems, with aphorisms, adages and proverbs of all ages and nations ... Translated and edited ... by Richard Pigot. *buckram, 4to. Lond., Longman, Green, Longman and Roberts, 1860.*

CAUNTER, HOBARD *and* DANIELL, WILLIAM. Caunter and Daniell's oriental annual, 1839. *buckram, 12mo. Lond., Whittaker, 1838.*

CAZAMIAN, LOUIS. The development of English humour. *buckram, 12mo. N.Y., Macmillan, 1930.*

CELEBRATED MRS. PILKINGTON'S JESTS, THE, or, The cabinet of wit and humor. *half-calf, 12mo. Lond., Nicoll, 1764.*

CENTURY BOOK OF IRISH WIT AND HUMOR. *buckram, 16mo. Chic., Henneberry, 1901.*

CERF, BENNETT, *ed.* Anything for a laugh. *paper, 24mo. N.Y., Bantam, 1946.*

_____ An encyclopedia of modern American humor. *buckram, 8vo. N.Y., Doubleday, 1954.*

_____ Good for a laugh. *buckram, 8vo. N.Y., Hanover Housem 1952.*

_____ Laughing stock. *buckram, 8vo. N.Y., Grosset & Dunlap, 1945.*

_____ The laugh's on me. *buckram, 8vo. N.Y., Doubleday, 1959.*

_____ Laughter incorporated. *buckram, 12mo. N.Y., Garden City, 1950.*

_____ Life of the party. *buckram, 8vo. N.Y., Doubleday, 1956.*

_____ Pocket book of war humor. *paper, 16mo. N.Y., Pocket books, 1943.*

_____ Shake well before using. *buckram, 8vo. N.Y., Simon & Schuster, 1948.*

_____ Try and stop me. *buckram, 8vo. N.Y., Simon & Schuster, 1944.*

CERNIKOFF, VLADIMIR. Humour and harmony. *buckram, 8vo. Lond., Barker, 1936.*

CERVANTES SAAVEDRA, MIGUEL DE. Don Quixote of the Mancha. *buckram, 8vo. Altrincham, J. Sherratt, n.d.*

_____ The living thoughts of Cervantes. Presented by L.B. Walton. *buckram, 12mo. Lond., Cassell, 1948.*

_____ Sancho Panza's proverbs. *buckram, 8vo. Lond., Pickering, 1872.*

_____ Wit and wisdom of Don Quixote. *buckram, 12mo. N.Y., Appleton, 1867.*

CHAMBERLAIN, FREDERICK. The sayings of Queen Elizabeth. *buckram, 8vo. Lond., J.Lane, 1923.*

CHAMBERS, F.W. Ever heard this? Over 390 good stories. *buckram, 16mo. Lond., Methuen, 1922. 5th ed.*

CHAMBERS, ROBERT, *ed.* The book of days; a miscellany of popular antiquities. *2v. buckram, 4to. Lond., Chambers, 1866.*

_____ Scottish jests and anecdotes. *boards, 24mo. Edinburgh, Paterson, n.d.*

CHAMBERS'S MISCELLANY. Interesting narratives and anecdotes. *buckram, 12mo. Bost., Gould, Kendall & Lincoln, n.d.*

CHAMBERS'S MISCELLANY OF USEFUL AND ENTERTAINING TRACTS. *half-calf, 12mo. Edinburgh, Chambers, n.d.*

CHAMBERS'S RESPOSITORY OF INSTRUCTIVE AND AMUSING TRACTS. *12v. in 4. half-calf, 12mo. Edinburgh, Chambers, 1854.*

CHAMFORT, SEBASTIAN ROCH NICHOLAS. Maxims and consideration of Chamfort. *2v. quarter-boards, 8vo. Lond., Golden Cockerel, 1926.*

CHAMISSON, ADELBERT *von.* The wonderful history of Peter Schlemihl. *buckram, 16mo. Lond., Longman, Brown, Green and Longman, 1843.*

CHAMPION, SELWYN GURNEY: Racial proverbs. *buckram, 4to. Lond., Routledge, Kegan Paul, 1950. 2d.ed.*

_____ Wayside sayings. *boards, 12mo. Lond., Duckworth, 1922.*

CHANEY, JACK. Foolish questions - Yellowstone's best. *paper, 16mo. Lincoln, Nebr., Woodruff, 1922.*

CHAPIN, HAROLD. Augustus in search of a father. *paper, 24mo. Lond., Gowans & Gray, 1911.*

_____ The dumb and the blind. *paper, 24mo. Lond., Gowans & Gray 1914.*

CHAPIN, HENRY. The adventures of Johnny Appleseed. *buckram, 12mo. N.Y., Grosset & Dunlap, 1930.*

CHAPMAN, H.S., *comp.* 1001 one minute stories. *buckram, 16mo. Bost., Mason, 1927.*

CHAPPELL, GEORGE S., *comp.* Dr. Traprock's memory book, or Aged in the wood. *buckram, 8vo. N.Y., Putnams, 1931.*

_____ Through the alimentary canal with gun and camera. *buckram, 12mo. N.Y., Stokes, 1930.*

CHAPPLE, JOE MITCHELL. The happy habit. *buckram, 12mo. Bost., Author, 1908.*

CHARACTERS AND ANECDOTES COLLECTED IN THE REIGNS OF WILLIAM RUFUS, CHARLES THE SECOND, AND KING GEORGE THE THIRD, by the celebrated Wandering Jew of Jerusalem. *half-calf, 8vo. Lond., Ridgway, 1791.*

CHARACTERS AND OBSERVATIONS; an 18th century manuscript, with a foreword by Lord Gorell. *buckram, 8vo. N.Y., Stokes, 1930.*

CHARNWOOD, GODFREY RATHBONE BENSON, *Lord.* Abraham Lincoln. *buckram, 8vo. N.Y., Holt, 1917. 3d.ed.*

CHARTERS, W.W. Heirs of democracy. *paper, 24mo. (Personal Growth Leaflets)*

CHASE, EDITHE LEA. Toasts for all occasions. *buckram, 12mo. N.Y., Barse, n.d.*

_____ Waes hael; the book of toasts. *buckram, 12mo. N.Y., Barse & Hopkins, 1904.*

CHASE, GEORGE. Tales out of school. *buckram, 12mo. Cambridge, Harvard, Univ. Press, 1947.*

CHASE, MARY. Bernadine; a comedy. *paper, 12mo. N.Y., Dramatists Play Service, 1954.*

CHASE, RICHARD. The Jack tales. *buckram, 8vo. Cambridge, Houghton, Mifflin, 1943.*

"CHATEDS" *pseud.* "Spoken in jest", or, The Traveller's deconfuser. *boards, 12mo. Lond., Hutchinson, 1924.*

CHATFIELD, PAUL. The tin trumpet; or, Heads and tails for the wise and waggish. *buckram, 12mo. N.Y., Appleton, 1859.*

CHAUCER, GEOFFREY. Canterbury tales; Chaucer for present-day readers. *buckram, 12mo. Lond., Murray, 1946.*

CHAUDON, LOUIS MAYEUL. Historical and critical memoirs of the life and writings of M. de Voltaire ... *calf., 8vo. Lond., G.G.J. and J. Robinson, 1781.*

CHAVAL. C'est la view; the best cartoons of Chaval. *boards, 4to. N.Y., Citadel, 1957.*

CHEARFUL, CHARLES, *pseud.* The comforts of human life, or, Smiles and laughter of Charles Chearful, and Martin Merryfellow. *quarter-leather, 16mo. Lond., Oddy, 1807.*

CHEKHOV, ANTON. Nine humorous tales. *boards, 12mo. Bost., Stratford, 1918.*

CHEEM ALIPH *see* YELDHAM, WALTER.

CHENEY, L.J., *comp. and ed.* The world of man, prose passages. *buckram, 12mo. Cambridge, Univ. Press, 1933.*

CHESHIN, SCHNEOR Z. Tears and laughter in an Israel courtroom. *buckram, 8vo. Phila, Jewish Pub. Soc., 1959.*

CHESTERFIELD, PHILIP DORMER STANHOPE, *4th earl of.* Letters, sentences and maxims. *buckram, 24mo. N.Y., Putnam's, n.d.*

_____ Same. Lond., Sampson, Low, n.d.

_____ Wit-a-la-mode, or Lord Chesterfield's witticisms. *quarter calf., large 16mo. Lond., Newport & Mallard, 1778.*

_____ Wit and wisdom of the Earl of Chesterfield. Edited by W. Ernst Browning. *buckram, 12mo. Lond., Bentley, 1875.*

CHESTERTON, GILBERT KEITH. Essays. *paper, 32mo. Girard, Kan., Haldeman-Julius, n.d. (Little Blue Books)*

_____ Tales of the long bow. *buckram, 12mo. N.Y., Sheed & Ward, 1956.*

_____ Magic. *buckram, 12mo. Lond., Secker, n.d.*

CHEVIOT, ANDREW. Proverbs, proverbial expressions and popular rhymes of Scotland. *buckram, 12mo. Paisely, Gardner, 1896.*

CHIDECKEL, MAURICE. Leaves from a doctor's diary. *boards, 8vo. Nutley, N.J., Hoffmann-La Roche, 1940.*

CHILD, HAROLD. A poor player, the story of a failure. *buckram, 16mo. Cambridge, Univ. Press, 1939.*

CHILDS, BREVARD S. Myth and reality in the Old Testament. *paper, 8vo. Lond., SCM press, 1960.*

CHINESE FABLES AND ANECDOTES. *paper, 12mo. Peking, Foreign language press, 1958.*

CHINESE LITERATURE. Spring, 1953. *paper, 4to. Peking, Foreign Language Press, 1953.*

CHINESE PROVERBS FROM OLDEN TIMES. *boards, 12mo. Mount Vernon, Peter Pauper, 1956.*

CHITTICK, V.L.C., ed. Ring-tailed roarers; tall tales of the American frontier. *buckram, 8 vo. Caldwell, Caxton, 1946.*

CHOICE DIALECT AND VAUDEVILLE STAGE JOKES. *paper, 16mo. Chic., Drake, 1902.*

CHOICE VARIETY JOKES. *paper, 24mo. Baltimore, Otten-heimer, 1908.*

CHOTZNER, J. Hebrew humour, and other essays. *buckram, 8vo. Lond., Luzac, 1905.*

_____ Hebrew satire. *buck-ram, 12mo. Lond., Kegan Paul, Trench & Trubner, 1911.*

CHEW, T.C. DUNCAN. Chinese fables of ancient times. *paper, 12mo. Hong Kong, English Language Pub. Co., n.d.*

CHRISMAN, ARTHUR BOWIE. Shen of the sea. *buckram, 12 mo. N.Y., Dutton, 1927.*

CHRISTIAN, W.E. Rhymes of the rookies; sunny side of soldier service. *buckram, 16mo. N.Y., Dodd, Mead, 1917.*

CHRISTMAS IN CALIFORNIA. Part I: Christmas at Sutter's Fort in 1847.
PART II: Christmas before the Americans came, by Jose Ramon Pico. *buckram, 12mo. San Francisco, Lawton Kennedy for the California Historical Society, 1956.*

CHRISTY, BYRON. Dime American joke book. *paper, 24mo. N.Y., DeWitt, n.d. but ca. 1867.*

CHRISTOPHER, MELESINA SETON. Life's little laughs. *buckram, 12mo. Lond., Longmans, Green, 1925.*

CHRYSTIE, FRANCES N. The first book of jokes and funny things. *buckram, wide 8vo. N.Y. Watts, 1951.*

CHRYSTY, ROBERT. Proverbs, maxims and phrases of all ages. *2v. in 1. quarter-calf., small 8vo. N.Y., Putnam's 1904.*

CHUANG TZU. Musings of a Chinese mystic. *buckram, 16 mo. Lond., Murray, 1920.*

CHUCKLE EVERY DAY; comedy cartoon calendar for 1961. *loose-leaf binder. N.Y., Chuckle-every-day, 1959.*

CHURCH, ALFRED J. Stories from the Greek comedians: Aristophanes, Philemon, Diphilus, Menander, Appolodorus. *buckram, 12mo. Lond., Seeley, 1893.*

CHURCHILL, ALLEN, ed. All in fun; an omnibus of humor, *buckram, 8vo. N.Y., McBride, 1940.*

_____ A treasury of modern humor. *buckram, 8vo. N.Y., Tudor, 1940.*

CHURCHILL, WINSTON SPENCER. Maxims and reflections. *buckram, 8vo. Lond., Eyre & Spottiswoode, 1947.*

_____ Same. *Bost., Houghton, Mifflin, 1949.*

_____ Wisdom of Winston Churchill. *buckram, 8vo. Lond., Allen & Unwin, 1956.*

CIBBER, COLLEY. The careless husband, a comedy. *calf., 16 mo. Lond., J. and R. Tonson, 1756.*

CIRCLE OF HUMOUR, or, Comic gleanings descriptive of life, character and manners for 1824. *boards, 24mo. Glasgow, Griffin, 1824.*

CLAPP, ROGER TILLINGHAST, comp. The beaver book. *paper, 8vo. Providence, R.I., Haley & Sykes, 1930.*

CLARK, B.F. Mirthfulness and its exciters, or Rational laughter and its promoters. *buckram, 12 mo. Bost., Lee & Shepard, 1875.*

CLARK, ELLA E. Indian legends of the Pacific Northwest. *paper, 8vo. Berkeley, Univ. of Calif. Press, 1958.*

CLARK, GEORGE. The neighbors' kids. *paper, 16mo. N.Y., Gold Medal Books, 1955.*

CLARK, G.J. Great sayings by great lawyers. *buckram, 8vo. Kansas City, Lawyers' International Pub. Co., 1922.*

CLARK, LOUIS GAYLORD. Knick-knocks. *buckram, 12mo. N.Y., Appleton, 1852.*

CLARKE, C.C. The hundred wonders of the world. *calf., 12 mo. New Haven, John Babcock, 1821. 1st American ed, from the 10th English ed.*

CLARKE, MARY COWDEN. Kit Bam's adventures; or, The yarns of an old mariner. *half-calf., 16mo. Lond., Grant & Griffith, 1849.*

CLARKE, VIRGINIA. Sunny hours. *paper, 16mo. Chic., Regensteiner, 1914.*

CLAYTON, DAVID and LANGTON, DAVID. Wake up and die. *buckram, 12mo. Lond., Wingate, 1952.*

CLAYTON, GEOFFREY. Footnotes, or The profession from inside out. A book of humor about music and those who make it. *buckram, 8vo. Lond., Melody Maker, n.d.*

CLEMENS, WILL M. The Depew story book. *buckram, 12mo. Lond., F.Tennyson Neely 1898.*

_____ Famous funny fellows. *paper, 12mo. N.Y., Munro's, 1897.*

CLEUGH, JAMES. The amorous Master Pepys. *buckram, 8vo. Lond., Muller, 1958.*

CLEVELAND, ANNE and ANDERSON, JEAN. Everything correlates; some observations on the educational continuum. *paper, 8vo. Vassar College, Vassar Cooperative Bookshop, 1946.*

_____ It's better with your shoes off. *boards, oblong 24mo. Tokyo, Tuttle, 1955.*

_____ The parent from zero to ten. *boards, 4to. N.Y., Simon & Schuster, 1957.*

CLINCHY, EVERETT R. Education and human relations. *paper, 24mo. (Personal Growth Leaflets)*

CLINTON-BADDELEY, V.C. The burlesque tradition in the English theatre after 1660. *buckram, 8vo. Lond., Methuen, 1952.*

CLODD, EDWARD. Tom Tit Tot; an essay on savage philosophy in folk-tale. *buckram, 12mo. Lond., Duckworth, 1898.*

CLOTHO *see* THE SPINNER'S CLUB.

CLOUGH, BEN C. The American imagination at work; tall tales and folk tales. *buckram, small 4to. N.Y., Knopf, 1947.*

CLOUSTON, W.A. The book of noodles; stories of simpletons, or, Fools and their follies. *buckram, 12mo. Lond., Stock, 1888.*

_____ Choice anecdotes and good sayings of the witty and wise. *buckram, 12mo. Lond., Ward, Lock & co., n.d.*

_____ Flowers from a Persian garden and other papers. *paper, 16mo. Lond., Nutt, 1894.*

_____ Popular tales and fictions. *2v. half-calf, 12mo. Edinburgh, Blackwood, 1887.*

CLUETT, JACK. Quiz fizzles; little gems of misinformation gathered from the radio's and television quiz programs. *boards, 12mo. N.Y., Lippincott, 1954.*

COBB, ELISABETH. My wayward parent; a book about Irvin S. Cobb. *buckram, 12mo. Indianapolis, Bobbs-Merrill, 1945.*

COBB, IRVIN SHREWSBURY. Alias Ben Alibi. *buckram, 12mo. N.Y., Grosset & Dunlap, 1925.*

_____ Back home. *buckram, 12mo. N.Y., Rev. of Rev., 1912.*

_____ Cobb's anatomy. *boards, 16mo. N.Y., Doran, 1912.*

_____ Cobb's bill-of-fare. *boards, 12mo. N.Y., Doran, 1913.*

_____ Eating in two or three languages. *boards, 12mo. Lond., Hodder & Stoughton, 1919.*

_____ The escape of Mr. Trimm. *buckram, 12mo. N.Y., Rev. of Rev., 1918.*

_____ Exit laughing. *buckram, 4to. Indianapolis, Bobbs-Merrill, 1941.*

_____ Fibble, D.D. *buckram, 8vo. N.Y., Doran, 1916.*

_____ From place to place. *buckram, 8vo. N.Y., Rev. of Rev. 1920.*

_____ Irvin Cobb at his best. *buckram, 8vo. N.Y., Sun Dial, 1923.*

_____ Kansas. *boards, 12 mo. N.Y., Doran, 1924.*

_____ A laugh a day keeps the doctor away. *buckram, 8vo. N.Y., Doran, 1923.*

_____ The life of the party. *boards, 12mo. N.Y., Doran, 1919.*

_____ Local color. *buckram, 12mo. N.Y., Rev. of Rev. 1916.*

_____ Many laughs for many days. *buckram, 8vo. N.Y., Doran, 1925.*

_____ New York. *boards, 12mo. N.Y., Doran, 1924.*

_____ North Carolina. *boards, 12mo. N.Y., Doran, 1924.*

_____ Oh! Well! You know how women are. *boards, 12mo. N.Y., Doran, 1919.* (Contains also: "Isn't that just like a man!" by Mary Roberts Rinhart. Separate title-page, and inverted)

_____ Old Judge Priest. *buckram, 12mo. N.Y., Rev. of Rev. 1916.*

_____ Snake doctor. *buckram, 8vo. N.Y., Rev. of Rev. 1923.*

_____ "Speaking of operations — " *boards, 12mo. N.Y., Doran, 1915.*

_____ Stickfuls - myself to date. *buckram, 12mo. N.Y., Rev. of Rev. 1923.*

_____ Sundry accounts. *buckram, small 8vo. N.Y., Rev. of Rev., 1922.*

_____ Those times and these. *buckram, small 8vo. N. Y., Rev. of Rev. 1917.*

_____ To be taken before sailing. *boards, 16mo. N.Y., Cosmopolitan, 1930.*

COBBES PROPHECIES, his signes and tokens, his madrigals, questions and answeres... Reproduced in facsimile by Charles Praetorius. *paper, 8vo. Lond., Printed for Private circulation, 1890. (Antient Drolleries, no. 2)*

COBBETT, MARTIN. Bottled holidays for home consumption. *buckram, 12mo. Lond., Sands, 1899.*

COBBIN, INGRAM, *comp.* Peter Parley's book of fables. *buckram, 16mo. Hartford, Conn., Andrus, 1855.*

COBBLE, ALICE D. Wembi, the singer of stories. *buckram, 8 vo. St. Louis, Bethany, 1959.*

COBEAN, SAM. Cartoons. *buckram, 4to. N.Y., Harper, 1952.*

_____ Cobean's naked eye. *paper, 16mo. N.Y., Pocket Books, 1952.*

COBLENTZ, STANTON. Villains
and vigilantes. *buckram, 8vo.*
*N.Y., Yoseloff, 1936.*

COCKBURN, HENRY THOMAS
COCKBURN, *lord.* Memorials of
his time. *buckram, 8vo. Edin-*
*burgh, Grant, 1946.*

COGGINS, HERBERT LEONARD.
Knick knacks. *boards, 12mo.*
*Phila., Penn. 1906.*

COCHRAN, CHARLES B. Show-
man looks on. *buckram, 8vo.*
*Lond., Dent. 1946.*

COHEN, A. Ancient Jewish
proverbs. *buckram, 16mo.*
*Lond., Murray, 1911.*

COHEN, INEZ LOPEZ. Our dark-
town press. *buckram, 16mo.*
*N.Y., Appleton, 1932.*

COHEN, JOHN MICHAEL. The
Penguin book of comic and
curious verse. *paper, 12mo.*
*Lond., Penguin, 1952.*

COHEN, LOUIS. Napoleonic anecdotes. *buckram, 8vo. Lond.,*
*Holden, 1925.*

COHEN, MYRON. Laughing out
loud. *boards, 8vo. N.Y.,*
*Citadel, 1958.*

COHEN ON THE TELEPHONE
*see* TWENTY DIFFERENT
ADVENTURES OF COHEN ON
THE TELEPHONE.

COHN, ART. The joker is wild;
the story of Joe E. Lewis.
*paper, 12mo. N.Y., Bantam,*
*1957.*

COLD NOSES AND WARM
HEARTS. *buckram, 4to.*
*Englewood Cliffs, Prentice-*
*Hall, 1958.*

COLE, E.W. Cole's fun doctor, the
funniest book in the world.
*cloth, 12mo. Lond., Routledge,*
*n.d.* (First series)

_____ *Same. 2d. series*

_____ The funniest book
but one. *buckram, 48mo. Lond.,*
*Scott, n.d.*

COLE, WILLIAM, *ed.* French
cartoons. *buckram, 12mo. Lond.,*
*Spearman, 1955.*

_____ More French
cartoons. *paper, 16mo. N.Y.,*
*Dell, 1955.*

_____ Women are wonder-
ful. *quarter-boards, 4to. Bost.,*
*Houghton, Mifflin, 1956.*

COLEMAN, ALBERT, *ed.* Grins
and giggles. *paper, 32mo.*
*Girard, Kan., Haldeman-Julius,*
*n.d. (Little Blue Books)*

COLLECTANEA: or, An as-
semblage of anecdotes,
aphorisms, and bon-mots ...
*half-calf., 12mo. Lond.,*
*Burton, 1802.*

COLLECTION OF ANECDOTES
ENTERTAINING AND
INTERESTING. *calf., 24mo.*
*Lebanon, Ohio, Van Vleet &*
*Camron, 1817.*

COLLEGE JOKER. *paper, 12mo.*
*N.Y., Ivers, 1907.*

COLLIER, JEREMY. A short view
of the profaness and immorality
of the English stage. *calf, 8vo.*
*Lond., Birt, 1738.*

COLLIER, JOHN PAYNE. A book
of Roxburghe ballads. *leather,*
*8vo. Lond., Longman, Brown,*
*Green and Longman, 1847.*

COLLIER, RONALD. Bees under
my bonnet. *buckram, 8vo. Lond.,*
*Motor Racing, n.d.*

COLLIERS. Colliers collects its wit. Edited by Gurney Williams. *boards, 4to. N.Y., McBride, 1944.*

_____ It's a funny world. Edited by Gurney Williams. *boards, 4to. N.Y., McBride, 1943.*

_____ Stop or I'll scream! Edited by Gurney Williams. *boards, 4to. N.Y., McBride, 1945.*

COLLINS, EDWIN, *tr.* The wisdom of Israel; being extracts from the Babylonian Talmud and Midrash Rabboth. *buckram, 16 mo. Lond., Murray, 1910.*

COLLINS, GILBERT. Extreme oriental mixture. *buckram, 8vo. Lond., Methuen, 1925.*

COLLINS, PETE. No people like show people. *buckram, 8vo. Lond., Muller, 1957.*

COLLINSON, CLIFFORD W. Life and laughter 'midst the cannibals. *buckram, 8vo. Lond., Hurst & Blackett, 1926.*

COLMAN, C., *comp.* The circle of anecdote and wit, a choice collection of pieces of humour. *boards, 24mo. Lond., William, 1926.*

COLMAN, GEORGE, *the younger.* Broad grins. *quarter vellum, 12 mo. Lond., Cadell & Davies, 1809.*

_____ *Same. 1815.*

_____ *Same, 1819.*

_____ *Same. John Camden Hotten, 1871.*

_____ The circle of anecdotes and wit. *boards, 16mo. Lond., Bumpus, 1822. 2d.ed.*

_____ Eccentric tales in verse. *half-russia, 16mo. Lond., Tegg, 1812.*

COLQUHOUN, DONALD. Jean, a comedy. *paper, 24mo. Lond., Gowans & Gray, 1914.*

COLTON, C. Hypocrisy; a satire. *boards, 8vo. Lond., Taylor & Hessey, 1812.*

_____ Lacon: or, Many things in few words. *2v. in 1. half-calf., 8vo. Lond., Longman, Hurst, Rees, Orme and Brown, 1822.*

THE COMIC ALMANACK, for 1835. An ephemeris in jest and earnest. *half-leather, 16mo. Lond., Tilt, 1835.*

THE COMIC ALPHABET. *paper, 12mo. Lond., Gregory, Collins & Renolds, ca. 1840.*

THE COMIC ANNUAL 1844; a book for every table. *half-calf., 4to. Lond., Orr, 1844.*

COMIC ARITHMETIC. *buckram, small 8vo. Lond., Bentley, 1844.*

THE COMIC COCKER, or, Figures for the million. *boards, 16mo. Lond., Ward & Lock, ca. 1850.*

COMIC EPITAPHS, from the best old grave-yards. *boards, 12mo. Mount Vernon, Peter Pauper 1957.*

COMIC GLEANINGS, an assemblage of the latest and best songs of humour. . . *half-calf, 24mo. Glasgow. Brown, 1826.*

THE COMIC LIBRARY. *7v. paper, 24mo. Lond., Kent, ca. 1850.* Contents.-Evening parties, by Albert Smith.-The bal masque! by Count Chicard.-Change for a shilling, by Horace Mayhew.- Stuck-up people, by Albert Smith.-The idler upon town, by Albert Smith.-A romance of a mince pie, by Angus B. Read.- Natural history of the Hawk tribe, by T.W. Carleton.

THE COMIC MAGAZINE, edited by "Figaro in London". *half-calf, 24mo. Lond., Isaac, 1836.*

THE COMIC OFFERING: or Ladies' melange of literary mirth. *5v. calf., 16mo. Lond., Smith, Elder, 1831-1835.*

COMIC POEMS (18th and 19th century). *paper, 32mo. Girard, Kan., Haldeman-Julius, n.d. (Little Blue Books).*

COMIC SONGS, FUNNY STORIES AND RECITATIONS. *paper, 12mo. Chic., M. Stein, 1928.*

COMIC TOKEN FOR 1836. A companion to The Comic Almanac. *paper, small 8vo. Bost., Ellms, 1836.*

THE COMPLETE JESTER: being a choice collection of jests, epigrams, bons mots, funny epitaphs, &c. &c. *paper, 12mo. Lond., Laidler's 1776.*

THE COMPLETE LONDON JESTER, or, Wit's companion. *leather, 12mo. Lond., Lowndes, 1785. 12th ed.*

CONDO, A.D. *and* RAPER, J.W. The outbursts of Everett True. *boards, 4to. N.Y., Sallfield, 1907.*

CONFUCIUS. The analects, or, The conversations of Confucius with his disciples and certain others. *buckram, 16mo. Lond., Oxford Univ. Press, 1937.*

———— The sayings of Confucius. *buckram, 12mo. Lond., Murray, 1910.*

———— The sayings of Confucius; a new translation. *buckram, 12mo. Lond., Murray, 1949.*

CONFUCIUS SAY: Cracks and gags collected and compiled by competent members of the coast-to-coast Confucius Clubs. *(Broadside in plastic case).*

CONNOLLY, BERTHA, *and* RAMSEY, HELEN. Modern toasts for all occasions. *paper, 12mo. Minneapolis, Northwestern, 1946.*

CONROY, JACK, *ed.* Midland humor. *buckram, 8vo. N.Y., Wyn, 1947.*

CONSCRIPT 2989; experiences of a drafted man. *buckram, 12mo. Lond., Methuen, 1940.*

CONSELMAN, DEIRDRE *and* CONSELMAN, WILLIAM. Keedle. *boards, 4to. N.Y., Hillman-Curl, 1940.*

CONSTANDUROS, MABEL *and* CONSTANDUROS, DENIS. 'anging around pubs. *buckram, 12mo. Lond., Methuen, 1940.*

CONTEMPORARY CARTOONS; an exhibition of original drawings of American artists at the Huntington Library, March-April, 1957. *pamphlet. San Marino, Ward Ritchie, 1937.*

CONTEMPORARY CHINESE SHORT STORIES. *paper, 12mo. HongKong, n.d.*

CONWELL, RUSSEL H. Why
Lincoln laughed. *buckram,
12mo. N.Y., Harper, 1922.*

CONWAY, MONCURE DANIEL.
George Washington's rules of
civility traced to their sources
and restored. *boards, 12mo.
Lond., Chatto & Windus, 1890.*

COOK, LYMAN E. Comics in the
law. *buckram, 8vo. Chic., Universal, 1938.*

COOK, TED. Adam Scofflaw's
journal.*(Newspaper clippings
pasted in scrap-book) Los
Angeles, Los Angeles Examiner,
1924.*

COOK, THEODORE A. An anthology of humorous verse. *buckram,
16mo. N.Y., Brentano's, 1902.*

COOKE, CHARLES. Lispings
from low latitudes; or, Extracts
from the journal of the Hon.
Impulsia Gushington. *half-calf,
8vo. Lond., Murray, 1863.*

COOKE, GRACE MACGOWAN.
Their first formal call. *buckram,
8vo. N.Y., Harper, 1906.*

COOLEY, HAZEL, *ed.* So say the
wisc. *buckram, 12mo. N.Y.,
Sully, 1929.*

COOP, J. WALLACE. Bulls and
bears; cartoons of members and
ring traders of Liverpool Cotton
Exchange. *buckram, folio.
Liverpool, Tinling, 1908.*

COOPER, GEORGE. Dutch dialect
readings and recitations. *paper,
16mo. N.Y., Wehman, 1891.*

_____ Yankee, Italian and
Hebrew dialect readings and
recitations. *paper, 16mo. N.Y.,
Wehman, 1891.*

COOPER, LEONARD. R. S.
Surtees. *buckram, 8vo. Lond.,
Barker, 1952.*

COOPER, PAGE, *ed.* The boudoir
companion. *buckram, 8vo. N.Y.,
Lexington, 1943.*

COOPER, WILLIAM M. Flagel-
lation and the flagellants.
*buckram, 12mo. Lond., Reeves,
n.d. New ed.*

COPE, HORACE. The Rev. Mr.
Sourball's European trip; the
recreations of a city parson.
*paper, 12mo. Phila., D.Ashmead,
1867.*

COPELAND, LEWIS, *ed.* 10,000
jokes, toasts & stories. *buckram, 8vo. Garden City, Garden
City Pub. Co., 1946.*

_____ The world's best
jokes. *buckram, 22cm. N.Y.,
Blue Ribbon Books, 1936.*

COPE'S MIXTURE: selected from
his tobacco plant. *paper, 12mo.
Liverpool, At the Office of
Cope's Tobacco Plant, 1893.*

COPPEE, FRANCOIS. Pater
noster. *paper, 12mo. N.Y.,
French, 1915.*

CORRELL, CHARLES J. *and*
GOSDEN, FREEMAN F.
Sam'n Henry. *paper, 12mo.
Chic., Shrewsbury, 1926.*

COSE, JO., *pseud.* Ginger snaps;
a collection of 2,000 scintil-
lations of wit. *buckram, 24mo.
Bost., Amsen, 1865.*

COULSON, F. RAYMOND. This
funny world. *buckram, 12mo.
Lond., S.Paul, n.d.*

"THE COUNCIL OF TEN" The
town. *v.1. no.1. N.Y.,
Andrews, Beaumont, 1845.*

THE COUNTRY PLUMBER: rebutting some arguments set forth by other noted specialists in America's backyard architecture. *boards, 24mo. Minneapolis, Country Press, n.d.*

COUNTRY PLUMBER'S CATALOG. *looseleaf.*

COUNTRYMAN, CARL C. Three senses. *paper, 24mo. Lyceumite Press, 1908.*

COURLANDER, HAROLD. Ride with the sun; an anthology of folk tales and stories from the United Nations. *buckram, 8vo. Whittlesey, 1955.*

COUTTS, HENRY T. Library jokes and jottings. *boards, 12 mo. Lond., Grafton, 1914.*

COWAN, W. The humorous side of the pulpit. *buckram, 12mo. Lond., Gibbings, 1913.*

COWARD, NOEL. To-night at 8:30. *3v. buckram, 12mo. Lond., Heinemann, 1936.*

COWPER, WILLIAM. The Yorkshire hunt; or, An extraordinary chase of the parson and the cat. *Lond., Marsh & Miller, 1930. (Bound in the volume entitled ODDITIES, q.v.)*

COX, COLEMAN. Think it over. *paper, 12mo. San Francisco, Author, 1924.*

COX, MARIAN ROALFE. Cinderella; three hundred and forty-five variants. *buckram, 8vo. Lond., Folk-lore Society, 1893.*

COX, PALMER. Frontier humor. *buckram, 16mo. Phila., Hubbard, 1895.*

—————— Same. *Chic., Donahue, Henneberry, n.d.*

COX, SAMUEL S. Why we laugh. *buckram, 12mo. N.Y., Harper, 1880. New and enl.ed.*

COZZENS, FRED'C S. The sayings of Dr. Bushwhacker, and other learned men. *buckram, 12mo. Lond., Simpson, 1867.*

—————— Sayings wise and otherwise. *buckram, 12mo. N.Y., Lovell, 1870.*

—————— Sparrograss papers; or, Living in the country. *buckram, 12mo. N.Y., Derby & Jackson, 1859.*

CRABB, JAMES. The gipsies' advocate; or, Observations on the origin, character, manners and habits of the English gipsies. *buckram, 12mo. Lond., Seeley, 1831.*

CRABTREE, SIMON. Hector Tumbler investigates. *buckram, 12mo. Lond., Jarrolds, n.d.*

CRACKED (magazine) The Cracked reader. *paper, 16mo. N.Y., Ace, 1960.*

CRAIG, A. Work of the wits. *buckram, 12mo. Chic., Craig, 1881.*

CRAIG, VIRGINIA JUDITH. Martial's wit and humor. *paper, 8vo. Phila., Steinman & Foltz, 1912.*

CRAMPTON, GERTRUDE, comp. Your own joke book. *paper, 12 mo. N.Y., Comet, 1948.*

CRANDALL, ARTHUR G. New England joke lore; the tonic of Yankee humor. *buckram, 8vo. Phila., Davis, 1922.*

CRANE, ROY. Captain Easy and Wash Tubbs. *boards, 8vo. Racine, Wis., Whitman, 1934.*

CRANE, WILLIAM H. Footprints and echoes. *buckram, 8vo. N.Y., Dutton, 1927.*

CRASCREDO. No joke. *buckram, 4to. Lond., Country Life, 1929.*

CRAVEN, TOM. Tom Craven's ("Dear readers") gag book. *paper, 12mo. Lond., French, n.d.*

CRAVEN, THOMAS, *ed.* Cartoon cavalcade. *buckram, 4to. Chic., Consolidated Book Pub. 1944.*

CRESSY, WILL M. Cressy's history of New England. *leaflet (in folder) San Francisco, Hall, n.d.*

———— Cressy's humorous history of Pennsylvania. *paper, 16mo. St. Petersburg, Condon, 1925.*

CREWDSON, CHARLES N. Tales of the road. *buckram, 12mo. Chic., Thompson & Thomas, 1905.*

CRICHTON, KYLE. The Marx brothers. *buckram, 8vo. N.Y., Doubleday, 1950.*

CRISSEY, FORREST. Tattlings of a retired politican. *buckram, 8vo. Chic., Clarkson & Cooper, 1904.*

CRITHANNAN, JOB. Fifty-one original fables with morals and ethical index. *half-calf, 8 vo. Lond., Hamilton, Adams, 1833.*

CROCOMBE, LEONARD. Written for fun; my favourite stories. *buckram, 16mo. Lond., Newnes, 1937.*

CROFT, JOHN. Scrapeana. Fugitive miscellany. *half-calf, 12 mo. Lond., Blanchard, 1792. 2d.ed.*

CROPPER, JAMES. Notes and memories. *buckram, 16mo. Kendal, Bateman & Hewitson, 1900.*

CROSBY, BING. Call me lucky. *paper, 12mo. N.Y., Simon & Schuster, 1953.*

CROSBY, P.L. Between shots. *boards, 8vo. N.Y., Harper, 1919.*

———— Skippy rambles. *buckram, 12mo. N.Y., Putnam's, 1932.*

CROSLAND, MARGARET. The happy yes; an anthology of marriage proposals, grave and gay. *buckram, 12mo. Lond., Benn, 1949.*

CROSLAND, T.W.H. Little stings. *buckram, 12mo. Bost., Luce, 1908.*

CROSS, E.A. Heritage of British literature. *buckram, 8vo. N.Y., Macmillan, 1954.*

CROTHERS, SAMUEL L. The mission of humour. *pamphlet.*

CROWCROFT, PETER. The life of the shrew. *buckram, 12mo. Lond., Reinhardt, 1957.*

CROWEST, FREDERICK. A book of musical anecdote. *2v. buckram, 12mo. Lond., Bentley, 1878.*

———— Musician's wit, humour and anecdote. *buckram, 12mo. Lond., Scott, 1902.*

CROWQUILL, ALFRED, *pseud. see* FORRESTER, ALFRED HENRY.

CROY, HOMER. Our Will Rogers. *buckram, 8vo. N.Y., Duell, Sloan & Pearce, 1953.*

———— What grandpa laughed at. *buckram, 8vo. N.Y., Duell, Sloan & Pearce, 1948.*

CRUIKSHANK, GEORGE. The comic almanack; an ephemeris in jest and earnest, containing merry tales, humorous poetry, quips and oddities ... *buckram, 12mo. Lond., John Camden Hotten, 1835-1843. First series.*

——————— *Same. Second series. 1844-1853.*

——————— Four hundred humorous illustrations. *buckram, 8vo. Lond., Simpkin, Marshall, Hamilton, Kent, n.d.*

——————— George Cruikshank's table-book. *buckram, 8vo. Lond., Bell, 1878.*

——————— Punch's real history. *buckram, 12mo. Lond., Tegg, 1844. 3d.ed.*

CRUIKSHANK, ISAAC ROBERT. Cruikshank at home; a new family album of endless entertainment. *buckram, 16mo. Lond., Blackwood, n.d.*

CRUIKSHANK, ROBERT. Facetiae; being a general collection of jeux d'esprits. *3v. quarter-calf; 16mo. Lond., Kidd, 1831.*

CUDLIPP, HUGH. Publish and be damned! The astonishing story of the Daily Mirror. *buckram, 8 vo. Lond., Dakers, 1953.*

CULLINAN, HOWELL. Pardon my accent. *buckram, 12mo. Norwood, Mass., Plimpton, 1934.*

CULOTTA, NINO. Cop this lot. *buckram, 8vo. Lond., Kaye, 1960.*

——————— they're a weird mob. *buckram, 8vo. Lond., Kaye, 1958.*

CUMINE, ERIC. Lunghua Cackles. *paper, 4to. Shanghai, Author, n.d.*

CUMMINGS, J.W. Italian legends and sketches. *buckram, 12mo. N.Y., Dunigan, 1858.*

CUMMINGS, PARKE. I'm telling you kids for the last time. *boards, 8vo. N.Y., Schuman, 1951.*

CUNNINGHAM, ALLAN. Traditional tales of English and Scotish peasantry. *half-boards, 16mo. Lond., Kerslake, 1874.*

CUNNINGHAM, CLARICE, *ed.* Best jokes. *paper, 32mo. Girard, Kan., Haldeman-Julius, n.d. (Little Blue Books) (Not the same as book with similar title)*

——————— Best jokes. *paper, 32mo. Girard, Kan., Haldeman-Julius, n.d. (Little Blue Books.)*

——————— Best jokes about lovers. *paper, 32mo. Girard, Kan., Haldeman-Julius, n.d. (Little Blue Books)*

——————— Best jokes about married life. *paper, 32mo. Girard, Kan., Haldeman-Julius, n.d. (Little Blue Books)*

——————— Toasts for all occasions. *paper, 32mo. Girard, Kan., Haldeman-Julius, n.d. (Little Blue Books)*

CUPID'S ALMANACK. *boards, 12 mo. Mount Vernon, Peter Pauper, n.d.*

CUPPY, WILL. The Great Bustard, and other people. Containing How to tell your friends from the apes, and How to become extinct. *buckram, 12mo. N.Y., Murray Hill Pub. Co., 1944.*

# C-D

_____ The decline and fall of practically everybody. *buckram, 8vo. N.Y., Holt, 1950.*

_____ How to become extinct. *buckram, 12mo. N.Y., Farrar & Rinehart, 1941.*

_____ How to get from January to December. *buckram, 8vo. N.Y., Holt, 1951.*

_____ How to tell your friends from the apes. *paper, 32mo. Chic., Royce, 1944.*

CURCIJA-PRODANOVIC, NADA. Yugoslav folk-tales. *boards, 8 vo. Lond., Oxford Univ. Press, 1957.*

CURIOSITIES OF LITERATURE, consisting of anecdotes, characters, sketches and observations. ... *2v. calf, 12mo. Lond., Murray & Highley, 1797. 4th ed.*

CURIOSITIES OF STREET LITERATURE, comprising "Cocks" and "Catchpennies". A large and curious assortment of street-drolleries, squibs, histories, comic tales in prose and verse. *buckram, 4to. Lond., Reeves & Turner, 1871.*

CURIOUS CASES AND AMUSING ACTIONS AT LAW, including some trials of witches in the seventeenth century. *buckram, 8vo. Lond., Sweet & Maxwell, 1916.*

CURRAN, WILLIAM, *comp.* Clean dirt; 500 anecdotes, stories, poems, toasts and wisecracks; and, How to become a raconteur. *buckram, 8vo. Buffalo, Author, 1948.*

CURTIS, CHARLES P. A commonplace book. *boards, 12 mo. N.Y., Simon & Schuster, 1957.*

CURTISS, FRED H. The comic cook book and dyspeptic's guide to the grave. *paper, 12mo. N.Y., Ogilvie, 1890.*

CUSTOMS AND ANECDOTES OF THE GREENLANDERS. *boards, 24mo. Phila., American Sunday-School Union, 1834.*

CUTTER, SARAH J. Conundrums, riddles, puzzles and games. *buckram, 16mo. Buffalo, Hausauer, 1902. Rev. and enl. ed.*

CYCLOPEDIA OF ANECDOTES OF LITERATURE AND THE FINE ARTS. *half-morocco, 4to. Bost., Gould & Lincoln, 1851.*

CYNIC'S CYCLOPEDIA. *boards, 16mo. Bost., Little, Brown, 1925.*

CYNICUS. Cartoons social and political. *buckram, 4to. Lond., Cynicus Pub. Co., 1893.*

_____ Cynicus, his humour and satire. *paper, 16mo. Lond., Cynicus Pub. Co., 1894.*

_____ The humour of Cynicus. *boards, 12mo. Lond., Cynicus Pub. Co., 1892.*

D.,R. Les eminent Victorians. *buckram, 4to. Lond., Davies, 1927.*

DACIER, ANDRE. The life of Pythagoras, with his symbols and golden verses. Now done into English by N. Rowe. *roan, 8vo. Lond., Tonson, 1707.*

DAHL, FRANCIS W. Dahl's Boston. *buckram, 8vo. Bost., Little, Brown, 1946.*

_____ Dahl's brave new world. *buckram, 8vo. Bost., Little, Brown, 1947.*

# D

DAILY MAIL QUIZ BOOK, number 11. Fact or fiction? *paper, 16mo. Lond., Daily Mail, 1958.*

———————— Number 12. Books. *paper, 16mo. Lond., Daily Mail, 1958.*

DALBIAC, PHILIP HIGH, *ed.* A dictionary of quotations. *buckram, 12mo. Lond., Nelson, n.d.*

DALE, ALAN. The great wet way. *buckram, 12mo. N.Y., Dodd, Mead, 1909.*

DALE, FELIX. He's a lunatic; a farce. *paper, 12mo. Lond., French, n.d.*

DALI, SALVADOR *and* HALSMAN, PHILIPPE. Dali's mustache; a photographic interview. *boards, 12mo. N.Y., Simon & Schuster, 1954.*

DALLAS, MARY KYLE. Aroused at last; a comedy. *paper, 12mo. Chic., Dramatic Pub. Co., n.d.*

DALY, AUGUSTIN. A night off; a comedy. *paper, 12mo. N.Y., Dick & Fitzgerald.*

DALY, T.A. Canzoni. *buckram, 12 mo. Phila., McKay, 1912.*

———————— McAroni ballads. *boards, 12mo. N.Y., Harcourt, Brace & Howe, 1919.*

———————— Madrigali. *buckram, 12mo. Phila., McKay, 1912.*

DAMMANN, CONRAD J. The ABC way to stop smoking cigarettes. *buckram, 16mo. N.Y., Worth, 1950.*

DANINOS, PIERRE. Major Thompson lives in France and discovers the French. *buckram, 8vo. Lond., Cape, 1955.*

———————— Sonia, je t'adore. *boards, 8vo. N.Y., Knopf, 1959.*

DARBY, ERASMUS FOSTER. Idy, the fox-chasing cow. *paper, 8vo. Chillicothe, O., Priv. Print., 1953.*

DARE, JOSIAH. Counsellor manners, his last legacy to his son. *calf, 16mo. Lond., Gough, 1726.*

DARK, RICHARD. The hilarious universe; being Angela's guide to Einstein, and that crush! *buckram, 12mo. Oxford, Blackwell, 1932.*

———————— Shakespeare and that crush! being Angela's guide to English literature. *buckram, 12 mo. Oxford, Univ. Press, 1931.*

DARK, SIDNEY. Twelve bad men. *buckram, 8vo. Lond., Hodder & Stoughton, n.d.*

DARNLEY, J.H. "The Barrister" a new and original farcical comedy. *paper, 12mo. Lond., French, n.d.*

DARROW, CLARENCE *and* HOLMES, JOHN HAYNES. Debate on prohibition. *boards, 12mo. N.Y., League for Public Discussion, 1924.*

DARROW, WHITNEY, *jr.* "Stop, Miss!" *boards, 4to. N.Y., Random, 1957.*

DART, HARRY GRANT. Sprightly adventure of Mr. Homesweet Home. *boards, 12mo. N.Y., Moffat Yard, 1914.*

DARWIN, BERNARD *and* DARWIN, ELINOR. The tale of Mr. Tootleoo. *boards, 12mo. Lond., Nonesuch, n.d.*

DASH, PAUL R. The Cook-ed-up Peary-oddical dictionary and who's hoot in these Arctic circles. *boards, 12mo. Bost., Luce, 1910.*

DASKAM, JOSEPHINE DODGE.
The best nonsense verses.
*boards, 12mo. Evanston,
Lord, 1902.*

DAUGHERTY, JAMES. West of
Boston. *buckram, small 4to.
N.Y., Viking, 1956.*

DAVENPORT, R.A. The commonplace book of epigrams. *leather,
32mo. Edinburgh, Anderson,
1825.*

DAVIDOFF, HENRY. A world
treasury of proverbs from
twenty-five languages. *buckram,
8vo. N.Y., Random House,
1946.*

DAVIDSON, ADOLPH. Here's a
new one; a book of after-dinner
stories. *buckram, 12mo. N.Y.,
Caldwell, 1913.*

DAVIDSON, ANGUS. Edward Lear,
landscape painter and nonsense
poet. *paper, 16mo. Harmondsworth, Middlesex, Penguin,
1950.*

DAVIDSON, BILL. Tall tales they
tell in the services. *buckram,
12mo. N.Y., Crowell, 1943.*

DAVIES, MAURICE. Fun, ancient
and modern. *2v. buckram, 12mo.
Lond., Tinsley, 1878.*

DAVIES, RANDALL. A lyttel book
of nonsense. *boards, 8vo. Lond.,
Macmillan, 1912.*

DAVIES, ROBERTSON. The table
talk of Samuel Marchbanks.
*buckram, 8vo. Lond., Chatto &
Windus, 1951.*

DAVIES, THOMAS. The characters
of George the First, Queen
Caroline, Robert Walpole, Mr.
Pulteney, &c. &c. *half-sheep,
24mo. Lond., Davies & Cadell,
1777.*

DAVIS, BERT. Crisp toasts. *paper,
24mo. Bost., Mutual, 1907.*

—————— Stung. *buckram, 16mo.
Bost., Mutual, 1907.*

DAVIS, CAESAR. The fine art of
punning, with a horrible example. *buckram, 12mo. Colorado
Springs, Apex, 1916.*

DAVIS, EDDIE. Campus joke book.
*paper, 16mo. N.Y., Ace, 1956.*

—————— Fun voyage. *buck-
ram, 8vo. N.Y., Citadel, 1958.*

—————— Laugh yourself well.
A merry mixture of medical
mirth. *buckram, 8vo. N.Y., Fell,
1954.*

—————— Laughter in bed; the
complete pepper-upper for
patients. *buckram, small 4to.
N.Y., Fell, 1958.*

—————— Gag writer's private
joke book. *paper, 12mo. N.Y.,
Ace, 1956.*

—————— Stories for stags.
*paper, 12mo. N.Y., Lion, 1956.*

—————— A treasure of
pleasure; how to be sexcessful.
*buckram, 12mo. N.Y., Fell,
1958.*

DAVIS, F. HADLAND. Myths and
legends of Japan. *buckram, 8
vo. Lond., Harrap, 1912.*

DAVIS, HASSOLDT. Bonjour, hang-
over! *buckram, 8vo. N.Y., Duell,
Sloan & Pearce, 1958.*

DAVIS, HERBERT. The satire of
Jonathan Swift. *buckram, 8vo.
N.Y., Macmillan, 1947.*

DAVIS, MAC. Great American
sports humor. *buckram, 8vo.
Garden City, Blue Ribbon, 1950.*

—————— Say it aint so! *buckram, 8vo. N.Y., Dial, 1953.*

DAVIS, RICHARD HARDING. The orator of Zepata City. *paper, 12mo. Chic., Dramatic Pub. Co., 1900.*

DAVIS, ROBERT H. Over my left shoulder. *buckram, 8vo. N.Y., Appleton, 1926.*

DAVISON, ARTHUR B. A thousand thoughts from various authors. *buckram, 12mo. Lond., Longmans, Green, 1880.*

DAWSON-SCOTT, C.A. Twenty-seven humorous tales. *buckram, 12mo. Lond., Hutchinson, n.d.*

DAY, CHON. Brother Sebastian carries on. *paper, 16mo. N.Y., Pocket Books, 1961.*

——————— I could be dreaming. *boards, 4to. N.Y., McBride, 1945.*

DAY, CLARENCE. The best of Clarence Day. *buckram, 8vo. N.Y., Knopf, 1948.*

DAY, DONALD. Uncle Sam's Uncle Josh. *buckram, 8vo. Bost., Little, Brown, 1953.*

DAY, LAL BEHARI. Folk-tales of Bengal. *buckram, 12mo. Lond., Macmillan, 1902.*

DAY, ROBERT. All out for the sack race! *boards, folio. N.Y., Random House, 1945.*

DAYRELL, E. Ikom folk stories from Southern Nigeria. *paper, 4to. Lond., Royal Anthropological Institute of Great Britain and Ireland. 1911.*

DEAN, ABNER. Cave drawings of the future. *boards, 8vo. N.Y., Dial, 1954.*

——————— Come as you are. *boards, 4to. N.Y., Simon & Schuster, 1952.*

——————— Not far from the jungle. *boards, 8vo. Cleveland, World, 1956.*

——————— Wake me when it's over. *boards, 8vo. N.Y., Simon & Schuster, 1955.*

——————— What am I doing here, *buckram, small 4to. N.Y., Simon & Schuster, 1947.*

DE BURGH, W.G. Legacy of the ancient world. *2v. paper, 12mo. Lond., Penguin, 1953.*

DEAMAN, JULIEN. Boola, boola! *paper, 8vo. N.Y., Coward McCann, 1950.*

DE FINOD, J. A thousand flashes of French wit, wisdom and wickedness. *buckram, 16mo. Lond., Paterson, 1890.*

——————— Same. *N.Y., Appleton, 1900.*

DE GEORGE, FRED. Spaghetti ballads. *buckram, 12mo. N.Y., Exposition, 1947.*

DELARUE, PAUL, *comp. and ed.* Borzoi book of French folk tales. *buckram, 8vo. N.Y., Knopf, 1956.*

DEL REGGO, BERYL. Ex-virgin. *boards, 12mo. Phila., Du Barry, 1930.*

DE MEYER, JOHN. Benjamin Franklin calls on the President. *buckram, 12mo. N.Y., Ives Washburn, 1939.*

DEMIDOFF, ALEX and DEMIDOFF, MARION. Laugh with us. *buckram, 8vo. N.Y., Exposition, 1957.*

DEMOCRITUS. Darwin on trial at the Old Bailey. *buckram, 4to. Lond., University, n.d.*

DEMOCRITUS, or, The laughing
philosopher. A collection of
merry stories, jests, epigrams,
riddles...*calf., 12mo.* Lond.,
*Hornton, Hills, n.d. but ca.1770.*

DEMOCRITUS JUNIOR. The magazine of mirth; being a choice
collection of good stories,
jests, bonmots, epigrams,
epitaphs, &c.&c. *buckram,
24mo.* Stanford, *Drakard, n.d.*

_____ Versatile ingenium.
The wittie companion, or, Jests
of all sorts from citie and
countrie, court and universitie.
*Amsterdam, 1679. (Photostatic
copy from the original in the
Library of Congress)*

DEMOCRITUS IN LONDON, with
the mad pranks and comical
conceits of Motley and Robin
Goodfellow. *buckram, 16mo.*
Lond., *Pickering, 1852.*

DE MORGAN, JOHN. In lighter
vein; a collection of witty
sayings, bon mots, bright
repartees, &c.&c. *paper, 16mo.*
San Francisco, *Elder, 1909.*

DENGEL, VERONICA. Hold your
man! *buckram, 12mo.* N.Y.,
*Coward-McCann, 1945.*

DENIS, CHARLES. Select fables.
*half-calf, 8vo.* Lond., *Tonson
& Draper, 1754.*

DENIS, PAUL, *comp.* Unexpected
answers (on radio and TV).
*paper, 8vo.* n.p., *Lyle Stuart,
1958.*

DENNY, NORMAN, *comp.* The
Yellow book. *buckram, 8vo.*
Lond., *Spring, n.d.*

DENNYS, N.B. Folk-lore of China.
*half-calf, 8vo.* Lond., *Trubner,
1876.*

DEPEW, CHAUNCY M. The Depew
story book. *buckram, 12mo.*
*Chic., Thompson & Thomas,
1903.*

DERBY, GEORGE H. Phoenixi-
ana; or, Sketches and burlesques, by John Phoenix, *pseud.*
*buckram, 12mo.* N.Y., *Appleton,
1856.*

_____ The Squibob papers.
*buckram, 12mo.* N.Y., *Carleton,
1865.*

_____ Squibbs and drol-
leries. *paper, 16mo.* Lond.,
*Ward, Lock, n.d.*

DERMENGHEM, EMILE.
Muhammad and the Islamic
tradition. *paper, 12mo.* N.Y.,
*Harper, 1958.*

DERRICK, JOSEPH. Confusion,
a farcical comedy. *paper, 12
mo.* N.Y., *French, 1900.*

DESAI, VALJI GOVINDI. A
Ghandi anthology, book 1.
*paper, 16mo.* Ahmedabad,
*Navajivan, 1952.*

DESCARTES, RENE. The living
thoughts of Descartes. Presented by Paul Valery. *buckram, 12mo.* Lond., *Cassell,
1948.*

DESCRIPTIVE, SENTIMENTAL,
AND HUMOROUS ALBUM,
THE. *morocco, 24mo.*
*Baltimore, Nickman, 1836.*

DESLANDES, ANDRE FRANCOIS
BOUREAU. Dying merrily, or
Historical and critical
reflexions on the conduct of
great men in all ages, who in
their last moments mock'd
death and died facetiously.
*buckram, 12mo.* Lond., *Cooper,
1745.*

DEUTSCH, MONROE E. Saint
Albert of San Francisco. In:
The Menorah Journal, Spring-
Summer, 1955.

DE VERE, WILLIAM. De Vere's
negro sketches, end-men's
gags and conundrums. *paper,
12mo. Chic., Powner, 1946.*

DEVEREUX, THOMAS H. Pointed
pickings from the Arkansaw
Traveler. *paper, 12mo. Chic.,
Lee, n.d.*

DEWEY, JOHN. Creative democracy; the task before us. *paper,
24mo. (Personal Growth
Leaflets)*

A DIARY OF THE GLADSTONE
GOVERNMENT. *paper, 16mo.
Edinburgh, Blackwood, n.d.*

DICK, WILLIAM B., *ed.* Dick's book
of toasts, speeches and re-
sponses. *boards, 16mo. N.Y.,
Dick & Fitzgerald, 1883.*

——————— Dick's comic dia-
logues. *paper, 16mo. N.Y.,
Dick & Fitzgerald.*

——————— Dick's Dutch, French
and Yankee dialect recitations.
*paper, 16mo. N.Y., Dick & Fitz-
gerald, 1879.*

DICKENS, CHARLES. Best fun from
the Pickwich papers. *paper,
32mo. Girard, Kan., Haldeman-
Julius, n.d. (Little Blue Books)*

——————— Humorous readings
from Charles Dickens, an
anthology by Peter Haworth.
*buckram, 12mo. Lond.,
Macmillan, 1951.*

——————— Humour and pathos of
Charles Dickens. Selected by
Charles Kent. *buckram, 12mo.
Lond., Chapman & Hall, 1884.*

——————— Humour of Dickens.
Chosen by R.J. Cruikshank.
*paper, 8vo. Lond., News
Chronicle, 1952.*

——————— Sketches by Boz.
*buckram, 8vo. Lond., Chapman
& Hall, 1877. New ed.*

——————— Wellerisms from
"Pickwick" and "Master
Humphrey's clock". *buckram,
16mo. Lond., Record, n.d.*

——————— *Same. Lond.,
Redway, 1886.*

——————— *Same. Lond., Record,
n.d. 2d.ed.*

——————— Wit and wisdom of
Dickens. *paper, 32m, . Girard,
Kan., Haldeman-Julius, n.d.
(Little Blue Books)*

DICKSON, NICHOLAS. The auld
Scotch precentor as sketched in
anecdote and story. *buckram,
16mo. Glasgow, Morison, 1894.*

DICKSON, SAMUEL. San Francisco
is your home. *buckram, 8vo.
Stanford, Stanford Univ. Press,
1947.*

DICTES AND SAYINGS OF THE
PHILOSOPHERS. A facsimile
reproduction of the first book
printed in England by William
Caxton, in 1477. *buckram, 4to.
Lond., Stock, 1877.*

DIGS AT DOC, AND OTHERS: a
collection of funny sayings
principally about the doctor and
his profession. *buckram, 8vo.
Perth Amboy, Perth Amboy
Evening News, 1915.*

DIME DIALOGUES NO. 27.
Original and specially prepared dialogues, colloquies,
farces ... *paper, 16mo. N.Y.,
Beadle & Adams, 1880.*

DIME SELECT SPEAKER; a fresh collection of gems of oratory ... *paper, 16mo. N.Y., Ivers, 1887.*

DIONNE, JACK. Cullud fun. *buckram, 12mo. Houston, Rein, 1932.*

_____ "Lotsa fun" a compilation of the favorite stories of this author. *Houston, Author, n.d.*

DIPROSES'S ANECDOTES ABOUT LAWYERS, DOCTORS, AND PARSONS. *half-calf., 16mo. Lond., Diprose & Bateman, n.d.*

DIPROSES'S ANNUAL BOOK OF FUN, FACT AND FICTION. *buckram, 8vo. Lond., Diprose & Bateman, 1877.*

DIPROSES'S BOOK OF EPITAPHS: humorous, eccentric, ancient & remarkable. *buckram, 12mo. Lond., Diprose & Bateman, n.d.*

DISHER, M. WILLSON. Clowns and pantomimes. *buckram, 4to. Lond., Constable, 1925.*

DISRAELI, BENJAMIN. Wit and wisdom of Disraeli. *paper, 32mo. Girard, Kan., Haldeman-Julius, n.d. (Little Blue Books)*

DISRAELI, ISAAC. Amenities of literature. *2v. buckram, 12mo. Lond., Routledge, Warnes & Routledge, 1859.*

_____ A dissertation on anecdotes. *boards, 8vo. Lond., Kearsley & Hunter, 1793.*

DIX, DOROTHY. Fables of the elite. *buckram, 16mo. N.Y., Fenno, 1902.*

DOBELL, BYRON. Child's book of funny animals. *boards, 4to. N.Y., Ziff-Davis, 1960.*

DOBREE, BONAMY. Timotheus, or The future of the theatre. *buckram, 16mo. N.Y., Dutton, 1925.*

DOBSON, AUSTIN. William Hogarth. *buckram, 4to. Lond., Sampson Low, Marston, 1891.*

DOBSON, WILLIAM T. Literary frivolities, fancies, follies and frolics. *buckram, 16mo. Lond., Chatto & Windus, 1880.*

DODD, HENRY PHILIP. The epigrammatists. *buckram, 8vo. Lond., Bell & Daldy, 1870.*

DODGE, DAVID. The crazy glass-pecker, or, High life in the Andes. *buckram, 8vo. N.Y., Random House, 1949.*

_____ How green was my father. *buckram, 8vo. N.Y., Simon & Schuster, 1950.*

_____ How lost was my weekend. *boards, 8vo. N.Y., Random House, 1948.*

_____ 20,000 leagues behind the 8 ball. *boards, 8vo. N.Y., Random House, 1951.*

DOESTICKS, Q.K. PHILANDER *see* THOMSON, MORTIMER.

DOLBIER, MAURICE. Nowhere near Everest. *boards, 8vo. Knopf, 1955.*

DOLE, NATHAN HASKELL, *ed.* Best humor of 1925. *buckram, 12mo. Bost., Stratford, 1926.*

_____ Joseph Jefferson at home. *buckram, 8vo. Bost., Estes & Lauriat, 1898.*

DOLSON, HILDEGARDE. Sorry to be so cheerful. *buckram, 8vo. Lond., Hammond & Hammond, 1956.*

DONAHUE, HAROLD W. Toastmaster's manual. *buckram, 8vo. Indianapolis, Droke, 1937.*

DONALD, DAVID. Lincoln's Herndon. *buckram, 8vo. N.Y., Knopf, 1948.*

DONNELLY, MILLY LOU *see* MOBLEY, MILLY LOU.

DOOKS' DOOMESDAY BOOK. *paper, 8vo. Lond., Paul, 1910.*

DORAN _____. History of court fools. *calf., 12mo. Lond., Bentley, 1858.*

DORR, FRANK I. Hayseed and sawdust. *buckram, 8vo. Bost., Wormsted, Smith, 1934.*

DORSON, RICHARD M. Jonathan draws the long bow. *buckram, 8vo. Cambridge, Harvard Univ. Press, 1946.*

_____ Negro folktales in Michigan. *boards, 8 vo. Cambridge, Harvard Univ. Press, 1956.*

DOUDOUIT, J.F.O. Elegant biographical extracts; consisting of interesting anecdotes, bonmots, judicious repartees, etc. *2v. boards, 16mo. Ludlow, Procter, 1802.*

DOUGLAS, JACK. My brother was an only child. *paper, 16mo. N.Y., Permabooks, 1959.*

_____ Never trust a naked bus driver. *paper, 16mo. N.Y., Permabooks, 1961.*

DOUGLAS, JAMES, *ed.* Scottish wit and humour; a collection of comical anecdotes. *buckram, 12 mo. Edinburgh, Gall & Inglis, n.d.*

DOUGLAS, NORMAN. An almanac. *buckram, 8vo. Lond., Chatto & Windus, 1945.*

DOWDALL, MARY FRANCES HARRIETT: Joking apart. *buckram, 12mo. Lond., Duckworth, 1915.*

DOWER *and* RIDDELL. Inside Britain. *buckram, 12mo. Lond., Heinemann, 1937.*

_____Outside Britain. *buckram, 8vo. Lond., Heinemann, 1938.*

DOWNEY, FAIRFAX, When we were rather older. *buckram, 12 mo. N.Y., Minton, Balch, 1926.*

_____ Young enough to know better! *buckram, 12mo. N.Y., Minton, Balch, 1927.*

DOWNEY, WILLIAM SCOTT. Proverbs. *morocco, 16mo. Bost., Hewes, 1853. 4th ed.*

DOWNING, CHARLES. Russian tales and legends. *buckram, 8 vo. Lond., Oxford Univ. Press, 1956.*

DOWNING, MAJOR JACK, *pseud. see* SMITH, SEBA.

DOWST, CHARLES. Second suds sayings, a collection of stories, sketches and articles regarding the laundry. *buckram, 12mo. Chic., National Laundry, Journal, 1919.*

DOWTY, A.A. Figaro's history of England, by P.P.Q. Philander Smiff, *pseud. paper, 16mo. Lond., Figaro, 1873.*

DOYLE, RICHARD. Foreign tour of Messrs. Brown, Jones and Robinson. *buckram, 4to. Lond., Bradbury & Evans, 1854.*

_____ Manners and customs of ye Englyshe, to which is added some extracts from Mr. Pips hys diary, contributed by Percival Leigh. *boards, wide 8 vo. Lond., Bradbury & Evans, 1849.*

D'OYLEY, *Sir* HASTINGS. Tales retailed of celebrities, and others. *buckram, 8vo. Lond., Lane, 1920.*

DRAKE, SAMUEL ADAMS. A book
of New England legends and
folk lore. *buckram, 8vo. Bost.,
Little, Brown, 1901. New. and
rev. ed.*

DREAMY BILL, pseud. The
Arkansaw I saw. *paper, 32mo.
Baltimore, Ottenheimer, n.d.*

DREIER, THOMAS. The silver
lining, or Sunshine on the
business trail. *buckram, 12mo.
N.Y., Forbes, 1923. Bound with
"Forbes Epigrams" by B.C.
Forbes)*

DRESSLER, ALBERT, *comp.*
California Chinese chatter.
*boards, 8vo. San Francisco,
Author, 1927.*

_____ California's pioneer
artist, Ernest Narjot. *paper, 8
vo. San Francisco, Author,
1936.*

_____ California's pioneer
circus, Joseph Andrew Rowe,
founder. *buckram, 8vo. San
Francisco, Crocker, 1926.*

_____ Emperor Norton. *paper,
8vo. San Francisco, Author,
1927. 2d.ed.*

_____ Letters to a pioneer
senator. *paper, 12mo. San
Francisco, Crocker, 1925.*

DRESSLER, MARIE. Life story of
an ugly duckling. *buckram, 8vo.
McBride, 1924.*

DROHAN, LEONARD. Come with
me to Macedonia. *boards, 8vo.
N.Y., Knopf, 1957.*

DROKE, MAXWELL. Anecdotes.
*paper, 12mo. Indianapolis,
Droke, 1935.*

_____ Anthology of anec-
dotes. *buckram, 8vo. Indianapolis, Droke, 1948.*

_____ Just a touch of
lavender. *boards, 12mo.
Indianapolis, Droke, 1935.*

_____ Speaker's handbook
of humor. *buckram, 8vo. N.Y.,
Harper, 1956.*

_____ Stag lines; an
anthology of virile verse.
*buckram, 12mo. N.Y., Phoenix,
1940.*

DRUMMER'S YARNS AND FUNNY
JOKES, SEVENTH CROP.
*paper, 8vo. N.Y., Excelsior,
1896.*

DRUMMOND, WILLIAM HENRY.
The habitant. *buckram, 12mo.
N.Y., Putnam, 1909.*

DRYDEN, CHARLES. On and off
the breadwagon. *buckram, 12mo.
Chic., Reilly & Britton, 1904.*

_____ Roughing it from New
York to the Pacific Coast.
*paper, 16mo. Chic., Stein, 1921.*

DRYDEN, JOHN. Fables ancient
and modern. *calf, 8vo. Lond.,
Tonson, 1713.*

_____ Fables ancient and
modern. *calf, 16mo. Lond.,
Tonson & Draper, 1955.*

DUBOIS, EDWARD. American
broad grins, edited by Rigdum
Funnidos, Gent. *buckram, 24
mo. Lond., Tyas, 1839. 2d.ed.*

_____ My pocket book; or,
Hints for "A ryghte merrie and
conceitede" tour, to be called
"The stranger in Ireland" in
1805. By a Knight Errant. *tree
calf., 12mo. Lond., Vernor
Hood & Sharpe, 1808.
New ed.*

DU BOIS, HENRI PENE. Witty
wise and wicked maxims.
*buckram, 16mo. Chic.,
Brentano's, 1897.*

DUBOUT, Dubout cartoons. *buckram, 4to. Lond., Spearman, 1957.*

——————— Dubout's raillery. *boards, 8vo. Lond., Putnam, 1956.*

DU BROCA, LOUIS. Interesting anecdotes of the heroic conduct of women, duri ng the French Revolution. *tree-calf., 16mo. Lond., Symonds, 1802.*

DUFF, *Sir* MOUNTSUART ELPHINSTONE GRANT. A Victorian vintage. *buckram, 8vo. Lond., Methuen, 1930.*

DUFF, BEN *and* POWEL, HARFORD. The world's greatest 99 days. *buckram, 8vo. N.Y., Harper, 1933.*

DUKES, ASHLEY. The man with the load of mischief. *paper, 12 mo. N.Y., French, 1930.*

DU MAURIER, GEORGE. English society. *buckram, wide 8vo. N.Y., Harper, 1897.*

DUMONT, FRANK. Ham(om)let, Prince of Dunkirk. *paper, 12 mo. N.Y., Witmark, 1905.*

——————— Burnt cork, or, The amateur minstrel. *paper, 12mo. N.Y., Wehman, 1881.*

——————— The Crest collection of stump speeches. *paper, 12mo. N.Y., Witmark, 1905.*

——————— The Witmark amateur minstrel guide and burnt cork encyclopedia. *cloth, 8vo. Chic., Whitmark, 1899.*

DUNCAN, ISADORA. My life. *buckram, 12mo. Lond., Gollanz, 1928.*

DUNCAN, SARA JEANNETTE. The simple adventures of a memsahib. *buckram, 12mo. Lond., Chatto & Windus, 1893.*

DUNHILL, ALFRED. The gentle art of smoking. *boards, 8vo. N.Y.. Putnam's 1954.*

DUNN, ALAN. Is there intelligent life on earth? *boards, folio. N.Y., Simon & Schuster, 1960.*

——————— Who's paying for this cab? *buckram, 12mo. N.Y., Simon & Schuster, 1945.*

——————— Should it gurgle? *boards, 4to. N.Y., Simon & Schuster, 1956.*

DUNN, ARTHUR WALLACE. Gridiron nights. *buckram, 4to. N.Y., Stokes, 1915.*

DUNN, BOB. I'm gonna be a father. *boards, 8vo. N.Y., McKay, 1941.*

——————— Knock knock, featuring Enoch Knox. *paper, 4to. N.Y., Dell, 1936.*

DUNN, SEYMOUR. The complete golf joke book. *buckram, 8vo. N.Y., Stravon, 1953.*

DUNNE, PETER FINLEY. Dissertations by Mr. Dooley. *buckram, 12mo. N.Y., Harper, 1906.*

——————— Mr. Dooley in peace and war. *buckram, 16mo. Bost., Small, Maynard, 1898.*

——————— Mr. Dooley says. *buckram, 16mo. Toronto, McLeod & Allen, 1910.*

——————— Mr. Dooley's opinions. *buckram, 12mo. N.Y., Russell, 1901.*

——————— Mr. Dooley's philosophy. *buckram, 12mo. N.Y., Russell, 1902.*

——————— Observations of Mr. Dooley. *buckram, 12mo. N.Y., Harper, 1906.*

# D-E

DUNSANY, EDWARD JOHN
MORETON DRAX PLUNKETT,
*baron* Five plays. *buckram, 12
mo. N.Y., Kennerley, 1914.*

DUNTON, JOHN *see* ATHENIAN
SOCIETY, LONDON.

DURANT, JOHN. Predictions;
pictorial predictions. *buckram,
small 4to. N.Y., Barnes, 1956.*

DURANT, WILL. Anatole France;
the man and his work. *paper,
32mo. Girard, Kan, Haldeman-
Julius, n.d. (Little Blue Books)*

D'URFEY, THOMAS. Wit and
mirth; or, Tom D'Urfey's Pills
to purge melancholy. *quarter-
calf, 8vo. Lond., Holland, 1719.*

DUTCH DIALECT RECITATIONS,
READINGS AND JOKES.
*paper, 16mo. Chic., Drake,
1903.*

DUTCH JOKES AND FUNNY
YARNS. *paper, 12mo. Phila.,
Royal, 1902.*

DUTHIE, D. WALLACE. The
church in the pages of "Punch"
*buckram, 8vo. Lond., Smith,
Elder, 1912.*

DUTHIE, ERIC. Tall short stories.
*buckram, 8vo. N.Y., Simon &
Schuster, 1959.*

DWIGGINS, CLARE VICTOR.
Toasts. *boards, 12mo. N.Y.,
Author, 1907.*

DYER, T.F. THISELTON. Great
men at play. *2v. buckram, 8vo.
Lond., Remington, 1889.*

DYRENFORTH, JAMES and
KESTOR, MAX. Adolf in
Blunderland; a political parody
of Lewis Carroll's famous story.
*boards, 4to. Lond., Muller,
1939.*

DYSON, VERNE. Forgotten tales
of ancient China. *buckram, 8vo.
Shanghai, Commercial press,
1934.*

DYSON, WILL. Cartoons. *paper,
folio. Lond., Daily Herald,
1914.*

——————— Kultur cartoons.
*paper, folio, Lond., S.Paul, n.d.*

EASTMAN, E.R. Another batch of
Eastman's chestnuts. *ring
binder, American Agriculturist,
1945.*

——————— Eastman's chestnuts.
*v.1,4 &5. paper, 16mo. American
Agriculturist, various dates.*

EASTMAN, MAX. Enjoyment of
laughter. *buckram, 12mo. N.Y.,
Simon & Schuster, 1936.*

——————— Great companions.
*boards, 8vo. N.Y., Farrar, Straus
& Cudahy, 1959.*

——————— The sense of humor.
*buckram, 16mo. Scribners, 1921.*

EASTMAN, REX. *comp.* The jumbo
joke book. *paper, 8vo. Girard,
Kan., Haldeman-Julius, 1936.*

EASY METHOD FOR LEARNING
VENTRILOQUISM. *paper, 24mo.
Baltimore, Ottenheimer, 1908.*

EATON, ARTHUR WENTWORTH,
*comp.* Funny epitaphs. *buckram,
8vo. Bost., Mutual, 1900.*

EBERHARD, WOLFRAM, *comp. and
tr.* Chinese fairy tales and folk
tales. *buckram, 8vo. N.Y.,
Dutton, 1938.*

ECCENTRICITIES, or, Whimsical
cabinet of comic tales, forming
a complete gallimaufry for the
humorist, either at home or
abroad. *paper, 48mo. Lond.,
Smith, 1820.*

# E

ECHOLS, LEE R. Dead aim. *buckram, 12mo. N.Y., Greenberg, 1951.*

ECKSTEIN, GUSTAV. Friends of mine. *buckram, 8vo. N.Y., Readers Club, 1942.*

EDGEWORTH, MARIA. Popular tales. *3v. calf., 12mo. Lond., Johnson, 1811. 4th ed.*

——————— Tales of fashionable life. *3v. half-calf, 12mo. Lond., Johnson, 1809.*

EDGEWORTH, RICHARD LOVELL. Essay on Irish bulls. *quarter-leather, 12mo. Lond., Johnson, 1802.*

——————— Same. *3d.ed. 1808.*

——————— Same, *4th ed. 1815.*

EDINBURGH BUDGET OF WIT AND AMUSEMENT. *half-calf, 24mo. Edinburgh, Moir, 1808.*

EDINBURGH MEDLEY OF ENTERTAINMENT. *half-calf, 24mo. Edinburgh, Brown, 1800.*

EDINGER, GEORGE. Pons asinorum, or, The future of nonsense. *buckram, 16mo. Lond., Kegan Paul, Trench, Trubner, 1929.*

EDMONDS, I.G. Solomon in kimono; tales of Oooka, a wise judge of old Yedo. *half-boards, 4to. Japan, Pacific Stars & Stripes, 1956.*

EDMONDS, WALTER D. Hound dog Moses and the promised land. *buckram, 8vo. N.Y., Dodd, Mead, 1954.*

EDMUND, PEGGY. Toaster's handbook; jokes, stories and quotations. *buckram, 12mo. N.Y., Wilson, 1916. 3d.ed.*

EDSON, C.L. The gentle art of columning; a treatise on comic journalism. *boards, 12mo. N.Y., Brentano, 1920.*

EDWARDES, MICHAEL, *ed.* The Reverend Mr. Punch; pictorial record of a sixty years' ministry. *boards, 8vo. Lond., Mowbray, 1956.*

EDWARDS, CHARLES. Pleasantries about courts and lawyers of the state of New York. *buckram, 8vo. N.Y., Richardson, 1867.*

EDWARDS, E.D. The dragon book. *buckram, 16mo. Lond., William Hodge, 1943.*

EDWARDS, FRANK. Strangest of all. *buckram, 8vo. Lond., Rider, 1958.*

EDWARDS, GUS C. Legal laughs; a joke for every jury. *buckram, 8 vo. Clarkesville, Legal pub.co., 1915.*

EDWARDS, HARRY STILLWELL. Aneas Africanus. *boards, 8vo. N.Y., Grosset & Dunlap, 1920.*

——————— Tenth generation. *paper, 24mo. (Personal Growth Leaflets.)*

——————— Pearls; or, The world's laconics. *half-morocco, 12mo. Bost., B.B. Russell, 1872.*

EDWIN'S JESTS, HUMOURS, FROLICS AND BON-MOTS. *quarter-calf., 12mo. Lond., Roach, 1794.*

EDYE, ALFRED. Woman's ways and wiles; home truths about love. *buckram, 12mo. Lond., Jarrolds, 1922.*

EELS, JOHN SHEPARD. Touchstone of Matthew Arnold. *buckram, 8vo. N.Y., Bookman Associates, 1955.*

EHRET, WENDELL. "Dear Gertrood" *boards, 4to. N.Y., McBride, 1945.*

EHRMANN, MAX. Poems. *buckram, 12mo. N.Y., Dodge, 1906.*

EIGHT ONE-ACT PLAYS. *buckram, 12mo. Lond., Rich & Cowan, 1933.*

EIMERL, SAREL. The cautious bachelor. *buckram, 8vo. N.Y., Crown, 1958.*

EISENBERG, FRANCES. My Uncle Newt. *buckram, 8vo. Phila., Lippincott, 1942.*

EISENSCHIML, OTTO. Why was Lincoln murdered? *buckram, 8 vo. Bost., Little, Brown, 1937.*

ELDRIDGE, PAUL. Lanterns in the night. *paper, 8vo. Girard, Kan., Haldeman-Julius, 1945.*

_____ Leaves from the Devil's tree. *paper, 8vo. Girard, Kan., Haldeman; Julius, 1946.*

_____ Maxims are gadflies. *paper, 8vo. Girard, Kan., Haldeman-Julius, 1950.*

ELEGANT EXTRACTS, or, Useful and entertaining passages. *calf, 8vo. Lond., Dilly, 1784. New ed.*

ELIOT, GEORGE. A moment each day with George Eliot. *boards, 8vo. Chic., Madison, 1903.*

_____ Wise, witty and tender sayings in prose and verse, selected ... by Alexander Main. *buckram, 12mo. Edinburgh, Blackwood, 1904.*

_____ Wit and wisdom. *buckram, 24mo. Bost., Roberts, 1874.*

ELIOT, JOHN. The parlement of pratlers ... published in the year 1593. *boards, 8vo. Lond., Franfrolico, 1928.*

"ELLINGOWAN" Sporting anecdotes. *buckram, 8vo. Lond., Hamilton, Adams, 1889.*

ELLIOT, ANDREW GEORGE. The bunion specialist. *buckram, 16 mo. Kingswood, Surrey, Right Way books 1954.*

ELLIOTT, ARTHUR H. The witty and humorous side of the English poets. *buckram, 8vo. Lond., Sampson, Low, Marston, Searle & Rivington, 1880.*

ELLIS, CHARLES *and* WEIR, FRANK. I'd rather be president; a handbook for expectant candidates. *boards, 8vo. N.Y., Simon & Schuster, 1956.*

ELLIS, EDITH. Seven sisters. *paper, 12mo. N.Y., Dramatists Play Service, 1937*

ELLIS, H.F. Much ado mostly about nothing. *buckram, 12mo. Lond., Methuen, 1934.*

_____ The papers of A.J. Wentworth, B.A. *buckram, 12 mo. Lond., Evans, 1949.*

_____ The pleasure's yours. *buckram, 12mo. Lond., Methuen, 1933.*

_____ Twenty five years hard. *buckram, 8vo. Lond., Parrish, 1960.*

ELLIS, WINIFRED. London - so help me! *buckram, 12mo. Lond., Macdonald, 1952.*

ELMO, HORACE T. Hollywood humor. *paper, 16mo. N.Y., Ace, 1957.*

_____ Honeymoon humor. *paper, 12mo. N.Y., Ace, 1956.*

_____ Modern Casanova's handbook. *paper, 16mo. N.Y., Ace, 1955.*

ELWELL-SUTTON, L.P. Persian proverbs. *buckram, 12mo. Lond., Murray, 1954.*

EMCEE COLLECTION OF HECKLER STOPPERS; comic dictionary, comic song titles. *paper, 8vo. Chic., Emcee Magazine, n.d.*

EMERSON, RALPH WALDO. Gems from Emerson. *paper, 32mo. Girard, Kan., Haldeman-Julius, n.d. (Little Blue Books.)*

——————— Pearls of wisdom. *buckram, 12mo. San Francisco, Z. Varney, n.d.*

——————— Selections from Ralph Waldo Emerson, by Joy Elmer Morgan. *paper, 24mo. (Personal Growth Leaflets.)*

——————— Wisdom of Ralph Waldo Emerson, being extracts from his prose and verse, selected by William B. Parker. *buckram, 24mo. N.Y., Brentano's 1904.*

ENCHIRIDION OF WIT; the best specimens of English conversational wit. *half-leather, 16mo. Phila., Lippincott, 1885.*

ENCYCLOPAEDIA OF ANECDOTE. *half-calf., 24mo. Dublin, Jackson, n.d.*

ENCYCLOPAEDIA OF WIT. *half-calf., 24mo. Lond., Baldwin, Cradock & Joy, 1823.*

ENCYCLOPAEDIA OF WIT FOR 1812. *calf., 32mo. Lond., Tegg, 1812.*

ENCYCLOPEDIA OF WIT. *half-calf, 24mo. Lond., Phillips, n.d. ca. 1840.*

——————— Same. *half-calf, 24 mo. Lond., Crosby, n.d. but ca. 1850. New ed.*

END MEN'S JOKER: an everlasting cornucopia of fun. *paper, 16mo. N.Y., Advance Pub. Co., n.d.*

ENDLESS AMUSEMENT, new series; containing nearly four hundred interesting experiments in various branches of science. *buckram, 16mo. Lond., Tegg, 1837.*

ENGELBACH, ARTHUR H. Anecdotes of bench and bar. *buckram, 12mo. Lond., Richards, 1913.*

——————— Anecdotes of the theatre. *buckram, 12mo. Lond., Richards, 1914.*

——————— More anecdotes of bench and bar. *buckram, 12mo. Lond., Richards, 1915.*

ENGLAND'S GENIUS; or, Wit triumphant. *quarter-morocco, 8vo. Lond., Roberts, 1734.*

ENGLISH AS SHE IS SPOKE: or, A jest in sober earnest. *paper, 24mo. Lond., Field & Tuer, n.d. 7th ed.*

——————— Same. *N.Y., Appleton, 1886.*

ENGLISH JESTS AND ANECDOTES. *half-buckram, 24mo. Edinburgh, Paterson, n.d.*

——————— Same. *Lond., Dent, n.d.*

ENGLISH WIT AND HUMOR. *limp leather, 24mo. Phila., Jacobs, 1898.*

ENTERTAINING MEDLEY; being a collection of genuine anecdotes, delightful stories, frolicks of wit and humour. *calf., 16mo. Lond., Parker, 1767. 2d.ed.*

EPIGRAMS, ORIGINAL AND SELECTED. *buckram, 16mo. Lond., Simpkin, Marshall, 1877.*

EPIGRAMS OF WIT, WISDOM AND WICKEDNESS. *paper, 32mo. Girard, Kan., Haldeman-Julius, n.d. (Little Blue Books.)*

EPITAPHS AND EPIGRAMS, CURIOUS QUAINT AND AMUSING. *buckram, 16mo. Lond., Palmer, 1869.*

ERASMUS, DESIDERIUS. The Apophthegms of the ancients. *2v. calf., 16mo. Lond., Millar, 1753.*

ERNST-BROWNING, WILLIAM. Memoirs of the life of Philip Dormer, 4th earl of Chesterfield. *buckram, 8vo. Lond., Sonnenschein, 1893.*

ERNST, MARGARET S. In a word. *buckram, 8vo. N.Y., Knopf, 1939.*

ERSKINE, JOHN. The delight of great books. *buckram, 8vo. Lond., Eveleigh Nash, 1928.*

ERSKINE, MEL. Thank God for laughter. *buckram, 12mo. N.Y., Kendall, 1936.*

ESAR, EVAN. Animal joker. *buckram, 8vo. N.Y., Harvest House, 1946.*

——— The dictionary of humorous quotations. *buckram, 8vo. N.Y., Doubleday, 1949.*

——— Esar's comic dictionary. *buckram, small 8 vo. N.Y., Harvest House, 1943.*

——— Esar's joke dictionary. *buckram, small 8vo. N.Y., Harvest House, 1945.*

——— The humor of humor. *buckram, 8vo. N.Y., Horizon, 1952.*

——— The legend of Joe Miller. *paper, folio. San Francisco, Grabhorn, 1957. Anecdota Scowah, 2. (Contains also: A prefatory fragment with Joe Milleriana, by Nat Schmulowitz.)*

ESCAPADE. Famous cartoons from Escapade. *paper, 12mo. Derby, Conn., Monarch, 1960.*

ESQUIRE. Esquire cartoon album. 25th anniversary volume. *buckram, folio. Garden City, Doubleday, 1957.*

——— Pocket book of Esquire cartoons. *paper, 16mo. N.Y., Pocket books, 1959.*

AN ESSAY ON LAUGHTER, wherein are displayed its natural and moral causes, with the arts of exciting it. Quid rides? *calf., 16mo. Lond., Davies, 1769.*

AN ESSAY ON THE ART OF INGENIOUSLY TORMENTING, with proper rules for the exercise of that pleasant art. *calf., 12mo. Lond., Millar, 1757.*

ESSLEMONT, PETER. Stories frae Aberdeen; grave and gay - mostly gay. *paper, 8vo. Aberdeen, Avery, n.d.*

ETHRIDGE, WILLIE SNOW. This little pig stayed home. *buckram, 12mo. N.Y., Vanguard, 1944.*

EULENSPIEGL. The legend of Ulenspiegel and Lamme Goedzak, by Charles de Coster. *2v. buckram, 8vo. Lond., Heinemann, 1922.*

——— The legend of the glorious adventures of Tyl Ulespiegel in the land of Flanders & elsewhere, by Charles de Coster. *buckram, 8vo. Lond., Chatto & Windus, 1918.*

——————— The marvellous adventures and rare conceits of Master Tyll Owlglass, newly collected, chronicled and set forth by Kenneth R.H. Mackenzie. *buckram, 12mo. Lond., Trubner, 1860.*

——————— *Same. Bost., Ticknor, 1860.*

——————— *Same. Lond., Trubner, 1890. New ed.*

——————— Till Eulenspiegel the clown. Retold by Erich Kastner. *buckram, 4to. N.Y., Messner, 1957.*

——————— Tyll Ulenspiegel's merry pranks, by M. Jagendorf. *buckram, 8vo. N.Y., Vanguard, 1938.*

EUWER, ANTHONY. The limeratomy; a compendium of the universal knowledge. *buckram, 12mo. N.Y., Pond, 1917.*

EVANS, BERGEN. The natural history of nonsense. *buckram, 8vo. N.Y., Knopf, 1949.*

——————— *Same. paper, Lond., Joseph, 1953.*

——————— The spoor of spooks, and other nonsense. *buckram, 8vo. N.Y., Knopf, 1954.*

EVANS, HENRY. Bohemian San Francisco. *paper, 24mo. San Francisco, Porpoise, 1955.*

——————— Curious lore of San Francisco's Chinatown. *paper, 24mo. San Francisco, Porpoise, 1955.*

——————— San Francisco's Fisherman's Wharf. *paper, 24 mo. San Francisco, Porpoise, 1957.*

EVANS, TREVOR, *ed.* The great Bohunkus; tributes to Ian Mackay. *buckram, 8vo. Lond., Allen, 1953.*

EVENING BRUSH, or, Laughable jester. For 1807. *paper, 16mo. Lond., Leel, 1807.*

EVERITT, GRAHAM, English caricaturists and graphic humourists of the 19th century. *buckram, 4to. Lond., Sonnenschein, 1893. 2d.ed.*

EVERYBODY'S BOOK OF JOKES. *buckram, 24mo. Lond., Saxon, 1890.*

——————— *Same. leather, Lond., Saxon, 1899.*

EWEN, DAVID, *comp.* Listen to the mocking words; a medley of anecdotes about music and musicians. *buckram, 8vo. N.Y., Arco, 1945.*

THE EXAMINER, San Francisco. A little army fun. *paper, 16mo. San Francisco, Examiner, n.d.*

EXTRA SEXTRA SPECIAL. *buckram, 8vo. N.Y., Scylla, 1954.*

FABLES FOR THE FEMALE SEX. *calf., 8vo. Lond., Francklin, 1744.*

FABLES OF PILPAY. *buckram, 12 mo. Lond., Warne, n.d. Rev. ed.*

FABLES, ORIGINAL AND SELECTED, by the most esteemed European and Oriental authors. *buckram, 4to. Lond., Willoughby, 1842.*

FAIRBANKS, DOUGLAS, Laugh and live. *buckram, 12mo. N.Y., Britton, 1917.*

FAIRBURN'S LAUGHABLE JESTER, or, Flights of humour for the song of mirth, calculated to promote mirth, drive away care, kill the blue devils and raise the spirits of all the laughing sons of Momus. By an Odd Fellow. *paper, 12mo. Lond., Fairburn, n.d.*

# F

FAIRHOLT, F.W. Gog and Magog.
The giants in Guildhall, their
real and legendary history.
*buckram, 16mo. Lond., John
Camden Hotten, 1859.*

FAIRY LEGENDS AND TRA-
DITIONS OF THE SOUTH OF
IRELAND. *buckram, 16mo.
Lond., Murray, 1838.*

FALK, BERNARD. He laughed in
Fleet Street. *buckram, 8vo.
Lond., Hutchinson, 1937. Popu-
lar ed. rev.*

FALLOWS, J.A. Realistic
aphorisms and purple patches.
*buckram, 12mo. Lond., Pioneer,
1922.*

FALSTAFF'S NEW COMIC
ANNUAL FOR 1831. *buckram,
16mo. Lond., Hurst, Chance,
1831.*

FAMILY JARS; a musical farce.
*paper, 12mo. N.Y., French, n.d.*

FARBER, MILTON. Blackstone
and white rock. *buckram, 8vo.
N.Y., Dutton, 1948.*

FAREWELL, NINA. The unfair
sex. *paper, 16mo. N.Y., Popular library, 1960.*

FARRINGTON, FRANK. Back in
the harness; a sequel to Talks
by the old storekeeper. *buckram,
12mo. Delhi, N.Y., Merchants'
Helps Pub.co., 1908.*

——————— Talks by the old
storekeeper. *buckram, 12mo.
Delhi, N.Y., Merchants' Helps
co., 1906.*

FARRIS, J.D. The significance of
friendship. *paper, 24mo. (Personal Growth Leaflets.)*

FARROW, G.E. Absurd ditties.
*buckram, 16mo. Lond.,
Routledge, 1903.*

FARTHEST FROM THE TRUTH:
a series of dashes. *paper, 12
mo. Lond., Pitman, 1909.*

FASHIONABLE TELL-TALE, containing a great variety of
curious and interesting anecdotes. *2v. calf., 12mo. Lond.,
Baldwin, 1778.*

FATOUT, PAUL. Indiana
University presents Mark Twain
on the Lecture circuit. *buckram,
8vo. Bloomington, Indiana,
Univ. of Indiana Press, 1960.*

FAUGHT, MILLARD C. Care and
feeding of executives. *buckram,
8vo. N.Y., Wormwood, 1945.*

——————— How to scratch a
match and other secrets of suc-
cessful pipe smoking. *boards,
16mo. N.Y., Garden City, 1947.*

FAY, FRANK. How to be poor.
*buckram, 8vo. N.Y., Prentice-
Hall, 1945.*

FEAST OF REASON, AND THE
FLOW OF SOUL; or, Humorous
respository. *quarter-calf., 24mo.
Dublin, Charles, 1821.*

FEDER, EDWARD L. Comic book
regulation. *paper, 4to.
Berkeley, Calif., Univ. of
California. Bureau of Public
Administration. (1955 legis-
lative problems, no.2. 1955.)*

FEDER, MARK. It's a living; a
personalized collection of
Jewish humor. *buckram, 8vo.
N.Y., Bloch, 1948.*

FEELEY, DAN. Dan Feeley's
original joke book. *paper, 12mo.
Phila., Royal, 1905.*

FEENEY, LEONARD. Your second
childhood. *buckram, 8vo. Milwaukee, Bruce, 1945.*

FELLER, ARTHUR. Naked Hollywood, by Weegee. *buckram, 4to.*
*N.Y., Pelligrini & Cudahy,*
*1953.*

FELSEN, HENRY GREGOR.
Doctor - it tickles! *boards,*
*8vo. N.Y., Prentice-Hall,*
*1955.*

——————— Medic mirth. *paper,*
*16mo. N.Y., Ace, 1956.*

FENN, GEORGE MANVILLE, *ed.*
World of wit and humour. *buck-*
*ram, 4to. Lond., Cassell,*
*Petter & Galpin, n.d.*

——————— *Same. Hartford,*
*Conn. American pub.co.,n.d.*

FENNER, MILDRED SANDISON.
The growing teacher. *paper,*
*24mo. (Personal Growth*
*Leaflets)*

——————— Susan B. Anthony,
apostle of freedom. *paper, 24*
*mo. (Personal Growth Leaflets)*

FERGUSON, J.A. Campbell of
Kilmhor. *paper, 24mo. Lond.,*
*Gowans & Gray, 1915.*

FERGUSON, JAMES. A few
etceteras grave and gay, collected by J. *paper, 12mo.*
*Birmingham, Priv. Print., n.d.*

——————— A new biographical
dictionary. *half-calf., 24mo.*
*Lond., Tegg, 1810.*

FERGUSON, JAMES. The table in
a roar, or, If you've heard it,
try and stop me. Compiled by
"Fergy". *buckram, 12mo. N.Y.,*
*Dutton, 1933.*

FERNANDEZ FLOREZ, WEN-
CESLAO. Laugh and the ghosts
laugh with you ... *buckram, 16*
*mo. Lond., British Technical*
*and General Press, 1951.*

FERRIER, ANNE. The high price
of Paradise. *buckram, 8vo.*
*Lond., Hollis & Carter, 1958.*

FERRILL, HELEN *and* FOLSON,
ANNE. The indoor bird
watcher's manual. *boards, 8vo.*
*N.Y., Duell, Sloan & Pearce,*
*1950.*

FERRIS, BENJAMIN. Letters,
fables and sayings of
"Amicus". *buckram, 12mo.*
*N.Y., Mutual Life Insurance*
*Co., of New York, 1897.*

FESTIVAL OF PUNCH. *see*
PUNCH FESTIVAL.

THE FESTOON: a collection of
epigrams ancient and modern,
panegyrical, satyrical, amorous
moral, humorous, monumental.
*half-calf, 12mo. Lond.,*
*Robinson & Roberts, 1767.*

FFOLKES, MICHAEL. ffanfare!
*boards, folio. Lond., Faber &*
*Faber, 1953.*

FIEDLER, LESLIE A. Duplicitous
Mark Twain. *pamphlet.*

FIELD, AL G. Watch yourself go
by. *buckram, 12mo. Columbus,*
*Ohio, n.d. 1912.*

FIELD, CECIL. I always was
lucky. *boards, 12mo. Lond.,*
*Macdonald, 1948.*

FIELD, CHARLES KELLOGG.
The story of Cheerio, by
himself. *buckram, 8vo. N.Y.,*
*Garden City, 1936.*

FIELD, EUGENE. The clink of the
ice. *buckram, 12mo. Chic.,*
*Donohue, 1905.*

——————— The complete Tribune
primer. *buckram, 12mo. Bost.,*
*Mutual, 1901.*

——————— Hoosier lyrics. *buck-*
*ram, 12mo. Chic., Donohue,*
*1905.*

——————— In wink-a-way land.
*buckram, 12mo. Chic., Donohue,*
*1905.*

_____ John Smith, U.S.A. *buckram, 12mo. Chic., Donohue, 1905.*

_____ Love affairs of a bibliomaniac. *buckram, 12mo. N.Y., Scribner's, 1896.*

_____ Nonsense for old and young. *buckram, 12mo. Bost., Dickerman, 1901.*

_____ The Tribune primer. *buckram, 16mo. Bost., Dickerman, 1900.*

_____ Works. *9v. buckram, 12mo. N.Y., Scribners, 1897.*

**FIELD, JOHN EDWARD.** The myth of the pent cuckoo; a study in folklore. *buckram, 8vo. Lond., Stock, 1913.*

**FIELDING, HOWARD.** Col. Evans from Kentucky, and other humorous sketches. *paper, 12 mo. N.Y., Manhattan Therapeutic co., 1889.*

**FIELDING, JOHN.** Sir John Fielding's jests; or, New fun for the parlour and kitchen. Compiled by a Justice of the Peace. *half-calf., 12mo. Lond., Hogg & Lewis, n.d.*

**FIELDING, THOMAS.** Select proverbs of all nations. *leather, 24mo. Lond., Longman, Hurst, Rees, Orme, Brown & Green, 1824.*

**FIELDS, WILLIAM,** *comp.* The scrap-book; consisting of tales and anecdotes. *buckram, 8vo. Phila., Claxton, Remsen, 1872.*

**FIFTH OVER SEXTEEN.** *buckram, 8vo. N.Y., Grayson, 1956.*

**FIFTY-ONE ORIGINAL FABLES,** with morals and ethical index. Also, a translation of Plutarch's Banquet of the seven sages. *buckram, 8vo. Lond., Hamilton, Adams, 1833.*

**FIFTY TRUE LOVE STORIES.** *buckram, 8vo. Lond., Odhams, 1958.*

**FILLERS;** a sampling of vaudeville and radio gags. *paper, 32 mo. Girard, Kan., Haldeman-Julius, (Little Blue Books).*

**FINCH, MATTHEW.** Teething troubles. *buckram, 8vo. Lond., Dobson, 1956.*

**FINCK, BENNET.** The curate's egg; a book of anecdotes chiefly clerical. *buckram, 12 mo. Lond., T.Werner Laurie, 1942.*

**FINCK, HENRY T.** Musical laughs, jokes, tittle-tattle and anecdotes mostly humorous about musical celebrities. *buckram, 12mo. N.Y., Funk & Wagnalls, 1924.*

**FINDLATER, RICHARD.** Grimaldi, king of clowns. *buckram, 8vo. Lond., MacGibbon & Kee, 1955.*

**FINGER, CHARLES J.** The gist of Burton's Anatomy of melancholy. *paper, 32mo. Girard, Kan., Haldeman-Julius, 1924. (Little Blue Books.)*

_____ Mark Twain the philosopher who laughed at the world. *paper, 32mo. Girard, Kan., Haldeman-Julius, n.d. (Little Blue Books.)*

**FINN, J.F.** The brighter side of public speaking. *buckram, 12 mo. Lond., Hutchinson, n.d.*

**FIRENZUOLA.** Tales of Firenzuola, Benedictine monk of Vallombrosa (XVIth century). *paper, 16mo. Paris, Liseux, 1889.*

FISCHER, MARTIN H. Fischer-isms, being a sheaf of sundry and divers utterances. *buckram, 24mo. Springfield, Ill., Thomas, 1944.*

FISHBACK, MARGARET. I feel better now. *buckram, 12mo. N.Y., Dutton, 1932.*

FISHBEIN, MORRIS. Doctors and specialists. *buckram, 12mo. Indianapolis, Bobbs-Merrill, 1930.*

——————— The medical follies. *buckram, 12mo. N.Y., Boni & Liveright, 1925.*

FISHER, ANNE. Live with a man and love it! The gentle art of staying happily married. *buckram, 12mo. Lond., Duckworth, 1937.*

FISHER, GRAHAM. Best after dinner stories. *paper, 16mo. Lond., Foulsham, n.d.*

FISHER, HENRY W. Abroad with Mark Twain and Eugene Field. *buckram, 8vo. N.Y., Brown, 1922.*

FISHER'S COMIC ALMANAC, 1844. *paper, small 8vo. Bost., Fisher, 1844.*

FISKE, DWIGHT. Why should penguins fly? and other stories. *buckram, 8vo. Lond., Hale, 1937.*

FISKE, JOHN. Myths and myth-makers; old tales and super-stitions interpreted by com-parative mythology. *buckram, 12mo. Bost., Houghton, Mifflin, 1886.*

FISKE, MARY H. The giddy gusher papers. *buckram, 12mo. N.Y., Dramatic Mirror, 1889.*

FITZGERALD, ED., ed. Tales for males. *boards, 8vo. N.Y., Cadillac, 1945.*

FITZGERALD, PERCY. The book of theatrical anecdotes. *boards, 16mo. Lond., Routledge, n.d.*

——————— The book of wit. *buckram, 12mo. Lond., Roxburghe Press, n.d.*

——————— Life of Laurence Sterne. *2v. buckram, 8vo. Lond., Chapman & Hall, 1864.*

FLAGG, JAMES MONTGOMERY. "If", a guide to bad manners. *boards, 12mo. N.Y., Life, 1905.*

——————— Tomfoolery. *boards, 12mo. N.Y., Life, 1904.*

FLANNER, JANET. An American in Paris. *buckram, 8vo. N.Y., Simon & Schuster, 1940.*

FLASHES AND SPARKS OF WIT AND HUMOR BY OUR AMERI-CAN HUMORISTS. *paper, 16mo. N.Y., Ivers, 1880.*

FLASHES OF WIT, AND SPARKS OF HUMOUR; an extensive collection of modern witty sayings, anecdotes, Ameri-canisms, bon-mots, conundrums, epigrams, repartees, &c.&c.&c. *buckram, 32mo. Lond., Milner & Sowerby, 1867.*

FLASHES OF WIT; pointed pickings from the Arkansaw traveler. *paper, 12mo. Chic., Stein, 1948.*

FLAUBERT, GUSTAVE. A diction-ary of platitudes. *buckram, 8vo. Lond., Rodale, 1954.*

FLECKENSTEIN, NINON TRAVER. Widow's wisdom. *buckram, 12 mo. N.Y., Caldwell, 1909.*

FLEISCHMAN, HARRY. Let's be human. *paper, 8vo. N.Y., Coeana, 1960.*

FLEMING, PETER. Variety. *buckram, 16mo. Lond., Cape, 1933.*

FLEMING, R.M. Ancient tales from many lands. *buckram, 8vo.* Lond., Benn, 1922.

FLEMING, THOMAS. Around the "Pan" with Uncle Hank; his trip through the Pan-American exposition. *buckram, 8vo.* N.Y., Nut Shell Pub. Co., 1901.

FLOETHE, RICHARD, *comp.* The world's best limericks. *boards, 12mo.* Mt. Vernon, N.Y., Peter Pauper, 1951.

FLORA, PAUL. Flora's fauna; cartoons & drawings. *buckram, 4to.* Indianapolis, Bobbs-Merrill, 1959.

FLOWERS, OF ANECDOTE, WIT, HUMOUR, GAIETY AND GENIUS. *buckram, 24mo.* Lond., Newman, 1842. New ed.

_____ Same. Lond., Tilt, 1831. 2d.ed.

FLUGEL, J.C. Humour; some modern approaches to an ancient problem. *In:* The Rationalist annual, 1956.

FOGG, WALTER. One thousand sayings of history, presented as pictures in prose. *buckram, 8vo.* Bost., Beacon, 1929.

FOLK-LORE AND LEGENDS. English. *buckram, 16mo.* Phila., Lippincott, 1891.

FOLK-LORE AND LEGENDS. North American Indians. *buckram, 16mo.* Phila., Lippincott, 1891.

FOLK-LORE AND LEGENDS. Oriental. *buckram, 16mo.* N.Y., White & Allen, 1889.

FOLK-LORE AND LEGENDS. Russian and Polish. *buckram, 16mo.* Lond., Gibbins, 1890.

FOLK-LORE AND LEGENDS. Scandinavian. *buckram, 16mo.* Phila., Lippincott, 1891.

FOLK TALES FROM CHINA: first series. *boards, 8vo.* Peking, Foreign Languages Press, 1957.

FOLK TALES FROM CHINA. Second series. *boards, 8vo.* Peking, Foreign Languages Press, 1958.

FOLK TALES FROM CHINA. Fifth series. *boards, 8vo.* Peking, Foreign Languages Press, 1960.

FOLKLORE OF THE SANTAL PARGANAS. *buckram, 8vo.* Lond., Nutt, 1909.

FOLLMER, LUCILLE. Your sports are showing. *buckram, 4to.* N.Y., Pellegrini & Cudahy, 1949.

FOLSOM, ANNE. Care and feeding of husbands. *boards, 8vo.* N.Y., Duell, Sloan & Pearce, 1950.

FONTAINE, ROBERT. Hello to springtime. *buckram, 8vo.* N.Y., Crowell, 1955.

FOOD FOR THE MIND. or, A new riddle book. *boards, 32mo.* Lond., Carnan & Newbery, 1778.

FOOLISH ALMANACK FOR YEAR OF 1906 A.D. *buckram, 12mo.* Lond., Luce, 1905.

THE FOOLISH ALMANACK FOR ANOTHER YEAR. *cloth, 12mo.* Bost., Luce, 1905.

FOOT, FERDINANDO. The Nutcracker, containing an agreeable and great variety of well-seasoned jests, epigrams, epitaphs, etc. *calf, 16mo.* Lond., Carnan, 1760.

FOOTE, SAMUEL. Bon-mots of Samuel Foote and Theodore Hook. Ed. by Walter Jerrold. *buckram, 32mo.* Lond., Dent, 1894.

———————— New theatre of fun, or, The modern Aristophanes in high glee. *boards, 12mo. Lond., Durfey & Curdell, 1778.*

———————— Wit for the ton! The convivial jester, or, Sam Foote's last budget opened. *half-calf, 8 vo. Lond., Adlard, 1777.*

———————— The table-talk and bon-mots of Samuel Foote. Ed. by the late William Cooke. *boards, 8vo. New Southgate, Rogers, 1889.*

FOOTNER, HULBERT. Thieves' wit. *buckram, 12mo. N.Y., Doran, 1918.*

FOR LAUGHING PURPOSES ONLY. 62 gag cartoons. *paper, 32mo. Girard, Kan., Haldeman-Julius, n.d. (Little Blue Books.)*

FORBES, ATHOL. Cassock and comedy; the humorous side of clerical life. *buckram, 12mo. Lond., Skeffington, 1898.*

FORBES, BERTIE CHARLES. Forbes epigrams. 1000 thoughts on life and business. *buckram, 12mo. N.Y., Forbes, 1922. Bound with: The silver lining, or Sunshine on the business trail.*

———————— 499 Scottish stories for the price of 500. *buckram, 12mo. N.Y., Forbes, 1945.*

FORBES, ESTHER. Paul Revere and the world he lived in. *buckram, 12mo. Bost., Houghton Mifflin, 1942.*

FORD, ALLA T. *and* MARTIN, DICK. The musical fantasies of L. Frank Baum. *buckram, 8vo. Chic., Wizard, 1958.*

FORD, COREY. The day nothing happened. *boards, 8vo. N.Y., Doubleday, 1959.*

———————— Has anybody seen me lately? *buckram, 8vo. N.Y., Doubleday, 1958.*

———————— How to guess your age. *boards, 12mo. N.Y., Doubleday, 1950.*

———————— The office party. *boards, 8vo. N.Y., Doubleday, 1951.*

———————— Never say diet; how to live older and look longer. *boards, 8vo. N.Y. Holt, 1954.*

FORD, ED. Can you top this? *buckram, 12mo. Garden City, Blue Ribbon, 1946.*

———————— Cream of the crop. *buckram, 12mo. N.Y., Grosset & Dunlap, 1947.*

———————— My home town. *buckram, 12mo. N.Y., Howell, Soskin, 1945.*

FORD, EDWARD HASTINGS. After dinner speaking and other forms of insanity. *boards, 16mo. N.Y. Flatow, 1930.*

FORD, ROBERT. Thistledown; a book of Scotch humour, character, folk-lore, story and anecdote. *buckram, 8vo. N.Y., Stokes, 1891.*

———————— *Same. Paisley, A. Gardner, n.d. New and enl. ed.*

FORD, SIMEON. A few remarks. *buckram, 12mo. N.Y., Grosset & Dunlap, 1903. 4th rev. ed.*

FOREMAN, ROBERT L. The hot half hour. *buckram, 8vo. N.Y., Criterion, 1958.*

THE FORGET-ME-NOT SONGSTER, containing a choice collection of old ballad songs as sung by our grandmothers. *paper, boxed. 32mo. N.Y., Nafis & Cornish, 184?*

FORNEY, JOHN W. Anecdotes of public men. *buckram, 12mo. Harper, 1874.*

FORREST, S.J. Time for a rhyme. *boards, 8vo. Lond., Mowbray, 1957.*

FORRESTER, ALFRED HENRY. Phantasmagoria of fun, by Alfred Crowquill, pseud. *2v. buckram, 12mo. Lond., Bentley, 1843.*

FOSTER, ELON. New cyclopedia of prose illustrations. Second series. *buckram, 8vo. N.Y., Crowell, 1870?*

FOSTER, JAMES R., *ed.* Great folktales of wit and humor. *buckram, 8vo. N.Y., Harper, 1955.*

FOUGASSE, *pseud. See* BIRD, KENNETH.

FOUNDLING HOSPITAL FOR WIT. Intended for the reception and preservation of such brats of wit and humour, whose parents chose to drop them. *half-calf., 8vo. Lond., Reprinted 1743 ed. W.Webb, 1763.*

4 WHEEL FUN. *paper, 24mo. n.p., n.d.*

FOURTH BOOK OF ARTEMAS. *buckram, 12mo. Lond., Holden, 1925.*

FOWLER, GENE. Father Goose; the story of Mack Sennett. *buckram, 8vo. N.Y., Covici-Friede, 1934.*

——————— Schnozzola; the story of Jimmy Durante. *buckram, 8vo. N.Y., Viking, 1951.*

FOWLER, NATHANIEL C. Stories and toasts for after dinner. *buckram, 12mo. N.Y., Burt, 1914.*

FOY, EDDIE. Clowning through life. *buckram, 8vo. N.Y., Dutton 1928.*

FRA ALBERTUS, *pseud. see* HUBBARD, ELBERT.

FRAMPTON, J. Three dialogues on the amusements of clergymen. *quarter-leather, 12mo. Lond., Cadell, 1797. 2d.ed.*

FRANCE, ANATOLE. Epigrams of love, life and laughter. *paper, 32mo. Girard, Kan., Haldeman-Julius, n.d. (Little Blue Books)*

——————— The merrie tales of Jacques Tournbroche. *buckram, 8vo. Lond., Lane, 1923.*

——————— Merry tales. *paper, 32mo. Girard, Kan., Haldeman-Julius, n.d. (Little Blue Books)*

——————— Merry tales of childhood. *paper, 32mo. Girard, Kan., Haldeman-Julius, n.d. (Little Blue Books)*

FRANCE, HECTOR. Musk, hashish and blood. *buckram, 8 vo. N.Y., Panurge, n.d.*

FRANCIS & DAY'S "JOKELETS" as performed by the Mohawk, Moore, and Burgess minstrels. *paper, 12mo. Lond., Francis, Day & Hunter, n.d.*

FRANCOIS, ANDRE. Double bedsidebook. *buckram, 4to. Lond., Deutsch, 1952.*

——————— The half-naked knight; cartoons and drawings. *boards, 4to. Lond., Deutsch, 1958.*

——————— The tattooed sailor. *boards, 4to. N.Y., Knopf, 1954.*

FRANCOIS DE SALES, *Saint.* Spiritual maxims. *buckram, 24 mo. N.Y., Harper, 1953.*

FRANK LESLIE'S COMIC ALMANAC FOR THE YEARS 1870, 1874. *paper, folio. N.Y., Leslie, 1870, 1874.*

FRANKLIN, BENJAMIN. Auto-
biography. Poor Richard.
*Letters. buckram, 8vo. N.Y.,
Appleton, 1900.*

—————— Autobiography of
Benjamin Franklin. The un-
mutilated and correct version,
compiled and edited by John
Bigelow. *buckram, 8vo. N.Y.,
Putnam's, n.d.*

—————— Ben Franklin's wit
and wisdom. *boards, 12mo.
Mount Vernon, Peter Pauper,
n.d.*

—————— Benjamin Franklin on
marriage. *boards, 12mo. n.p.,
n.d.*

—————— Franklin's wit and
folly. The bagatelles. *buckram,
8vo. New Brunswick, Rutgers
Univ. Press, 1953.*

—————— On the choice of a
mistress, and other satires and
hoaxes. *boards, 8vo. Mount
Vernon, N.Y., Peter Pauper
Press, n.d.*

—————— The papers of Ben-
jamin Franklin. v.1, January 6,
1806 through December 31,
1734. *buckram, 8vo. New Haven,
Yale Univ. Press, 1959.*

—————— Poor Richard's
almanac. *paper, 24mo.
(Personal Growth Leaflet)*

—————— Poor Richard's
almanac. *boards, 12mo. Mount
Vernon, N.Y., Peter Pauper
Press, n.d.*

—————— "The sayings of Poor
Richard" *buckram, 16mo. N.Y.,
Putnam's n.d.*

FRANKLIN, MAX, *comp.* Anthology
of wit and humor. *buckram, 16
mo. N.Y., Author, 1923.*

FRANKLY, I DON'T GET IT.
*boards, 8vo. N.Y., Hanover
House, 1954.*

FRANKLYN, JULIAN. The
cockney, a survey of London
life and language. *Lond.,
Deutsch, 1953. Rev. ed.*

FRANZERO, CARLO MARIA.
Beau Brummell, his life and
times. *buckram, 8vo. N.Y.,
Day, 1958.*

FRASER, J.A. A delicate
question. *paper, 12mo. Chic.,
Dramatic Pub. Co., 1896.*

FRAZER, JAMES GEORGE.
Folk-lore in the Old Testament. *buckram, 8vo. N.Y.,
Macmillan, 1927. Abridged
ed.*

—————— Psyche's task; a
discourse concerning the
influence of superstition on
the growth of institutions.
*buckram, 8vo. Lond., Mac-
millan, 1909.*

FREDERICK, C.O. *and* E.E.
Wise cracks; wit, wisdom and
fun for all occasions. *buckram,
16mo. N.Y., Putnam's, 1929.*

FREDERICK, J. GEORGE.
Breezy. *buckram, 16mo. N.Y.,
Doubleday, Page, 1909.*

FREDERICKS, PIERCE G. The
people's choice; the issues of
the campaign; as seen by the
nation's best political car-
toonists. *buckram, 4to. N.Y.,
Dodd, Mead, 1956.*

FREDERICKS, VIC. Crackers in
bed. *paper, 16mo. N.Y., Pocket
books, 1953.*

—————— Jest married; a gay
gift lift for the newlywed.
*boards, 12mo. N.Y., Fell,
1958.*

FREEMAN, ROBERT MASSIE. A diary of the great warr, by Samuel Pepys, junr. *buckram, 12mo. Lond., Lane, 1917.*

FRENCH ANAS, THE. *3v. half-morocco, 16mo. Lond., Phillips, 1805.*

FRENCH, JOSEPH LEWIS, *ed.* Sixty years of American humor; the best of American humor from Mark Twain to Benchley. *buckram, 12mo. N.Y., Garden City, 1941.*

FRENCH, MARION N. Myths and legends of the ages. *buckram, 8vo. N.Y., Hart, 1956.*

FRENCH POSTCARDS. *paper, 16mo. N.Y., Avon, 1954.*

FRENCH WIT AND WISDOM. *boards, 12mo. Mount Vernon, N.Y., Peter Pauper, 1956.*

FRENCH'S FUNNY RECITALS. Part 1. A collection of new and hitherto unpublished humorous recitations. *paper, 12mo. Lond., Reynolds, n.d.*

FRESH LOT OF RUBE JOKES, A. *paper, 32mo. Baltimore, Otten-heimer, 1913.*

FRIEDERICH II, *der Grosse, King of Prussia.* Characteristic anecdotes and miscellaneous papers. *half-calf, 8vo. Lond., Stockdale, 1788.*

FRIEDMAN, I.K. Autobiography of a beggar. *buckram, 12mo. Bost., Small, Maynard, 1903.*

FRISKY JESTER, THE, or, A feast for the funny, containing a banquet for choice spirits, good fellows and merry souls. *boards, 12mo. Lond., Sudbury, ca.1780.*

FRITH, HENRY. How to read character in features, forms & faces. *buckram, 12mo. Lond., Ward, Lock, n.d.*

FRITH, WILLIAM POWELL. John Leech, his life and work. *2v. half-calf., 8vo. Lond., Bentley, 1891.*

FROESCHELS, EMIL. Philosophy in wit. *buckram, 8vo. N.Y., Philosophical Library, 1948.*

FROHMAN, DANIEL. Memories of a manager; reminiscences of the Old Lyceum and of some players of the last quarter century. *buckram, 12mo. Lond., Heinemann, 1911.*

FROLICS OF THE SPHYNX, or, An entirely original collection of charades, riddles and conundrums. *half-calf, 12mo. Oxford, Munday & Slatter, 1812.*

FROST, A.B. Stuff and nonsense. *buckram, 4to. N.Y., Scribners, 1888.*

FROST, JOHN. The book of anecdotes, or, The moral of history taught by real examples. *buckram, 12mo. Hartford, Belknap & Hamersley, 1849.*

FROST, MAX GILBERT. The merry stories omnibus book. 2397 stories for all occasions. *buckram, 12mo. Lond., T. Werner Laurie, 1953.*

FROST, RALPH. What cheer? Merry stories for all occasions. *buckram, 12mo. Lond., T. Werner Laurie, 1929.*

FROY, HERALD. How to avoid matrimony; the layman's guide to the laywoman. *buckram, 12 mo. Lond., Muller, 1957.*

—————— How to survive matrimony. *buckram, 12mo. Lond., Muller, 1958.*

FRYE, RALPH. Uncle 'Lish. *buckram, 12mo. N.Y., Knopf, 1945.*

FULLER, EDMUND, *ed.* Thesaurus of anecdotes. *buckram, 8vo. N.Y., Crown, 1942.*

—————— *Same,* with title, 2,500 anecdotes.

—————— Thesaurus of epigrams. *buckram, 8vo. N.Y., Crown, 1943.*

FULLER, HORACE, *ed.* The green bag, a useless but entertaining magazine for lawyers. *quarter-calf., 4to. Bost., Boston Book co., 1890.*

FULLER, THOMAS, *comp.* Gnomologia: Adages and proverbs, wise sentences and witty sayings, ancient and modern, foreign and British. *half-calf., 16mo. Lond., Barker, 1782.*

—————— Wise words and quaint counsels. *buckram, 12 mo. Oxford, Clarendon, 1892.*

FUN ALIVE O! or, The merry mortal's companion, *half-leather, 8vo. Lond., Langley, n.d.*

FUN DOCTOR. First series. Laugh cure. Fun is better than physic and more pleasant to take. *buckram, 12mo. Phila., McKay, n.d.*

FUN FOR ALL. A novel collection of jokes and jests for all readers. *paper, 8vo. Lond., Ward, Lock, 1880.*

FUN FOR THE MILLION. A gathering of choice wit and humor, good things and sublime nonsense. *paper, 8vo. Lond., John Camden Hotten, 1874.*

FUN FOR THE MILLION, or, The laughing philosopher, consisting of several thousand of the best jokes, witticisms, puns, epigrams. &c. *quarter-russia, 24mo. Lond., Sherwood, Gilbert & Piper, 1835. New ed.*

FUNK, WILFRED J. When the merry-go-round breaks down! *buckram, 12mo. N.Y., Funk & Wagnalls, 1938.*

FUNNIEST OF ALL FUN AND THE WITTIEST OF ALL WIT *half-calf., 32mo. Halifax, Nicholson, 1866.*

FUNNY EPITAPHS. title-page lacking. *Spine reads Mutual Pub. co.*

FUNNY FACTS AND FICTION. v.1. no.1. *paper, 8vo. St. Paul, Minn., Keller, 1931.*

FUNNY FELLOW, THE, comprising his humorous sketches and comical tales together with his droll songs, witty sayings, laughing adventures, and startling anecdotes. *paper, 16 mo. Lond., Ward, Lock, 1862.*

FUNNY FOLLIES OF 1922, THE, including the best wit and humor of 1921. *paper, 12mo. n.p., 1922.*

FUNNY SIDE UP. *paper, 16mo. N.Y., Dell, 1952.*

FUNNY STORIES ABOUT THE FORD. *paper, 16mo. Hamilton, Ohio, Preston, 1915.*

FUNNYMAN, BILLY, *pseud.* On a fast train through Georgia and what we saw there. *paper, 12 mo. N.Y., Ogilvie, 1904.*

FURNEAUX, RUPERT. Legend and reality. *buckram, 8vo. Lond., Wingate, 1959.*

FURNESS, WILLIAM HENRY. Folk-lore in Borneo. *buckram, 8vo. Wallingford, Pa., Priv. Print., 1899.*

FURNISS, GRACE L. A box of monkeys; a parlor farce. *paper, 12mo. Bost., Baker, n.d.*

FURNISS, HARRY. Confessions of a caricaturist. *2v. buckram, 8vo. N.Y., Harper, 1902.*

————————*Same. paper, in 1v., Lond., T.Fisher, Unwin, n.d.*

———————— Harry Furniss at home. *buckram, 8vo. Lond., T.Fisher, Unwin, 1904.*

FURST, HERBERT. New anecdotes of painters and painting. *buckram, 12mo. Lond., Lane, 1926.*

FURTHER SUNBEAMS. Anecdotes, jokes and stories for all occasions. *buckram, 16mo. Lond., S.Paul, 1924.*

FURTHERMORE OVER SEXTEEN. *buckram, 8vo. N.Y., Grayson, 1956.*

FYVIE, JOHN. Some famous women of wit and beauty; a Georgian galaxy. *buckram, 8vo. N.Y., Pott, 1905.*

G., J.F. The silly season. *buckram, 12mo. Lond., E.Mathews, 1910.*

GABRIEL, PHILIP LOUIS. The executive. *buckram, 4to. N.Y., Citadel, 1959.*

GAER, JOSEPH. The legend of the Wandering Jew. *paper, 16 mo. N.Y., Mentor, 1961.*

GAG, WANDA. Gone is gone. *buckram, 24mo. N.Y., McCann, 1935.*

GAGGING THE DICTATORS; the comedy of terrors. *paper, 4to. N.Y., Ace, n.d.*

GAGS AND PUNS. *pamphlet. N.Y. Ceagee Pub. co., 1944.*

GAINES, FRANK LESLIE. Short furrows. *buckram, 12mo. Indianapolis, Stine & McClure, 1938.*

GAINES, M.G. Narrative illustration; the story of the comics. *paper, 4to. Reprinted from Print, v.3. no.2. (Inserted: Haggard, Ernest A. A projective technique using comic strip characters.)*

GAINES, WILLIAM M. The bedside Mad. *paper, 12mo. N.Y., Signet, 1959.*

———————— The brothers Mad. *paper, 12mo. N.Y., Ballantine, 1958.*

————————Fighting Mad. *paper, 12mo. N.Y., Signet, 1961.*

————————Inside Mad. *paper, 12mo. N.Y., Ballantine, 1958.*

———————— The organization Mad. *paper, 12mo. N.Y., Signet, 1960.*

————————Son of Mad. *paper, 12mo. N.Y., Signet, 1959.*

————————Utterly Mad. *paper, 12mo. N.Y., Ballantine, 1956.*

GALAXY OF WIT: or, Laughing philosopher, being a collection of choice anecdotes, many of which originated in or about "The Literary Emporium" *2v. in 1. buckram, 16mo. Lond., Dombey, 1851.*

# G

GALAXY OF WIT AND WISDOM: or, Fun for the million. *buckram, 16mo. N.Y., Miller, 1875.*

GALBRAITH, V.H. An autograph MS of Ranulph Higden's Polychronicon. (Reprinted from Huntington Library Quarterly).

GALLAHER, J.E. Best Lincoln stories tersely told. *buckram, 16mo. Chic., Donohue, 1898.*

GALLERY OF LITERARY MORCEAUX: containing innumerable anecdotes and jests, embracing the serious, the lively, the gay and the pathetic. *calf., 24mo. Lond., Daly, 1835.*

GALLERY OF 140 COMICALITIES, which have appeared from time to time, in that most Popular Sporting Sunday paper, "Bell's life in London." *paper, Lond., Goodger, 1831.* (Followed by three issues titled: The Gallery of Comicalities ... from October 1834 to the present period. *Lond., William Clement, n.d.*)

GALLIMAUFRY; or, Theatrical speaker's entertaining repository. *buckram, 8vo. Lond., Smith, 1828.*

GALSWORTHY, JOHN. A bit of love. *buckram, 12mo. N.Y., Scribner's, 1915.*

——————— A family man. *buckram, 12mo. Lond., Duckworth, 1922.*

——————— The pigeon. *buckram, 12mo. N.Y., Scribner's 1912.*

——————— Six short plays. *buckram, 16mo. Lond., Duckworth, 1921.*

GAMBLE, E.L. Gamble's gag & joke collection, no. 1. *paper, 8vo. East Liverpool, Ohio, Author, n.d.*

GAMES AND AMUSEMENTS. *buckram, 12mo. Lond., Ward, Lock, n.d.*

GAMLIN, LIONEL *and* GILBERT, ANTHONY. Don't be afreud! a short guide to youth control. *boards, 8vo. Lond., Methuen, 1906.*

GAMMOND, PETER *and* CLAYTON, PETER. 101 things; a survey of their influence on British life and language. *paper, 24mo. Lond., Elek, 1959.*

GANGULEE, N. Folk tales of India. *boards, 8vo. Bombay, Hind Katabs, 1953.*

GARD, ALEX. More ballet laughs. *boards, 4to. N.Y., Scribner's, 1946.*

——————— Sailors in boots. *boards, 8vo. N.Y., Scribner's, 1943.*

GARDINER, FLORENCE HERRICK. Limericks arranged and illustrated. *boards, 16mo. Phila., Lippincott, 1921.*

GARDNER, ED. Duffy's First reader, by Archie. *paper, 16 mo. N.Y., Bristol-Mayers, 1943.*

GARDNER, HY. Champagne before breakfast. *buckram, 8vo. N.Y., Holt, 1954.*

——————— Tales out of night school. *paper, 16mo. N.Y., Permabooks, 1959.*

GARDNER, MARTIN. Fads and fallacies in the name of science. *paper, 8vo. N.Y., Dover, 1957.*

GARIS, HOWARD R. Uncle Wiggily in the country. *buckram, 8vo. N.Y., Platt & Munk, 1940.*

GARNETT, TAY. Tall tales from Hollywood. *buckram, 12mo. N.Y., Liveright, 1932.*

GARNETT, WILLIAM. Morals from the beastly world. *buckram, 12 mo. Lond., Hart-Davis, 1958.*

GARRETT, PHINEAS, *comp.* One hundred choice selections. *half-calf, 12mo. Phila., Garrett, 1877.* (Scattered volumes.)

GARRISON, FIELDING H. John Shaw Billings; a memoir. *buckram, 8vo. N.Y., Putnam's, 1915.*

GARROD, H.W. Epigrams. *paper, 12mo. Oxford Blackwell, 1946.*

GASTER, MOSES. *tr.* Ma'aseh book; book of Jewish tales and legends translated from the Judeo-German. *2v. buckram, 16 mo. Phila., Jewish Pub. Soc., 1934.*

GATCHELL, CHARLES. They say, by Thorold King, *pseud. buckram, 12mo. Chic., Era, 1899.*

GATES, W. FRANCIS. Anecdotes of great musicians. *buckram, 8vo. Lond., Weekes, 1896.*

GAULT, JOSEPH. Joseph Gault's fifth edition of his REPORTS, entitled A coat of many colors. *buckram, 8vo. Americus, Ga. Americus Law Book Co., 1902.*

GAY, FRANCIS. The friendship book. *boards, 12mo. Lond., Thomson, 1961.*

GAY, JOHN. Plays. *2v. buckram, 16mo. Lond., Chapman & Dodd, 1923.*

GAYER-ANDERSON, R.G. "JOHN". Legends of the Bait al-Kretliya, as told by Sheikh Sulaiman al-Kretli. *boards, 4to. Ipswich, East Anglian Daily Times, 1951.*

GAYER, JACK *and* STANLEY, DAVE. There's laughter in the air! Radio's top comedians and their best shows. *buckram, 8vo. N.Y., Greenberg, 1945.*

GEAKE, CHARLES, *and* GOULD F. CARRUTHERS. John Bull's adventures in the fiscal wonderland. *buckram, 12mo. Lond., Methuen, 1904.*

GEE, H.L. Five hundred tales to tell again. *buckram, 12mo. Lond., Epworth, 1955.*

GEISEL, THEODOR SEUSS. Boners, by Dr. Seuss, *pseud. buckram, 16mo. N.Y., Viking, 1931.*

—————— The Seven Lady Godivas. *buckram, 4to. N.Y., Random House, 1939.*

GENLIS, STEPHANIE FELICITE DUCREST DE ST. AUBIN. Selections from the works of ... *boards, 12mo. Lond., Albion, 1806.*

GENTLEMAN, A, formerly of Brazen-Nose College, Oxford. Interesting collection of curious anecdotes, scarce pieces and genuine letters. *half-calf, 8vo. Lond., Author, 1790.*

GENTLEMAN, B.A. The Bumpus family of Baltimore. *paper, 12 mo. Los Angeles, Gem, 1926.*

GENTLEMAN'S COMPANION, THE; or, An assemblage of anecdotes, aphorisms, and bon-mots. *half-calf., 12mo. Lond., Minerva Press for A.K. Newman, 1810.*

GEORGE, DANIEL, *ed.* A book of anecdotes. *buckram, 8vo. Bath, Hulton, 1957.*

——————— A book of characters. *buckram, 8vo. Bath, Hulton, 1959.*

——————— A peck of troubles, or, An anatomy of woe. *buckram, 8vo. Lond., Cape, 1936.*

——————— Pick and choose; a gallimaufry. *buckram, 8vo. Lond., Cape, 1936.*

GEORGIS, TAKISS, *comp.* Modern Greek proverbs. *paper, 32mo. Girard, Kan., Haldeman-Julius, n.d. (Little Blue Books.)*

GERMAN WIT AND HUMOR. *buckram, 16mo. Phila., Jacobs, 1903.*

GERMANIA. (Cartoons with captions in English, Italian, Spanish and Portuguese). *paper, 4to. Paris, L'Edition Franciase Illustree, 1916.*

GESTA ROMANORUM. A record of ancient histories entituled in Latin Gesta Romanorum. *calf, small 16mo. Lond., Chiswell & Walford, 1703.*

——————— Selections, translated by Charles Small, *boards, 8vo. Bost., Lriv. print. by Nathan Haskell Dole, 1904.*

——————— Tales of the Gesta Romanorum. Translated from the Latin by Charles Swan. *buckram, 8vo. N.Y., Everest, 1959.*

——————— Tales of the monks, from the Gesta Romanorum. *buckram, 8vo. N.Y., Tudor, 1933.*

GHAZZALI-al. The alchemy of happiness. *buckram, 12mo. Lond., Murray, 1910.*

GHOSE, AUROBINDO, *sri.* Thoughts and aphorisms. *paper, 8vo. Pondicherry, India, Sri Aurobindo Ashram Press, 1958.*

——————— Thoughts and glimpses. *paper, 12mo. Pondicherry, India, Sri Auborindo Ashram Press, 1950.*

GIBB, LEE. The Joneses: how to keep up with them. *buckram, 12mo. Lond., Muller, 1959.*

GIBBS, WOLCOTT. Bird life at the pole, by Commander Christopher Robin. *buckram, 12mo. N.Y., Morrow, 1931.*

GIBRAN, KAHLIL. The prophet. *buckram, 8vo. N.Y., Knopf, 1925.*

——————— Sand and foam; a book of aphorisms. *buckram, 8vo. N.Y., Knopf, 1926.*

——————— Tears and laughter. *paper, 12mo. N.Y., Philosophical Library, 1949.*

GIBSON, PRESTON. S.O.S. and five one act plays. *buckram, 8vo. N.Y., French, 1912.*

GIBSON, W. BOLTE *and* BECK, HENRY C. Clerical errors. *buckram, 8vo. N.Y., Messner, 1955.*

——————— Fun in church. *paper, 8vo. Flemington, N.J., Calvary Church, 1952.*

GIELOW, MARTHA S. Old Andy the moonshiner. *boards, 12mo. N.Y., Revell, 1909.*

GILBERT, MARK. Wisdom of the ages. *buckram, 12mo. Lond., Saint Catherine Press, 1948. 2d.ed.*

GILBERT, WILLIAM SCHWENCK. The "Bab" ballads. *buckram, 12mo. Phila., McKay, n.d.*

_____ The Mikado. (Libretto). *paper, 12mo. n.p., n.d.*

_____ "Pinafore" an entirely original comic opera. *paper, 12mo. N.Y., Seer, 1879.*

_____ Pygmalion and Galatea; a mythological comedy. *paper, 12mo. Phila., Penn., 1912.*

GILBO, F.C. Father Goose. *buckram, 8vo. N.Y., Vantage, 1954.*

GILBRETH, FRANK B. *and* CAREY, ERNESTINE GIL-BRETH. Belles on their toes. *buckram, 8vo. N.Y., Crowell, 1950.*

_____ Innside Nantucket. *buckram, 8vo. N.Y., Crowell, 1954.*

GILES. Sunday Express and Daily Express cartoons. 6th series. *paper, 12mo. Lond., Daily Express, 1952.*

_____ *Same. 9th series. 1955.*

_____ *Same. 11th series, 1957.*

_____ *Same. 14th series, n.d.*

GILES, HERBERT A., *tr.* Quips from a Chinese jest-book. *paper, 16mo. Shanghai, Kelly & Walsh, 1925.*

GILL, E.W.B. War, wireless and wangles. *paper, 12mo. Oxford, Blackwell, 1934.*

GILL, WILLIAM DAVIS. Texas yarns and jokes. *buckram, 8vo. San Antonio, Naylor, 1952.*

GILLESPIE, JOHN. The humours of Scottish life. *buckram, 12 mo. Edinburgh, Blackwood, 1904.*

GILLETTE, WILLIAM. All the comforts of home. *paper, 12mo. N.Y., Dick & Fitzgerald, 1897.*

GILHAM, C.E. Medicine men of Hooper Bay, or The Eskimo's Arabian Nights. *buckram, 12mo. Lond., Batchworth, 1955.*

GILLILAN, STRICKLAND. Laugh it off, including Songs of sanity. *buckram, 12mo. Chic., Forbes, 1924.*

_____ A sample case of humor. *buckram, 12mo. Chic., Forbes, 1920.*

GILLY. With the walnuts and wine. *buckram, 16mo. Lond., Mills & Boon, 1922. 3d.ed.*

GILPATRIC, GUY. The Glen-cannon omnibus. *buckram, 8vo. N.Y., Dodd, Mead, 1944.*

GINGOLD, HERMIONE. My own unaided work. *boards, 8vo. Lond., T.Werner Laurie, 1952.*

_____ The world is square. *buckram, 12mo. Lond., Home & Van Thal, 1945.*

GINGRICH, ARNOLD, *ed.* The bed-side Esquire. *buckram, 12mo. Lond., Barker, 1948.*

GINZBERG, LOUIS. Legends of the Bible. *boards, 8vo. Phila., Jewish Pub. Soc., 1956.*

_____ On Jewish law and lore. *buckram, 8vo. Phila., Jewish Pub. Soc., 1955.*

GIOVANNETTI, PERICLE LUIGI. Max. *boards, folio, Zurich, Sanssouci, 1954.*

_____ Max presents. *boards, folio. N.Y., Macmillan, 1956.*

GIOVANNI FIORENTINO. The Pecorone of Ser Giovanni, now first translated into English by W.G. Waters. *3v. buckram, 8vo. Bost., Priv. Print. for Members of the Burton Ethnological Soc., n.d.*

GLADSTONE A.B.C., THE. *pamphlet. Edinburgh, Blackwood, n.d.*

GLADSTONE UMBRELLA, THE. *boards, 12mo. Lond., Quaritch, 1885.*

GLADSTONE, WILLIAM EWART. Thoughts from the writings and speeches of ... *buckram, 12mo. Lond., Ward, Lock & Bowden, 1894.*

GLAENZER, RICHARD BUTLER, *ed.* Spoofs. *buckram, 12mo. N.Y., Laugh Club, 1933.*

GLASGOW MAGAZINE OF WIT, original and selected. *calf, 12 mo. Glasgow, Falconer, 1803.*

GLASS, MONTAGUE. Potash and Perlmutter settle things. *buckram, 12mo. N.Y., Harper, 1919.*

——————— Potash and Perlmutter; their copartnership, ventures and adventures. *buckram, 12mo. N.Y., Grosset & Dunlap, 1911.*

——————— You can't learn 'em nothin'. *buckram, 12mo. N.Y., Doubleday, Doran, 1930.*

GLEANINGS OF WIT, being a choice collection of tales, anecdotes, occurrences ... from the works of an Old Military Officer. *3v. in 1. half-calf, 16mo. Lond., Ginger, 1805.*

GLOTZ, HERMAN. Spicy stories. *paper, 12mo. Los Angeles, Crown, 1943.*

GLYN, ELINOR. The sayings of Grandmamma and others. *boards, 24mo. N.Y., Duffield, 1908.*

GOBINEAU, JOSEPH ARTHUR, *comte de.* The dancing girl of Shamakha and other Asiatic tales. *buckram, 8vo. Lond., J. Cape, n.d.*

GODFREY, ARTHUR. Stories I like to tell; 306 of the best jokes and anecdotes I have heard in twenty years. *paper, 12mo. N.Y., Simon & Schuster, 1952.*

GOD'S MESSAGE: a book of 365 daily meditations. *buckram, 24 mo. Chic., Winston, 1931.*

GOETHE, JOHANN WOLFGANG von. The wisdom of Goethe, an anthology chosen by Emil Ludwig. *buckram, 8vo. N.Y., Carlton House, n.d.*

GOGARTY, OLIVER ST. JOHN. Start from somewhere else. *buckram, 8vo. N.Y., Doubleday, 1955.*

GOGGS, DIDIMUS *see* LLOYD, HENRY.

GOKHALE, ARAVIND. The unmarried widow and other stories. Translated from Marathi. *paper, 16mo. Bombay, Jaico, 1957.*

GOLD DUST: a collection of golden counsels. *leather, 16 mo. Phila., Altemus, n.d.*

GOLDBERG, HYMAN. How I became a girl reporter. *buckram, 12mo. Garden City, Doubleday, 1950.*

GOLDBERG, ISAAC, *ed.* Great Yiddish poetry. *paper, 32mo. Girard, Kan., Haldeman-Julius, n.d. (Little Blue Books.)*

_____ What we laugh at —
and why. *paper, 8vo. Girard,
Kan., Haldeman-Julius, n.d.*

_____ Yiddish short
stories. *paper, 32mo. Girard,
Kan., Haldeman-Julius, n.d.
(Little Blue Books.)*

GOLDBERG, RUBE. How to
remove the cotton from a
bottle of aspirin. *boards,
8vo. N.Y., Doubleday, 1959.*

_____ Is there a doctor in
the house? *buckram, 12mo.
N.Y., Day, 1929.*

_____ Rube Goldberg's
guide to Europe. *boards, 12mo.
N.Y., Vanguard, 1954.*

_____ Rube Goldberg plan
for the post-war world. *boards,
8vo. N.Y., Watts, 1944.*

GOLDEN, FRANCIS LEON.
Fellow citizens. *paper, 8vo.
N.Y., Fell, 1950.*

_____ For doctors only.
*buckram, 12mo. N.Y., Fell,
1949.*

_____ Jest what the doctor
ordered. *buckram, 12mo. N.Y.,
Fell, 1949.*

_____ Laughter is legal.
*buckram, 12mo. N.Y., Fell,
1950.* (Contains ALS to Nat
Schmulowitz.)

_____ Notes on being a
boss. *pamphlet. From Coronet,
Nov. 1936.*

_____ Tales for salesmen.
*buckram, 8vo. N.Y., Fell, 1951.*

GOLDEN, HARRY. Only in
America. *paper, 16mo. N.Y.,
Permabooks, 1958.*

GOLDEN, W. ECHARD. Hearts, a
comedy. *paper, 12mo. Chic.,
Dramatic Pub. Co., 1892.*

GOLDEN TREASURY OF INDIAN
LITERATURE. *boards, 8vo.
Lond., Sampson Low, Marston,
1938.*

GOLDSMITH, OLIVER. She stoops
to conquer; a comedy. *paper,
12mo. N.Y., De Wit, 1876.*

_____ She stoops to con-
quer, and The good-natured
man. *paper, 24mo. Lond.,
Cassell, 1906.*

_____ Vicar of Wakefield.
v.1. of MIRROR OF AMUSE-
MENT, *q.v.*

GOLDSMITH, ROBERT HILLS.
Wise fools in Shakespeare.
*buckram, 8vo. Liverpool. Liver-
pool Univ. Press, 1958.*

GOLD DIGEST. Fun in the rough.
*buckram, 4to. Englewood
Cliffs, N.J., Prentice-Hall,
1957.*

GOOD, RICHARD. Facetiae
Cantabrigienses; consisting of
anecdotes, smart sayings,
satirics, retorts, &c. &c. by
Socius. *boards, 16mo. Lond.,
Cole, 1825.*

_____ Same. *Lond., Mason,
1836. 3d.ed.*

_____ Nuts to crack, or,
Quips, quirks, anecdotes and
facete of Oxford and Cam-
bridge scholars. *quarter-
morocco, 12mo. Lond., Baily,
1834.*

_____ Same. *2d.ed.*

GOOD BUSINESS. Prayer in the
market place. *buckram, 16mo.
Lee's Summit, Mo., Unity
School of Christianity, 1950.*

GOOD-FELLOW'S CALENDAR AND ALMANACK OF PERPETUAL JOCULARITY, THE; containing a choice collection of laughable narratives, facetious anecdotes, singular facts and mirth-yielding details... *boards, 12mo. Lond., Sherwood, Gilbert & Piper, 1826.*

GOOD THINGS OF LIFE, THE. *buckram, wide 8vo. N.Y., White Stokes & Allen, 1884.*

——————— *Same. Second series.*

GOODMAN, JACK, *ed.* The fireside book of dog stories. *buckram, 8vo. N.Y., Simon & Schuster, 1943.*

——————— How to do practically anything. *buckram, 12mo. N.Y., Simon & Schuster, 1942.*

——————— I wish I'd said that! *buckram, 16mo. N.Y., Simon & Schuster, 1935.*

GOODMAN, PHILIP. Rejoice in thy festival; a treasury of wisdom, wit and humor for the Sabbath and Jewish holidays. *buckram, 8vo. N.Y., Bloch, 1956.*

GOODRICH, SAMUEL GRISWOLD. Peter Parley's merry stories, or, Fact, fancy and fiction. *buckram, small 8vo. N.Y., Knox, 1869.*

——————— Peter Parley's tales about Great Britain. *buckram, 32mo. Lond., Allman, 1839.*

——————— Tales of animals, comprising quadrupeds, birds, fishes, reptiles and insects. *calf., 16mo. Lond., Tegg, 1833. 3d.ed.*

——————— Wit bought; or, The life and adventures of Robert Merry. *buckram, 24mo. Lond., Daton & Compy, 1842.*

GOODWIN, I. Bury me in lead. *buckram, 12mo. Lond., Wingate, 1952.*

GOODWIN, J.JOSEPH. The "Sinker" stories of wit and humor. *buckram, 12mo. N.Y., Ogilvie, 1902.*

GOOGE, BARNABE. Eglogs, epytaphes & sonettes. 1563. From the copy in the posession of Henry Huth. Carefully edited by Edward Arber. *paper, 16mo. Lond., 1871. (English reprints.)*

GORDON, A.C. *and* PAGE, THOMAS NELSON. Befo' de war; echoes in negro dialect. *buckram, 12mo. N.Y., Scribner's, 1888.*

GORDON, A.M.R. Hoch der Kaiser. Myself und Gott. By Rose A. McGregor, pseud. *buckram, 12mo. Lond., Abbey, 1900.*

GORDON, ANTOINETTE K., *tr.* Tibetan tales; stories from the Dsangs Blun. *buckram, 12mo. Lond., Luzac, 1953.*

GORDON, HANFORD L. Laconics. *buckram, 8vo. Los Angeles, Author, 1914. 4th. ed. rev.*

GORDON, I. *and* FRUEH, A.J. The log of the ark, by Noah. *buckram, 12mo. N.Y., Dutton, 1936.*

GORDON, IRWIN L., *ed.* Who was who, 5000 B.C. to date. *buckram, 12mo. Phila., McKay, 1914.*

GORDON, RALPH. Pioneer daze; a history a la carte and a la cartoon (of Seattle) *boards, 12 mo. Seattle, Lowman & Hanford, 1930.*

GORDON, RICHARD, *pseud. see* OESTLERE, GORDON

GORDON, THOMAS. A cordial for low-spirits; being a collection of curious tracts. *calf, 16mo. Lond., Griffiths, n.d.*

GORE, *Mrs.* MOODY P. *and* SPEARE, *Mrs.* GUY E. New Hampshire folk tales. *buckram, 12mo. New Hampshire Federation of Women's Clubs, 1932.*

GORER, GEOFFREY *and* SEARLE, RONALD. Modern types. *buckram, 12mo. Lond., Cresset, 1955.*

GOREY, EDWARD. The unstrung harp, or, Mr. Earbrass writes a novel. *boards, 12mo. N.Y., Duell, Sloan & Pearce, 1953.*

GORHAM, MAURICE. Showmen and suckers. *buckram, 8vo. Lond., Marshall, 1951.*

GOSCINNY, RENE, *ed.* French and frisky. *paper, 16mo. N.Y., Lion, 1956.*

GOSSE, EDMUND. Gossip in a library. *buckram, 12mo. Lond., Heinemann, 1893.*

GOSSE, PHILIP. Dr. Viper; the querulous life of Philip Thicknesse. *buckram, 8vo. Lond., Cassell, 1952.*

———— Rest billets. *boards, 8vo. Lond., Dulau, 1927.*

GOSSETT, MARGARET. The real book of jokes. *buckram, 8vo. Garden City, Garden City Books, 1954.*

GOSSIP, GILES. Coronation anecdotes; or, Select and interesting fragments of English coronation ceremonies. *buckram, 12mo. Lond., Jennings, 1828. 2d.ed.*

GOULD, FRANCIS CARRUTHERS. Froissart's modern chronicles. *buckram, 8vo. Lond., T.Fisher Unwin. 1902.*

———— Political caricatures, 1903. *buckram, 4to. Lond., Arnold, 1903.*

———— Political caricatures, 1904. *buckram, 4to. Lond., Arnold, 1904.*

GOULD, GERALD. Democritus; or, The future of laughter. *buckram, 16mo. Lond., Kegan Paul, Trench, Trubner, 1929.*

GOULD, JOHN. The fastest hound dog in the State of Maine. *boards, 12mo. N.Y., Morrow, 1953.*

GOULD, R.E. Yankee drummer. *buckram, 8vo. N.Y., McGraw-Hill, 1947.*

GOULD, RUPERT T. Enigmas, another book of unexplained facts. *buckram, 8vo. Lond., G. Bles, 1946. 2d.ed.*

———— Oddities, a book of unexplained facts. *buckram, 8vo. Lond., G.Bles, 1945. Rev.*

GOURMONT, REMY de. Epigrams. *paper, 32mo. Girard, Kan. Haldeman-Julius, n.d. (Little Blue Books.)*

GOVION BROGLIO SOLARI, CATHERINE HYDE, *marquis de*. Venice under the yoke of France and of Austria; with memoirs of the courts, governments and people of Italy ... By a lady of rank. *quarter-calf., 8vo. Lond., Whittaker, 1824.*

GOWER, RONALD. My reminiscences. *2v. half-calf, 8vo. Lond., Kegan Paul, Trench, 1883.*

GRABOWSKI, Z.A. Your undiscovered island. *buckram, 12 mo. Lond., Johnson, 1950.*

GRADY, LESTER. Drink and be merry. *paper, 12mo. Greenwich, Conn., Fawcett, 1959.*

GRADY, RONAN C. The collected works of Ducrot Pepys. *buckram, 8vo. Newburgh, N.Y., Moore, 1943.*

GRAHAM, HARRY. The complete sportsman. *buckram, 12mo. Lond., Arnold, 1924. 3d.ed.*

———————— Deportmental ditties. *boards, 12mo. N.Y., Duffield, 1909.*

———————— More misrepresentative men. *boards, 16mo. N.Y., Fox, Duffield, 1905.*

————————More ruthless rhymes for heartless homes. *buckram, 24mo. Lond., Arnold, 1930.*

———————— Motley muse (Rhymes for the times). *buckram, 8vo. Lond., Arnold, 1913.*

———————— Methuen's Library of humour. Harry Graham. *buckram, 16mo. Lond., Methuen, 1934.*

———————— The world we laugh in (More deportmental ditties) *buckram, 12mo. Lond., Methuen, 1924. 2d.ed.*

———————— *Same. Lond., Methuen, 1928. 8th ed.*

———————— The world's workers. *buckram, 16mo. Lond., Methuen, 1928.*

GRAHAM, JORY. I'm driving my analyst crazy. *paper, 12mo. N.Y., Citadel, 1959.*

———————— *Same. Lond., Hammond & Hammond.*

GRAHAM, VIRGINIA. A cockney in the country. *paper, 8vo. Lond., Harvill, 1958.*

GRANDGENT, CHARLES HALL. Getting a laugh, and other essays. *boards, 8vo. Cambridge, Harvard Univ. Press, 1924.*

GRANT, E.W.M., MIZNER, ADDISON *and* HERFORD, OLIVER. The perfectly good cynic's calendar, with astronomical attachment. *cloth, 24mo. San Francisco, Paul Elder, 1908.*

GRAUER, ALVIN. So I went to Japan. *paper, small 4to. Tokyo, Nippon Times, 1946.*

GRAVES, CHARLES *and* LONGHURST, HENRY. Candid caddies. *boards, 8vo. Lond., Duckworth, 1935.*

GRAVES, MERLE DIXON. Bubblin's an' b'ilin's at the center. *buckram. 8vo. Rutland, Vt. Tuttle, 1934.*

GRAVES, ROBERT. !Catacrok! mostly stories, mostly funny. *buckram, 8vo. Lond., Cassell, 1956.*

———————— The future of swearing and improper language. *buckram, 12mo. Lond., Kegan Paul, Trench, Trubner, 1936.*

_____ Lars Porsena; or, The future of swearing and improper language. *buckram, 16 mo. N.Y., Dutton, 1927.*

_____ Mrs. Fisher, or, The future of humour. *boards, 16mo. Lond., Kegan Paul, Trench, Trubner, 1928.*

GRAVES, W.W. Tricks of rascals. *paper, 12mo. St. Paul, Kan., A.H.T.A. Weekly News, 1906.*

GRAY, ARTHUR. Bath robes and bachelors, and other good things. *suede, 16mo. N.Y., Caldwell, 1897.*

_____ Toast and tributes; a happy book of good cheer. *buckram, 16mo. N.Y., Rohde & Haskins, 1905.*

GRAY, JAMES *and* MAIDMENT, J.J.B. The banquet of wit, being a varied selection of anecdotes, bon mots, et cetera. *buckram, 12mo. Lond., Pickering, 1882.*

GRAY, R.L. Wit, wisdom and eloquence. *buckram, small 4to. Atlanta, Harrison, 1930. 4th ed. rev. and enl.*

GREAT FABLES, THE, *buckram, 8vo. Lond., Harrap, n.d.* (The Library of Living Classics)

GREAT FRENCH SHORT STORIES. *buckram, 12mo. Cleveland, World, 1926.*

GREAT LINGARD JOKER, THE. Full of Al side-splitters, funny stories, natty anecdotes, tip-top jests, and heaps of "bully" conundrums. *paper, 24mo. N.Y., Brady, 1870.*

GREAT THOUGHTS; a collection of exalted thoughts ancillary to success in life. *paper, 16mo. Calcutta, Industry Pub. Co., n.d.*

GREEN, ABLE, *ed.* The spice of Variety. *buckram, 8vo. N.Y., Holt, 1952.*

GREEN, BERT. Love letters of an interior decorator; romantic outbursts of a bootlegger. *boards, 12mo. N.Y., Stokes, 1929.*

GREEN, KENSAL. Premature epitaphs mostly written in malice. *boards, 12mo. Lond., Palmer, 1927.*

GREEN, MARK. Illustrations for argumentation; a book of tools, not rules... *buckram, 8vo. Washington, Author, 1937.*

GREEN, PAUL D. Fabulous Freddie and the Saints and Sinners. *buckram, 12mo. N.Y., Funk, 1951.*

GREEN, ROGER LANCELYN, *ed.* Century of humorous verse, 1850-1950. *buckram, 12mo. Lond., Dent, 1959.*

GREENING, ARTHUR. The better yarn, being some chronicles of the Merrythought Club. *buckram, 16mo. Lond., Jarrolds, 1919.*

GREENLEAF, BENJAMIN. The California almanac for 1849. *boards, 8vo. San Marion, reprinted from the copy in the Huntington Library, 1942.*

GREEN'S DIARY ALMANAC FOR 1885-1886. *paper, 8vo. Woodbury, N.J., Author, 1885.*

GREENWOOD, JAMES. Legends of savage life. *buckram, 8vo. Lond., John Camden Hotten, 1867.*

GREGORY, J.C. The nature of laughter. *buckram, 8vo. Lond., Kegan Paul, Trench, Trubner, 1924.*

GREIG, J.Y.T. The psychology of laughter and comedy. *buckram, 8vo. Lond., Allen and Unwin, 1923.*

GRIDLEY, ELEANOR. The story of Abraham Lincoln. *buckram, 8vo. Juvenile Pub. Co., 1900.*

GRIERSON, FRANCIS, The humour of the underman. *buckram, 12mo. Lond., Lane, 1923. 2d.ed.*

GRIFFIN, RICHARD. Bug house poetry. *buckram, 12mo. Priv. Print., 1928. Rev. and enl.*

GRIMM, JAKOB. Fairy tales. *8vo. buckram, N.Y., Pantheon, 1944.*

———————— Grimm's fairy tales. *buckram, 8vo. Lond., Dakers, n.d.*

———————— Grimm's household tales. Trans. by Margaret Hunt. *2v. buckram, 12mo. Lond., Bell, 1892.*

GRIMMELSHAUSEN, HANS JACOB CHRISTOPH *von.* The adventurous Simplicissimus. *boards, 12mo. Lond., Heinsmann, 1912.*

GRIMMER, WILLIAM HENRY. Anecdotes of the bench and bar. *buckram, 8vo. Lond., Hope, 1852.*

GRIN, GEOFFREY, *pseud.* Rhyming reminiscences in comical couplets. *half-calf., 24mo. Lond., Arnold, 1826.*

GRINDLAYE, GABRIEL. The Lord Mayor's fool, or, Maxims of Kit Largosse. *boards, 16mo. Lond., Tyas, 1840.*

GRISET, ERNEST. Griset's grotesques; or, Jokes drawn on wood with rhymes by Tom Hood. *cloth, 4to. Lond., Routledge, 1867.*

GRONOW, REES HOWELL. Recollections and anecdotes of the camp, the court and the clubs. *buckram, 12mo. Lond., Smith, Elder, 1877. New ed.*

GROSE, FRANCIS. The olio. *half-calf, 8vo. Lond., Hooler, 1792.*

GROSS, MILT. Dear dollink; momma writes to her Frankie at the front. *buckram, 12mo. N.Y., Putnams, 1945.*

———————— I shoulda ate the eclair. *buckram, 4to. Chic., Ziff Davis, 1946.*

———————— Nize baby. *buckram, 12mo. N.Y., Doran, 1926.*

———————— What's this? *boards, 12mo. N.Y., Simon & Schuster, 1936.*

GROSS, NATE. The town tattler. *clippings from newspapers, in binder.*

GROSSMAN, RICHARD *and* ROSE, CARL. A new leash on life. *buckram, 8vo. N.Y., Random House, 1950.*

GROSSMAN, WILLIAM, *ed.* Jewish humor in the home and synagogue. *paper, 16mo. Passaic, N.J., Columbia, 1940.*

GROSSMITH, GEORGE. A society clown. *half-calf, 16mo. Bristol, Arrowsmith, 1888.*

GROVER, EDWIN OSGOOD. Just being happy; a little book of happy thoughts. *boards, 16mo. Chic., Volland, 1916.*

GROVER, J. HOLMES. That rascal Pat; a farce. *paper, 12 mo. N.Y., French, 1863.*

GUBBINS, NATHANIEL. Dear Sir, unless ... Gubbins' and Hendry's Guide to dodging income tax. *buckram, 12mo. Lond., Routledge, 1936.*

GUERBER, HELENE A. Myths and Legends of the Middle Ages. *buckram, 8vo. Lond., Harrap, 1903.*

GUILD, LEO. You bet your life! *buckram, 12mo. Hollywood, M.Rodd, 1946.*

GUILPIN, EVERARD. Skialetheia, 1598. *boards, 8vo. Lond., Milford for the Shakespeare Association, 1931. Facsimile.*

GUITERMAN, ARTHUR. Chips of jade. *cloth, 12mo. N.Y., Dutton, 1921.*

——————— The laughing muse. *buckram, 12mo. N.Y., Harper, 1915.*

——————— A poet's proverbs. *buckram, 12mo. N.Y., Dutton, 1924.*

GUNN, BATTISCOMBE G., *tr.* The instruction of Ptahhotep and the instruction of Ke'gemni, the oldest books in the world. *buckram, 16mo. Lond., Murray, 1906.*

GUNN, JOHN W., *comp.* Best jokes. *paper, 32mo. Girard, Kan., Haldeman-Julius, n.d. (Little Blue Books.)*

——————— Life and works of Jonathan Swift. *paper, 32mo. Girard, Kan., Haldeman-Julius, n.d. (Little Blue Books.)*

GURY, JEREMY. The wonderful world of Aunt Tuddy. *boards, folio. N.Y., Random House, 1958.*

GWATHNEY, JOHN H. Justice John, tales from the courtroom of the Virginia judge. *boards, 8vo. Richmond, Va., Dietz, 1934.*

——————— Legends of Virginia courthouses. *boards, 8vo. Richmond, Va., Dietz, 1933.*

——————— Legends of Virginia lawyers. *boards, 8vo. Richmond, Va., Dietz, 1934.*

"H." Meditations of a profane man, by "H". *buckram, 12mo. N.Y., Grosset & Dunlap, 1926.*

H.,K. *and* H.,M.B. 100 riddles and 101 things to do. *buckram, 12mo. N.Y., Grosset & Dunlap, 1928.*

HA! HA!! HA!!! Everybody's book of humorous stories and jokes. *paper, 24mo. Lond., Foulsham, n.d.*

HABBERTON, JOHN. Helen's babies. *buckram, 12mo. Lond., Routledge & Kegan Paul, 1948.*

HADDON, ARCHIBALD. Green room gossip. *buckram, 12mo. Lond., S.Paul, 1922.*

HADDOW, J.G. Amber, all about it. *paper, 12mo. Liverpool, "Cope's Tobacco Plant," 1892.*

HADLEY, ARTHUR T. Do I make myself clear? *boards, 8vo. N.Y., Holt, 1956.*

HADLEY, M.A. Korea? I've had it! *boards, 12mo. Rutland, Vt. Tuttle, 1954.*

HAESTIER, RICHARD. Dead men tell tales; a survey of exhumations, from earliest antiquity to the present day. *buckram, 8vo. Lond., Long, 1934.*

HAHN, EMILY. Spousery: his edition (her edition by Eric Hatch.) *boards, 12mo. N.Y., Watts, 1956.*

# H

HAINES, JENNIE DAY. Sovereign woman versus mere man. *boards, 12mo. San Francisco, Elder, 1905.*

HAISELY, WAYNE G. New teeth in old saws; a collection of well-known sayings done in the modern manner. *boards, 16mo. N.Y., Sears, 1928.*

HALDEMAN-JULIUS, E. Brief burlesques and epigrams. *paper, 32mo. Girard, Kan., Haldeman-Julius, n.d. (Little Blue Books.)*

HALE, LUCRETIA P. The Peterkin papers. *buckram, 8vo. Bost., Houghton, Mifflin, 1924.*

HALF-HOURS WITH GREAT HUMORISTS: the choicest humor of great writers, by Charles Lamb, Tom Hood, F.C. Burnand, Mark Twain and others. *buckram, 12mo. Chic., Belford, Clarke, 1888.*

HALF PORTIONS. *buckram, 8vo. N.Y., Life, 1900.*

HALIBURTON, THOMAS CHANDLER. The attache; or, Sam Slick in England. *2v. buckram, small 8vo. Lond., Bentley, 1843.*

——————— The clockmaker; or, The sayings and doings of Samuel Slick of Slickville. *2v. half-calf., 12mo. Lond., Bentley, 1838.*

——————— *Same. 1v. Phila., Lea & Blanchard, 1839.*

——————— The old judge; or, Life in a colony. *buckram, 12mo. Lond., Hurst & Blackett, n.d.*

——————— Piney woods tavern; or, Sam Slick in Texas. *buckram, 12mo. Phila., Peterson, 1858.*

——————— Sam Slick. *buckram, 8vo. N.Y., Doran, 1923.*

——————— Sam Slick in England. *buckram, 12mo. Lond., Routledge, 1858.*

——————— Sam Slick's wise saws and modern instances. *2v. buckram, 8vo. Lond., Hurst & Blackett, 1853. 2d.ed.*

——————— Sayings and doings of Samuel Slick, esq. *buckram, 12mo. N.Y., Dick & Fitzgerald, n.d.*

——————— Traits of American humor. *buckram, 12mo. Lond., Hurst & Blackett, n.d.*

——————— Wise saws, or, Sam Slick in search of a wife. *buckram, 12mo. N.Y., Dick & Fitzgerald, n.d.*

——————— *Same. N.Y., Stringer & Townsend, 1855.*

——————— Yankee notions, or, The American Joe Miller, by Sam Slick. *half-calf., 16mo. Lond., Bell, Arnold, 1839.*

HALL, GORDON LANGLEY. Me papoose sitter. *buckram, 8vo. Lond., Hutchinson, 1956.*

HALL, ROBERT A. Italian stories. *paper, 12mo. N.Y., Bantam, 1961.*

HALL, S.C. A book of memories of great men and women of the age. *buckram, 8vo. Lond., Virtue, 1877. 2d.ed.*

HALL, S.C. Tales of Irish life and character. *cloth, 8vo. Edinburgh, Foulis, 1909.*

HALL, W.W. Fun better than physic; or, Everybody's life-preserver. *buckram, 12mo. Springfield, Mass., Fisk, 1871.*

HALLIDAY, W.R. Folklore studies ancient and modern. *buckram, 12mo. Lond., Methuen, 1924.*

HALLIWELL, JAMES ORCHARD. A dictionary of archaic and provincial words. *quarterleather. 8vo. Lond., Routledge, 1924. 7th ed.*

——————— The jokes of the Cambridge coffee-houses of the seventeenth century. *paper, 24 mo. Lond., Tilt & Bogue, 1842.*

HALSEY, ASHLEY, *jr. ed.* The perfect squelch. *boards, 8vo. N.Y., Barnes, 1952.*

——————— You be the judge. *boards, 8vo. N.Y., Barnes, 1952.*

HALSEY, MARGARET. Some of my best friends are soldiers. *buckram, 8vo. N.Y., Simon & Schuster, 1944.*

HAMER, J. The smoker's text book. *paper, 12mo. Liverpool. "Cope's Tobacco Plant" 1890.*

HAMID-UD-DIN KHAN BAHADUR. *see* ANECDOTES OF AURANGZIB.

HAMILTON, A.E. Psychology and "The great god fun". *buckram, 8vo. N.Y., Julian, 1955.*

HAMILTON, ELIZABETH. Memoirs of the life of Agrippina, wife of Germanicus. *3v. calf., 12mo. Bath, Cruttwell, 1804.*

HAMILTON, GEORGE ROSTREVOR. Epigrams, *buckram, 16mo. Lond., Heinemann, 1928.*

——————— The soul of wit; a choice of English verse epigrams. *buckram, 12mo. Lond., Heinemann, 1924.*

HAMMERTON, J.A. English humorists of to-day. *buckram, 12mo. Lond., Hodder & Stoughton, 1907.*

——————— The fun library. *10v. buckram, 12mo. Lond., Educational Book Co., n.d.*

——————— George Meredith in anecdote and criticism. *buckram, 8vo. Lond., Richards, 1909.*

——————— Stevensoniana; an anecdotal life and appreciation of Robert Louis Stevenson. *buckram, 8vo. Edinburgh, Grant, 1910.*

HAMMOND, PERCY. Poker, smoke and things. *buckram, 12mo. Chic., Reilly & Britton, 1907.*

HANAUER, J.E. Folk-lore of the Holy Land: Moslem, Christian and Jewish. *buckram, 8vo. Lond., Sheldon, 1935. New and enl.ed.*

HANEMANN, HENRY WILLIAM. As is, a book of miscellaneous revelations. *boards, 12mo. N.Y. Harcourt, Brace, 1923.*

HANSER, RICHARD. The laughing Lincoln. *(From the Saturday Review, Feb. 8, 1958.)*

——————— Meet Mr. Lincoln. *paper, 4to. N.Y., Ridge, 1960.*

HA'PORTH OF WIT, WISDOM, FICTION, PASTIME AND GENERAL INFORMATION, 1892-1893, THE. *buckram, 4to. Bradford, Wood, Holdsworth, Oates, etc., 1892-1893.*

HARBIN, E.O. Phunology. *buckram, 8vo. N.Y., Abingdon-Cokesbury, 1923.*

HARBOTTLE, THOMAS BEN-
FIELD. Dictionary of quo-
tations (classical) *buckram,
8vo. Lond., Sonnenschein,
1897.*

_____ Dictionary of quo-
tations (Italian) *buckram, 12
mo. Lond., Sonnenschein,
1909.*

_____ Dictionary of quo-
tations (Spanish) *buckram, 12
mo. Lond., Sonnenschein, 1907.*

HARCOURT, JOHN. John
Harcourt's original jests.*paper,
24mo. Lond., Cowie & Strange,
1827.*

HARDCASTLE, EPHRAIM. Wine
and walnuts; or, After-dinner
chit-chat. *2v. buckram, 16mo.
Lond., Longman, Hurst, Rees,
Orme, Brown & Green, 1824.*

HARDIE, KEIR. The Keir Hardie
calendar. *paper, 24mo. Girard,
Kan., Appeal to Reason, n.d.*

HARDING, GILBERT. A treasury
of insult. *buckram, 12mo. Lond.
Widenfeld & Nicolson, 1953.*

HARDING, T. SWANN. Aren't men
rascals? *buckram, 12mo. N.Y.,
Dial, 1930.*

HARE, JULIUS CHARLES.
Guesses at truth, by Two
Brothers. First series. *calf.,
16mo. Lond., Watson & Maberly,
1851. 4th ed.*

_____ *Same. Second
series. 1855.*

HARE, WALTER BEN. Comics; an
anthology of readings, monologues, pianologues and encore
bits. *buckram, 16mo. Bost.,
Baker, 1924.*

_____ Readings and mono-
logues a la mode. *paper, 12mo.
Minneapolis, Denison, 1921.*

HARGROVE, JOHN. Propaganda
the mightiest weapon of all.
Words win wars. *buckram, 8vo.
Lond., Wells, Gardner, Darton,
1940.*

HARGROVE, MARION. See here,
Private Hargrove. *buckram, 8
vo. N.Y., Holt, 1942.*

HARIRI. *see* KASIM IBN ALI,
*called Al-Hariri.*

HARLEY, A.B., *comp. and ed.*
Another five-minute recitations.
*paper, 12mo. Edinburgh, Oliver
& Boyd, 1958.*

_____ More story recitals in
poem and prose. *paper, 12mo.
Edinburgh, Oliver & Boyd,
1958. 2d.ed.*

_____ Story recitals in poem
and prose. *paper, 12mo. Edinburgh, Oliver & Boyd, 1958.
3d.ed.*

HARMON, BOB, *and* KETCHAM,
HANK. Baby sitter's guide, by
Dennis the Menace. *boards, 8
vo. N.Y., Holt, 1954.*

HARMSWORTH, CECIL. Immortals
at first hand; famous people as
seen by their contemporaries.
*buckram, 8vo. Lond., Harms-
worth, 1933.*

HARPER, HENRY HOWARD.
Merely the patient. *buckram,
12mo. N.Y., Balch, 1930.*

HARPER, T.H. Boonastiel; a
volume of legend, story and
song in "Pennsylvania Dutch."
*buckram, 8vo. Bellefonte, Pa.,
"The Keystone Gazette"
1904.*

HARRIS, FRANCIS A. A majority
of one; a farce. *paper, 12mo.
Bost., Baker, 1892.*

HARRIS, GEORGE W. Sut Loving-good. Yarns spun by a "nat'ral born durn'd fool" warped and wove for public wear. *buckram, 12mo. N.Y., Dick & Fitzgerald, 1867.*

HARRIS, JOEL CHANDLER. Nights with Uncle Remus. *buckram, 12mo. Bost., Houghton, Mifflin, 1900.*

HARRIS, MABEL ARUNDEL. Riddles and laughter; a book of fun for young folks. *buckram, 12mo. N.Y., Burt, 1928.*

HARRIS, RENDEL. Testimonies. *2v. buckram, 8vo. Cambridge, Univ. Press, 1916.*

HARRISON, JOHN. After dinner stories. *buckram, 24mo. Phila., Penn, 1923.*

HARRISON, W.H. The humourist, a companion for the Christmas fireside. *morocco, 12mo. Lond., Ackermann, 1831.*

HARRISON, WILFRED H. Humour in the East End. *paper, 8vo. Lond., Epworth, 1933.*

HARRISON, WILMOT. The social circle of anecdote. *leather, 24 mo. N.Y., Brentano's, n.d.*

HARRY, PHILIP W. French anec-dotes. *buckram, 16mo. N.Y., American Book Co., 1915.*

HART, FRED H. The Sazerac lying club; a Nevada book. *paper, 8vo. San Francisco, S. Carson, 1878. 5th ed.*

HART, HAROLD, *ed.* Top stuff. *buckram, 8vo. N.Y., Parker, 1945.*

HART, HAROLD H. Grab a pencil. *paper, 4to. N.Y., Author, 1958.*

HART, HENRY H., *tr.* Seven hundred Chinese proverbs. *buckram, 8vo. Stanford, Stanford Univ. Press, 1937.*

HART, LAURENCE H. Selections from George Washington. *paper, 24mo. (Personal Growth Leaf-let.)*

HARTE, FRANCIS BRET. Unpublished limericks & car-toons. *cloth, 8vo. Atherton, Calif., Camino de Lago Press, 1933.*

HARTLAND, EDWIN SIDNEY. English fairy and other folk tales. *buckram, 12mo. Lond., Scott, n.d.*

——————— The science of fairy tales. *buckram, 16mo. Lond., Scott, 1891.*

HARTLIB, SAMUEL. A facsimile edition of Samuel Hartlib's 1641 pamphlete "A description of the famous kingdome of Macaria". *paper, 8vo. Sausalito, Calif., Elan, 1961.*

HARTMAN, J.F. Monologues and parodies. *buckram, 12mo. N.Y., Vernon, 1910.*

——————— Spice and parody; a unique collection of funny rhymes, epitaphs and parodies. *buckram, 12mo. N.Y., Carey-Stafford, 1906.*

HARTWELL, DICKSON *and* ROONEY, ANDREW A. Off the record; the best stories of foreign correspondents. *buck-ram, 8vo. N.Y., Doubleday, 1952.*

HARVARD LAMPOON. Fortune. *paper, 4to. Bost., Harvard Lampoon, 1933.*

——————— Hits from the Harvard Lampoon; cartoons and editorials, poems and parodies, wit and whimsey by Cambridge jesters, old and new. *paper, 8vo. (Bost., Harvard Lampoon, 1950?)*

HARVEY, PAUL. Remember these things. *boards, 8vo. Garden City, Heritage Foundation, 1952.*

HARVEY, PETER. Reminiscences and anecdotes of Daniel Webster. *buckram, 8vo. Bost., Little, Brown, 1877.*

HARVEY, WILLIAM. Irish life and humour in anecdote and story. *buckram, 12mo. Lond., Maclaren, 1906.*

——————— *Same. Stirling, Eneas Mackay, 1899.*

——————— *Same. Abridged edition. Lond., Maclaren, 1908.*

HARZBERG, HILER, *and* MOSS, ARTHUR. Slapstick and dumbbell; a casual survey of clowns and clowning. *boards, 4to. Paris, Lecram, 1924.*

HASELDEAN, W.K. The sad adventures of big and little Willie during the first six months of the great war. *paper, folio. Lond., Fine Art Society, 1915.*

HASLEWOOD, JOSEPH. Green room gossipp or, Gravity gallinipt; a gallimaufry ... gathered and garnished by Gridiron Gribble, Gent., godson to Mother Goose. *half-calf., 12mo. Lond., Barker, 1809.*

HATCH, JAMES NOBLE. Mirthful musings. *boards, 8vo. Chic., Author, 1925.*

HATCH, PREBLE D.K. Don't shoot the bill collector. *buckram, 8vo. N.Y., Crowell, 1950.*

HATLO, JIMMY. Another new Jimmy Hatlo book. *paper, 16mo. N.Y., Avon, 1958.*

——————— Cartoons. *paper, 16mo. N.Y., Avon, 1955.*

——————— Hatlo cartoons — 1956. *paper, 16mo. N.Y., Avon, 1956.*

——————— Jimmy Hatlo's office party. *paper, 4to. N.Y., Grosset & Dunlap, 1959.*

——————— New Jimmy Hatlo book. *paper, 16mo. N.Y., Avon, 1953.*

HAUFF, WILHELM. Caravan tales, and some others. *buckram, 8 vo. Lond., Wells Gardner, Darton, 1912.*

HAVE YOU HEARD THIS ONE? Best Scottish, Jewish & Irish jokes. *paper, 16mo. Lond., Foulsham, n.d.*

——————— *Same. buckram, with sub-title only.*

HAWGOOD, ALISON. A family is fun. *buckram, 12mo. Lond., Nicholson & Watson, 1948.*

HAWEIS, H.R. American humorists. *buckram, 12mo. N.Y. Funk & Wagnalls, 1883?*

——————— American humorists: Artemas Ward. *paper, 24mo. N.Y., Alden, 1883.*

HAWKES, JACQUETTA. Fables. *buckram, 8vo. Lond., Cresset, 1953.*

HAWKINS, CHARLES HALFORD. Noctes Shaksperianae; a series of papers. *buckram, 8vo. Lond., Simpkin, 1893.*

HAWKS, WELLS. Red wagon stories, or, Tales under the tent. *paper, 12mo. Baltimore, Ottenheimer, 1904.*

HAWTREY, CHARLES. The
private secretary; a farcical
comedy. *paper, 12mo. N.Y.,
French, 1907.*

HAY, GEORGE D. Howdy judge.
*buckram, 12mo. Nashville,
McQuiddy, 1926.*

HAY, IAN *see* BEITH, JOHN
HAY.

HAYES, GABBY. The Gabby
Hayes treasure chest of tall
tales. *paper, 4to. Bost.,
Wilson-Hill, 1952.*

HAYKLAN, ELIZABETH.
Impossible people. *buckram,
12mo. Lond., Hutchinson,
n.d.*

HAYMAN, JOE. Twenty different
adventures of Cohen on the
telephone, and other different
samples of Hebrew humour.
*paper, 12mo. Lond., Rogers,
1927.*

HAYNES, E.S.P. Lycurgus, or,
The future of law. *boards, 16mo.
Lond., Kegan Paul, Trench,
Trubner, n.d.*

"HAYSEED" JOKER, THE. *paper,
12mo. Cleveland, Westbrook,
1903.*

HAYTER, H.W.G. Caricatures by
H.H. *boards, folio, Shanghai,
Kelly & Walsh, 1902.*

HAYVE, O.B. *see* TOWNE,
CHARLES WAYLAND.

HAZLEWOOD, C.H. For honor's
sake. *paper, 12mo. Chic.,
Dramatic Pub. Co., n.d.*

HAZLITT, WILLIAM CAREW.
English proverbs and pro-
verbial phrases. *buckram, 12mo.
Lond., Reeves & Turner, 1907.*

——————— Hazlitt painted by
himself, and presented by
Catherine Macdonald Maclean.
*buckram, 8vo. Lond., Temple,
1948.*

——————— Jests new and old,
containing anecdotes of celebrities, living and deceased.
*half-leather, 8vo. Lond., Jarvis,
1886.*

——————— Lectures on the
English comic writers, delivered at the Surrey Institution.
*boards, 8vo. Lond., Taylor &
Hessey, 1819.*

——————— Lectures on the
English comic writers with
miscellaneous essays. *quarter-
calf., 12mo. Lond., Dent, n.d.*

——————— New London jest
book. *buckram, 12mo. Lond.,
Reeves & Turner, 1871.*

——————— Old English jest
books. Pasquil's jests mixed
with Mother Bunches merriments. Whereunto is added a
Doozen of Gulles, 1604. Reprinted from the rare original.
*quarter-calf., 12mo. Lond.,
Willis & Sotheran, 1866.*

——————— Studies in jocular
literature. *boards, 16mo.
Lond., Stock, 1904.*

——————— What I have learned
about life from fools and sages
(Characteristics). *paper, 32mo.
Girard, Kan., Haldeman-
Julius, n.d. (Little Blue Books)*

——————— Wit and humour, and
other essays. *leather, 32mo.
N.Y., Dutton, n.d.*

HEARD, FRANKLIN FISKE.
Curiosities of the law reporters.
*buckram, 12mo. Bost., Lee &
Shepard, 1871.*

HEARD ANY GOOD SHAGGY DOG STORIES LATELY? Leaflet advertising Walt Disney's motion picture "The shaggy dog".

HEARN, LAFCADIO. Some Chinese ghosts. *buckram, 16mo. N.Y., Modern Library, 1927.*

HEART THROBS IN PROSE AND VERSE. *buckram, 12mo. N.Y., Grosset & Dunlap, 1905.*

HEATH, ROYAL VALE. Mathemagic; magic, puzzles, and games with numbers. *paper, 8vo. N.Y., Dover, 1933.*

HEATON, JOHN LANGDON. The book of lies. *buckram, 12mo. N.Y., Morse, 1896.*

HEAVENLY HUMOR ... An incense-laden garland of irreverent revelry. *paper, 16mo. St. Louis, Mo., Rationalist Association, 1958.*

HEBRAIC LITERATURE: translations from the Talmud, Midrashim and Kabbala. *buckram, 8vo. N.Y., Tudor, 1901.*

HEBREW JOKES AND DIALECT HUMOR. *paper, 12mo. Phila., Royal, 1902.*

HECHT, ANDREW. Hollywood merry-go-round. *buckram, 8vo. N.Y., Grosset & Dunlap, 1947.*

HECHT, BEN *and* BODENHEIM, MAXWELL. Cutie, a warm mamma. *buckram, 8vo. N.Y., Boar's Head, 1952.*

——————————— I hate actors! *buckram, 12mo. N.Y., Crown, 1944.*

——————————— Tales of Chicago streets. *paper, 32mo. Girard, Kan., Haldeman-Julius, n.d. (Little Blue Books.)*

HEDGES, SID G. Fun for the not-so-young. *buckram, 12mo. N.Y., Philosophical Library, 1958.*

HEGERMANN-LINDENCRONE, LILY. The sunny side of diplomatic life, 1875-1912. *buckram, 8vo. N.Y., Harper, 1914.*

HEINE, HEINRICH. The wit of Heinrich Heine. *paper, 32mo. Girard, Kan., Haldeman-Julius, n.d. (Little Blue Books.)*

——————————— Wit, wisdom and pathos, from the prose of Heinrich Heine. *buckram, 12 mo. Lond., Gardner, 1888. 2d.ed.*

——————————— Wit, wisdom, and pathos, from the prose of Heinrich Heine, with a few pieces from the "Book of Songs". Selected and translated by J. Snodgrass. *buckram, 12mo. Lond., Trubner, 1879.*

HEINZ-LEHMANN, ARTHUR. The noble stallion. *buckram, 8vo. N.Y., Holt, 1954.*

HELD, JOHN. Held's angels. *buckram, 8vo. N.Y., Crowell, 1952.*

——————————— The saga of Frankie & Johnny. *buckram, 4to. N.Y., McKee, 1930.*

HELLER, JACK. Sex-clusive. *paper, 16mo. N.Y., Belmont, 1960.*

——————————— Strictly (monkey) business. *paper, 4to. N.Y., Star, 1954.*

H-E-L-L-O BILL! a book of after-dinner stories. *boards, 12mo. N.Y., Dodge, 1915.*

HENDERSON, ANDREW. Scottish proverbs. *buckram, 12mo. Glasgow, Morison, 1881.*

HENDERSON, JACK. Down south. *buckram, 16mo. N.Y., Hurst, 1905.*

HENDREN, PATSY. Silly point.
*boards, 8vo. Lond., Duckworth,*
*1939.*

HENREY, T. SELBY. Attic salt;
the saving grace of humour.
*buckram, 16mo. Lond.,*
*Nisbet, 1913.*

——————— Good stories from
Oxford and Cambridge and the
dioceses. *buckram, 12mo.*
*Lond., Simpkin, Marshall,*
*1925. Enl.ed.*

HENRY, L.E. Napoleon's war
maxims with his social and
political thoughts. *buckram,*
*8vo. Lond., Gale & Polden,*
*1899.*

HENRY, LEWIS C. 5,000 quotations for all occasions. *buck-*
*ram, 8vo. Phila., New Home*
*Library, 1945.*

——————— Humorous anecdotes
about famous people. *buckram,*
*8vo. Garden City, Halcyon,*
*1948.*

HERACLITUS RIDENS; or, A discourse between jest and
earnest ... *2v. calf., 24mo.*
*Lond., Tooke, 1713.*

HERBERT, ALAN PATRICK.
A.T.I. "There is no need for
alarm" *boards, 12mo. Lond.,*
*Ornum, 1944.*

——————— Ballads for broad-
brows, and others. *buckram,*
*12mo. N.Y., Doubleday, Doran,*
*1931.*

——————Godd's last case,
and other misleading cases.
*buckram, 12mo. Lond.,*
*Methuen, 1952.*

——————— Holy deadlock. buckram, *12mo. N.Y., Doubleday,*
*Doran, 1934.*

——————— Honeybubble and co.
*buckram, 12mo. Lond.,*
*Methuen, 1928.*

——————— Laughing Ann, and
other poems. *buckram, 12mo.*
*N.Y., Doubleday, Page, 1926.*

——————Look back and laugh.
*buckram, 12mo. Lond., Methuen,*
*1960.*

——————Leave my old morale
alone. *buckram, 8vo. N.Y.,*
*Doubleday, 1948.*

——————'Less nonsense!'
*buckram, 12mo. Lond., Methuen,*
*1944.*

——————Let us be glum.
*buckram, 12mo. Lond.,*
*Methuen, 1941.*

——————— Light articles only.
*buckram, 12mo. Lond.,*
*Methuen, 1921.*

——————— *Same. 3d.ed. 1939.*

——————— Methuen's library of
humour. A.P. Herbert. *buckram,*
*16mo. Lond., Methuen, n.d.*

——————— Misleading cases in
the common law. *buckram, 12mo.*
*Lond., Methuen, 1930. 5th ed.*

——————— More misleading
cases. *buckram, 12mo. Lond.,*
*Methuen, 1930.*

——————— "No fine on fun" the
comical history of the entertainments duty. *buckram, 12mo.*
*Lond., Methuen, 1957.*

——————Plain Jane. *buckram,*
*12mo. N.Y., Doubleday, Page,*
*1927.*

——————*Same. Lond., T.*
*Fisher Unwin, 1927.*

——————— The point of parliament. *buckram, 8vo. Lond.,*
*Methuen, 1946.*

——————— She-shanties. *buckram, 12mo. Lond., T.Fisher Unwin, 1926.*

——————— Sip! swallow! *buckram, 12mo. Lond., Methuen, 1937.*

——————— Still more misleading cases. *buckram, 12mo. Lond., Methuen, 1933.*

——————— The Topsy omnibus. *buckram, 12mo. Lond., Benn, 1949.*

——————— Topsy turvy. *buckram, 12mo. Lond., Benn, 1947.*

——————— The trials of Topsy. *buckram, 12mo. Lond., Benn, 1928.*

——————— Uncommon law. *buckram, 12mo. Lond., Methuen, 1937. 3d.ed.*

——————— What a word! *buckram, 12mo. Lond., Methuen, 1935.*

——————— Wisdom for the wise. *buckram, 12mo. Lond., Methuen, 1930.*

**HERBERT, GEORGE.** The remains of that sweet singer of the temple. *leather, 16mo. Lond., Pickering, 1848.*

**HERFORD, CHARLES H.** Studies in the literary relations of England and German in the 16th century. *buckram, 12mo. Cambridge, Univ. Press., 1886.*

**HERFORD, OLIVER** *(and others).* The complete cynic being bunches of wisdom culled from the calendars of Oliver Herford, Ethel Watts Mumford and Addison Mizner. *boards, 12mo. San Francisco, Elder, 1910.*

——————— Cupid's cyclopedia. *boards, 16mo. N.Y., Scribner, 1910.*

——————— Cynic's calendar of revised wisdom for 1904. *buckram, 24mo. San Francisco, Elder, 1903.*

——————— The deb's dictionary. *buckram, 12mo. Phila., Lippincott, 1931.*

——————— Same. *Lond., Methuen, 1932.*

——————— The laughing willow. *boards, 12mo. N.Y., Doran, 1918.*

——————— A little book of bores. *buckram, 16mo. Lond., Gay & Hancock, 1908.*

——————— Neither here nor there. *buckram, 12mo. N.Y., Doran, 1922.*

——————— The simple jography, or, How to know the earth and why it spins. *boards, 12mo. Bost., Luce, 1908.*

——————— This giddy globe, by Peter Simple. *boards, 12mo. N.Y., Doran, 1919.*

——————— What'll you have? *boards, 12mo. N.Y., Holt, 1925.*

**HERMAN, VIC.** Winnie the Wac. *boards, 12mo. Phila., McKay, 1945.*

**HEROLD, DON.** Drunks are driving me to drink. *boards, 12mo. N.Y., Barnes, 1953.*

——————— Our companionate goldfish. *buckram, 12mo. N.Y., Doubleday, Doran, 1928.*

**HERRICK, MARVIN T.** Comic theory in the 16th century. *paper, 8vo. Urbana, Univ. of Illinois Press, 1950.*

**HERRIMAN, ———** Adventures of Krazy Kat and Ignatz Mouse in Koko Land. *boards, 48mo. Akron, O., Saalfield, 1934.*

HERSCH, PHIL. The war between the mates. *paper, 12mo. N.Y., Pyramid, 1961.*

HERSCHELL, WILLIAM. The smile-bringer, and other bits of cheer. *buckram, small 8vo. Indianapolis, Bobbs-Merrill, 1926.*

HERSCHFIELD, HARRY. Jewish jokes. *buckram, 16mo. N.Y., Simon & Schuster, 1932.*

HERSHFIELD, HARRY. Laugh louder, live longer. *buckram, 8vo. N.Y., Grayson, 1959.*

_____ "Now I'll tell one". *buckram, 8vo. N.Y., Greenberg, 1938.*

HERSEY, HAROLD. *comp.*, G.I. laughs; real U.S. army humor. *buckram, 8vo. N.Y., Sheridan, 1944.*

HERSEY, JOHN. Hiroshima. *In: New Yorker magazine, August 31, 1946.*

HERZBERG, MAX. Insults; a practical anthology of scathing remarks and acid portraits. *buckram, 8vo. N.Y., Greystone, 1942.*

HERZOG, F. BENEDICT. College cuts, chosen from the Columbia Spectator, 1880-81-82. *buckram, 12mo. N.Y., White & Stokes, 1882.*

HERZOG, GEORGE. Jabo proverbs from Liberia; maxims in the life of a native tribe. *buckram, 8vo. Lond., International Institute of African Languages and Cultures, 1936.*

HESELTINE, OLIVE. Conversation. *buckram, 12mo. Lond., Methuen, 1927.*

HESTON, WATSON. Old Testament stories comically illustrated. *boards, 16mo. N.Y., Truth Seeker Co., 1892.*

HEWITT, W.C. The best after dinner stories and how to tell them. *buckram, 12mo. Oshkosh, Wis., Castle-Pierce, 1916.*

_____ Same. *Chic., Powner, 1946.*

HEWLETT, JOHN. The Blarney stone. *buckram, 8vo. N.Y., Appleton-Century-Crofts, 1951.*

HEWLETT, Sir MEYRICK. Forty years in China. *buckram, 8vo. Lond., Macmillan, 1943.*

HEYWOOD, JOHN. A dialogue of wit and folly. *paper, 8vo. Lond., Percy Society, 1846.*

HICKS, SEYMOUR. Chestnuts reroasted; a collection of perhaps funny stories. *buckram, 12mo. Lond., Hodder & Stoughton, n.d.*

_____ Laugh with me; some of the world's best stories. *buckram, 12mo. Lond., Cassell, 1936.*

HIEROCLES OF ALEXANDRIA. Hierocles upon the Golden Verses of the Pythagoreans. Trans. out of the Greek. *half-calf., 16mo. Lond., M.Flesher for Thomas Fickus, 1682.*

HIEROCLES, *grammarian.* The jests of Hierocles and Philagrius. Trans. from the Greek by Charles Clinch Bubb. *photostat, Cleveland, Rowfant Club, 1920.*

HIKEN, NAT. Sergeant Bilko. *paper, 12mo. N.Y., Ballantine, 1957.*

HIKMET, MURAT. One day the Hodja. *paper, 12mo. Ankara, Tarhan, 1959.*

HILDITCH, NEVILLE, *ed.* In praise of humour; an anthology of enjoyment. *boards, 24mo. Lond., Muller, 1949.*

HILL, A.F. John Smith's funny adventures on a crutch; or, The remarkable peregrinations of a one-legged soldier after the war. *buckram, 12mo. Phila., Potter, 1869.*

HILL, AARON. The tragedy of Zara. *calf., 16mo. Lond., Tonson, 1758.* (Bound with: The careless husband, by Colley Cibber.)

HILL, BENSON EARLE. A pinch of snuff, composed of curious particulars and original anecdotes of snuff-taking ... by Dean Swift, of Brazen-nose. *half-calf., 16mo. Lond., R.Tyas, 1840.*

HILL, W.E. *and* ADAMS, F.P. Among us mortals. *buckram, 12 mo. Bost., Houghton, Mifflin, 1917.*

HILTON, AUDREY, *ed.* This England: selections from the New Statesman "This England column" 1953-57. *paper, 8vo. Lond., New Statesman, 1957.*

HINDI PUNCH. Cartoons from the Hindi Punch. *boards, 4to. Bombay, Hindi Punch, 1903.*

HINDLEY, CHARLES. The old book collector's miscellany; or, A collection of readable reprints of literary rarities. *4v. buckram, 8vo. Lond., Reeves & Turner, 1871.*

———————— Tavern anecdotes and sayings; including the origin of signs, and reminiscences connected with taverns, coffee-houses, clubs, &c. &c. *buckram, 12mo. Lond., Tinsley, 1875.*

HINGSTON, EDWARD P. The genial showman, being reminiscences of the life of Artemas Ward. *buckram, 8vo. N.Y., Harper, 1870.*

"HINTS" AND "HITS" FOR PUBLIC SPEAKERS. *simulated leather, 12mo. Washington, Leewin B. Williams, 1936. Rev.ed.*

HIRSCHFELD, AL. Show business is no business. *buckram, 8vo. N.Y., Simon & Schuster, 1951.*

HISLOP, ALEXANDER, *ed.* Adversaria, ana, and table talk; a literary commonplace book. *buckram, 16mo. Edinburgh, Author, n.d.*

———————— Book of Scottish anecdote: humorous, social, legendary and historical. *half-calf, 12mo. Edinburgh, Edinburgh Pub. Co., 1874.*

———————— Same. First series. *buckram, 12mo. Edinburgh, Edinburgh Pub. Co., 1875. New and rev.ed.*

———————— Same. Glasgow, Morison, 1881. *New and rev. ed.*

HISTORICAL AND ENTERTAINING ANECDOTES; or, The pocket remembrancer. *sheep, 16mo. Lond., Lane, 1775. 2d.ed.*

HISTORICAL COMPANION AND AGREEABLE ENTERTAINER. *buckram, 16mo. Lond., Axtell, n.d.*

HISTORY OF MISS ETTIE REYNOLDS, THE MADAGASCAR LADY. *paper, 16mo. N.Y., Popular Pub. Co., n.d.*

HITOPADESA. ENGLISH. The book of good counsels. Transl. by Edwin Arnold. *buckram, 12 mo. Edinburgh, Grant, 1924.*

_____ Fables and proverbs from the Sanskrit. Transl. by Charles Wilkins. *buckram, 8 vo. Lond., Routledge, 1885.*

_____ *Same. 2d.ed. 1888.*

HIX, ELSIE. Strange as it seems. *buckram, 8vo. N.Y., Hanover House, 1953.*

HOBART, GEORGE VERE. Back to the woods, by Hugh McHugh, *pseud. buckram, 12mo. N.Y., Dillingham, 1902.*

_____ Boobs as seen by John Henry. *buckram, 12mo. N.Y., Dillingham, 1914.*

_____ Dinkelspiel's letters to Looey. *buckram, 12mo. N.Y. Dillingham, 1908.*

_____ Down the line with John Henry. *buckram, 16mo. N.Y., Dillingham, 1901.*

_____ Get next! *cloth, 12 mo. N.Y., Dillingham, 1905.*

_____ I need the money. *buckram, 12mo. N.Y., Dillingham, 1903.*

_____ I'm from Missouri (They had to show me). *buckram, 12mo. N.Y., Dillingham, 1904.*

_____ It's up to you. *buckram, 12mo. N.Y., Dillingham, 1902.*

_____ Jim Hickey; a story of the one-night stands. *buckram, 16mo. N.Y., Dillingham, 1904.*

_____ Out for the coin. *cloth, 12mo. N.Y., Dillingham, 1903.*

_____ The silly syclopedia, by Noah Lott, *pseud. buckram, 12mo. N.Y., Dillingham, 1905.*

_____ Skiddoo! *buckram, 12mo. N.Y., Dillingham, 1906.*

_____ You can search me. *buckram, 12mo. N.Y., Dillingham, 1905.*

_____ You should worry, says John Henry. *buckram, 12 mo. N.Y., Dillingham, 1914.*

HOBBS, J. WALTER. Lodge and after-dinner speaking; a collection of chapters compiled with a view to improve Masonic speaking. *buckram, 12mo. Lond., Masonic Record, n.d.*

HOBO'S SIDE-SPLITTING JOKES AND MONOLOGUES, as told by the greatest tramp comedians. *paper, 12mo. Chic., Donohue, 1910.*

HODGINS, J. GEORGE. Her Majesty the Queen, the late prince consort and other members of the Royal Family. Sketches and anecdotes. *buckram, 16mo. Montreal, Lovell, 1868.*

HOFF, SYD. Mom, I'm home! *buckram, 4to. N.Y., Doubleday, Doran, 1945.*

_____ Oops! wrong stateroom! *buckram, 8vo. N.Y., Ives Washburn, 1953.*

_____ Okay, you can look now! *boards, 8vo. N.Y., Duell, Sloan & Pearce, 1955.*

_____ Out of gas! *buckram, 4to. N.Y., Ives Washburn, 1954.*

HOFFENSTEIN, SAMUEL. Pencil in the air. *buckram, 12mo. N.Y., Doubleday, 1947.*

_____ Poems in praise of practically nothing. *buckram, 12mo. N.Y., Boni & Liveright, 1928.*

_____ A treasury of humorous verse. *buckram, 8vo. N.Y., Liveright, 1946.*

HOFFER, ERIC. The passionate state of mind, and other apho- isms. *buckram, 12mo. N.Y., Harper, 1955.*

HOFFNUNG, GERARD. Birds, bees and storks. *buckram, 16 mo. Lond., Dobson, 1960.*

_____ Hoffnung's acoustics. *boards, 12mo. Lond., Dobson-Putnam, 1959.*

_____ Hoffnung's musical chairs. *boards, 12mo. Lond., Dobson-Putnam, 1958.*

HOFMANN, WERNER. Caricature from Leonardo to Picasso. *buckram, 4to. N.Y., Crown, 1957.*

HOGARTH, WILLIAM. Hogarth's time. Edited by Michael Alexander. *boards, 8vo. Emmaus, Pa., Rodale, 1956.*

HOGARTH'S FROLIC. The five days peregrination around the Isle of Sheppey by William Hogarth and his fellow pilgrims. *buckram, 8vo. Lond., John Camden Hotten, 1872.*

HOGG, JAMES. Familiar anecdotes of Sir Walter Scott. *quarter- calf., 16mo. N.Y., Harper, 1884.*

HOGUE, CHARLES E. Hot lava; the torrid loves of Madame Pele, goddess of all volcanoes. *paper, 16mo. Honolulu, Author, 1958.*

HOIG, STAN. The humor of the American cowboy. *buckram, 8vo. Caldwell, Idaho, Caxton, 1958.*

HOKE, HELEN, ed. The family book of humor. *buckram, 8vo. N.Y., Hanover, 1957.*

_____ Jokes, jokes, jokes. *buckram, 8vo. N.Y., Watts, 1954.*

_____ Jokes, riddles, puns; the best brief humor. *buckram, 8vo. N.Y., Watts, n.d.*

HOKE, NEWTON WILSON. Double entendre. *paper, 16mo. N.Y., Pocket books, 1957.*

HOKEY-POKEY JOKER. *paper, 12mo. N.Y., Wehman, 1870.*

HOKINSON, HELEN E. My best girls. *buckram, 4to. N.Y., Dutton, 1943.*

_____ So you're going to buy a book! *boards, folio. N.Y., Minton, Balch, 1931.*

_____ There are ladies present. *buckram, 4to. N.Y., Dutton, 1952.*

_____ When were you built. *buckram, 4to. N.Y., Dutton, 1948.*

HOLCOMB, MAURICE *and* GOODWIN, LANG. Poppin' a button. *paper, 12mo. Seattle, Authors, 1945. 3d.ed.*

HOLDCRAFT, PAUL E. Snappy stories that preachers tell. *paper, 8vo. Baltimore, Stockton, 1932.*

HOLE, S.REYNOLDS. A little tour in Ireland. *buckram, 8vo. Lond., Arnold, 1896. 3d.ed.*

HOLLEY, HORACE. Read-aloud plays. *buckram, 12mo. N.Y., M. Kennerley, 1916.*

HOLLEY, MARIETTA. Around the world with Josiah Allen's wife. *buckram, 8vo. N.Y., Dillingham, 1905.*

_____ Josiah Allen's wife as a P.A. and P.I. Samantha at the centennial, *buckram, 8vo. Hartford, Conn. American, 1878.*

_____ My opinions and Betsey Bobbet's. *buckram, 12 mo. Hartford, Conn., American, 1888.*

_____ My wayward pardner; or, My trials with Josiah, America, the Widow Bump, and etcetery. *buckram, 12mo. Hartford, Conn., American, 1888.*

_____ Samantha among the brethren. *buckram, 8vo. N.Y., Funk & Wagnalls, 1892.*

_____ Samantha among the colored folks. "My ideas on the race problem". *buckram, 12mo. N.Y., Dodd, Mead, 1898.*

_____ Samantha at Coney Island, and a thousand other Islands. *buckram, 12mo. N.Y., Christian Herald, 1911.*

_____ Samantha at Saratoga, or, "Racing after fashion". *buckram, 8vo. N.Y., Hubbard, 1887.*

_____ Samantha at the world's fair. *buckram, 8vo. N.Y., Funk & Wagnalls, 1893.*

_____ Samantha in Europe. *buckram, 12mo. N.Y., Funk & Wagnalls, 1895.*

_____ Sweet Cicely, or, Josiah Allen as a politician. *buckram, 12mo. N.Y., Funk & Wagnalls, 1887. 8th ed.*

HOLLIDAY, CARL. The wit and humor of colonial days (1607-1800). *buckram, 12mo. Phila., Lippincott, 1912.*

HOLLIS, CHRISTOPHER. The ayes and the noes. *buckram, 12mo. Lond., Macdonald, 1957.*

HOLLOWOOD, BERNARD. An innocent at large. *buckram, 12mo. Lond., Sidgwick & Jackson, 1947.*

_____ Money is no expense. *buckram, 12mo. Lond., Sidgwick & Jacksons, n.d.*

_____ Scowle, and other papers with some drawings. *paper, 12mo. West Drayton, Middlesex, 1948.*

HOLLYWOOD JOKE BOOK. *paper, 16mo. Los Angeles, Hollywood Pub. Co., 1945. 2d.ed.*

HOLMES, ALFRED I., *comp.* The cute sayings of our little ones, and Poems of childhood. *buckram, 12mo. Brooklyn, Author, 1889.*

HOLMES, OLIVER WENDELL. The autocrat of the breakfast table. *leather, 16mo. Phila., Altemus, n.d.*

HOLUB, WILLIAM M. On the humor side. *buckram, 12mo. Milwaukee, Bruce, 1951.*

HOLZ, LOUIE E. Tokyo harvest; thirty short stories. *buckram, 8vo. Tokyo, Tokyo News Service, 1954.*

HOME BOOK OF QUIZZES, GAMES AND JOKES. *buckram, 8vo. N.Y., Blue Ribbon, 1941.*

HOME REFERENCER, N.Y.,
Buchanan, n.d. (Eureka Library,
no. 1)

HOME SECRETS. pamphlet.
Milwaukee, Pabst Brewing Co.,
1898.

HOMER TRAVESTIE: A burlesque
translation of Homer. 2v.
boards, 8vo. Lond., Robinson,
1797. 4th ed.

HONE, WILLIAM. Ancient mysteries described. buckram, 8vo.
Lond., Author, 1823.

_____ Facetiae and miscellanies. boards, 8vo. Lond.,
Hunt & Clarke, 1827.

_____ The three trials of
William Hone. paper, 8vo.
Lond., Hone, 1818.

HONE'S TRACTS. half-calf, 8vo.
various publishers & dates.
Contents.-The second trial of
William Hone, 1818.-The third
trial of William Hone, 1818.-
Final examination and committal of Henry Hunt, esq,
1819.-Caluminous aspersions
contained in the Report of the
subcommittee of the Stock
Exchange, exposed and refuted.-Letter to Lord Erskine
containing expose of conspiracy against Queen Caroline
Amelia Elizabeth, 1820.-
Dramatic censor, or Monthly
epitome of taste, fashion and
manners, 1820.-A peep at the
peers, 1820.-The road to ruin,
1821.-A peep at the divan,
1821.-Substance of the speech
of the Right Honourable Charles
James Cox.-The trial of Lord
George Gordon for high
treason.-The Whigs exposed.-
The every-day book.-Blood for
gold.

HOOD, EDWIN PAXTON. Gold
fringes. buckram, 12mo. Lond.,
Partridge & Oakey, 1852.

_____ The world of anecdote. buckram, 12mo. Lond.,
Hodder & Stoughton, 1897.

_____ The world of moral
and religious anecdote. buckram, 8vo. Phila., Lippincott,
1872.

_____ The world of proverb
and parable. buckram, 4to.
Lond., Hodder & Stoughton,
1885.

HOOD, THOMAS, ed. The book of
modern anecdotes, humour, wit
and wisdom. English - Irish -
Scotch. buckram, 8vo. Lond.,
Routledge, n.d.

_____ Choice works of
Thomas Hood, in prose and
verse, including the cream of
the comic annuals. buckram,
12mo. N.Y., Alden, 1883.

_____ The Comic Annual.
5v. quarter-calf, 16mo. Lond.,
Tilt, 1830-1834.

_____ The Comic Annual,
1875-1882. half-calf, 8vo.
Lond., Fun Office, 1875-1882.

_____ English, Scotch and
Irish anecdotes. 3v. in 1. half-
calf, 16mo. Toronto, Warwick,
n.d.

_____ Humorous poems.
buckram, 12mo. Lond., Macmillan, 1893.

_____ Life in lodgings.
paper, 12mo. Lond., Fun Office,
n.d.

_____ Poems of wit and
humour. calf, 16mo. Lond.,
Moxon, 1864. 13th ed.

_____ Same. 14th ed. 1865.

———————— The rhymster; or,
The rules of rhyme. *buckram,
16mo. N.Y., Appleton, 1923.*

———————— Up the Rhine. *buckram, 8vo. Lond., Baily, 1840.*

———————— Whims and oddities
in prose and verse. *buckram,
8vo. Lond., Moxon, n.d.*

———————— Whimsicalities. *buckram, 12mo. N.Y., Putnam, 1852.*

———————— Works of Thomas
Hood, comic and serious, in
prose and verse. *7v. buckram,
12mo. Lond., Moxon, 1863.*

HOOD'S OWN, or, Laughter from
year to year. *buckram, 8vo.
Lond., Baily, 1839.*

———————— Same. *Lond., Moxon,
1873. New ed.*

———————— Same. *Lond., Ogden,
1883. (Bound with "Happy
thoughts")*

———————— Same. Second series.
*Lond., Moxon, 1862.*

HOOK, THEODORE. Choice
humorous works; ludicrous
adventures, bons mots, puns
and hoaxes. *buckram, 12mo.
Lond., Chatto & Windus, 1889.
New ed.*

HOOLE, W. STANLEY. Sam Slick
in Texas. *buckram, 8vo. San
Antonio, Naylor, 1945.*

HOOVER, IRWIN HOOD. Forty-two
years in the White House. *buckram, 8vo. Bost., Houghton
Mifflin, 1934.*

HOPE, BOB. Bob Hope's own
story of his trip abroad. I never
left home. *paper, 4to. N.Y.,
Simon & Schuster, 1944.*

———————— Have tux, will
travel. *paper, 8vo. N.Y., Simon
& Schuster, 1954.*

———————— So this is peace.
*buckram, 8vo. N.Y., Simon &
Schuster, 1946.*

HOPE, JANE. Don't do it! (A complete guide to teaching). *buckram, 12mo. Lond., Muller, 1947.*

HOPKINS, HIRAM, *pseud. see*
SELTZER, CHARLES A.

HOPKINS, LIVINGSTON. A comic
history of the United States.
*buckram, 16mo. N.Y., American
Book Exchange, 1880.*

HOPPER, DEWOLF. Remi-
niscences of DeWolf Hopper.
Once a clown always a clown.
*buckram, 8vo. Garden City,
Garden City Pub. Co., 1927.*

HOPPNER, J. Oriental tales,
translated into English. *verse,
boards, 12mo. Lond., Murray,
1806.*

HOPTON, RALPH Y. Bed
manners; how to bring sunshine
into your nights. *boards, 12mo.
N.Y., Vanguard, 1934.*

———————— Better bed manners.
*boards, 12mo. N.Y., Vanguard,
1936.*

HORACE GREELEY'S JOKES,
written by old-time editors and
reporters of the Tribune. *paper,
24mo. N.Y., Gilluly, 1872.*

HORSELESS JOKES, being a collection of the funniest things
about silent steeds. *paper, 4to.
N.Y., Judge, 1901.*

HOT STUFF BY FAMOUS FUNNY
MEN ... Eli Perkins, Josh
Billings, Alex. Sweet, Mark
Twain, Robert J. Burdette ...
*et al. buckram, 8vo. Chic.,
Reilly & Britton, 1901.*

HOT STUFF JOKELETS, by
America's funny men. *paper,
12mo. N.Y., Ogilvie, 1903.*

HOTALING, RICHARD M. The twilight of the kings; a masque of democracy. *paper, 8vo. San Francisco, Bohemian Club, 1928.*

HOTCHKIS, KATHARINE BIXBY. Christmas at Rancho Los Alamitos. *buckram, 12mo. San Francisco, Lawton Kennedy for the California Historical Society, 1957.*

HOUGHTON, GEORGE. Golf addicts through the ages. *paper, 8vo. Lond., Museum, 1956.*

—————— Golf on my pillow. *paper, 12mo. Lond., Paul, 1960.*

HOUGHTON, STANLEY. Five one act plays. *paper, 12mo. Lond., Sidgwick & Jackson, 1903.*

HOURMOUZIOS. S.-L. Salute to Greece; an anthology of cartoons published in the British press. *buckram, wide 12mo. Lond. Evans, 1942.*

HOUSE, BOYCE. As I was saying. *buckram, 8vo. San Antonio, Naylor, 1957.*

—————— Friendly feudin'; Alaska vs. Texas. *buckram, 12mo. San Antonio, Naylor, 1959.*

—————— I give you Texas! 500 jokes of the Lone Star State. *buckram, 8vo. San Antonio, Naylor, 1943.*

—————— Laugh parade of states; star-spangled wit and humor. *buckram, 8vo. San Antonio, Naylor, 1948.*

—————— Roundup of Texas humor. *buckram, 8vo. San Antonio, Naylor, 1949.*

—————— Tall talk from Texas. *buckram, 8vo. San Antonio, Naylor, 1946.*

—————— Texas laughs, and The amazing truth about Texas. *buckram, 8vo. San Antonio, Naylor, 1950.*

—————— Texas proud and loud. *buckram, small 8vo. San Antonio, Naylor, 1945.*

—————— Texas rhythm, and other poems. *buckram, 12mo. San Antonio, Naylor, 1950.*

—————— You can always tell a Texan (but you can't tell him very much). *buckram, 8vo. San Antonio, Naylor, 1955.*

HOUSE, BRANT. Cartoon annual, no.2. *paper, 12mo. N.Y., Ace, 1955.*

—————— The little monsters. *paper, 16mo. N.Y., Ace, 1956.*

—————— Love and hisses. *paper, 16mo. N.Y., Ace, 1956.*

—————— Squelches. *paper, 16mo. N.Y., Ace, 1956.*

—————— They goofed! *paper, 16mo. N.Y., Ace, 1956.*

—————— Words fail me! *paper, 12mo. N.Y., Ace, 1954.*

HOUSEHOLD BOOK OF WIT AND HUMOR. *buckram, 12mo. N.Y., Hurst, n.d.*

HOW, WALSHAM. Lighter moments from the notebook of Bishop Walsham How. *buckram, 12mo. Lond., Isbister, 1900.*

HOW TO DIE LAUGHING IN 62 EASY LESSONS. *paper, 32mo. Girard, Kan., Haldeman-Julius, n.d. (Little Blue Books.)*

HOW TO MAIL A LETTER IN 5 EASILY AND UTTERLY PREPOSTEROUS LESSONS. *paper, 4to. Stamford, Conn., Pitney-Bowes, n.d.*

HOW WOULD YOU LIKE TO WIN $1,000.00 FREE! Games, tricks, recipes, horoscopes. *paper, 8vo. Los Angeles, n.p. 1938.*

HOWARD, CLARENCE J. Howard's book of conundrums and riddles. *boards, 16mo. N.Y., Dick & Fitzgerald, 1869.*

HOWARD, VERNON. Humorous monologues. *buckram, 12mo. N.Y., Sterling, 1958.*

HOWE, E.W. Notes for my biographer. *paper, 32mo. Girard, Kan., Haldeman-Julius, n.d. (Little Blue Books.)*

HOWE, W.H. English wit and humour. *cloth, 16mo. Phila., Jacobs, 1898.*

——————Everybody's book of Scotch wit and humour. *limp leather, 24mo. Lond., Howe, n.d.*

—————— Everybody's book of wit and humour. (1) English (2) Scotch (3) Irish. *leather, 24mo. N.Y., Brentano's n.d.*

—————— "Here lies" being a collection of ancient and modern, humorous and queer inscriptions from tombstones. *buckram, 16mo. N.Y., New Amsterdam Book Co., 1901.*

HOWLAND, HEWITT H. Humor by vote. *buckram, 8vo. N.Y., Laugh Club, 1933.*

HOYT, HARLOWE R. Town Hall tonight. *quarter-buckram, 4to. Englewood Cliffs, N.J., Prentice-Hall, 1955.*

HSIAO, CH'IEN. Spinners of silk. *buckram, 12mo. Lond., Allen & Unwin, 1946.*

HSIEH, TEHYI. Chinese epigrams inside out and proverbs. *buckram, 8vo. N.Y., Exposition, 1948.*

HSU, RUTH. Chinese children's rhymes. *buckram, 12mo. Shanghai, Commercial Press, 1935.*

HTIN AUNG, U. Burmese folk-tales. *buckram, 8vo. Lond., Oxford Univ. Press, 1959.*

HUBBARD, ELBERT. Concerning slang, and other droll stories. *quarter-calf., 16mo. East Aurora, N.Y., Roycrofters, 1920.*

—————— The Elbert Hubbard book; wise and witty sayings. *boards, 12mo. Racine, Wis., Whitman, 1934.*

—————— Elbert Hubbard's scrap book. *buckram, 8vo. N.Y., Wise, 1923.*

——————Little journeys to the homes of the great. *14v. buckram, 8vo. Cleveland, World, 1923.*

—————— The motto book, by Fra Elbertus, pseud. *paper, 16 mo. East Aurora, N.Y., Roy-crofters, 1917.*

—————— The philosophy of Elbert Hubbard. *buckram, 4to. N.Y., Wise, 1934.*

HUBBARD, ELBERT, II. Right adjustment. *paper, 24mo. East Aurora, N.Y., Author, 1947.*

HUBBARD, KIN. Abe Martin of Brown county, Indiana. *cloth, 8vo. Indianapolis, Indianapolis News, 1906. 3d.ed.*

_____ Abe Martin on the war and other things. *boards, 16mo. Indianapolis, Abe Martin Pub. Co., n.d.*

_____ Abe Martin, the joker on facts. *boards, 16mo. Indianapolis, Abe Martin Pub. Co., n.d.*

_____ Abe Martin's almanack. *buckram, 8vo. Indianapolis, Bobbs-Merrill, 1907.*

_____ Abe Martin's almanack, 1908.

_____ Abe Martin's almanack, 1911.

_____ Abe Martin's back country sayings. *buckram, 12 mo. Indianapolis, Abe Martin Pub. Co., n.d.*

_____ Abe Martin's primer. *boards, 16mo. Indianapolis, Abe Martin Pub. Co., n.d.*

_____ Back country folks. *buckram, 16mo. Indianapolis, Abe Martin Pub. Co., n.d.*

_____ Brown County folks. *boards, 16mo. Indianapolis, Abe Martin Pub. Co., 1911.*

HUDSON, ARTHUR PALMER. Humor of the old deep south. *buckram, 8vo. N.Y., Macmillan, 1936.*

HUDSON, HOYT HOPEWELL. The epigram in the English renaissance. *buckram, 12mo. Princeton, Princeton Univ. Press, 1947.*

HUDSON, THOMAS. Comic songs. *buckram, 12mo. Lond., Gold & Walton, 1822.*

HUGHES, MARION. The Dam family. *paper, 12mo. Chic., Donohue, 1905.*

_____ Fun and trouble. *paper, 12mo. Stillwater, Sy & Maud, 1907.*

_____ Three years in Arkansaw. *paper, 12mo. Chic., Donohue, 1905.*

HULME, F. EDWARD. Proverb lore. *buckram, 8vo. Lond., Stock, 1902.*

HUMANIORA: essays in literature, folklore, bibliography, honoring Archer Taylor on his seventieth birthday. *buckram, 4to. Locust Valley, N.Y., J-J. Augustin, 1960.*

HUMBUG DIGEST. *paper, 16mo. N.Y., Ballantine, 1957.*

HUME, BILL. Babysan; a private look at the Japanese occupation. *paper, 12mo. Tokyo, Tuttle, 1953.*

_____ Babysan's world; the Hume'n slant on Japan. *paper, 12mo. Rutland, Vt., Tuttle, 1955.*

_____ When we get back home. *paper, 12mo. Rutland, Vt., Tuttle, 1956.*

HUMORISTS OF THE PENCIL: L. Raven-Hill. Charles Keene, Phil May. *half-calf, 8vo. Lond., Punch, n.d.*

HUMOROUS MASTERPIECES FROM AMERICAN LITERATURE. *3v. buckram, 16mo. N.Y., Putnam, 1886.*

HUMOROUS POEMS BY ENGLISH AND AMERICAN WRITERS. *buckram, 12mo. Lond., Ward Lock, n.d.*

HUMOROUS RECITATIONS AND STORIES. *buckram, 12mo. Lond., Foulsham, n.d.*

HUMOROUS VERSE (17th and 18th
century). *paper, 32mo. Girard,
Kan., Haldeman-Julius, n.d.
(Little Blue Books.)*

HUMOUR AND COUNTER
HUMOUR. *buckram, 12mo.
Shrewsbury, Wilding, n.d.*

HUMOUR VARIETY. No. 28.
*paper, 12mo. Lond., Mellifont
press, n.d.*

HUMOURIST, THE; a collection of
entertaining tales, anecdotes,
epigrams, illustrated ... by
Geo. Cruikshank. *4v. buckram,
small 8vo. London., Nimmo,
1892.*

HUMOURIST'S MISCELLANY,
containing original and select
articles of poetry on mirth, wit,
gaiety, and entertainment. To
which is prefixed the celebrated "Lecture on heads", by
G.A. Stevens. *calf., 16mo.
Lond., Cundee, n.d.*

——————Same. *Lond., Crosby
& Letterman, 1801.*

HUMOURIST'S OWN BOOK, THE;
a cabinet of original and
selected anecdotes, bon mots,
sports of fancy, and traits of
character. *russia, 24mo. Phila.,
Key & Biddle, 1834.*

HUMOURS OF THE TIMES, being
a collection of several curious
pieces in verse and prose.
*calf., 16mo. Lond., n.p. 1771.*

HUN HUNTERS, THE: cautionary
tales from the trenches.
*boards, 8vo. Lond., Richards,
1916.*

HUNDRED MERRY TALES: or,
Shakespeare's jest book.
*boards, 16mo. Lond., Chidley,
1831.*

HUNDRED MERRY TALES: the
earliest English jest-book. Now
first reproduced in photo-
lithography from the unique
copy of 1526 in the Royal
Library of Gottingen. With an
introduction, notes, and
glossarial index, by W. Carew
Hazlitt. *buckram, 8vo. No. 45
of 137 copies.*

HUNEKER, JAMES GIBBON. Old
Fogy; his musical opinions and
grotesques. *boards, 16mo.
Phila., Presser, 1913.*

HUNT, CECIL. The best howlers.
*buckram, 12mo. Lond., Benn,
1949. 2d.ed.rev.*

——————The book of howlers.
*paper, 12mo. Lond., Lane,
1930.*

—————— Fun with the famous.
*paper, 12mo. Lond., Benn,
1929.*

—————— Hand-picked
howlers. *boards, 8vo. Lond.,
Methuen, 1937.*

—————— Hand-picked pro-
verbs. *boards, 12mo. Lond.,
Methuen, 1940.*

—————— Here I lie. *boards,
12mo. Lond., Cape, 1931.*

—————— Howlers. *paper, 12
mo. Lond., Benn, 1928.*

—————— The "Howlers"
omnibus. *buckram, 12mo. Lond,
Benn, 1928.*

—————— Last words; a col-
lection of singular authentic
epitaphs. *buckram, 12mo.
Lond., Methuen, 1944.*

—————— Latest howlers.
*buckram, 12mo. Lond., Harrap,
1934.*

—————— Laughing gas; the
best jokes. *buckram, 12mo.
Lond., Methuen, 1940.*

—————— More hand-picked howlers. *boards, 12mo. Lond., Methuen, 1938.*

—————— My favourite howlers. *buckram, 12mo. Lond., Benn, 1951.*

—————— Quips; an index for occasions. *paper, 12mo. Lond., Allan, 1930.*

—————— Ripe howlers. *boards, 12mo. Lond., Methuen, 1939.*

HUNT, JOSEPH P. A few notes on a famous trolley. *(In: American book collector, v.7., no. 9, June, 1957.)*

HUNT, LEIGH. Readings for railways; or, Anecdotes and other short stories, reflections, maxims, characteristics, passages of wit, &c &c. *boards, 16mo. Lond., Gilpin, 1849.*

—————— Wit and humour. *buckram, 24mo. Lond., Smith, Elder, 1846.*

—————— *Same.* Cheap edition. *Lond. Murray, 1910.*

—————— *Same. Lond., Smith, Elder, 1875.*

HUNT, RIDGELEY *and* CHAPPELL, GEORGE S. The saloon in the home, or, A garland of rum blossoms. *boards, 8vo. N.Y., Coward-McCann, 1930.*

HUNTER, WILLIAM C. Brass tacks. *buckram, 16mo. Chic., Reilly & Britton, 1910.*

—————— Evening round-up; more good stuff life PEP. *buckram, 12mo. Kansas City, Hunter, 1915.*

—————— Laughing gas. Sunshine capsules to cure the blues. *buckram, 24mo. Kansas City, Hunter, 1916.*

HUNTLEY, STANLEY. Mr. and Mrs. Spoopendyke. *paper, 8vo. Lond., Ward, Lock, n.d.*

HUPFELD, HENRY. Encyclopedia of wit and wisdom. *buckram, 8vo. Phila., McKay, 1897.*

HURON, HORACE. A bunch of laughs. *paper, 12mo. Rock Island, Ill., Author, 1909.*

HURST, THOMAS. Off in a bunch. *paper, 12mo. Chic., McKnight, 1908.*

HUSTLED HISTORY, or, As it might have been. *paper, 12mo. Lond., Pitman, 1908.*

HUTCHISON, FRANK. The philosophy of Johnnie the gent. *paper, 12mo. Chic., Donohue, 1905.*

HUXLEY, ALDOUS. Vulgarity in literature; digressions upon a theme. *boards, 12mo. Lond., Chatto & Windus, 1930.*

HUXLEY, THOMAS. Aphorisms. *paper, 32mo. Girard, Kan., Haldeman-Julius, n.d. (Little Blue Books.)*

—————— Aphorisms and reflections. *buckram, 16mo. Lond., Macmillan, 1907.*

HUZII, OTOO. Japanese proverbs. *paper, 12mo. Tokyo, Japanese Tourist Bureau, 1940.*

HYLAND, STANLEY. Curiosities from Parliament. *buckram, 8vo. Lond., Wingate, 1955.*

# H-I

HYMAN, DICK. It's still the law. *buckram, 8vo. N.Y., McKay, 1961.*

_____ It's the law. *buckram, 8vo. N.Y., Doubleday, 1936.*

_____ Nonsense, U.S.A., a collection of nonsensical Americana. *buckram, 8vo. N.Y., Dutton, 1953.*

_____ Of all fool things. *buckram, 12mo. N.Y., Duell, Sloan & Pearce, 1948.*

HYMAN, MAC. No time for sergeants. *buckram, 8vo. N.Y., Random, 1954.*

HYNES, EDWARD S. Cocktail cavalcade. *boards, 4to. Lond., T.Werner Laurie, 1937.*

IBSEN, HENRIK. Ibsen's epigrams. *paper, 32mo. Girard, Kan., Haldeman-Julius, n.d. (Little Blue Books.)*

IMMEN, LORAINE, *comp.* Shoemaker's best selections for readings and recitations, No. 22. *buckram, 12mo. Phila., Penn, 1894.*

IN PRAISE OF ALE. The lamentable complaints of Nick Froth the tapster and Rulerost the Cooke. The lamentable complaints of Hop the Brewer and Kilcalfe, the Butcher. The whole tryal and indictment of Sir John Barley-Corn, knight. *paper, 12mo. Priv. Print.*

INDOOR PASTIMES FOR PROFIT AND PLEASURE; a thousand hints on how to pass away your leisure hours. *buckram, 12mo. Lond., Foulsham, n.d.*

INFORMERS OUTWITTED, THE: a tragi-comical farce. As it has been rehearsed at the New Exchange in Rag-Fair. Written originally in Hebrew and translated by Solomon Bung-your-eye, Gent. *half-tree calf, 12mo. Lond., Cooper, 1738.*

INGE, WILLIAM RALPH. Wit and wisdom of Dean Inge. *buckram, 12mo. Lond., Longmans, Green, 1927.*

INGERSOLL, ROBERT G. Ingersolliana. Gems of thoughts from the lectures, speeches and conversations. *buckram, 12mo. Chic., Belford, Clarke, 1888.*

_____ Wisdom of Ingersoll. *paper, 32mo. Girard, Kan., Haldeman-Julius, n.d. (Little Blue Books.)*

INGOLD, ERNEST. Tales of a peddler. *buckram, 8vo. San Francisco, Kibbee, 1942.*

INGOLDSBY, THOMAS, *pseud. see* BARHAM, ROBERT HARRIS.

INGRAHAM, EDWARD D., *comp.* Singular surnames. *paper, 4to. Phila., Campbell, 1873.*

INGRAM, JOHN. Humorous Scottish anecdotes; Scottish life and character in anecdote and story. *buckram, 12mo. Edinburgh, Nimmo, Hay & Mitchell, n.d.*

INNOMINATA: a collection of the merriest tales of the most famous authors of the Renaissance. *buckram, 8vo. N.Y., Priv. Print, 1930.*

# I-J

INTERNATIONAL LADIES
GARMENT WORKERS UNION:
*Education Department.* "That
reminds me" jokes and stories
for use by union organizers and
papers. *pamphlet, mimeo-
graphed. N.Y., ILGWU, n.d.*

IRISH JESTS AND ANECDOTES,
collected from various sources.
*half-calf., 24mo. Edinburgh,
Paterson, n.d.*

IRISH WIT AND HUMOR. *paper,
16mo. Chic., Drake, 1903.*

IRISH WIT AND HUMOR. *buckram,
16mo. Phila., Jacobs, 1898.*

IRISH WIT AND HUMOR; anecdote
biography of Swift, Curran,
O'Leary and O'Connell. *buckram, 12mo. Ratisbon, Postet,
1916.*

IRVIN COBB, HIS BOOK. Friendly
tributes upon the occasion of a
dinner tendered to Irvin Shrewsbury Cobb at the Waldorf-
Astoria Hotel, N.Y., April
twenty-fifth, MCMXV. *boards,
4to. n.p., 1925.*

IRVINE, ST. JOHN G. Four Irish
plays. *buckram, 12mo. N.Y.,
Macmillan, 1914.*

IRWIN, WALLACE. At the sign of
the dollar. *buckram, 12mo.
N.Y., Duffield, 1905.*

———————— Love sonnets of a
car conductor. *boards, 12mo.
San Francisco, Elder, 1908.*

———————— Mr. Togo: maid of
all work. *buckram, 12mo. N.Y.,
Duffield, 1913.*

———————— The Rubaiyat of
Omar Khayyam, jr. *paper, 8vo.
San Francisco, Elder &
Shepard, 1902.*

IS YOUR HALO ON STRAIGHT?
Published for the Ethics and
Professional Conduct Council
of the Alumni Association of
the School of Medicine of the
College of Medical Evange-
lists. *paper, 12mo. Los
Angeles, San Lucas Press,
1955.*

IT'S A TOUGH WAR. *boards,
8vo. Garden City, Garden City
Pub. Co., 1942.*

"IT'S ALL IN THE MIND!" Adult
"eye-opening" captions.
*pamphlet. N.Y., Donen, n.d.*

IVERS' IRISH JOKER, no. 3; a
collection of good Irish humor.
*paper, 12mo. N.Y., Ivers, 1909.*

IVERS' VARIETY JOKER, no. 2.
*paper, 12mo. N.Y., Ivers, 1909.*

IVERS' VAUDEVILLE JOKER,
no. 3; new jokes by new
jokers. *paper, 12mo. N.Y.,
Ivers, 1909.*

J.J.B. *see* BELL, JOHN JOY

JABET, GEORGE. Nasology: or,
Hints towards a classification
of noses, by Eden Warwock,
*pseud. buckram, 8vo. Lond.,
Bentley, 1848.* (Reprinted in
1852 with title: Notes on
noses, *q.v.)*

———————— Notes on noses.
*paper, 16mo. Lond., Bentley,
1852.*

JACK JUNK'S NEW JESTER: or,
Bony taken in tow in a new
way. *Lond, J. Ker, n.d.*

JACKE OF DOVER'S QUEST OF
INQUIRIE; or, His privy search
for the veriest foole in
England, 1604. Reprinted from
the rare original, and edited, by
C. Carew Hazlitt. *quarter-calf.,
12mo. Lond., Clay & Taylor,
1866.*

# J

JACKS, L.P. Near the brink; observations of a nonagenarian. *buckram, 8vo. Lond., Allen & Unwin, 1952.*

JACKSON, ARTIE. It's a smaller world. *boards, 32mo. Lond., Dobson, 1960.*

JACKSON, HARRY G. On a fast streamliner, fun from New York to Frisco. A trainload of loud laughs. *paper, 12mo. Chic., Jackson, 1950.*

JACKSON, HOLBROOK. Book-man's pleasure; a recreation for booklovers. *buckram, 12mo. Lond., Farrar, Straus, 1947.*

JACKSON, JOHN. Rational amuse-ment for winter evenings; or, A collection of above 200 curious and interesting puzzles and paradoxes relating to arithme-tic, geometry, geography, etc. .. *quarter vellum, 12mo. Lond., Longman, Hurst, Rees, Orme and Brown, 1821.*

JACKSON, JOHN HENRY, *ed.* Bawdy ballads and lusty lyrics. *boards, 12mo. Indianapolis, Droke, 1935.*

JACKSON, THOMAS W. Don't miss it! *paper, 12mo. Chic., Jackson, 1908.*

——————— *Same. Rev. 1950.*

——————— From Rhode Island to Texas. *paper, 12mo. Chic., Jackson, 1939.*

——————— *Same. Rev. 1950.*

——————— "I'm from Texas, You can't steer me!" *paper, 12mo. Chic., Jackson, 1948. Rev. ed.*

——————— O U Auto C the United States with Jackson. A million laughs. *paper, 12mo. Chic., Jackson, 1951.*

——————— On a slow train through Arkansaw. Funny rail-road stories - sayings of the Southern darkies - all the latest and best minstrel jokes of the day. *paper, 12mo. Chic., Jackson, 1903.*

——————— See America first. *paper, 12mo. Chic., Jackson, 1949. Rev. ed.*

——————— Take a joy ride with Thos. W. Jackson to the land of smiles. He has all the good ones. *paper, 12mo. Chic., Jackson, 1945. Rev.ed.*

——————— Thos. W. Jackson catches a fish and tells the story. *paper, 12mo. Chic., Jackson, 1910.*

——————— *Same. Rev. 1951.*

——————— Thos. W. Jackson coming with good stuff. One hundred percent fun. *paper, 12mo. Chic., Jackson, 1951. Rev.ed.*

——————— Thos. W. Jackson with all the funny ones. He makes them smile. *paper, 16mo. Chic., Jackson, 1949. Rev.ed.*

——————— Through Missouri on a mule. Funny railroad stories, old time darky sayings, minstrel jokes. All the late and funny sayings of the day. *paper, 12mo. Chic., Jackson, 1946.*

——————— You can't beat it. Thos. W. Jackson getting off the good ones. *paper, 12mo. Chic., Jackson, 1952. Rev. ed.*

JACKSON, W. SPENCER. Merry minstrelsy; everybody's book of humorous poetry. *buckram, 24mo. Lond., Saxon, 1892.*

JACKSON, WILLIAM. Old
fashioned wit and humor: in
verse. *buckram, 12mo. Lond.,
Blackwood, 1860.*

JACOBS, JOSEPH. Indian fairy
tales. *buckram, 8vo. Lond.,
Nutt, 1892.*

JACOBS, WILLIAM WYMARK.
Methuen's library of humour.
W.W. Jacobs. *buckram, 16mo.
Lond., Methuen, 1933.*

JACOT, B.L. Frogs don't grow
feathers, *buckram, 8vo. Lond.,
Hutchinson, n.d.*

JAGENDORF, MORRIS A. The
merry men of Gotham. *buckram,
8vo. N.Y., Vanguard, 1950.*

———— Noodlehead stories
from around the world. *buckram, 8vo. N.Y., Vanguard,
1957.*

———— The priceless cats,
and other Italian folk stories.
*buckram, 8vo. N.Y., Vanguard,
1956.*

JAMES, CAIRNS. The golden
humorous reciter. *buckram,
8vo. Lond., Seeley, 1908.*

JAMES, CROAKE. Curiosities of
law and lawyers, *buckram, 8vo.
Lond., Low, Marston, Searle &
Rivington, 1882.*

JAMES, EDGAR. Told on the
train. *paper, 12mo. Baltimore,
Ottenheimer, n.d.*

JAMES, HENRY. Daumier, caricaturist. *boards, 8vo. Lond.,
Rodale, 1954.*

JAMES THE CHAUFFEUR, *pseud.*
Automobile jokes and stories.
*paper, 12mo. Baltimore,
Ottenheimer, 1913.*

JANDA, JANE. Mother Goose gets
caught in the draft. *paper, 8vo.
Author, 1942.*

JANSON, J. MELVILLE. Encyclopedia of comedy for professional entertainers. *buckram,
8vo. Phila., McKay, 1899.*

———— Stump speeches,
monologues, conundrums, etc.
*paper, 8vo. Phila., McKay,
1900.*

JARRELL, MACKIE L. The pro-
verbs in Swift's Polite Conver-
sation. (In: Huntington Library
Quarterly, v.20, no.1. *San
Marino, California, Huntington
Library, 1956.)*

JARVIS, C.S. The back garden of
Allah. *buckram, 8vo. Lond.,
Murray, 1939.*

———— Heresies and
humours. *buckram, 8vo. Lond.,
Country Life, 1943.*

JAUSS, ANNE MARIE. Wise and
otherwise; the do's and dont's
of sundry proverbs. *buckram,
4to. N.Y., McKay, 1953.*

JAY, THOMAS. The seaside
guyed. *boards, 8vo. Lond.,
Collins, 1923.*

JEAFFRESON, J. CORDY. A
book about doctors. *buckram,
12mo. N.Y., Rudd & Carleton,
1861.*

JEFFERSON, JOSEPH. "Rip van
Winkle" The autobiography.
*buckram, 8vo. Lond., Reinhardt
& Evans, 1949.*

JEFFERSON, THOMAS. The
living thoughts of Thomas
Jefferson. Presented by John
Dewey. *buckram, 12mo. Lond.,
Cassell, 1941.*

JEGERLEHNER, JOHANNES. Alp
legends. *buckram, 8vo. Manchester, Sherratt & Hughes,
1926.*

JENNINGS, GEORGE HENRY, comp. Anecdotal history of the British Parliament, from the earliest periods to the present time. *buckram, 8vo. N.Y., Appleton, 1881.*

_____ *Same. Lond., Cox, 1883. New ed.*

JENNINGS, H.J. Chestnuts and small beer. *buckram, 8vo. Lond, Chapman & Hall, 1920.*

JENNINGS, PAUL. Even oddlier. *buckram, 12mo. Lond., Reinhardt, 1952.*

_____ Gladly oddly. *buckram, 12mo. Lond., Reinhardt, 1958.*

_____ Model oddlies. *buckram, 12mo. Lond., Reinhardt, 1956.*

_____ Next to oddliness. *buckram, 12mo. Lond., Reinhardt, 1956.*

_____ Oddly Bodlikins. *buckram, 12mo. Lond., Reinhardt, 1953.*

_____ Oddly enough. *boards, 12mo. Lond., Reinhardt, 1951.*

JENNISON, KEITH. The half-open road; a handy guide to chaos on the highway. *buckram, 8vo. N.Y., Doubleday, 1953.*

JEROME, JEROME KLAPKA. Funny facts about stageland. *paper, 32mo. Girard, Kan., Haldeman-Julius, n.d. (Little Blue Books.)*

_____ Funny ghost stories told after supper. *paper, 32mo. Girard, Kan., Haldeman-Julius, n.d. (Little Blue Books.)*

_____ A miscellany of sense and nonsense. *buckram, 12mo. Lond., Arrowsmith, 1923.*

_____ Sunset. *paper, 12mo. Chic., Dramatic Pub. Co., 1888.*

_____ Three men in a boat. *buckram, 12mo. Bristol, Arrowsmith, 1889.*

_____ Told after supper. *buckram, 12mo. Lond., Leadenhall, 1891.*

_____ When Greek meets Greek. *paper, 12mo. Phila., Penn, 1906.*

JERROLD, DOUGLAS. The barber's chair, and The hedgehog letters. *buckram, 12mo. Lond., Chatto & Windus, 1874.*

_____ Essays. *calf., 12mo. Lond., Dent, 1903.*

_____ Jokes and wit. *paper, 16mo. Lond., Ward, Lock, n.d.*

_____ Mrs. Caudle's curtain lectures. *buckram, 8vo. Lond., Bradbury, Evans, 1866.*

_____ Mrs. Caudle's curtain lectures. Mrs. Bib's baby. *buckram, 16mo. Lond., Bradbury, Evans, 1874.*

_____ Mrs. Caudle's curtain lectures. The story of a feather, and The sick giant and the Doctor Dwarf. *buckram, 12mo. Lond., Bradbury, Evans, 1852.*

_____ The popular tales. *buckram, 8vo. Glasgow, Morison, n.d.*

_____ Specimens of Douglas Jerrold's wit. *buckram, 12mo. Bost., Ticknor & Fields, 1858.*

———————— Whimsical tales of Douglas Jerrold. *buckram, 8vo. Allentown, Pa., Story Classics, 1948.*

JERROLD, W. BLANCHARD. The life of Douglas Jerrold. *buckram, 12mo. Lond., Bradbury, Evans, n.d.*

JERROLD, WALTER, *ed.* Bon-mots of the eighteenth century. *buckram, 24mo. Lond., Dent, 1897.*

———————— Bon-mots of the 19th century. *buckram, 24mo. Lond., Dent, 1897.*

———————— Book of famous wits. *buckram, 8vo. Lond., Methuen, 1912.*

———————— Bulls, blunders and howlers. *buckram, 12mo. Lond., Brentano's 1928.*

———————— Century of parody and imitation. *buckram, 12mo. Lond., Humphrey Milford, 1913.*

———————— Douglas Jerrold and "Punch". *buckram, 8vo. Lond., Macmillan, 1910.*

———————— Epigrams; wit and wisdom in brief. *boards, 12mo. N.Y., Crowell, 1926.*

———————— Jerrold's jest book, series 1. *boards, 16mo. Lond., Simpkin, Marshall, Hamilton, Kent, 1916.*

———————— *Same. Series II.*

JESSE, EDWARD. Anecdotes of dogs. *buckram, 12mo. Lond., Bell, 1878. New ed.*

JESSEL, GEORGE. "Hello, momma". *buckram, 8vo. Cleveland, World, 1946.*

———————— Jessel, anyone? *buckram, 8vo. Englewood Cliffs, N.J., Prentice-Hall, 1960.*

———————— So help me; the autobiography of George Jessel. *buckram, 8vo. N.Y., Random House, 1943.*

———————— This way, miss. *buckram, 8vo. N.Y., Holt, 1955.*

———————— You too can make a speech. *quarter buckram, 8vo. N.Y., Grayson, 1956.*

JEST ON SEX; sexplosively sex-sational sinerama of life ... for he and she from ages sexteen to sexty. *buckram, 8vo. N.Y., Encore, 1953.*

JESTERS IN EARNEST: cartoons by the Czechoslovak artists Z.K., A. Hoffmiester, A. Pelo-Stephen, W. Trier. *buckram, 4to. Lond., Murray, 1944.*

JESTIANA: or, Joke upon joke. *buckram, 32mo. Lond., Hodgson, n.d.*

JEST BOOKS. 6v. in 1. *calf., 16mo.* Contents.-The monstrous good jester, Lond., Stalker, n.d.-Ben Johnson's Jests, or, The banquet of fun. Lond., Stalker, n.d.-The Buck's jester, or, The annals of gallantry, glee and pleasure. Lond., Stalker, n.d.-The St. James jester, or, The humors of high-life. Lond., Stalker, 1792.-The jolly sailors jester. Lond., Stalker, 1793.-The original Covent Garden jester. South-wark, Sudbury, 1793.

JESTS OF THE SHIP, or, Wooden walls of old England. *buckram, 16mo. Lond., Hughes, n.d.* (Bound with: The Toast master's guide.)

JEUDWINE, J.W. *comp.* An antholo-gy of sayings and anecdotes of Samuel Johnson. *typescript, n.p. 1921.*

JOAD, C.E.M. Thrasymachus, or, The future of morals. *boards, 16mo. Lond., Kegan Paul, Trench, Trubner, 1928.*

JOE MILLER *see* MILLER, JOSEPH.

JOHN CHEAP, the Chapman's Library; the Scottish chap literature of the last century, classified. Comic and humorous. *quarter-calf., 12mo. Glasgow, Lindsay, 1877.*

Contents.-The witty and entertaining exploits of George Buchanan, commonly called the King's fool.-A brief relation of the adventures of Bamfylde Moore Carew, who was for more than forty years, King of the Beggars.-Daniel O'Rourke's wonderful voyage to the moon. Also, Master and man, or, The adventures of Billy MacDaniel.- The comical tricks of Lothian Tom, with a selection of anecdotes.-The comical history of the King and the cobbler.- Entertaining history of John Cheap the Chapman.-The comical history of Simple John and his twelve misfortunes.-The merry tales of the wise men of Gotham.-The life of Mansie Wauch, tailor in Dalkeith.-The whole proceedings of Jocky and Maggy's courtship.-The coalman's courtship to the creel-wife's daughter.-The history of Buchaven in Fifeshire, containing the witty and entertaining exploits of Wise Willie, and Witty Eppy, the ale wife.- The dominie deposed, with the sequel, to which is added Maggy Johnston's elegy.-Odds and ends, or, A groat's worth of fun for a penny.-Comical sayings of Paddy from Cork, with his coat buttoned behind.-Fun upon fun, or, Lepter the Tailor.-John Falkirk's cariches, to which is added Tom Merrilees, a capital story.-Grinning made easy; or, Funny Dick's unrivalled collection of jests, jokes, bulls, epigrams, &c.-The Scotch haggis, a selection of choice bon-mots, Irish blunders, repartees, anecdotes, &c.

JOHNSON, BEN, *pseud.* Ben Johnson's jests; or, The wit's pocket companion. *sheep, 16mo. Lond., Baldwin, n.d.* (Bound with: Joe Miller's jests. Lond., Hodges, n.d.)

*see also* JEST BOOKS

JOHNSON, BURGES. Bashful ballads. *buckram, 12mo. N.Y., Harper, 1911.*

_____ Beastly rhymes. *buckram, 12mo. N.Y., Crowell, 1906.*

_____ Little book of necessary nonsense. *buckram, 16mo. N.Y., Harper, 1929.*

_____ Lost art of profanity. *buckram, 12mo. Indianapolis, Bobbs-Merrill, 1948.*

_____ More necessary nonsense. *buckram, 16mo. N.Y., Harper, 1931.*

_____ Rhymes of little boys. *buckram, 12mo. N.Y., Crowell, 1905.*

JOHNSON, CLIFTON, *comp.* What they say in New England; a book of signs, sayings and superstitions. *buckram, 12mo. Bost., Lee & Shepard, 1896.*

JOHNSON, CONSTANCE, *ed.* A year book of humor. *suede, 12mo. N.Y., Crowell, 1910.*

JOHNSON, EDGAR. A treasury of satire. *buckram, 8vo. N.Y., Simon & Schuster, 1945.*

JOHNSON, GERALD W. The lines are drawn; American life since the first world war as reflected in the Pulitzer Prize cartoons. *buckram, 8vo. Phila., Lippincott, 1958.*

JOHNSON, HELEN KENDRICK, *ed.* Short sayings of famous men. *2v. buckram, 16mo. N.Y., Putnam's 1884.*

JOHNSON, J.H., *ed.* The laughter library. *buckram, 12mo. Indianapolis, Droke, 1936.*

JOHNSON, LUCY BLACK *and* JOHNSON, PYKE, *eds.* Cartoon treasury; a collection of the world's funniest cartoons. *buckram, 4to. Lond., Collins, 1956.*

JOHNSON, MAURICE. The sin of wit. *boards, 8vo. Syracuse, Syracuse Univ. Press, 1950.*

JOHNSON, S.C. Schoolboy and other howlers. *paper, 24mo. Lond., Foulsham, n.d.*

JOHNSON, SAMUEL.
Dr. Johnson's Table-talk, containing aphorisms on literature, life and manners. *half-calf., 8vo. Lond., Dilly, 1798.*

_____ History of Rasselas, prince of Abissinia. *v.2. of Mirror of Amusement, q.v.*

_____ Johnsoniana; or, Supplement to Boswell. *boards, 8vo. Lond., Murray, 1836.*

_____ Sermons attributed to Samuel Johnson and left for publication by John Taylor. *calf., 8vo. Lond., Ebers, 1812.*

_____ Wisdom of Dr. Johnson. *buckram, 8vo. Lond., Harrap, 1948.*

_____ Wit and wisdom of Samuel Johnson, selected and arranged by George Birkbeck Hill. *buckram, 16mo. Oxford, Clarendon, 1888.*

JOHNSON, W. BRANCH. Folktales of Brittany. *buckram, 12mo. Lond., Methuen, 1927.*

JOHNSTON, ALVA. The incredible Mizners. *buckram, 8vo. Lond., Hart-Davis, 1953.*

JOHNSTON, CHARLES. Why the world laughs. *buckram, 8vo. N.Y., Harper, 1912.*

JOHNSTON, ELIZABETH BRYANT. George Washington, day by day. *buckram, 8vo. N.Y. Cycle, 1895.*

JOHNSTON, WILLIAM. The fun of being a fat man. *boards, 12mo. Bost., Little, Brown, 1922.*

JOHNSTON, WILLIAM T. Bill Johnston's joy book. *buckram, 12mo. Cincinnati, Kidd, 1922.*

_____ Bill Johnston's second joy book. *buckram, 12mo. N.Y., Appleton, 1925.*

JOKE BOOK ONE. *paper, 32mo. Girard, Kan., Haldeman-Julius, n.d. (Little Blue Books.)*

JOKE BOOK TWO. *paper, 32mo. Girard, Kan., Haldeman-Julius, n.d. (Little Blue Books.)*

JOKE BOOKS. *15v. paper, 48vo. Ceagee, 1944.*

Contents.-Button busters.- Deluxe jokes.-Les extases.- Gags and puns.-Full of jokes for rich man and poor man.- Keen cracks, chips'o' the old block.-Laughs de luxe!-Purely entertainment plus!-Favorite party jokes.-Reel fun.-Sheer nonsense.-Smiles to cure the blues.-Snappy chuckles.-Good clean fun, sizzling wit and humor.-Wit and humor.

JOKES! Cartoons from American magazines pasted in scrapbook.

JOKES FOR ALL OCCASIONS. Selected and edited by one of America's foremost public speakers. *buckram, 12mo. N.Y, Clode, 1921.*

_____ *Same.* With title: 2,088 jokes, toasts and anecdotes. *N.Y., Grosset & Dunlap, 1923.*

JOKES FOR THE PEOPLE BY THE PEOPLE. *paper, 16mo. Dundee, Thomson, 1889.*

JOKES, RIDDLES AND CONUNDRUMS. *paper, 12mo. N.Y., Wehman, n.d.*

"JOKEY-POKEY" JOKER, THE. *paper, 12mo. N.Y., Wehman, 1870.*

JOLLY JOKER: or, A laugh all around! *paper, 8vo. N.Y., Dick & Fitzgerald, n.d.*

JOLLY TIT-BITS FOR MIRTHFUL MORTALS. *buckram, 8vo. N.Y., Hurst, 1876.*

"JON" The two types. *paper, wide 24mo. Lond., Benn, 1960.*

JONES, GWYN. Scandinavian legends and folk tales. *buckram, 8vo. Lond., Oxford Univ. Press, 1957.*

_____ Welsh legends and folk tales. *buckram, 8vo. Lond, Oxford Univ. Press, 1957.*

_____ Welsh short stories. *buckram, 16mo. Lond., Oxford, 1956.*

JONES, HENRY A. A bed of roses. *paper, 12mo. Lond., French, n.d.*

JONES, HOWARD MUMFORD. The pursuit of happiness. *buckram, 8vo. Cambridge, Harvard Univ. Press, 1953.*

JONES, HUGH PERCY. Dictionary of foreign phrases and classical quotations. *buckram, 8vo. Edinburgh, Grant, 1958. New and rev.ed.*

JONES, J.S. Solon Shingle; a comedy. *paper, 12mo. Chic., Dramatic Pub. co., n.d.*

JONES, JOSEPH. Emerson and Bergson on the comic. *pamphlet. Reprinted from Comparative Literature, Winter, 1949.*

_____ Humor in Moby Dick. *pamphlet. Reprinted from University of Texas Studies in English. 1945-1946.*

_____ Josh Billings meets James Marshall. *leaflet. Reprinted from Pacific Historical Review, Dec. 1944.*

JONES, LOUIS C. Things that go bump in the night. *buckram, 8vo. N.Y., Hill & Wang, 1959.*

JONES, R.C. Prominent San Franciscans (in caricature). *buckram, 12mo. San Francisco, Murdock, n.d.*

JONES, SAM. Hot shots, or, Sermons and sayings. *buckram, 12mo. Nashville, Tenn., Pub. House of the M.E. Church, South, 1905.*

JONES, WALTER. "Jiglets" a series of sidesplitting gyrations reeled off. *paper, 12mo. N.Y., Street & Smith, 1903.*

JORDAN, CHARLOTTE BREWSTER. Sphinx-lore. *buckram, 16mo. N.Y., Dutton, 1897.*

JORDAN, W.C. Ancient Hebrew stories and their modern interpretation. *buckram, 12mo. Lond., Hodder & Stoughton, 1922.*

JOSTEN, JOSEF, *ed.* The great challenge, as seen by international artists. *paper, 8vo. Lond., Pub. for the First International Exhibition of Political Cartoons, 1958.*

JOUBERT, JOSEPH. Pensees, selected and translated by Henry Attwell. *buckram, 8vo. Lond., Macmillan, 1877.*

JOURNAL OF EDUCATIONAL PSYCHOLOGY. Comics as reading for children. *December 1949 issue.*

JOURNAL OF SOLOMON SIDE-SPLITTER; a collection of witticisms. *buckram, 12mo. Phila., Pickwick, 1884.*

JOVIAL JESTER: or, Tim Grin's delight. *half-calf, 16mo. Lond., Lane, 1791.*

JOYFUL TALES; jingles and jokes for little folks. *paper, 8vo. N.Y., McLoughlin, 1869.*

JOYNSON, CECILE. In search of Henry. *buckram, 8vo. Lond., Hammond, Hammond, 1960.*

JUAN MANUEL, *Infante of Spain.* Count Lucanor, or, The fifty pleasant stories of Patronio. *boards, 12mo. Westminster, Pickering, n.d.*

JUDELL, MAXSON FOXHALL. The fun shop; the mirth of a nation. *buckram, 8vo. N.Y., Doran, 1927.*

JUILLERAT, IDA H. Jingles for singles. *boards, 16mo. Oakland, Calif. Author, 1910.*

JULIEN, ANNA *and* JULIEN, HERBERT. The scrap book; choice bits of wit, humor and philosophy. *paper, 12mo. n.p. 1941.*

JULLIAN, PHILIPPE. The snob spotter's guide. *buckram, 8vo. Lond., Weidenfeld & Nicolson, 1958.*

JUNIOR, ALLAN. The Aberdeen Jew. *boards, 8vo. Dundee, Valentine, 1927. 6th ed.*

—————— Canny tales fae Aberdeen. *paper, 8vo. Dundee, Valentine, 1927. 19th ed.*

—————— Mair canny tales fae Aberdeen. *paper, 8vo. Dundee, Valentine, 1926.*

JUNIPER, WILLIAM. A merry ingenious, and diverting work entitled The law of drinking. *buckram, 12mo. San Francisco, Fahey, 1935.*

JUNIUS. Stat nominis umbra. *2v. leather, 8vo. Lond., Bensley, 1801.*

JUNIUS, *pseud.* Junius, including letters by the same writer under other signatures. *2v. buckram, 12mo. Lond., Bell & Daldy, 1873.*

JUPPENSHA IKKU. Shanks' Mare, being a translation of the Tokaido volumes of Hizakurige, faithfully rendered into English by Thomas Setchell. *buckram, 8vo. Tokyo, Tuttle, 1960.* (See also version in Japanese.)

—————— Hizakurige. Shanks' mare tour of the Tokaido. *boards, 12mo. Tokyo, Toa Bungei Sha, n.d.*

JUVENALIS, DECIMUS JUNIUS. The satires, translated into English verse by William Gifford. *half-calf, 8vo. Lond., Bulmer, 1806.*

# K

K_____. G_____. The
festival of wit, or Small talker,
being a collection of bons-
mots, anecdotes &c of the most
exalted characters, procured
and selected by G_____
K_____ summer resident
at Windsor (purported to be
George III). *calf, 32mo. Lond.,
Kearsley, 1783. 16th ed.*

_____ *Same. Dublin, Porter,
1783.*

_____ *Same. Lond.,
Davison, 1800. 17th ed.*

KAHN, E.J. The merry partners.
The age and stage of Harrigan
and Hart. *buckram, 8vo. N.Y.,
Random, 1955.*

KAHN, EDGAR MYRON. Bret
Harte in California; a character
study. *boards, 8vo. San
Francisco, Haywood Hunt for
the Roxeburgh Club, 1951.*

KANE, HARNETT. Have pen, will
autograph. *buckram, 8vo.
Garden City, Doubleday, 1959.*

KANEKO, NORBERT N. Modern
Japanese humor. *paper, 12mo.
Tokyo, World Information
Service, 1950.*

_____ Old Japanese
humor. *paper, 12mo. Tokyo,
Tokyo News Service, 1959.*

KANIN, FAY. Goodbye, my fancy;
a comedy. *paper, 12mo. N.Y.,
French, 1950.*

KANNON, JACKIE. Poems for the
john. *buckram, 8vo. N.Y.,
Kanrom, 1960.*

KANSAS CITY (MO.) PUBLIC
LIBRARY. Three years of
laughter; a selection of books
on humor, 1946-1949.
*Mimeographed pamphlet.*

KANT, IMMANUEL. The living
thoughts of Kant. Presented by
Julien Benda. *buckram, 12mo.
Lond., Cassell, 1948. 2d.ed.*

KAO, GEORGE. Chinese wit and
humor. *buckram, 8vo. N.Y.,
Coward-McCann, 1946.*

KARINTHY, FREDERICK. Solilo-
quies in the bath. *buckram,
12mo. Lond., Hodge, 1937.*

KASER, ARTHUR LEROY. Good
toasts and funny fellows.
*paper, 12mo. Chic., Denison,
1923.*

KASIM IBN ALI, *called Al-Hiriri.*
Makamat, or Rhetorical anec-
dotes. Translated from the
original Arabic by Theodore
Preston. *buckram, 8vo. Lond.,
Madden, 1850.*

KASTNER, ERICH. Don Quixote.
*buckram, 4to. N.Y., Messner,
1957.*

_____ The simpletons.
*buckram, 4to. N.Y., Messner,
1957.*

KATIBAH, H.I. Arabian romances
and folk-tales. *buckram, 8vo.
N.Y., Scribner's, 1929.*

KATKOV, NORMAN. Fabulous
Fanny. *buckram, 8vo. N.Y.,
Knopf, 1953.*

KATZIN, OLGA *and* WEISS,
VICTOR. Up the poll! the sap's
guide to the general election,
by Sagittarius and vicky,
*pseuds. paper, 8vo. Lond.,
Turnstile press, 1950.*

KATZIN, WINIFRED, *ed.* Eight
European plays. *buckram, 8vo.
N.Y., Brentano's, 1927.*

KAUFMAN, GEORGE S. *and*
RYSKIND, MORRIE. Of thee I
sing. *buckram, 12mo. N.Y.,
Knopf, 1932.*

KAUFMAN, GERALD LYNTON.
The book of modern puzzles.
*paper, 8vo. N.Y., Dover, 1954.
2d.rev.ed.*

KATZMAN, LAWRENCE. Nellie
the nurse. *paper, 16mo. N.Y.,
Dell, 1958.*

KAZ *see* KATZMAN, LAWRENCE.

KEARNEY, PAUL w. Toasts and
anecdotes. *buckram, 12mo.
N.Y., Clode, 1923.*

——————— 1226 jokes. *buckram,
12mo. N.Y., Clode, 1929.*

KEATING, WALTER S., *ed.* The
omnibus of pleasure; a
pleasure primer. *paper, small
8vo. N.Y., Plaza, 1943.*

KEATON, BUSTER. My wonderful
world of slapstick. *buckram,
8vo. N.Y., Doubleday, 1960.*

KEENE, CHARLES. Pictures by
Charles Keene. *paper, 24mo.
Lond., Gowans & Gray, 1909.*
(Humorous masterpieces.)

KETIGES, JOHN, *comp.* Proverbs
and quotations for school and
home. *buckram, 12mo. Chic.,
Flanagan, 1905.*

KELLER, REAMER. Mating
manual. *paper, 12mo. N.Y.,
Bantam, 1957.*

——————— Why the long puss?
*paper, 12mo. N.Y., Bantam,
1956.*

KELLOGG, FRANK E. Flip flap
fables; a bunch of twenty
seven tales. *buckram, 12mo.
N.Y., Dillingham, 1907.*

KELLY, EMMETT. Clown. *buckram, 8vo. Lond., Hale, 1956.*

KELLY, ETHEL. Home. James.
*boards, 12mo. N.Y., Knopf,
1927.*

KELLY, FRED C. The life and
times of Kin Hubbard, creator
of Abe Martin. *buckram, 8vo.
N.Y., Farrar, Straus & Young,
1952.*

KELLY, H.P. Gems of Irish wit
and humor. *buckram, 12mo.
N.Y., Sully, 1906.*

——————— *Same,* with title:
Irish bulls and puns, 500 gems
of modern Irish wit and humor.
*N.Y., Vernon, 1906.*

——————— *Same.* without sub-
title, *Lond., Skeffington, n.d.*

KELLY, JAMES. Complete collection of Scotish proverbs.
*calf., 8vo. Lond., Innys,
1721.*

——————— *Same. Lond., Rod-
well & Martin, 1818.*

KELLY, JOHN F. A bunch of
junk, gathered from the wits of
the world. *paper, 12mo. N.Y.,
Kelly & Lewis, 1920.*

KELLY, WALT. Uncle Pogo so-so
stories. *buckram, 4to. N.Y.,
Simon & Schuster, 1953.*

KELLY, WALTER K. Proverbs of
all nations, compared, explained and illustrated. *buckram, 12mo. Lond., Kent, 1861.*

KELSEY, ALICE GEER. Once the
Mullah. *buckram, 12mo.
Leicester, Brockhampton, 1957.*

KELVIN, KIT, *pseud.* Kernels.
*buckram, 12mo. N.Y., Rollo,
1860.*

KEMBLE, JOHN R. Four hundred
laughs, or, Fun without vulgarity. *buckram, 12mo. N.Y.,
New Amsterdam, 1901.*

KENDALL, EZRA. Good gravy; a
pure tonic of wit and humor.
*paper, 12mo. Cleveland,
Helman, Taylor, 1901.*

_____ Hot ashes all new and original. *paper, 12mo. Cleveland, Savage, 1908.*

_____ Spots of wit and humor (original). *paper, 12mo. Cleveland, Helman, Taylor, 1899.*

_____ Tell it to me; all new and original. *paper, 12mo. Cleveland, Helman, Taylor, 1903.*

_____ Top soil rich in wit and humor. *buckram, 12mo. Cleveland, Savage, 1909.*

_____ The vinegar buyer. *buckram, 12mo. Cleveland, Savage, 1909.*

KENDALL, PARK. Gone with the draft; love letters of a trainee. *buckram, 8vo. N.Y., Grosset & Dunlap, 1941.*

_____ ... Still in the draft. *buckram, 12mo. N.Y., Grosset, 1942.*

KENNEDY, CHARLES RANN. The terrible meek. *buckram, 8vo. N.Y., Harper, 1912.*

KENNEDY, H.C. A damphool in the Kentucky legislature. *buckram, 8vo. Chic., Conkey, 1909.*

KENNEDY, JOHN S. Pleased to meet you. *buckram, 8vo. N.Y., McMullen, 1952.*

KENNEDY, PATRICK, *ed.* The book of modern Irish anecdotes, humour, wit and wisdom. *buckram, 16mo. Lond., Routledge, 1886.*

KENT, MARGERY., *trans.* Fairy tales from Turkey. *buckram, 8vo. Lond., Routledge, 1946.*

KENWORTHY, JAN. Don't do it, doctor. *boards, 8vo. N.Y., Beechhurst, 1948.*

KERNEL ALMOND *see* THOMAS, CHARLES J.

KERNER, FRED. Love is a man's affair. *buckram, 12mo. Lond., Souvenir, 1958.*

KERR, JEAN. Please don't eat the daisies. *buckram, 12mo. Lond., Heineman, 1958.*

KERR, JOE. The cheery book. *buckram, 12mo. N.Y., Dillingham, 1897.*

KERR, ORPHEUS C., *pseud. see* NEWELL, ROBERT HENRY.

KERR, RODERICK WATSON. Style of me; letters of Eula from the U.S.A. *buckram, 12mo. Lond., Muller, 1945.*

KESELING, PETER C. *and* KINNEY, JOHN. Summa cum laughter; the best cartoons and jokes from American college humor magazines. *boards, 4to. N.Y., Waldorf, 1956.*

KETCHAM, HANK. Dennis the menace ... teacher's pet. *paper, 12mo. Greenwich, Crest, 1960.*

_____ Wanted: Dennis the menace. *paper, 12mo. N.Y., Pocket Books, 1955.*

KETT, HENRY. The flowers of wit; or, A choice collection of bon mots, both antient and modern. *2v. half-calf, 16mo. Lond., Lackington, Allen, 1814.*

KEY, TED. "Grand central station:" Original sketch presented to Nat Schmulowitz.

_____ Fasten your seat belts: *buckram, 4to. N.Y., Dutton, 1956.*

_____ Hazel. *paper, 16mo. N.Y., Bantam, 1955.*

_____ Hazel rides again. *buckram, 4to. N.Y., Dutton, 1955.*

_____ Here's Hazel. *paper, 12mo. N.Y., Bantam, 1956.*

_____ Many happy returns. *buckram, 4to. N.Y., Dutton, 1951.*

_____ Ted Key's Phyllis. *buckram, 8vo. N.Y., Dutton, 1957.*

KEYS TO KASHMIR. *boards, 8vo. Srinagar, Lalla Rookh, 1953.*

KHARAS, H.A. Limericks of India. *boards, 12mo. Bombay, Thacker, 1943.*

KHUSRAU, AMIR. Bagh o Bahar, or, Tales of the four darweshes, translated from the Hindu-stani of Mir Amman of Dihli, by Duncan Forbes. *buckram, 8vo. Lond., Crosby Lockwood, 1857.*

KIEFFER, HENRY MARTYN. The funny bone; short stories and amusing anecdotes for a dull hour. *buckram, 16mo. N.Y., Dodge, 1910.*

_____ It is to laugh. *limp leather, 16mo. N.Y., Dodge, 1907.*

_____ Laugh again; short stories and amusing anecdotes for a dull hour. *buckram, 16mo. N.Y., Dodge, 1913.*

_____ More laughs; short stories and amusing anecdotes for a dull hour. *buckram, 16mo. N.Y., Dodge, 1923.*

KIM SO-UN. The story bag; a collection of Korean folk tales. *paper, 12mo. Rutland, Vt., Tuttle, 1955.*

KIMBO. Tropical tales. *buckram, 8vo. n.p., n.d.*

KIMMINS, C.W. Springs of laughter. *buckram, 12mo. Lond, Methuen, 1928.*

KING, ALEXANDER. May this house be safe from tigers. *paper, 12mo. N.Y., Signet, 1960.*

KING, STODDARD. What the queen said, and further facetious fragments. *buckram, 12mo. N.Y., Doran, 1926.*

KING, WILLIAM. A miscellany of the wits. *buckram, 8vo. Lond., Allen, 1920.*

_____ Political and literary anecdotes of his own times. *calf., 12mo. Lond., Murray, 1819. 2d.ed.*

KINGSMILL, HUGH *see* LUNN, HUGH KINGSMILL.

KINGSTON, CHARLES. A gallery of rogues. *buckram, 8vo. Lond., S. Paul, 1924.*

_____ Society sensations. *buckram, 8vo. N.Y., Dutton, 1922.*

KINKEAD, EUGENE *and* MALONEY, RUSSELL. Our own Baedeker from the New Yorker. *boards, 8vo. N.Y., Simon & Schuster, 1947.*

KINNAIRD, CLARK, *ed.* Encyclopedia of puzzles and pastimes. *buckram, 8vo. N.Y., Grosset & Dunlap, 1946.*

KINNEY, JAMES R. *and* HONEY-CUTT, ANN. How to raise a dog in the city and in the suburbs. *buckram, 8vo. Lond., Hamilton, 1939.*

KIRCHER, RALF. There's a fly in this room! *buckram, 12mo. N.Y., Rinehart, 1946.*

KIRK, WILLIAM F. The Norsk
nightingale, being the lyrics of
a "Lumberyack". boards, 12mo.
Bost., Small, Maynard, 1917.

KIRKLAND, FRAZAR. The pictorial book of anecdotes of
the Rebellion ... buckram, 8vo.
St. Louis, Mason, 1889.

——————Cyclopaedia of com-
mercial and business anecdotes. 2v. calf., 8vo. N.Y.,
Appleton, 1864.

KIRKPATRICK, JOHN. The dab-
blers; a one-act farce. paper,
12mo. N.Y., French, 1945.

—————— Married at sunrise; a
comedy. paper, 12mo. N.Y.,
French, 1946.

KIRTON, JOHN WILLIAM. One
thousand temperance anec-
dotes, jokes, riddles, puns
and smart sayings. buckram,
16mo. Lond., Smart & Allen,
1867.

—————— Standard comic
reciter. buckram, 16mo. Lond.,
Ward, Lock, n.d.

KISER, S.E. It is to laugh; a book
of jokes. buckram, 12mo. N.Y.,
Sully, 1927.

KIT O' WIT: the funny side of life.
paper, 8vo. Chic., Wood, 1944.

KITCHENS, C.B. X-syrups from
the Trickem News Chronic.
buckram, 8vo. San Antonio,
Naylor, 1959.

—————— Trickem on Gooch
Creek. buckram, 8vo. San
Antonio, Naylor, 1957.

KITT, ERTHA. Thursday's child.
buckram, 8vo. N.Y., Duell,
Sloan & Pearce, 1956.

KLEBERG, AL. Slang fables from
afar. buckram, 12mo. Baltimore,
Phoenix, 1903.

KLEIN, ALEXANDER, comp. and
ed. The double dealers, adventures in grand deception.
buckram, 8vo. Phila., Lippincott, 1958.

——————Grand deception; a
selection from the provocative
best-seller. paper, 12mo. N.Y.,
Ballantine, 1955.

KLEISER, GRENVILLE. How to
argue and win. buckram, 16mo.
N.Y., Funk & Wagnalls, 1912.

——————Humorous hits, and,
How to hold an audience. buck-
ram, 12mo. N.Y., Funk &
Wagnalls, 1909. 3d. ed.

—————— Same. 5th ed. 1912.

—————— "Ladies and gentlemen: There's a story ..." buckram, 8vo. N.Y., Funk &
Wagnalls, 1935.

——————Stories that take.
buckram, 16mo. N.Y., Funk &
Wagnalls, 1910.

KLEY, HEINRICH. Drawings.
paper, 4to. N.Y., Dover, 1961.

KLOPFINGER, HERMAN. Hateful
thoughts for happy occasions.
paper, 8vo. N.Y., Citadel,
1959.

KNEEBONE, PETER. Look before
you elope. boards, 16mo. Lond,
Longmans, 1952.

KNIGHT, GRANT C. Superlatives.
buckram, 12mo. N.Y., Knopf,
1925.

KNIGHT ERRANT, A. see
DUBOIS, EDWARD.

KNOTT, TINA SPENCER. Keep
it clean. buckram, 8vo. Lond.,
Hammond, Hammond, 1958.

KNOX, CHARLES VICTOR.
Vick's parade, 1932. paper,
narrow 4to. Chic., Evening
Post, 1932.

KNOX, D.B. Children's funny sayings; an amusing book for everybody. *buckram, 12mo. N.Y., Dutton, n.d.*

——————— Everybody's anecdotes. *buckram, 12mo. Lond., T.Fisher Unwin, 1928.*

——————— Laugh and grow fat; eight hundred humorous stories. *buckram, 12mo. Lond., Clarke, n.d.*

——————— Laugh and live longer; an amusing book for everybody. *buckram, 12mo. Lond., Clarke, n.d.*

——————— More quotable anecdotes. *buckram, 12mo. Lond., T.Fisher Unwin, 1926.*

——————— Quotable anecdotes for various occasions. *buckram, 16mo. Lond., T.Fisher Unwin, 1924.*

KNOX, EDWARD VERRALL. Blue feathers. *buckram, 12mo. Lond, Chatto & Windus, 1929.*

——————— The brazen lyre. *buckram, 12mo. Lond., Smith, Elder, 1911.*

——————— Folly calling. *buckram, 16mo. Lond., Methuen, 1932.*

——————— Humorous verse; an anthology. *boards, 12mo. Lond., Chatto & Windus, 1931.*

——————— I'll tell the world! *buckram, 12mo. Lond., Chatto & Windus, 1927.*

——————— It occurs to me. *buckram, 16mo. Lond., Methuen, 1926.*

——————— The mechanism of satire. *paper, 12mo. Cambridge, Univ. Press, 1951. (The Leslie Stephen lecture, 10, May, 1951)*

——————— Methuen's library of humour. E.V. Knox. *buckram, 16mo. Lond., Methuen, 1934.*

——————— Quaint specimens. *buckram, 16mo. Lond., Methuen, 1925.*

KNOX, RONALD A. Essays in satire. *buckram, 12mo. Lond., Sheed & Ward, 1954.*

KOBER, ARTHUR. Oooh, what you said! *buckram, 8vo. N.Y., Simon & Schuster, 1958.*

KOMROFF, MANUEL. The great fables of all nations. *buckram, 8vo. N.Y., Tudor, 1935.*

KOPPE, RICHARD, *comp. and ed.* A treasury of college humor. *buckram, 8vo. N.Y., Penn, 1950.*

KOPPLIN, DOROTHEA, *comp. and ed.* Something to live by. *boards, 16mo. N.Y., Perma-books, 1948.*

KOUNTZ, WILLIAM J., *jr.* Billy Baxter's letters. *buckram, 16mo. Harmarville, Duquesne, 1899.*

KOURY, PHIL A. Yes, Mr. DeMille. *buckram, 8vo. N.Y., Putnam's 1959.*

KOVARSKY, ANATOL. Kovarsky's world; cartoons. *boards, folio. N.Y., Knopf, 1956.*

KOVNER, B. Laugh, Jew, Laugh; short humorous stories. *buckram, 12mo. N.Y., Bloch, 1936.*

KRAMER, DALE. Ross and the New Yorker. *buckram, 12mo. Lond., Gollancz, 1952.*

KRAMER, SAMUEL NOAH. History begins at Sumer. *paper, 12mo. N.Y., Doubleday, 1959.*

KREBS, FLORENCE KELLOGG.
Army Goose melodies. *boards*,
*8vo. San Francisco, Elder,
1910.*

KRICH, A.M., *ed.* The second
ribald reader. *paper, 16mo.
N.Y., Dell, 1956.*

KROKODIL *(Periodical).* The
Crocodile album of Soviet
humour. *paper, 16mo. Lond.,
Pilot, 1943.*

_____ Out of the croco-
dile's mouth; Russian cartoons
about the United States of
America, from "Krokodil".
Edited by William Nelson.
*buckram, 8vo. Washington,
Public Affairs Press, 1949.*

KRONENBERGER, LOUIS, *ed.*
An anthology of light verse.
*buckram, 12mo. N.Y., Modern
Library, 1935.*

_____ Reader's companion.
*buckram, 12mo. N.Y., Viking,
1945.*

KRUMPELMANN, JOHN T. Mark
Twain and the German
language. *paper, 8vo. Baton
Rouge, Louisiana Univ. Press,
1953.*

KRYLOV, IVAN ANDREEVICH.
Kriloff's fables. Translated
from the Russian by C. Filling-
ham Coxwell. *buckram, 16mo.
Lond., Kegan Paul, Trench &
Trubner, n.d.*

_____ Kriloff's original
fables. Translated by I. Henry
Harrison. *buckram, 12mo.
Lond., Remington, 1883.*

KUBLY, HERBERT. Varieties of
love. *boards, 8vo. N.Y., Simon
& Schuster, 1958.*

KUKA, MEHERJIBHAI NOSHER-
WANJI. Wit and humour of the
Persians. *buckram, 8vo.
Bombay, Education Society,
1894.*

KURTZMAN, HARVEY. The mad
reader. *paper, 12mo. N.Y.,
Ballantine, 1955.*

KUSTOMER, *pseud,* A. P.S. What
do you think of the market?
*boards, 12mo. N.Y., Guenther,
1919.*

# L

LACONICS: or, New maxims of state and conversation relating to the affairs and manners of the present times. In three parts. *calf., 12mo. Lond., Hodgson, 1701.*

LACONICS: or, The best works of the best authors. *3v. half-calf, 24mo. Lond., Tilt, 1840. 7th ed.*

LADIES HOME JOURNAL. Good stories, reprinted from the Ladies Home Journal. *boards, 16mo. Phila., Altemus, 1907.*

LAELAND, HERBERT. Lies and liars. *buckram, 12mo. Lond., Gay & Bird, 1896.*

LA FONTAINE, JEAN *de.* The tales and novels of Jean de La Fontaine, completely translated into English. *2v. buckram, 8vo. N.Y., Priv. Print, 1929.*

LAIDLER, GRAHAM. The British carry on, a collection of wartime drawings by Pont. *buckram, 12mo. Lond., Collins, 1940.*

——————— The British character studied and revealed by Pont. *buckram, 8vo. Lond., Collins, 1938.*

——————— Most of us are afraid, by Pont. *buckram, 12mo. Lond., Collins, 1946.*

LAING, ALLAN M. Laughter and applause; anecdotes for speakers. *buckram, 12mo. Lond, Allen & Unwin, 1953.*

LAIT, JACK. Gus the bus and Evelyn, the exquisite checker. *buckram, 12mo. N.Y., Doubleday, Page, 1917.*

——————— Our Will Rogers. *buckram, 12mo. N.Y., Greenberg, 1935.*

LAMB, CHARLES. Bon-mots of Charles Lamb and Douglas Jerrold. Ed. by Walter Jerrold. *buckram, 32mo. Lond., Dent, 1893.*

——————— *Same. 3d. ed. 1904.*

——————— Charles Lamb in pipefuls, selected and arranged by Walter Lewis. *paper, 12mo. Liverpool, "Cope's Tobacco Plant" 1890.*

——————— Final memorials of Charles Lamb. *half-calf, 12mo. N.Y., Derby, 1861.*

——————— Letters. *2v. buckram, 12mo. Lond., Macmillan, 1897.*

——————— Life and letters of Charles Lamb. By Thomas Noon Talfourd. *half-calf, 12mo. N.Y., Derby, 1861.*

——————— Rosamund Gray, essays, lectures and poems. *half-calf, 12mo. N.Y., Derby, 1861.*

——————— Specimens of English dramatic poets who lived about the time of Shakspeare. *half-calf., 12mo. N.Y., Derby, 1861. New ed.*

——————— Wit and wisdom of Charles Lamb. *paper, 32mo. Girard, Kan., Haldeman-Julius, n.d. (Little Blue Books.)*

LAMBETH AND THE VATICAN: or, Anecdotes of the Church of Rome, of the Reformed churches and sects and sectaries. *3v. half-calf., 16mo. Lond., J. Knight & H. Lacey, 1825.*

LAMPTON, WILLIAM J. Yawps and other things. *buckram, 8vo. Phila., Altemus, 1900.*

**LANCASTER, OSBERT.** The alarms and excursions of Lady Littlehampton. *buckram, 8vo. Bost., Houghton Mifflin, 1952.*

—————— Etudes; new pocket cartoons. *buckram, 16mo. Lond, Murray, 1958.*

—————— Facades and faces. *buckram, Murray, 1950.*

—————— Lady Littlehampton and friends. *buckram, 16mo. Lond., Gryphon, 1952.*

—————— New pocket cartoons. *buckram, 12mo. Lond., Murray, 1941.*

—————— Pocket cartoons. *paper, 16mo. Lond., Murray, 1940.*

—————— Private views; new pocket cartoons. *buckram, 16mo. Lond., Gryphon, 1956.*

—————— Studies from the life; new pocket cartoons. *buckram, 16mo. Lond., Gryphon, 1954.*

—————— Tableux vivants; new pocket cartoons. *buckram, 16mo. Lond., Gryphon, 1955.*

**LANDON, MELVILLE D.** American lecturers and humorists. *buckram, 4to. Akron, Saalfield, 1890.*

—————— Comical hits by famous wits, comprising wit, humor, pathos, ridicule, satire, &c. *buckram, 8vo. Chic., Thompson & Thomas, 1900.*

—————— Eli Perkins (at large) his sayings and doings. *buckram, 12mo. N.Y., Ford, 1875.*

—————— Eli Perkins thirty years of wit. *buckram, 12mo. N.Y., Cassell, 1891.*

—————— Eli Perkins' wit, humor and pathos. *buckram, 12mo. Chic., Donohue, Henneberry, 1890.*

—————— Kings of the platform and pulpit. *half-morocco, 4to. Chic., Werner, 1908.*

—————— Library of wit and humor from the writings of the world's greatest humorists. *buckram, 8vo. Chic., Thompson, 1901.*

—————— Masters of mirth. *buckram, large 8vo. Chic., Clarkson, 1890.*

—————— Saratoga in 1901. *buckram, 8vo. N.Y., Sheldon, 1872.*

**LANE-NORCOTT, MAURICE.** As I see it. *buckram, 16mo. Lond., Harmsworth, 1932.*

**LANGDON, DAVID.** A banger for a monkey. *buckram, 8vo. Lond., Wingate, 1957.*

—————— "All buttoned up" a scrapbook of R.A.F. cartoons. *paper, 12mo. Lond., Sylvan, n.d.*

—————— Funnier still. *boards, 8vo. Lond., Methuen, 1956.*

—————— I'm only joking. *buckram, 4to. Lond., Barker, 1960.*

—————— Langdon at large. *buckram, 4to. Lond., Wingate, 1958.*

—————— Laugh with me! *buckram, 8vo. Lond., Faber & Faber, 1954.*

—————— Look at you. *buckram, 12mo. Lond., Methuen, 1952.*

—————— More in fun. *boards, 8vo. Lond., Methuen, 1955.*

LANGLEY, NINA SCOTT *and*
"A.W.B." *of Punch.* Darwin
was right! *buckram, 8vo. Lond.,*
*Collins, 1938.*

LANGLEY, NOEL. There's a
porpoise close behind us.
*buckram, 12mo. Lond.,*
*Methuen, 1942. 8th ed.*

LANGNAS, ISAAC A., *comp. and*
*tr.* 1200 Russian proverbs.
*buckram, 12mo. N.Y., Phil-*
*osophical Library, 1960.*

LANGNER, LAWRENCE. The
magic curtain. *cloth, 8vo. N.Y.,*
*Dutton, 1951.*

LANGSTAFF, LAUNCELOT *see*
PAULDING, JAMES K.

LANIGAN, G.T. Fables, by
G. Washington Aesop. *boards,*
*24mo. N.Y., World, 1878.*

LANSING, MARION FLORENCE.
Great moments in freedom.
*buckram, 8vo. N.Y., Doubleday,*
*Doran, 1937.*

LAO TZU. The book of Lieh-tzu,
a new translation by
A.C. Graham. *buckram, 12mo.*
*Lond., Murray, 1960.*

——————— The sayings of Lao
tzu, translated from the
Chinese, with an introduction
by Lionel Giles. *buckram,*
*16mo. Lond., Murray, 1909.*

——————— Tao te ching; a new
translation by Ch'u Ta-Kao.
*buckram, 12mo. Lond., Allen,*
*& Unwin, 1959.*

LA PRADE, ERNEST. Alice in
Orchestralia. *buckram, 12mo.*
*Garden City, Doubleday, Doran,*
*1936.*

LARCOM, LUCY, *comp.* Beckon-
ings for every day; a calendar
of thought. *buckram, 16mo.*
*Bost., Houghton, Mifflin, 1886.*

LARDNER, RING. The portable
Ring Lardner. *buckram, 16mo.*
*N.Y., Viking, 1946.*

——————— Treat 'em rough;
letters from Jack the Kaiser
killer. *buckram, 12mo.*
*Indianapolis, Bobbs-Merrill,*
*1918.*

——————— What of it? *buckram,*
*12mo. N.Y., Scribner's 1925.*

——————— You know me, Al; a
busher's letters. *buckram,*
*12mo. Cleveland, World, 1945.*

LARIAR, LAWRENCE. Bed and
bored. *buckram, 4to. N.Y.,*
*Whittlesey, 1945.*

——————— Best cartoons from
abroad. *buckram, 4to. Lond.,*
*Redman, n.d.*

——————— Best cartoons of the
years 1943-1946, 1948, 1954,
1958. *buckram, 4to. N.Y.,*
*Crown.*

——————— Beat and be
damned. *buckram, 4to. Engle-*
*wood Cliffs, Prentice-Hall,*
*1957.*

——————— Cartooning for
everybody. *buckram, 4to. N.Y.,*
*Crown, 1941.*

——————— Fixit and be
damned. *buckram, 4to. Lond.,*
*Hammond, Hammond, 1957.*

——————— How green was my
sex life. *paper, 12mo. N.Y.,*
*Signet, 1955.*

——————— Hunt and be damned.
*boards, 4to. Englewood Cliffs,*
*Prentice-Hall, 1956.*

——————— Oh! Dr. Kinsey!
*paper, 8vo. N.Y., Cartwrite,*
*1953.*

——————— The salesman's
treasury. *buckram, 8vo. N.Y.,*
*Crown, 1951.*

—————— Teensville USA. *buckram, 4to. N.Y., Dodd, Mead, 1959.*

—————— Treasury of sports cartoons. *buckram, 4to. Lond., Hammond, Hammond, 1957.*

—————— Yankee Yiddish. *paper, 8vo. N.Y., Cartwrite, 1953.*

—————— You've got me - and how! *buckram, 4to. Lond., Hammond, Hammond, 1957.*

—————— You've got me behind the wheel. *buckram, 4to. Lond., Hammond, Hammond, 1957.*

—————— You've got me from 9 to 5. *buckram, 4to. Lond., Hammond, Hammond, 1957.*

—————— You've got me in a hole. *buckram, 4to. Lond., Hammond, Hammond, 1956.*

—————— You've got me in stitches. *buckram, 4to. Lond., Hammond, Hammond, 1956.*

—————— You've got me in the nursery. *buckram, 4to. N.Y., Dodd, Mead, 1958.*

—————— You've got me in the suburbs. *buckram, 4to. Lond., Hammond, Hammond, 1957.*

—————— You've got me on the hook. *boards, 4to. Lond., Hammond, Hammond, 1956.*

—————— You've got me seeing double. *buckram, 4to. Lond., Hammond, Hammond, 1957.*

LA ROE, C. WARDEN. Making laughs pay. *buckram, 8vo. N.Y., Writer's Digest, 1930.*

LA ROUCHEFOUCAULD, FRANCOIS *de.* Maxims. *boards, 8vo. Lond., Haworth, 1931.*

—————— Maxims. *paper, 32 mo. Girard, Kan., Haldeman-Julius, n.d. (Little Blue Books)*

LARWOOD, JACOB. Anecdotes of the clergy; or, The antiquities, humours, and eccentricities of "The Cloth". *half-buckram, 12mo. Lond., Chatto & Windus, 1890.*

—————— Book of clerical anecdotes. *buckram, 16mo. Lond., John Camden Hotten, n.d.*

—————— Forensic anecdotes, or, Humour and curiosities of the law and of the men of law. *buckram, 16mo. Lond., Chatto & Windus, 1882.*

—————— History of sign-boards, from the earliest times to the present day. *buckram, 12mo. Lond., Chatto & Windus, n.d. 7th ed.*

—————— Theatrical anecdotes, or, Fun and curiosities of the play, the playhouse, and the players. *buckram, 16mo. Lond., Chatto & Windus, 1882.*

LASKI, MARGHANITA. Apologies. *paper, 12mo. Lond., Harvill, 1955.*

—————— Love on the super-tax. *buckram, 12mo. Lond., Cresset, 1944.*

LASSWELL, MARY. High time. *buckram, 12mo. Bost., Houghton, Mifflin, 1944.*

—————— Suds in your eye. *buckram, 8vo. Bost., Houghton, Mifflin, 1942.*

—————— Tooner schooner. *buckram, 8vo. Bost., Houghton, Mifflin, 1953.*

—————— Wait for the wagon. *buckram, 12mo. Bost., Houghton, Mifflin, 1951.*

LATCHFORD, HENRY. Wit and
wisdom of Parliament.
*half-calf, 16mo. Lond.,*
*Cassell, Petter, Galpin, n.d.*

LATEST HOLLYWOOD JOKES OF
STAGE, SCREEN AND
RADIO. *paper, 8vo. n.p., n.d.*

LAUCK, CHESTER *and* GOFF,
NORRIS. Jot 'em down store
catalogue, calendar and game
and party book for 1939, by
Lum and Abner. *buckram, 12mo.*
*N.Y., Blue Ribbon, 1939.*

LAUDER, HARRY. Between you
and me. *buckram, 8vo. N.Y.,*
*McCann, 1919.*

——————— A minstrel in France.
*buckram, 12mo. N.Y.,*
*Cosmopolitan, 1918.*

——————— Roamin' in the
gloamin'. *buckram, 8vo. Phila.,*
*Lippincott, 1928.*

LAUGH A MINUTE, A. *paper,*
*8vo. n.p., n.d.*

LAUGH PARADE: a collection of
the funniest cartoons of the
day. *boards, folio, N.Y.,*
*Grosset & Dunlap, 1945.*

LAUGH ROUND-UP; a collection
of the funniest cartoons of the
day. *boards, 4to. N.Y.,*
*Grosset & Dunlap, 1946.*

LAUGHER, THE: or, The art of
jesting; shewing every man in
his humour, from the throne to
the cottage. *half-calf; 24mo.*
*Lond., Reeve, 1755.*

LAUGHING LEECH, THE; laugh
and grow fit. *buckram, 16mo.*
*Lond., Muller, 1935.*

LAUGHING PHILOSOPHER, THE;
being the entire works of
Momus, jester of Olympus,
Democritus, the merry philosopher of Greece and their
illustrious disciples ... *half-*
*calf., 24mo. Lond., Sherwood,*
*Jones, 1825.*

LAUGHING PHILOSOPHER, THE;
consisting of several thousand
of the best jokes, witticisms,
puns, epigrams, humorous
stories and witty compositions..
*boards, 24mo. Lond., Sherwood,*
*Gilbert & Piper, 1835.*

LAUGHTER: gems of the world's
best humor. *buckram, 12mo.*
*N.Y., Ernst, 1927. (Not the*
*same as the paper ed.)*

LAUGHTER: gems of the world's
best humor. *paper, 8vo. N.Y.,*
*Ernst, 1927. (Not the same as*
*the hard bound ed.)*

LAUGHTER FOR THE MILLIONS.
*paper, 8vo. N.Y., Larch, 1943.*

LAURENTS, ARTHUR. The time
of the cuckoo, a comedy. *paper,*
*12mo. N.Y., French, 1954.*

LAVATER, JOHN CASPAR.
Aphorisms on man. *morocco,*
*16mo. Lond., Johnson, 1794.*

LAVRIN, JANKO. Russian humorous stories. *buckram, 12mo.*
*Lond., Sylvan, 1946.*

LAW IS A BOTTOMLESS-PIT.
Exemplify'd in the case of the
Lord Strutt, John Bull,
Nicholas Frog and Lewis
Baboon, who spent all they had
in a law-suit. Printed from a
manuscript found in the cabinet
of the famous Sir Humphrey
Polesworth. *buckram, 12mo.*
*Lond., Morphew, 1712. 4th ed.*

LAWRENCE, JOHN B. Oracles of the office. *buckram, 12mo. Bost., Badger, 1919.*

LAWSON, J. GILCHRIST. World's best conundrums and riddles of all ages. *buckram, 12mo. N.Y., Doran, 1924.*

_____ World's best humorous anecdotes. *buckram, 12mo. N.Y., Doran, 1923.*

LAWSON, LIZZIE *and* MATEAUX, C.L. Old proverbs with new pictures. *boards, 8vo. Lond., Cassell, Petter, Galpin, n.d.*

LAWSON, MARIE A. Strange sea stories; legends, lore, and superstitions of the mysterious waters. *buckram, 8vo. N.Y., Viking, 1955.*

LAWSON, ROBERT. Country colic. *buckram, 8vo. Bost., Little, Brown, 1944.*

LAWSON, WILFRID *and* GOULD, F. CARRUTHERS. Cartoons in rhyme and line. *buckram, 8vo. Lond., T.Fisher Unwin, 1905.*

LAWYER, THE: Pace's scrap book of bench and bar. Choice selections. *paper, 8vo. Dallas, Pace, n.d.*

LEACH, HENRY GODDARD. My last seventy years. *buckram, 8vo. N.Y., Bookman Associates, 1956.*

LEACOCK, STEPHEN. Afternoons in Utopia; tales of the new time. *buckram, 12mo. Lond., Lane, 1932.*

_____ A book of funny dramatics. *paper, 32mo. Girard, Kan., Haldeman-Julius, n.d. (Little Blue Books.)*

_____ A book of ridiculous stories. *paper, 32mo. Girard, Kan., Haldeman-Julius, n.d. (Little Blue Books.)*

_____ The boy I left behind me. *buckram, 12mo. Garden City, Doubleday, 1946.*

_____ College days. *buckram, 12mo. N.Y., Dodd, Mead, 1923.*

_____ Essays of serious spoofing. *paper, 32mo. Girard, Kan., Haldeman-Julius, n.d. (Little Blue Books.)*

_____ The greatest pages of American humour. *buckram, 12mo. Lond., Methuen, 1937.*

_____ Further foolishness. *buckram, 12mo. N.Y., Lane, 1916.*

_____ Happy stories just to laugh at. *buckram, 12mo. N.Y., Dodd, Mead, 1943.*

_____ The Hohenzollerns in America, with the Bolsheviks in Berlin, and other impossibilities. *buckram, 12mo. Toronto, Gundy, 1919.*

_____ Humor and humanity. *buckram, 8vo. N.Y., Holt, 1938.*

_____ Humor, its theory and technique, with examples and samples; a book of discovery. *buckram, 12mo. N.Y., Dodd, Mead, 1935.*

_____ The iron man and the tin woman, with other such futurities. *buckram, 12mo. N.Y., Dodd, Mead, 1929.*

_____ Laugh parade. *buckram, small 8vo. N.Y., Dodd, Mead, 1940.*

_____ Laugh with Leacock. *buckram, 12mo. N.Y., Dodd, Mead, 1952.*

_____ Literary lapses. *buckram, 12mo. N.Y., Lane, 1921.*

_____ Methuen's library of humour. Stephen Leacock. *buckram, 16mo. Lond., Methuen, 1934.*

_____ Nonsense novels. *boards, 12mo. Lond., Lane, 1913. 5th ed.*

_____ Too much college; or, Education eating up life. *buckram, 12mo. N.Y., Dodd, Mead, 1942.*

_____ Wet wit and dry humour. *buckram, 12mo. N.Y., Dodd, Mead, 1931.*

_____ Winnowed wisdom; a new book of humour. *buckram, 12mo. N.Y., Dodd, Mead, 1926.*

**LEAF, MUNRO.** Lo, the poor Indian. *boards, 12mo. N.Y., Leaf, Mahony, Seidel & Stokes, 1934.*

_____ The story of Ferdinand. *boards, 8vo. N.Y., Viking, 1936.*

**LEAR, EDWARD.** A book of laughable lyrics. *paper, 32mo. Girard, Kan., Haldeman-Julius, n.d. (Little Blue Books)*

_____ Complete nonsense of Edward Lear. *buckram, 8vo. N.Y., Dover, 1951.*

_____ Nonsense books. *buckram, 16mo. Bost., Roberts, 1896.*

_____ Nonsense botany and nonsense alphabets. *buckram, 8vo. Lond., Warne, 1896.*

_____ Nonsense songs and stories. *buckram, 8vo. Lond., Warne, 1894.*

_____ Teapots and quails, and other new nonsense. *boards, 4to. Lond., Murray, 1953.*

**LEARNED, A.G.** *and* **SPRAGUE, LEILA.** Adam's sons. *cloth, 8vo. N.Y., Sparrell, 1906.*

**LEARSI, RUFUS.** The book of Jewish humor. *buckram, 8vo. N.Y., Bloch, 1941.*

**LE BRETON, THOMAS.** Mrs. May; some chapters from the life of a charlady. *buckram, 8vo. Lond., Jenkins, 1922.*

**LECOMTE, EDWARD S.,** *comp.* Dictionary of last words. *buckram, 8vo. N.Y., Philosophical Library, 1955.*

**LEDERER, WILLIAM J.** Ensign O'Toole and me. *buckram, 12mo. Lond., Cassell, 1958.*

**LEE, ELIZABETH,** *ed. and trans.* The humour of France. *buckram, 12mo. Lond., Scott, 1893.*

**LEE, F.J.,** *ed.* Folk tales of all nations, *buckram, 8vo. N.Y., Coward-McCann, 1930.*

**LEE, JAMES ZEE-MIN.** Chinese potpourri. *buckram, 8vo. Hongkong, Oriental Pub. Co., 1951. 2d.ed.*

**LEECH, JOHN.** Drawings. *boards, 16mo. N.Y., Henderson, n,d.*

_____ Pictures by John Leech. Second series. *paper, 24mo. Lond., Gowans & Gray, 1907.*

_____ Pictures of life and character from the collection of Mr. Punch. *5v. quarter-calf., wide folio. Lond., Bradbury & Evans, 1863.*

_____ Same. 1886.

**LEGEND OF THE WANDERING JEW, THE,** a series of twelve designs by Gustave Dore. *boards, folio, Chic., Belford, Clarke, n.d.*

LEGEY, FRANCOISE. The folk-
lore of Morocco. *buckram, 8vo.
Lond., Allen & Unwin, 1935.*

LEGLER, HENRY E. Library
ideals. *buckram, 8vo. Chic.,
Open Court Pub. Co., 1918.*

LEHMANN, ADOLPH. Vignettes.
*boards, 8vo. San Francisco,
Priv. Print., 1951.*

LEHR, LEW. Lew Lehr's cook-
book for men. *buckram, 8vo.
N.Y., Didier, 1949.*

——————— Stop me if you've
heard this one. *boards, 24mo.
N.Y., Permabooks, 1949.*

LEIGH, HENRY S., *ed.* Jeux
d'esprit, written and spoken
by French and English wits
and humourists. *buckram,
12mo. Lond., Chatto &
Windus. 1877.*

LEIGH, PERCIVAL. The comic
English grammar. *buckram,
12mo. Lond., Bentley, 1840.*

LEIGHTON, JOHN. Comic art
manufactures, collected by
Luke Limner, esq., *pseud.
buckram, 24mo. Lond., Bogue,
n.d.*

——————— Money: how Old
Brown made it and how young
Brown spent it. *2v. paper,
wide 24mo. Lond., Ackermann,
n.d.*

LEIMAN, EUGENE A. Lyrics
from "Lost in the stacks" a
musical review. *paper, 8vo.
N.Y., Association of the Bar
of the City of New York, 1953.*

LEISER, CLARA, *ed.* Lunacy
becomes us, by Adolf Hitler
and his associates. *buckram,
12mo. N.Y., Liveright, 1939.*

LELAND, CHARLES G. Hans
Breitmann in Germany. Tyrol.
*buckram, 12mo. Lond.,
T.Fisher Unwin, 1895.*

——————— Pidgin-English sing-
song, or Songs and stories in
the China-English dialect.
*buckram, 16mo. Lond., Kegan
Paul, Trench, Trubner, 1918,
9th ed.*

LE MAY, REGINALD, *trans.*
Siamese tales, old and new.
The four riddles and other
stories. *buckram, 8vo. Lond.,
Probsthain, 1958.*

——————— *Same:* with title:
Thai tales, old and new. *paper,
8vo. Shanghai, n.p. 1945.*

LEMON, MARK, *comp. and ed.*
The jest book; the choicest
anecdotes and sayings. *half-
calf., 16mo. Lond., Macmillan,
1864.*

——————— *Same. 1865, 1866,
1879, 1891.*

——————— Legends of Number
Nip. *buckram, 16mo. Lond.,
Macmillan, 1864.*

LEMONS, A PHEW, *pseud.* A
bunch of lemons. *cloth, 16mo.
N.Y., Caldwell, 1908.*

LENNON, FLORENCE BECKER.
Lewis Carroll. *buckram, 8vo.
Lond., Cassell, 1947.*

LENO, DAN. Dan Leno, hys booke.
*paper, 12mo. Lond., Greening,
1901. New and cheaper ed.*

LEONARD, HENRY. Open your
mouth and say "Oy". *paper,
8vo. N.Y., Crown, 1960.*

LEONARD, R.M. The book-lovers'
anthology. *buckram, 12mo.
Lond., Oxford Univ. Press,
1911.*

LEOPOLD, JULES. Check your wits! games, puzzles, and fun for all the family. *buckram, 8vo. N.Y., Whittlesey, 1948.*

LERNER, LEON L. Gob humor. *buckram, 8vo. Baltimore, Ottenheimer, 1953.*

LEROW, CAROLINE B. English as she is taught, being genuine answers to examination questions in our public schools. ..with a commentary thereon by Mark Twain. *paper, 24mo. Lond., T.Fisher Unwin, 1889. 3d.ed.*

LESLIE, JOHN. Interesting anecdotes, memoirs, allegories, essays and poetical fragments tending to amuse the fancy. *boards, 8vo. Aberdeen, Chalmers, 1882.*

LESSING, BRUNO. Jake or Sam. *boards, 12mo. N.Y., Fitzgerald, 1908.*

L'ESTRANGE, ALFRED GUY KINGAN. History of English humour, with an introduction upon ancient humour. *2v. buckram, 12mo. Lond., Hurst & Blackett, 1878.*

LETSLAFF, IKE'ENSMILE, *pseud.* Broad grins of the Laughing Philosopher. *paper, 16mo. N.Y., Dick & Fitzgerald, 1809?*

LETTERS FROM A CHINESE OFFICIAL: being an Eastern view of Western civilization. *boards, 16mo. N.Y., McClure, Phillips, 1906.*

LETTERS OF SHAHCOOLEN, a Hindu philosopher residing in Philadelphia to his friend El Hassan, an inhabitant of Delhi. *tree calf, 12mo. Bost., Russell & Cutler, 1802.*

LETTERS TO EGBERT FROM HIS UNCLE HEREWARD. *buckram, 8vo. Lond., Century, n.d.*

LETTICE, JOHN. Fables for the fire-side. *calf, 12mo. Lond., Black, 1812.*

LEVANT, OSCAR. A smattering of ignorance. *buckram, 8vo. N.Y., Doubleday, Doran, 1940.*

LEVENSON, SAMMY. Meet the folks; a session of American-Jewish humor. *buckram, 12mo. N.Y., Citadel, 1946.*

LEWIS, CHARLES LEE. Comic sketches; or, The comedian his own manager. *tree calf., 16mo. Lond., Symonds, 1804.*

LEWIS, CHARLES BERTRAND. Brother Gardner's Lime-Kiln Club, being the regular proceedings of the regular club for the last three years. With some philosophy, considerable music, a few lectures, and a heap of advice worth reading. Not compiled in the interest of Congress, or any department of government, by M.Quad and Brother Gardner. *buckram, 12mo. Chic., Donohue, Henneberry, 1890.*

———— "Quad's odds" by "M.Quad, the Detroit Free Press man." Anecdote, humor and pathos, and other things. *buckram, 8vo. Detroit, Tyler, 1875.*

———— Sawed-off sketches, humorous and pathetic. *buckram, 12mo. N.Y., Carleton, 1884.*

———— Sparks of wit and humour, by M.Quad. *paper, 12mo. Lond., Routledge, n.d.*

LEWIS, CLIVE STAPLES.
Surprised by joy. *buckram,*
*8vo. Lond., Bles, 1955.*

LEWIS, D.B. WYNDHAM, *ed.* I
couldn't help laughing! An
anthology of war-time humour.
*buckram, 8vo. Lond., Drum-*
*mond, 1941.*

_____ The nonsensibus.
*buckram, 12mo. Lond.,*
*Methuen, 1936.*

LEWIS, E.C., *comp.* After dinner
stories. *buckram, 12mo. Bost.,*
*Mutual, 1905.*

_____ Aint it awful?
*buckram, 24mo. Bost., Mutual,*
*1910.*

_____ Cheer up. *buckram,*
*24mo. Bost., Mutual, 1912.*

_____ Everybody up, a book
of toasts. *buckram, 16mo. Bost.*
*Mutual, 1901.*

_____ Irish and Scotch
mixed; an Irish bull. *buckram,*
*16mo. Bost., Mutual, 1912.*

_____ Ish ga bibble (I
should worry). *buckram, 16mo.*
*Bost., Mutual, 1914.*

_____ Smile, don't worry.
*buckram, 24mo. N.Y., Caldwell,*
*1909.*

_____ Stung again. *buck-*
*ram, 24mo. N.Y., Caldwell,*
*1908.*

_____ Up-to-date conun-
drums. *buckram, 24mo. Bost.,*
*Mutual, 1903.*

LEWIS, FREDERICK W. One
man's philosophy. *buckram,*
*8vo. N.Y., American Book-*
*Stratford Press, 1957.*

LEWIS, JERRY D., *ed.* Dealer's
choice; the world's greatest
poker stories. *buckram, 8vo.*
*N.Y., Barnes, 1955.*

LEWIS, LLOYD. Myths after
Lincoln. *buckram, 12mo. N.Y.,*
*Blue Ribbon, 1929.*

LEWIS, OSCAR. Bay window
Bohemia. *buckram, 8vo. N.Y.,*
*Doubleday, 1956.*

_____ Fabulous San
Simeon. *paper, 8vo. San*
*Francisco, California*
*Historical Society, 1958.*

_____ The town that died
laughing; the story of Austin,
Nevada. *buckram, 8vo. Bost.,*
*Little, Brown, 1955.*

LEWIS, OSWALD, *comp.* After
dinner; being a collection of
quotations and stories suitable
for after dinner speeches.
*boards, 12mo. Lond., Newman*
*Neame, 1955.*

LEWIS, THOMAS H. That's a good
one! The lighter side of business in story, epigram and
verse. *buckram, 12mo. Lond.,*
*May & Curtis, 1938.*

LIANG SHIH-CH'FU. The fine art
of reviling. *boards, 16mo. San*
*Francisco, Kibbee, 1949.*

LIAS, JOHN JAMES. Are miracles
credible? *buckram, 12mo. Lond,*
*Hodder & Stoughton, 1889.*

LIBER FACETIARUM, being a
collection of curious and interesting anecdotes. *calf., 16mo.*
*Newcastle upon Tyne, Aken-*
*head, 1809.*

_____ Same. *Bost.,*
*Williams, 1811.*

LIBRARY OF ANECDOTE AND
INFORMATION. *buckram, 12mo.*
*Lond., Lacey, n.d.*

LICHTY, GEORGE. Grin and bear it. *boards, 8vo. N.Y., McGraw-Hill, 1954.*

LIEBLING, A.J. Mink and red herring; the wayward pressman's casebook. *buckram, 8vo. N.Y., Doubleday, 1949.*

LIEDERMAN, AL. Li'l leaguer. *paper, 16mo. N.Y., Pocket Books, 1960.*

LIFE. *see also* NEW YORK LIFE.

LIFE. v.1. no.1. January 4, 1883. *miniature copy. N.Y., Life Office, 1883.*

LIFE AND ADVENTURES OF BILLY PURVIS, containing many humorous incidents and anecdotes not hitherto published. *paper, 12mo. Newcastle-on-Tyne, Bowman, 1875.*

LIFE AND ADVENTURES, SONGS, SERVICES AND SPEECHES OF PRIVATE MILES O'REILLY, 47th regiment, New York Volunteers. *buckram, 12mo. N.Y., Carlton, 1864.*

LIFE AND MEMOIRS OF WILLIAM WARREN, Boston's favorite comedian, with a full account of his golden jubilee. *buckram, 12mo. Bost., Daly, 1882.*

LIFE OF JAMES ALLAN, the celebrated Northumberland piper, and other branches of his extra-ordinary family. *boards, 8vo. Blyth, Guthrie, 1818. New ed.*

LIFE OF MR. JAMES QUIN, comedian, with the history of the stage from commencing actor to his retreat to Bath ... to which is added a supplement of original facts and anecdotes, arranged from authentic sources. Together with his trial for the murder of Mr. Bowen. *boards, 16mo. Lond., Reader, 1887.*

LIFE, PROPHECIES AND DEATH OF THE FAMOUS MOTHER SHIPTON. *pamphlet. Acton, Wainwright, n.d.*

LILLARD, JOHN F.B. The medical muse, grave and gay. *paper, 12mo. N.Y., Booth, 1895.*

LILLY, WILLIAM SAMUEL. Four English humourists of the nineteenth century. *buckram, 8vo. Lond., Murray, 1895.*

LIMNER, LUKE, *pseud.* see LEIGHTON, JOHN.

LIN YUTANG. Between tears and laughter. *buckram, 12mo.Lond., Crisp, 1945.*

——————— The importance of understanding. *buckram, 8vo. Lond., Heinemann, 1961.*

——————— On the wisdom of America. *buckram, 8vo. N.Y., Day, 1950.*

——————— Tales and parables of old China. *paper, 8vo. San Francisco, Book Club of California, 1943. (Guardians of the Pacific, no.2.)*

——————— The wisdom of China and India. *buckram, 8vo. N.Y., Random, 1942.*

LINCOLN, ABRAHAM. Abraham Lincoln's stories and speeches. *buckram, 12mo. Chic., Rhodes & McClure, 1896.*

_____ Anecdotal Lincoln; speeches, stories, and yarns of the "Immortal Abe". *buckram, 12mo. Chic., Thompson & Thomas, 1900.*

_____ Anecdotes of Abraham Lincoln and Lincoln's stories. Ed. by J.B. McClure. *buckram, 8vo. Chic., Rhodes & McClure, 1879.*

_____ Concise Lincoln dictionary; thoughts and statements. Compiled and arranged by Ralph B. Winn. *buckram, 12mo. N.Y., Philosophical Library, 1959.*

_____ Humor and wisdom of Abraham Lincoln. *paper, 32mo. Girard, Kan., Haldeman-Julius, n.d. (Little Blue Books.)*

_____ Lincoln encyclopedia. Compiled by Archer Shaw. *buckram, 4to. N.Y., Macmillan, 1950.*

_____ The Lincoln reader. Edited by Paul M. Angle. *buckram, 8vo. New Brunswick, Rutgers, 1947.*

_____ The Lincoln story book. Compiled by Henry L. Williams. *buckram, 12mo. N.Y., Dillingham, 1907.*

_____ Lincoln talks; a biography in anecdote, collected, collated and edited by Emanual Hertz. *buckram, 12mo. N.Y., Viking, 1939.*

_____ Lincoln's own stories, collected and edited by Anthony Gross. *buckram, 12mo. N.Y., Harper, 1912.*

_____ Lincoln's stories and speeches. Edited by Edward Frank Allen. *buckram, 8vo. N.Y., Books, inc., n.d.*

_____ Lincoln's wit. Edited by Brant House. *paper, 16mo. N.Y., Ace, 1958.*

_____ Lincoln's yarns and stories. Edited by A.K. McClure. *buckram, 8vo. Toronto, Winston, n.d.*

_____ *Same;* with title: "ABE" Lincoln's yarns and stories. *Chic., Thompson & Thomas, 1901.*

_____ Literary works of Abraham Lincoln. Selected and arranged by Carl Van Doren. *buckram, 8vo. N.Y., Readers Club, 1942.*

_____ Mr. Lincoln's funnybone; wherein the White House Joker retells his best yarns and fables. Edited by Loyd Dunning. *buckram, 16mo. N.Y., Howell, Soskin, 1942.*

_____ Selections from Abraham Lincoln. Edited by Joy Elmer Morgan. *paper, 24mo. (Personal growth leaflets.)*

_____ Wit and wisdom of Abraham Lincoln as reflected in his briefer letters and speeches. *buckram, 8vo. Cleveland, World, 1943.*

LINCOLN, GEOFFREY. No moaning of the bar. *buckram, 12mo. Lond., Bles, 1957.*

LINCOLN AND DEMOCRATIC LEADERSHIP; a radio discussion by Avery Craven, Charles Merriam and T.V. Smith. *pamphlet. Chic., Univ. of Chicago Press, 1947.*

LINCOLN IN CARICATURE: a
historical collection with
descriptive and biographical
commentaries by Rufus Rockwell Wilson. *buckram, 4to.
N.Y., Horizon, 1953.*

LINCOLN WHO LIVES IN ANEC-
DOTE, THE. *pamphlet,
Reader's Digest, Feb. 1959.*

LINCOLNIANA; a catalogue of
historic autograph letters and
documents from the Justin G.
Turner Collection of Americana. Exhibited at Occidental
College, Los Angeles, April
15-May 15, 1957. *pamphlet.*

LINDNER, CLARENCE R.
Private Lindner's letters,
censored and uncensored.
*buckram, 4to. San Francisco,
Priv. Print., 1939.*

LINDSAY, CYNTHIA. The climate
of lunacy, an unnatural history
of Southern California. *buckram, 8vo. Lond., Hamilton,
1960.*

——————— Mother climbed trees.
*buckram, 8vo. Lond., Hamilton,
1958.*

LINDSLEY, PHILIP. The humor
of the court room, or, Jones
vs. Johnson. *buckram, 12mo.
Dallas, Worley, 1899.*

LINE O'TYPE OR TWO, A.
*boards, 8vo. n.p., n.d.*

LINKLETTER, ART. Kids say the
darndest things! *buckram, 8vo.
Kingswood, Surrey, World's
Work, 1957.*

——————— People are funny.
*buckram, 12mo. Garden City,
Doubleday, 1947.*

——————— The secret world of
kids. *paper, 16mo. N.Y., Pocket
Books, 1960.*

LINKS, MARTY. Bobby sox; the
life and times of Emmy Lou.
*boards, 8vo. N.Y., Hawthorn,
1954.*

LINN, S. POLLOCK. Living
thoughts of leading thinkers; a
thesaurus. *buckram, 12mo.
Pittsburg, Foster, 1872.*

LINSCOTT, HILDA BATES.
Bright ideas for entertaining.
*buckram, 8vo. N.Y., Grosset &
Dunlap, 1935. New and enl.ed.*

LINSCOTT, ROBERT N., *ed.* Best
American humorous short
stories. *buckram, 12mo. N.Y.,
Modern Library, 1945.*

——————— Comic relief; an
omnibus of modern American
humor. *buckram, 12mo. N.Y.,
Laugh Club, 1942.*

LINTON, RALPH. The lore of
birthdays. *buckram, 12mo.
Lond., Rider, 1953.*

LITERARY GEMS: or, 1000 anecdotes and jests, being a selection of humourous, gay,
sentimental and pathetic
morceaux, for the amusement
and instruction of those who in
journeying through life like to
be enlivened and enlightened
by the way. *buckram, 24mo.
Lond., Thomas, 1834. 2d.ed.*

LITTLE, CHARLES, *comp.*
Historical lights, 6000 quotations from standard histories
and biographies. *buckram, 4to.
Lond., Funk & Wagnalls, 1910.*

LITTLE JOKE BOOK, THE.
*boards, 12mo. Mount Vernon,
N.Y., Peter Pauper Press, n.d.*

LITTLE LIMERICK BOOK.
*boards, 12mo. Mount Vernon,
N.Y., Peter Pauper Press, 1955.*

LITTLE PILGRIM'S PEEPS AT PARNASSUS, A. *buckram, 4to. Lond., Holden, 1927.*

LITTLE STORIES. *mimeographed pamphlet. Cleveland, National Reference Library, 1951.*

LIVES AND PORTRAITS OF REMARKABLE CHARACTERS, drawn from the most authentic sources. *2v. leather, 8vo. Lond., Lewis, 1819. New ed.*

LLOYD, HENRY. The smoking concert reciter. *buckram, 12mo. Lond., Hutchinson, 1890.*

LOAR, JACQUES. Ersatz war jokes. *paper, 12mo. Ghent, Snoeck-Ducaju, 1944.*

LOARING, HENRY JAMES, *comp.* Curious records, being a collection of beautiful and interesting epitaphs, with remarks on obsequies. *half-calf, 16mo. Lond., Tegg, 1872.*

——————— Epitaphs; quaint, curious and elegant. *buckram, 16mo. Lond., Tegg, 1873?*

LOBSENZ, MARGERY DARRELL. Her bedside companion. *buckram, 8vo. Englewood Cliffs, N.J., Prentice-Hall, 1957.*

LOBSENZ, NORMAN M. His bedside companion. *buckram, 8vo. Englewood Cliffs, N.Y., Prentice-Hall, 1957.*

LOCHNER, LOUIS P. Always the unexpected; a book of reminiscences. *buckram, 8vo. N.Y., Macmillan, 1956.*

LOCKE, DAVID ROSS. Divers views, opinions and prophecies, by Petroleum V. Nasby, pseud. *buckram, 8vo. Cincinnati, Carroll, 1867. 6th ed.*

——————— Ekkoes from Kentucky. *buckram, 12mo. Bost., Lee & Shepard, 1868.*

——————— Morals of Abou Ben Adhem. *buckram, 12mo. Bost., Lee & Shepard, 1875.*

——————— Let's laugh. *paper, 32mo. Girard, Kan., Haldeman-Julius, n.d. (Little Blue Books)*

——————— Nasby in exile; or, Six months of travel in England, Ireland, Scotland, France, Germany, Switzerland and Belgium; with many things not of travel. *buckram, 8vo. Toledo, Locke, 1882.*

——————— The Nasby letters, being the original Nasby letters as written during his lifetime. *boards, 8vo. Toledo, Toledo Blade, 1893.*

——————— "Swingin round the cirkle" ideas of men, politics and things ... *buckram, 12mo. Bost., Lee & Shepard, 1867.*

LOCKMAN, JOHN. The entertaining instructor. *calf., 12mo. Lond., Millar, 1765.*

LOCKRIDGE, NORMAN, *ed.* Golden treasury of the world's wit and wisdom. *buckram, 8vo. N.Y., Black Hawk Press, 1936.*

——————— Waggish tales of the Czechs; originally entitled Gesta Czechorum. *buckram, 8vo. Candide Press, 1947.*

LOEB, SOPHIE IRENE. Epigrams of Eve. *boards, 8vo. N.Y., Doran, 1913.*

LOFTING, HUGH. Doctor Dolittle's zoo. *buckram, 8vo. N.Y, Stokes, 1925.*

LOMAX, STAN. *and* STANLEY, DAVE. Treasury of baseball humor. *buckram, 8vo. N.Y., Lantern, 1950.*

LONDON BUDGET OF WIT. *half-calf., 24mo. Lond., Walker & Edwards, 1817.*

LONDON ANECDOTES. 6 pts in 2v. *half-calf.*, *32mo. Lond., Bogue, 1848?*

LONDON CHARACTERS AND THE HUMOROUS SIDE OF LONDON LIFE. *buckram, 12mo. Lond., Rivers, n.d.*

LONDON JESTER, or Museum of mirth, wit and humour. Illustrated by G.Cruikshank. *buckram, 8vo. Lond., Hogdson, n.d.*

—————— Same. *Lond., Smeeton, n.d.*

LONDON MATHEWS; containing an account of this celebrated comedian's trip to America. *paper, 16mo. Phila., Morgan & Yeager, 1824.*

LONG, J. Eastern proverbs and emblems illustrating old truths. *buckram, 8vo. N.Y., Funk & Wagnalls, n.d.*

LONG, W.H., *ed.* Naval yarns, letters and anecdotes, comprising accounts of sea fights and wrecks, actions with pirates and privateers, &c. from 1616 to 1831. *buckram, 12mo. Lond., Gibbins, 1899.*

LONGSTREET, AUGUSTUS BALDWIN. Georgia scenes, characters, incidents, &c. in the first half century of the Republic. By a Native Georgian. *buckram, 12mo. N.Y., Harper, 1860.*

LONSDALE, FREDERICK. The last of Mrs. Cheyney. *paper, 12mo. N.Y., French, 1929.*

LOOMIS, CHARLES BATTELL. Cheer up! *boards, 12mo. N.Y., Pott, 1906.*

—————— Cheerful Americans. *buckram, 12mo. N.Y., Holt, 1903.*

—————— More cheerful Americans. *buckram, 12mo. N.Y., Holt, 1904.*

LOOS, ANITA. "Gentlemen prefer blondes." *buckram, 12mo. N.Y., Boni & Liveright, 1925.*

LORANT, STEFAN. The lilliput pocket omnibus. *buckram, 12mo. Lond., Pocket Pub. n.d.*

LORD, PHILLIPS H. Seth Parker's album, by Seth Parker, *pseud. buckram, 8vo. N.Y., Century, 1930.*

LORENZ, KONRAD Z. Man meets dog. *buckram, 8vo. Lond., Methuen, 1954.*

LORIMER, GEORGE HORACE. Letters from a self-made merchant to his son. *buckram, 12mo. Bost., Small, Maynard, 1905.*

LOT OF BALLYHOO, A. *boards, 16mo. Racine, Whitman, 1933.*

LOT OF ROT, A; funny stories. *paper, 12mo. Lond., Success Pub. n.d.*

LOTT, NOAH, pseud. see HOBART, GEORGE VERE.

LOUNGER'S COMMON-PLACE BOOK, or, Alphabetical arrangement of miscellaneous anecdotes. *3v. quarter-calf., 8vo. Lond., Kerby, 1792.*

LOUYS, PIERRE. Collected works. *buckram, 8vo. N.Y., Liveright, 1932.*

LOVE LETTERS OF MEN AND WOMEN OF GENIUS. *paper, 32mo. Girard, Kan., Haldeman-Julius, n.d. (Little Blue Books)*

LOVERIDGE, ARTHUR. Many happy days I've squandered. *buckram, 8vo. N.Y., Harper, 1944.*

LOW, DAVID. Europe since
Versailles. *paper, 32mo.
Harmondsworth, Penguin,
1940.*

—————— Lions and lambs,
with interpretations by "Lynx".
*buckram, 4to. Lond., Cape,
1928.*

—————— Low again; a pag-
eant of politics. *boards, 8vo.
Lond., Cresset, 1938.*

—————— Low and Terry.
*buckram, 8vo. Lond.,
Hutchinson, 1934.*

—————— Low visibility; a
cartoon history, 1945-1953.
*buckram, 4to. Lond., Collins,
1953.*

—————— *Same;* with title:
Low's cartoon history, 1945-
1953. *N.Y., Simon & Schuster,
1953.*

—————— Low's Russian
sketchbook. Text by Kingsley
Martin. *buckram, 8vo. Lond.,
Gollancz, 1932.*

—————— Man, the lord of
creation. *paper, 12mo. Lond.,
Putnams, n.d.*

—————— Years of wrath; a cartoon history, 1931-1945. *buckram, 4to. N.Y., Simon &
Schuster, 1946.*

—————— Ye madde designer.
*buckram, 4to. Lond., Studio,
1935.*

LOWE, ED. *comp. and ed.*
Sextasy. *paper, 16mo. N.Y.,
Hillman, 1960.*

LOWE, H.Y. Stories from Chinese
drama. *paper, 8vo. Peking,
Peking Chronicle, 1952.*

LOWE, PAUL E., *ed.* After-dinner
stories. *buckram, 12mo. Phila.,
McKay, 1916.*

—————— Hot stuff joke book.
*paper, 32mo. Baltimore, Otten-
heimer, 1920.*

—————— The minstrel guide
and joke book, a comprehen-
sive guide to the organization
and conducting of a minstrel
show. *paper, 12mo. Baltimore,
Ottenheimer, 1912.*

—————— New tramp joke
book. *paper, 16mo. Baltimore,
Ottenheimer, 1907.*

—————— Twentieth century
book of toasts, gems of thought
from master minds. *paper,
12mo. Phila., McKay, n.d.*

LOWE, T.A. We all go the
pictures. *buckram, 12mo.
Lond., Hodge, 1937.*

LOWELL, JAMES RUSSELL. The
Biglow papers. *paper, 16mo.
Lond., John Camden Hotten,
1864. 4th English ed.*

LOWELL, JULIET. Dear Doctor.
*paper, 16mo. N.Y., Dell, 1958.*

—————— Dear folks. *paper,
16mo. N.Y., Permabooks, 1960.*

—————— Dear Hollywood.
*buckram, 16mo. N.Y., Duell,
Sloane & Pearce, 1950.*

—————— Dear Justice.
*boards, 16mo. N.Y., Mill, 1958.*

—————— Dear Mr. Congress-
man. *buckram, 16mo. N.Y.,
Duell, Sloan & Pearce, 1948.*

—————— Dear Sir: *buckram,
24mo. N.Y., Duell, Sloan &
Pearce, 1944.*

—————— Dear Sir or Madam.
*buckram, 16mo. N.Y., Duell,
Sloan & Pearce, 1946.*

—————— Dumb belles-lettres,
lallapaloozas from the morning
mail. *paper, 12mo. N.Y., Simon
& Schuster, 1935.*

LU HSUN. A brief history of Chinese fiction. *boards, 12mo. Peking, Foreign Languages Press, 1959.*

LUBBOCK, *Sir* JOHN. Tact. *paper, 16mo. Jersey City, Wells, 1954. Rev.ed.*

LUCAS, EDWARD VERRALL. A Boswell of Baghdad with diversions. *buckram, 12mo. Lond., Methuen, 1917.*

——————— Character and comedy. *buckram, 12mo. Lond., Methuen, 1907. 2d.ed.*

——————— Events and embroideries. *paper, 12mo. N.Y., Doran, 1927.*

——————— The gentlest art, and The second post; a choice of letters by entertaining hands. *buckram, 16mo. Lond., Methuen, 1925.*

——————— Good company, a rally of men. *buckram, 12mo. Lond., Methuen, 1909.*

——————— Quoth the raven. *paper, 12mo. Lond., Methuen, 1919.*

——————— Some more good ones; a bookful of funny stories. *buckram, 12mo. Lond., Foulsham, n.d.*

LUCAS, W.T. That's a good one! A fine collection of snappy laughter-making tales. *buckram, 12mo. Lond., Foulsham, 1930.*

LUCIANUS SAMOSATENSIS. True history, and Lucius, or the Ass. *buckram, 8vo. Bloomington, Indiana Univ. Press, 1958.*

LUDOVICI, ANTHONY M. The secret of laughter. *buckram, 16mo. Lond., Constable, 1932.*

LUM AND ABNER *see* LAUCK, CHESTER.

LUNN, HUGH KINGSMILL. An anthology of invective and abuse, by Hugh Kingsmill, *pseud.*

——————— More invective. *buckram, 12mo. Lond., Eyre & Spottiswoode, 1930.*

——————— What they said at the time; an anthology. *buckram, 12mo. Lond., Wishart, 1935.*

——————— The worst of love, an anthology. *buckram, small 8vo. Lond., Eyre & Spottiswoode, 1931.*

LUPTON, MARTHA, *ed.* Speaker's desk book. *buckram, 8vo. N.Y., Grosset & Dunlap, 1948.*

——————— The treasury of modern humor. *buckram, 8vo. Indianapolis, Droke, 1938.*

LURIE, CHARLES N. Make 'em laugh! humorous stories for all occasions. *buckram, 16mo. N.Y., Putnam's, 1927.*

——————— Make 'em laugh again! *buckram, 16mo. N.Y., Putnam's 1928.*

LUSTY CARTOON LAUGH-GUIDE TO THE WONDERFUL WORLD OF GIRLS, A. *paper, 16mo. N.Y., Zenith, 1960.*

LY HOI SANG. Book of everlasting gifts from ancient sages. *boards, 12mo. N.Y., Long Sang Ti Chinese Curios co., 1927.*

LYLY, JOHN. Euphues. The anatomy of wit. Editio princeps, 1579. Euphues and his England. Editio princeps, 1580. Collected with early subsequent editions. Carefully edited by Edward Arber. *paper, 16mo. Lond., Murray, 1868.*

——————— *Same. Lond., Constable, 1919.*

LYNES, RUSSELL. Guests, or, How to survive hospitality. *boards, 12mo. N.Y., Harper, 1951.*

——————— Snobs; a guidebook to your friends, your enemies, your colleagues and yourself. *buckram, 12mo. N.Y., Harper, 1950.*

LYNN, KENNETH S., *ed.* The comic tradition in America. *buckram, 12mo. Lond., Gollancz, 1958.*

LYONS, JIMMY, *comp.* Encyclopedia of stage material, containing witty jokes, recitations, sidewalk conversation, monologues &c. &c. *boards, 8vo. Bost., Baker, 1925.*

——————— The mirth of a nation. *buckram, 8vo. N.Y., Vantage, 1953.*

LYTTON, CHARLES EDWARD BULER-LYTTON, *baron.* The Siamese twins; a satirical tale of the times. *half-calf., 8vo. Lond., Colburn & Bentley, 1831.*

# M

"MAC" Cartoons of the great war. 3v. buckram, folio. Cape Town, Cape Times, 1914-1919.

MCASTOCKER, DAVID P. Flash lights. buckram, 16mo. Milwaukee, Bruce, 1929.

MCCABE, JOSEPH. The Epicurean doctrine of happiness. paper, 32mo. Girard, Kan., Haldeman-Julius, n.d. (Little Blue Books)

MACCALLUM TELLS FUNNY STORIES. buckram, 12mo. Munchen, Piper, 1929.

MACCAMPBELL, DONALD. Reading for enjoyment. boards, 16mo. N.Y., Permabooks, n.d.

MCCANN, REBECCA. The cheerful cherub. buckram, 12mo. Chic., Covici, 1927.

MCCARTHY, JUSTIN. More Brother Juniper. paper, 16mo. N.Y., Pocket Books, 1961.

MCCLURE, J.B. Entertaining anecdotes from every available source. buckram, 8vo. Chic., Rhodes & McClure, 1880.

——————— 2,000 jokes and jests. Wit, humor and anecdote. buckram, 12mo. Chic., Rhodes & McClure, 1882.

MCCLURE, JOHN. The stag's hornbook. buckram, 16mo. N.Y., Knopf, 1918.

MCCLURE'S MAGAZINE. Humor. Tales from McClure's. buckram, 24mo. N.Y., Doubleday & McClure, 1897.

MCCORD, DAVID. The camp at Lockjaw. boards, 12mo. N.Y., Doubleday, 1952.

——————— Odds without ends. buckram, 8vo. Bost., Little, Brown, 1954.

——————— Once and for all. buckram, 8vo. N.Y., Coward-McCann, 1929.

——————— What cheer; an anthology of American and British humorous and witty verse. buckram, 12mo. N.Y., Coward-McCann, 1945.

MCCORMICK, DELL J. Paul Bunyan swings his axe. buckram, 8vo. Caldwell, Idaho, Caxton, 1955.

——————— Tall timber tales; more Paul Bunyan stories. buckram, 8vo. Caldwell, Caxton, 1951.

MCCORMICK, ELSIE. The unexpurgated diary of a Shanghai baby. buckram, 8vo. Shanghai, China Press, n.d.

MCCOY, PAUL S. Holiday chuckles; a collection of comedies to celebrate the various holidays. paper, 12mo. Minneapolis, Northwestern Press, 1938.

MCCUTCHEON, JOHN T. Congressman Pumphrey, the people's friend. buckram, 8vo. Indianapolis, Bobbs-Merrill, 1907.

——————— The mysterious stranger and other cartoons. boards, folio, N.Y., McClure, Phillips, 1905.

MACDONALD, BETTY. The plague and I. buckram, 8vo. Lond., Hammond, Hammond, 1948.

MACDONALD, NORMAN. Maxims and moral reflections. boards, 12mo. N.Y., Collins & Hannay, 1827.

MACDONALD, W.H. Yarns,
ancient and modern. *paper,*
*12mo. Lond., Hodge, 1942.*

MACDOUGALL, CURTIS D.
Hoaxes, *paper, 8vo. N.Y.,*
*Dover, 1958.*

MCDOWELL, CHARLES. One
thing after another. *buckram,*
*8vo. Richmond, Va. Dietz,*
*1960.*

MCELROY, JOHN. Si Klegg; his
transformation from a raw
recruit to a veteran. *paper,*
*12mo. Washington, National*
*Tribune Co., 1910. 2d.ed.*

MCEVOY, J.P. Slams of life.
*quarter-boards, 8vo. Chic.,*
*Volland, 1919.*

MCGINTY'S JOKE BOOK, and the
true story of the life of the
celebrated Daniel. *paper, 8vo.*
*N.Y., Ivers, 1889.*

MCGIVERN, WILLIAM P. *and*
MCGIVERN, MAUREEN.
Mention my name in Mombasa.
*boards, 8vo. N.Y., Dodd,*
*Mead, 1958.*

MCGOWAN, NORMAN. My years
with Churchill. *buckram, 8vo.*
*N.Y., British Book Centre,*
*1958.*

MACGREGOR, ALEXANDER.
Highland superstitions. *buck-*
*ram, 8vo. Stirling, Mackay,*
*1901.*

MACGREGOR, FORBES *comp. and*
*ed.* Scots proverbs and rhymes.
*paper, 12mo. Edinburgh, Moray,*
*1948.*

MCGROARTY, JOHN, WALSH, M.
H. *and* BAXTER, J.K. Mac-
walbax; a collection of poems,
cartoons and comment. *paper,*
*4to. Panama City, Benedetti,*
*1926.*

MACHIAVELLI, NICCOLO. The
living thoughts of Machiavelli.
Presented by Count Carlo
Sforza. *buckram, 12mo. Lond.,*
*Cassell, 1949, 3d.ed.*

MCHUGH, HUGH, pseud. *see*
HOBART, GEORGE VERE.

MCHUGH, VINCENT. Caleb
Catlums America. *buckram,*
*8vo. N.Y., Stackpole, 1936.*

MCINTYRE, O.O. Another "Odd"
book, 25 selected stories.
*buckram, 12mo. N.Y., Cosmo-*
*politan, 1932. Second series.*

MCIVOR, IVOR BEN. Scottish
toasts. *boards, 16mo. N.Y.,*
*Caldwell, 1908.*

MACK, CHARLES E. Two black
crows in the A.E.F. *buckram,*
*12mo. Indianapolis, Bobbs-*
*Merrill, 1928.*

MACKAY, CHARLES. Extra-
ordinary popular delusions and
the madness of crowds.
*buckram, 8vo. N.Y., Page,*
*1932.*

MACKAY, WALLIS. His horn book
for the use of greenhorns and
others who would learn of the
anthropophagi and divers
strange things existing at the
end of the XIXth century.
*papers, 12mo. Lond., McQueen,*
*n.d.*

MACKAYE, PERCY. Yankee
fantasies. *buckram, 12mo.*
*N.Y., Duffield, 1912.*

MACKECHNIE, JOHN. Gaelic
without groans! *paper, 12mo.*
*Stirling, Mackay, n.d.*

MACKECHNIE, SAMUEL.
Popular entertainments through
the ages. *buckram, 8vo. Lond.,*
*Sampson Low, Marston, 1931.*

MCKEE, JOHN HIRAM, *comp.*
Coolidge wit and wisdom; 125
short stories about "Cal".
*buckram, 16mo. N.Y., Stokes,
1933.*

MCKEITHAN, D.M. Court trials in
Mark Twain, and other essays.
*buckram, 8vo. 's-Gravenhage,
Nijhof, 1958.*

MCKENNEY, RUTH. The loud
Red Patrick. *buckram, 12mo.
Lond., Hart-Davis, 1949.*

MACKENZIE, ALEXANDER. The
prophecies of the Brahan Seer
(Coinneach Odhar Fiosaiche).
*buckram, 12mo. Stirling,
Mackay, 1957.*

MACKENZIE, DONALD A. Indian
myth and legend. *buckram,
8vo. Lond., Gresham, n.d.*

MACKENZIE, HENRY. Anecdotes
and egotisms of Henry Mackenzie, 1745-1831. Edited by
Harold William Thompson.
*buckram, 8vo. Lond., Milford,
1927.*

MACKENZIE, WILLIAM J. The
cream o'Scottish humour.
*buckram, 8vo. Lond., Lane,
1933.*

MACKEY, JOSEPH. The froth
estate. *buckram, 12mo. N.Y.,
Prentice-Hall, 1946.*

MCKINNEY, LAURENCE. Lines
of least resistance. *buckram,
12mo. N.Y., Dutton, 1941.*

——————— People of note; a
score of symphony faces.
*buckram, 12mo. N.Y., Dutton,
1940.*

MCLAREN, MORAY. Understanding the Scots. *buckram, 12mo.
Lond., Muller, 1956.*

MACLAREN-ROSS, J. The funny
bone. *buckram, 8vo. Lond.,
Elek, 1956.*

——————— The stuff to give
the troops. *buckram, small
8vo. Lond., Cape, 1944.*

MACLEOD, NORMAN I., *ed.*
Moral and religious anecdotes.
*buckram, 8vo. Lond., Hamil-
ton, Adams, n.d.*

MACMANUS, GEORGE. Fun for
all; a collection of jokes, anecdotes and epigrams. *buckram,
8vo. Cleveland, World, 1948.*

MACMILLAN, MARY. More short
plays. *buckram, 12mo. Cinncinnati, Stewart & Kidd, 1917.*

——————— Short plays. *buckram,
12mo. Cinncinnati, Stewart &
Kidd, 1917.*

MACMURRAY, CLAIRE. ———————
and beat him when he sneezes.
*buckram, 8vo. N.Y., Stokes,
1941.*

MACNAMARA——————— *Dr.*
School-room humour. *paper,
16mo. Bristol, Arrowsmith,
1907. New and enl.ed.*

MCNEAL, T.A. Tom McNeal's
fables. *buckram, 12mo.
Topeka, Crane, 1900.*

MCNISH, ROBERT. The book of
aphorisms, by a Modern Pytha-
gorean. *buckram, 12mo. Glasgow, M'Phun, 1834.*

MCNULTY, JOHN. The world of
John McNulty. *buckram, 8vo.
N.Y., Doubleday, 1957.*

MCPHARLIN, PAUL. Love and
courtship in America. *boards,
16mo. N.Y., Hastings, 1946.*

MCQUEEN, SHERMAN J. A wee
bit o'Scotch. *paper, 12mo.
Monrovia, Calif., Author,
1931.*

MACRAE, DAVID. National
humour: Scottish-English-Irish-
Welsh-Cockney-American.
*buckram, 8vo. N.Y., Stokes,
n.d.*

—————— *Same. Paisley, A.
Gardner, 1915.*

MACTAVISH, ANGUS J. *comp.*
More Scotch, or, It's smart to
be thrifty. A new volume of
the best Scotch jokes. *buckram, 16mo. N.Y., MacSimon &
MacSchuster, 1932.*

—————— Scotch, or, It's
smart to be thrifty. *buckram,
16mo. N.Y., MacSimon &
MacSchuster, 1931.*

—————— *Same. Lond., Mel-
rose, n.d.*

MCVICKAR, HARRY WHITNEY.
The evolution of woman.
*buckram, 4to. N.Y., Harper,
1896.*

MACY, ALBERT WILLIAM.
Short-cut philosophy, home-
made and hand-turned. *boards,
16mo. N.Y., Sturgis & Walton,
1909.*

MAD. More trash from Mad, a collection of humor satire and
garbage from past issues.
*paper, 4to. N.Y., E.C. Publi-
cations, 1958.*

MAD *see also* GAINES,
WILLIAM M.

MAD PRANKS AND MERRY
JESTS OF ROBIN GOOD-
FELLOW. Reprinted from the
edition 1628. *half-calf, 12mo.
Lond., Percy Society, 1841.*

MAD STRIKES BACK! *paper,
16mo. N.Y., Ballantine, 1958.*

MADDEN, HENRY MILLER.
German travelers in Calif-
ornia. *boards, 8vo. Fairfax,
Calif., Mallette Dean for the
Roxburghe Club of San
Francisco, 1958.*

MADEMOISELLE FROM
ARMENTIERES. Illustrated by
Herb Roth with a discussion
of the song and origin by
John T. Winterich. *boards,
12mo. Mount Vernon, N.Y.,
Peter Pauper, 1953.*

MADISON'S BUDGET; a year book
of comedy material for vaudeville entertainers, containing
original monologues, sketches,
minstrel-first-parts, sidewalk
patter, farces, parodies on
popular songs and other kinds
of stage fun. *Volumes 17, 18,
20, N.Y., Madison.*

MADRANO, DAN M. Heap big
laugh. *buckram, 8vo. Tulsa,
Okla., Western Printing Co.,
1955.*

MAGNIAC, ADAM. Loopy lim-
ericks. *paper, 12mo. Lond.,
Jarrolds, n.d.*

MAHAFY, J.P. The principles of
the art of conversation. *buckram, 12mo. Lond., Macmillan,
1888. 2d. ed.*

MAHONY, PATRICK. Barbed wit &
malicious humor. *buckram,
8vo. N.Y., Citadel, 1956.*

MAHOOD, M.M. Fore! *boards,
wide 32mo. Lond., Hammond,
Hammond, 1959.*

—————— Not a word to a soul.
*buckram, 4to. Lond., Hammond,
Hammond, 1958.*

—————— Shakespeare's word-
play. *buckram, 8vo. Lond.,
Methuen, 1957.*

MAIR, JAMES ALLAN, *ed.* A handbook of proverbs. *half-calf, 16mo. Lond., Routledge, n.d.*

——————— 2000 familiar quotations. *boards, 16mo. Lond., Routledge, n.d.*

MAISTER, AL. An-am-ated verse. *buckram, 8vo. Bost., Humphries, 1946.*

MAJESTY OF THE LAW: a book of legal stories. *buckram, 12mo. Lond., Simpkin, Marshall, Hamilton, Kent, n.d.*

MAJOR IN WASHINGTON CITY, THE. Second series. *paper, 12mo. Chic., Neely, 1894.*

MAKER, ANN. Monologues for moderns. *paper, 12mo. Minneapolis, Northwestern Press, 1945.*

MALAMUD, BERNARD. The magic barrel. *boards, 8vo. Phila., Jewish Publication Society, 1958.*

MALCOLM-SMITH, GEORGE. The square peg. *buckram, 12mo. N.Y., Doubleday, 1952.*

MALLESON, MILES. Youth, a play in three acts. *paper, 12mo. Lond., Hendersons, 1916.*

MALLETT, RICHARD. Doggerel's dictionary. *buckram, 12mo. Lond., Cape, 1946.*

MALLOCH, D. MACLEOD. The book of Glasgow, anecdote. *boards, 8vo. Lond., Foulis, 1913.*

MALLOCH, DOUGLAS. Resawed fables. *buckram, 12mo. Chic., American Lumberman, 1911.*

MALONE, TED. *ed.* Yankee Doodles. *buckram, 8vo. N.Y., Garden City, 1943.*

MALONEY, RUSSELL. It's still Maloney, or, Ten years in the big city. *buckram, 12mo. Garden City, 1945.*

MAN WHO SOLD A GHOST, THE; Chinese tales of the 3d-6th centuries. *boards, 8vo. Peking, Foreign Languages Press, 1958.*

MANCHESTER, R.H. Ditty box ditties; a review of the season's best in cartoon and wit. *paper, 8vo. San Francisco, Naval Publication Co., 1921.*

MANCHESTER, WILLIAM ANGUS DROGO MONTAGU, *9th duke of.* My candid recollections. *buckram, 8vo. Lond., Grayson & Grayson, 1932.*

MANCHESTER GUARDIAN. The Bedside Guardian. Nos. 3,6,7, 8,9. *buckram, 8vo. Lond., Collins, 1954, 1957-1959.*

MANDEL, GEORGE, *ed.* From the horse's mouth. *buckram, small 8vo. N.Y., McBride, 1956.*

MANIS, J.J., *ed.* Proverbs of Turkey. *paper, 32mo. Girard, Kan., Haldeman-Julius, n.d.*

MANKOWITZ, WOLF. Make me an offer. *buckram, 12mo. Lond., Deutsch, 1952.*

MANN, HORACE. Horace Mann's letter to young Americans. *paper, 24mo. (Personal Growth Leaflets.)*

——————— Selections from Horace Mann. Edited by Joy Elmer Morgan. *paper, 24mo. (Personal Growth Leaflets.)*

MANN, LOUIS L. In quest of the bluebird. *buckram, 12mo. Chic., Glaser, 1938.*

MANNERS, J. HARTLEY. Happiness and other plays. *buckram, 12mo. N.Y., Dodd, Mead, 1914.*

MANNING, REG. Cartoon guide of California. *buckram, 12mo. N.Y., Augustin, 1939.*

MANNIX, DAN. Step right up! *buckram, 8vo. N.Y., Harper, 1951.*

MANSBRIDGE, NORMAN. The pale artist; studio peeps for the curious. *buckram, 12mo. Lond., Muller, 1947.*

MANYASIG, MUBIN. A brief selection of Turkish proverbs. *paper, 12mo. Istanbul, Turkish Press, Broadcasting and Tourist Department, n.d.*

———————— Nasreddin Hoca. *paper, narrow, 8vo. Istanbul, Turkish Press, Broadcasting and Tourist Department, 1959.*

MARBLE, THOMAS LITTLE-FIELD. Giuseppina; a play in one act. *paper, 12mo. Chic., Dramatic Pub. Co., 1909.*

MARCH, JOSEPH MONCURE. Fifteen lyrics. *buckram, 12mo. N.Y., Fountain, 1929.*

MARCH, WILLIAM. 99 fables. *buckram, 8vo. Mobile, Ala., Univ. of Alabama Press, 1960.*

MARCHANT, JAMES. An anthology of Jesus. *buckram, 12mo. N.Y., Harper, 1926.*

MARCOSSON, ISAAC F. Before I forget; a pilgrimage to the past. *buckram, 8vo. N.Y., Dodd, Mead, 1959.*

MARESCA, JAMES V. My flag is down; the diary of a New York taxi driver. *paper, 12mo. N.Y., Bantam, 1956.*

MARGOLIS, SIDNEY K. Turn your humor into money. *buckram, 8vo. N.Y., House of Little Books, 1938.*

MARIS, FAITH. African negro folk tales. *paper, 32mo. Girard, Kan., Haldeman-Julius, n.d. (Little Blue Books.)*

MARK TWAIN BIRTHPLACE MEMORIAL SHRINE. *(In: Missouri Historical Review, July, 1960.)*

MARKETOS, B.J., comp. A proverb for it; 1510 Greek sayings. *buckram, 8vo. N.Y., New World, 1945.*

MARKS, HENRY STACY. Pen and pencil sketches. *2v. buckram, 8vo. Lond., Chatto & Windus, 1894.*

MARKUN, LEO. The psychology of laughter. *paper, 32mo. Girard, Kan., Haldeman-Julius, n.d. (Little Blue Books.)*

MARMERY, J. VILLIN. Wit, wisdom and folly; pen and pencil flashes. *buckram, 8vo. Lond., Digby Long, n.d.*

MARMONTEL, JEAN FRANCOIS. Marmontel's moral tales. *buckram, 12mo. Lond., Allen, 1895.*

———————— Moral tales. 3v. in 1. *calf., 16mo. Lond., Cadell & Daves, 1800.*

MARPLES, MORRIS. Public school slang. *buckram, 12mo. Lond., Constable, 1940.*

———————— University slang. *buckram, 12mo. Lond., Williams & Norgate, 1950.*

MARQUIS, DON. archy and
mehitabel. *buckram, 12mo.
N.Y., Doubleday, Doran, 1937.*

——————— Best of Don Marquis.
*buckram, 12mo. N.Y., Double-
day, 1946.*

——————— the lives and times
of archy and mehitabel. *buckram, 12mo. N.Y., Doubleday,
1933.*

——————— The old soak. *buckram, 8vo. N.Y., Sun Dial, 1937.*

MARRIAGE JOKER, THE; com-
prising a house full of the
comicalities of connubial bliss.
*paper, 12mo. N.Y., Ivers, 1908.*

MARROU, HENRI. St. Augustine
and his influence through the
ages. *boards, 12mo. N.Y.,
Harper, 1957.*

MARSH, DANIEL L. The place of
religion in education. *paper,
24mo. (Personal Growth Leaflets.)*

MARSHALL, ALAN. Bumping into
friends. *buckram, 8vo. Melbourne, Cheshire, 1950.*

MARSHALL, ARTHUR. Nineteen to
to the dozen. *buckram, 12mo.
Lond., Hamilton, 1953.*

MARSHALL, ROBERT. The duke
of Killicrankie, a farcical
romance. *paper, 12mo. Lond.,
French, 1910.*

MARTEN, AMBROSE. The Stanley
tales, original and select. 6v.
*calf., 24mo. Lond., Morgan,
n.d.*

MARTIALIS, MARCUS VALERIUS.
Martial: the twelve books of
epigrams, translated by J.A.
Pott and F.A. Wright. *buckram, 8vo. Lond., Routledge,
n.d.*

MARTIN, ABE. *see* HUBBARD,
FRANK MCKINNEY.

MARTIN, BEN. Mr. Smith and Mr.
Schmidt; a story in pictures.
*boards, 4to. N.Y., Vanguard,
1940.*

MARTIN, DOUGLAS VASS.
Expectant fathers, their care
and treatment. *boards, 12mo.
St. Louis, De Vass, 1930.*

MARTIN, GEORGE M. Fun among
the masons. *buckram, 16mo.
Dundee, Winter, 1931.*

MARTIN, HENRY R. Comic epitaphs from the very best old
graveyards. *buckram, 12mo.
Mount Vernon, N.Y., Peter
Pauper, 1957.*

MARTIN, J.L. It happened ———————
in West Texas. *buckram, 12mo.
Dallas, Van Nort, 1945.*

MARTIN, LILLIEN J. Round the
world with a psychologist.
*buckram, 8vo. San Francisco,
Stacey, 1927.*

MARTIN, PHIL. What's so funny?
*paper, 12mo. N.Y., Author,
1954.*

MARTINE, ARTHUR. Martine's
droll dialogues and laughable
recitations. *boards, 16mo.
N.Y., Dick & Fitzgerald, 1870.*

MARVIN, DWIGHT EDWARDS, *ed.*
Curiosities in proverbs. *buckram, 12mo. N.Y., Putnam's,
1916.*

MARX, ARTHUR. Life with
Groucho. *buckram, 8vo. N.Y.,
Simon & Schuster, 1954.*

MARX, GROUCHO. Beds. *boards,
12mo. N.Y., Farrar & Rinehart, 1930.*

MARZUBAN-NAMA. The tales of Marzuban, translated from the Persian by Reuben Levy. *buckram, 8vo. Bloomington, Indiana University Press, 1959.*

MASANI, R.P. Court poets of Iran and India; an anthology of wit and verse. *paper, 8vo. Bombay, New Book co., 1938.*

MASEFIELD, JOHN. Salt-water ballads. *buckram, 12mo. N.Y., Macmillan, 1913.*

MASIN, HERMAN. Curve ball laughs. *paper, 12mo. N.Y., Lion Library, 1955.*

——————— Sports laughs. *paper, 12mo. N.Y., Lion Library, 1956.*

MASON, DEXTER. The art of drinking, or, What to make with what you have. *buckram, 12mo. N.Y., Farrar & Rinehart, 1930.*

MASON, WALT. "Horse sense" in verses tense. *buckram, 8vo. Chic., McClurg, 1920.*

——————— Rippling rhymes to suit the times. *limp leather, 12mo. Chic., McClurg, 1913.*

——————— Uncle Walt; the poet philosopher. *buckram, 8vo. Chic., Adams, 1911.*

——————— Uncle Walt's philosophy. *paper, 12mo. Bost., Wilde, 1912.*

——————— Walt Mason, his book. *buckram, 8vo. N.Y., Barse & Hopkins, 1916.*

MASQUERADE, THE; a collection of new enigmas, logographs, charades, rebusses, queries and transpositions. 2v in 1. *calf., 16mo. Lond., Wilkie, 1797, 1798.*

——————— *Same. Dublin, Wogan & Smith, 1800.*

——————— Selections from the Masquerade. *quarter-calf., 16mo. Lond., Baker & Fletcher, 1826.*

MASSON, THOMAS L., *comp. and ed.* Best stories in the world. *2v. buckram, 16mo. N.Y., Doubleday, Page, 1922.*

——————— A corner in women and other follies. *paper, 8vo. N.Y., Moffat, Yard, 1905.*

——————— The humor of love. *buckram, 12mo. N.Y., Moffat, Yard, 1906.*

——————— Listen to these. *buckram, 16mo. N.Y., Doubleday, Page, 1922.*

——————— Little masterpieces of wit and humor. *6v. buckram, 16mo. N.Y., Doubleday, Page, 1903.*

——————— Tom Masson's annual, ye comically inclined people's vade mecum. *buckram, 12mo. N.Y., Doubleday, Page, 1925.*

——————— Tom Masson's book of wit and humor. *buckram, 12mo. N.Y., Sears, 1927.*

MASTERPIECES OF AMERICAN HUMOR. *paper, 32mo. Girard, Kan., Haldeman-Julius, n.d. (Little Blue Books.)*

MASTERPIECES OF AMERICAN WIT. *paper, 32mo. Girard, Kan., Haldeman-Julius, n.d. (Little Blue Books.)*

MASTERPIECES OF GERMAN
HUMOR. *paper, 32mo. Girard,
Kan., Haldeman-Julius, n.d.
(Little Blue Books.)*

MASTERPIECES OF ITALIAN
HUMOR. *paper, 32mo. Girard,
Kan., Haldeman-Julius, n.d.
(Little Blue Books.)*

MASTERPIECES OF RUSSIAN
HUMOR. *paper, 32mo. Girard,
Kan., Haldeman-Julius, n.d.
(Little Blue Books.)*

MASTERPIECES OF SPANISH
HUMOR. *paper, 32mo. Girard,
Kan., Haldeman-Julius, n.d.
(Little Blue Books.)*

MASTERS, EDGAR LEE. Spoon
River anthology. *buckram,
12mo. N.Y., Macmillan, 1916.*

MATHERS, E. POWYS, *tr.* Eastern
love; one hundred and one
ribald tales; a collection of
amorous tales of the Orient.
*paper, 16mo. Greenwich, Conn.,
Fawcett, 1958.*

MATHERS, JAMES. From gun to
gavel. *buckram, 8vo. Lond.,
Souvenir, 1955.*

MATHEW, THEOBALD. Fifty
forensic fables by O. *buckram,
12mo. Lond., Butterworth,
1949.*

MATHEWS, CHARLES. Memoirs of
Charles Matthews, comedian.
*4v. half-calf, 8vo. Lond.,
Bentley, 1838.*

MATHEWS, CHARLES. My awful
dad; a comedy. *paper, 12mo.
Chic., Dramatic Pub. Co., n.d.*

MATHEWS, WILLIAM. Wit and
humor; their use and abuse.
*buckram, 12mo. Chic., Griggs,
1893.*

MATHIEWS, FRANKLIN K., *ed.*
Chuckles and grins. *buckram,
4to. N.Y., Grosset & Dunlap,
1928.*

MATRIMONIAL CEREMONIES
DISPLAYED: collected from the
papers of a rambling batchelor.
To which is added the comical
adventures of Sir Harry Fitzgerald. *buckram, 12mo. Lond.,
Serjeant, n.d.*

MATTHEWMAN, LISLE DE VAUX.
Brevities. *buckram, 16mo.
Phila., Coates, 1903.*

——————— Completed proverbs.
*buckram, 16mo. Phila., Coates,
1904.*

——————— Crankisms. *buckram,
16mo. Phila., Coates, 1901.*

——————— Rips and raps. *buckram, 16mo. N.Y., Stokes, 1903.*

MAUGHAM, WILLIAM SOMERSET,
*comp.* Tellers of tales. *buckram, 8vo. N.Y., Doubleday,
Doran, 1940.*

——————— Cakes and ale.
*buckram, 12mo. N.Y., Double-
day, 1930.*

——————— The unattainable; a
farce. *paper, 12mo. Lond.,
Heinemann, 1923.*

MAULDIN, BILL. Back home.
*buckram, 8vo. N.Y., Sloane,
1947.*

——————— A sort of saga.
*buckram, 8vo. N.Y., Sloane,
1949.*

——————— Up front. *buckram,
8vo. N.Y., Holt, 1945.*

MAUNDER, SAMUEL. The
scientific and literary treasury.
*calf, 16mo. Lond., Longman,
Brown, Green, Longmans &
Roberts, 1858.*

_____ The treasury of knowledge. *calf, 16mo. Lond., Longman, 1845. 16th ed.*

MAUPASSANT, GUY *de.* The portable Maupassant. *buckram, 16mo. N.Y., Viking, 1947.*

_____ Selected tales. *buckram, 4to. N.Y., Random, 1945.*

MAUREY, MAX. Rosalie, a comedy in one act. *paper, 12mo. N.Y., French, 1913.*

MAURICE, JACQUES. K.N.Pepper and other condiments putup for general use. *buckram, 12mo. N.Y., Rudd & Carleton, 1859.*

MAXIMS, CHARACTERS AND REFLECTIONS, CRITICAL, SATIRICAL AND MORAL. *calf, 12mo. Lond., Cadell, 1768. 3d.ed.*

MAXWELL, MARJORIE ELEANOR. The blessings of old age. *buckram, 12mo. Lond., Faber & Faber, 1954.*

MAXWELL, WILLIAM BABING-TON. The last man in. *paper, 24mo. Lond., Gowans & Gray, 1910.*

MAY, PHIL. Phil May's illustrated annual, 1899. Winter number. *half-calf, 8vo. Lond., Thacker, 1899.*

_____ Pictures by Phil May. *paper, 24mo. Lond., Gowans & Gray, 1910.*

_____ Sketches from "Punch". *buckram, 4to. Lond., Punch, 1903.*

MAYFIELD, JOHN S. Mark Twain vs. The Street Railway Co. *paper, 8vo. Priv. Print., 1926.*

MAYHEW, HORACE. The tooth-ache. *accordion fold in boards, Lond., Bogue, n.d.*

MAYO, CHARLES HORACE *and* MAYO, WILLIAM JAMES. Aphorisms of Dr. Charles Horace Mayo, 1865-1939 and Dr. William James Mayo, 1861-1959. Collected by Fredrick A. Willius. *buckram, 16mo. Springfield, Thomas, 1951.*

MAYO, HERBERT. Letters on the truths contained in popular superstitions. *buckram, 12mo. Frankfort a. Main, Sauerlaender, 1849.*

MAYO, ISA FYVIE, *comp.* Old stories and sayings from Japan and China. *buckram, 16mo. Lond., Daniel, n.d.*

MAYORGA, MARGARET GARDNER. Representative one-act plays by American authors. *buckram, 8vo. Bost., Little, Brown, 1919.*

MAZZINGHI, THOMAS JOHN *de.* Sanctuaries. *buckram, 4to. Stafford, Halden, 1887.*

MAZZINI, GIUSEPPE. The living thoughts of Mazzini. Presented by Ignazio Silone. *buckram, 12mo. Lond., Cassell, 1946. 2d.ed.*

MEAD, SHEPHERD. How to succeed with women without really trying. *buckram, 8vo. Lond., Boardman, 1958.*

_____ How to get rich in TV without really trying. *buckram, 8vo. N.Y., Simon & Schuster, 1956.*

MEADER, HERMAN LEE. Reflections of the morning after. *buckram, 24mo. Bost., Caldwell, 1903.*

MEADOWS, KENNY. Heads of the people. Portraits of the English. First series. *buckram, 8vo. Lond., Routledge, 1878.*

_____ *Same. Second series.*

MEARNS, DAVID C. Lincoln collections in the Library of Congress. *pamphlet. Washington, D.C. Govt. Print.Off.,1943. 2d.ed.*

MEDITATIONS IN WALL STREET. *buckram, 12mo. N.Y., Morrow, 1940.*

MEECHAM, MARIAN *and* GOLLAGHER, ELSIE, *eds.* Dictionary of humorous definitions. *paper, 24mo. Indianapolis, Droke, 1948.*

MEGARRY, R.E. Miscellany-at-law; diversion for lawyers and others. *buckram, 8vo. Lond., Stevens, 1955.*

MEHTA, N.P. Glimpses of the truth as they came to me. *boards, 12mo. Bombay, Hind Kitabs, 1953.*

MEIER, FREDERICK, *comp. and ed.* The joke tellers joke book. *buckram, 8vo. Phila., Blakiston, 1944.*

MEIER, GEORGE FREDERICK. The merry philosopher, or, thoughts on jesting. Now first translated into English from the German original. *boards, 16mo. Lond., Newbery & Nicoll, 1764.*

——————— Thoughts on jesting. Translated in the year 1764 from the 2d. German edition. Edited by Joseph Jones. *boards, 8vo. Austin, Univ. of Texas Press, 1947.*

MEIERS, MILDRED *and* KNAPP, JACK. Thesaurus of humor. *buckram, 12mo. N.Y., Crown, 1940.*

MEILHAC, HENRY *and* HALEVY, LUDOVIC. Indian summer. *paper, 12mo. N.Y., French, 1913.*

MEINE, FRANKLIN J. Mark Twain's first story. *paper, 12mo. Chic., Prairie Press, 1952.*

MELFORD, MARK. Turned up; a farcical comedy. *paper, 12mo. Chic., Dramatic Pub. Co., 1886.*

MELLON, JASON C., *comp.* A treasure chest of humor for boys and girls. *buckram, 4to. N.Y., Hart, 1955.*

MELLON, ROBERT C. So you're laid up! *paper, 4to. N.Y., Hart, 1958.*

MELVILLE, HELEN *and* MELVILLE, LEWIS. Anthology of humorous verse from Robert Herrick to Owen Seaman. *buckram, 12mo. Lond., Harrap, 1913.*

MEMBER OF THE G.A.R., A. The picket line and camp fire stories; a collection of war anecdotes, both grave and gay.. *buckram, 12mo. N.Y., Hurst, n.d.*

MENCIUS. The sayings of Mencius; a new translation by James R. Ware. *paper, 12mo. N.Y., Mentor, 1960.*

MENCKEN, HENRY LOUIS. Christmas story. *buckram, 16mo. N.Y., Knopf, 1946.*

MENDELSOHN, S. FELIX. Here's a good one; stories of Jewish wit and wisdom. *buckram, 8vo. N.Y., Bloch, 1947.*

——————— The Jew laughs; humorous stories and anecdotes. *buckram, 8vo. Chic., Stein, 1935.*

——————— Let laughter ring. *buckram, 8vo. Phila., Jewish Pub. Soc., 1941.*

_____ The merry heart. *buckram, 8vo. N.Y., Bookman Associates, 1951.*

MENKE, FRANK G. Sport tales and anecdotes. *buckram, 8vo. N.Y., Barnes, 1953.*

MENNIS, *Sir* JOHN. Facetiae. Musarium deliciae, or, The muses recreation, containing several pieces of poetique wit. By Sir J.M. and Ja: S., 1656. Wit restor'd, in severall select poems not formerly publish't. 1658. Wits recreations, selected from the finest fancies of moderne muses, with a thousand outlandish proverbs. 1640. The whole diligently compared with the originals with all the wood engravings, plates, memoirs and notes. New edition. *2v. boards, 12mo. Lond., John Camden Hotten, 1817.*

MENTAL PLEASURES, or, Select essays, characters, anecdotes and poems. By the author of Pleasing reflections, &c. *2v. boards, 12mo. Lond., Hamilton, 1791.*

MEREDITH, GEORGE. An essay on comedy and the uses of the comic spirit. *buckram, 12mo. N.Y., Scribner's, 1911.*

_____ The pilgrim's scrip; or, Wit and wisdom of George Meredith. *buckram, 12mo. Bost., Roberts, 1888.*

MERIVALE, H.C. A husband in clover; a farce. *paper, 12mo. Chic., Dramatic Pub. Co., n.d.*

MERMAN, ETHEL. Don't call me madam. *buckram, 8vo. Lond., Allen, 1955.*

_____ Who could ask for anything more. *buckram, 8vo. N.Y., Doubleday, 1955.*

MERRIMAN, CHARLES EUSTACE. Who's it in America. *buckram, 12mo. N.Y., Dodge, 1906.*

MERRIMAN, EFFIE W. Comedies for children. *paper, 12mo. Chic., Dramatic Pub. Co., 1898.*

MERRY, MAT. The turf; its humour in anecdote and story! *paper, 12mo. Lond., Simpkin, Marshall, Hamilton, Kent, 1906.*

MERRY DROLLERY COMPLEAT; being jovial poems, merry songs, &c. *buckram, 12mo. Bost., Roberts, 1874.*

MERRY FROLICS OF THE COMICAL CHEATS OF SWALPO, A NOTORIOUS PICKPOCKET, and The merry pranks of Roger the clown. *buckram, 12mo. Lond., Reprinted by J. Jones, balladmonger, n.d. ca. 1820.*

MERRY PICTURES BY THE COMIC HANDS OF H. H. BROWNE, CROWQUILL, DOYLE, LEECH, MEADOWS HINES, AND OTHERS. *quarter morocco, wide 4to. Lond., Kent, n.d.*

MERRY TALES OF THE WISE MEN OF GOTHAM. Edited by James Orchard Halliwell. *paper, 16mo. Lond., John Russell Smith, 1840.*

MERRYFIELD'S JESTS, or, Wit's companion. *quarter-calf, 16mo. Lond., Roach, 1731.*

MERRYMAN, BRIAN. The midnight court; a rhythmical Bacchanalia from the Irish. Translated by Frank O'Connor. *boards, 8vo. Lond., Fridberg, 1945.*

MERRYWEATHER, F. SOMNER. Lives and anecdotes of misers. *buckram, 12mo. Lond., Simpkin, Marshall, 1850.*

METHUEN, A. An anthology of modern verse. *buckram, 16mo. Lond., Methuen, 1953.*

METZGER, BERTA. Picture tales from India. *buckram, 24mo. Phila., Stokes, 1942.*

MEYER, JEROME S. Fun for the family. *buckram, 8vo. N.Y., Greenberg, 1938.*

———————— Fun with mathematics. *paper, 12mo. Greenwich, Conn., Fawcett, 1957.*

———————— Puzzle quiz and stunt fun. *paper, 8vo. N.Y., Dover, 1956.*

MEYOUHAS, JOSEPH. Bible tales in Arab folk-lore. *buckram, 12mo. Lond., Knopf, 1928.*

MICHELET, JULES. Satanism and witchcraft; a study in medieval superstition. *paper, 8vo. N.Y., Citadel House, 1939.*

MICKEY FINN'S NEW IRISH JOKES. *paper, 12mo. N.Y., Ogilvie, 1902.*

MIDDLETON, GEORGE. Embers and other one-act plays. *buckram, 12mo. N.Y., Holt, 1913.*

———————— Tradition. *buckram, 12mo. N.Y., Holt, 1913.*

MIDDLING, THEOPHILUS. Johnny Appleseed's rhymes. *buckram, 12mo. St. Louis, Sigma, 1894.*

MIKES, GEORGE. Down with everybody! A cautionary tale for children over twenty-one. *buckram, 12mo. Lond., Wingate, 1951.*

———————— East is east. *buckram, 12mo. Lond., Deutsch, 1958.*

———————— Eight humorists. *buckram, 8vo. Lond., Wingate, 1954.*

———————— How to be an alien. *buckram, 12mo. Lond., Wingate, 1956.*

———————— How to be inimitable; coming of age in England. *buckram, 12mo. Lond., Deutsch, 1960.*

———————— How to scrape skies; the United States explored, rediscovered and explained. *buckram, 12mo. Lond., Wingate, 1947.*

———————— Milk and honey; Israel explored. *buckram, 12mo. Lond., Wingate, 1957.*

———————— Shakespeare and myself. *buckram, 12mo. Lond., Wingate, 1952.*

———————— Wisdom for others. *buckram, 12mo. Lond., Wingate, n.d.*

MILBURN, GEORGE, ed. Best hobo jokes. *paper, 32mo. Girard, Kan., Haldemann-Julius, n.d. (Little Blue Books)*

———————— Best Jewish jokes. *paper, 32mo. Girard, Kan., Haldeman-Julius, n.d. (Little Blue Books.)*

———————— Best jokes about doctors. *paper, 32mo. Girard, Kan., Haldeman-Julius, n.d. (Little Blue Books.)*

—————— Best jokes about drunks. *paper, 32mo. Girard, Kan., Haldeman-Julius, n.d. (Little Blue Books.)*

—————— Best jokes about lawyers. *paper, 32mo. Girard, Kan., Haldeman-Julius, n.d. (Little Blue Books.)*

—————— Best jokes about preachers. *paper, 32mo. Girard, Kan., Haldeman-Julius, n.d. (Little Blue Books.)*

—————— Best rube jokes. *paper, 32mo. Girard, Kan., Haldeman-Julius, n.d. (Little Blue Books.)*

—————— Best Scotch jokes. *paper, 32mo. Girard, Kan., Haldeman-Julius, n.d. (Little Blue Books.)*

—————— Best Yankee jokes. *paper, 32mo. Girard, Kan., Haldeman-Julius, n.d. (Little Blue Books.)*

—————— Book of college humor. *paper, 32mo. Girard, Kan., Haldeman-Julius, n.d. (Little Blue Books.)*

—————— Book of interesting and amusing puns. *paper, 32mo. Girard, Kan., Haldeman-Julius, n.d. (Little Blue Books.)*

—————— Book of popular recitations. *paper, 32mo. Girard, Kan., Haldeman-Julius, n.d. (Little Blue Books.)*

—————— Book of the best Ford jokes. *paper, 32mo. Girard, Kan., Haldeman-Julius, n.d. (Little Blue Books.)*

MILES, ALFRED H. The new anecdote book. *buckram, 12mo. N.Y., Whittaker, n.d.*

—————— Same. *Lond., Hutchinson, n.d.*

—————— Modern humour for reading or recitations. *buckram, 12mo. Lond., Hutchinson, 1892.*

—————— One thousand and one anecdotes, illustrations, incidents, episodes, yarns, stories, adventures, practical jokes, witticisms, epigrams and bon-mots. *buckram, 8vo. Lond., Hutchinson, n.d.*

MILLER, DONALD F. Bedside book for shut-ins. *paper, 12mo. Liguori, Mo., Liguorian Pamphlet Office Redemptorist Fathers, 1951.*

MILLER, HENRY. The smile at the foot of the ladder. *paper, small 8vo. San Francisco, Greenwood, 1955.*

(MILLER, JOSEPH)

THE AMERICAN JOE MILLER, a collection of Yankee wit and humour. Compiled by Robert Kempt. *buckram, 16mo. Lond., Adams & Francis, 1865.*

FAMILY JO MILLER, a drawing room jest book. *cloth, 16mo. Lond., Orr, 1848.*

FUNNY JESTER, or, Amorous Joe Miller. *boards, 16mo. Lond., Smith, n.d.*

GEMS OF AMERICAN WIT AND ANECDOTE: or, The American Joe Miller. *buckram, 32mo. Lond., Tilt, 1839.*

GENUINE EDITION OF JOE MILLER'S JESTS, or, Wits vade-mecum revived. *half-calf., 12mo. Lond., Setchel, 1761? New ed.*

JOE MILLER IN MOTLEY (The cream of Joe's jests). With an introduction by W. Carew Hazlitt. *boards, 12mo. Lond., Simpkin, Marshall, Hamilton, Kent, 1892.*

JOE MILLER'S COMPLETE JEST BOOK. *cloth, 32mo. Lond., Dove, 1832.*

JOE MILLER'S COMPLETE JEST BOOK. *buckram, 24mo. Lond., Bohn, 1859.*

JOE MILLER'S COMPLETE JEST BOOK. *cloth, 24mo. Lond., Scott, Webster & Geary, 1840.*

JOE MILLER'S JEST BOOK. *buckram, 12mo. N.Y., Hurst, n.d.*

JOE MILLER'S JEST BOOK, WITH ADDITIONS. *buckram, 16mo. Lond., Mason, 1836.*

JOE MILLER'S JESTS, or, The wit's vade-mecum. *quarter-russia, 8vo. Lond., Read, 1739.*

JOE MILLER'S JESTS, or, The wit's vade-mecum. *sheep, 16mo. Lond., Hodges, n.d. (Bound with Ben Johnson's jests.)*

JOE MILLER'S JESTS, or, The wit's vade-mecum. *boards, 12mo. Lond., Crowder, Nicol & Williams, 1739. 14th ed.*

JOE MILLER'S JESTS, or, The wit's vade-mecum. As originally edited by John Mottley. *buckram, 16mo. Lond., Barker, n.d. New ed.*

JOE MILLER'S JESTS, with copious additions. *buckram, 16mo. Lond., Whittaker, 1836.*

JOE MILLER'S JESTS, with copious additions. *buckram, 12mo. Lond., Whittaker, 1846. 2d.ed.*

JOE MILLER'S JESTS, with copious additions. Edited by Frank Bellew. *buckram, 12mo. N.Y., Northern Magazine, 1865.*

JOE MILLER'S JOKE BOOK. *paper, 12mo. N.Y., Padell, 1943.*

JOE MILLER'S NEW IRISH JEST BOOK. *paper, 24mo. Dublin, Warren, 1859.*

LEGEND OF JOE MILLER, by Evan Esar. *paper, folio. San Francisco, Grabhorn Press for the Roxeburgh Club, 1957. (Anecdota Scowah, 2.)*

MODERN JOE MILLER, his jest book. Edited by R.C.W. *buckram, 12mo. Phila., Lippincott, 1884. (Bound with Modern humour, anecdote and wit.)*

——————— *Same. Lond., Warne, n.d., with titles reversed.*

NEW JOE MILLER, or, The tickler. *calf, 24mo. Lond., Ridgway, 1800. 2d.ed.*

——————— *Same. Lond., Ridgway, 1801. 3d.ed.*

NEW JOE MILLER'S JEST BOOK. *boards, 16mo. Lond., Milner, n.d.*

NEW JOE MILLER'S JEST BOOK. *buckram, 24mo. Lond., Duncome, n.d.*

OLD JOE MILLER, or, The tickler. *calf., 24mo. Lond., Ridgway, 1801.*

OLD JOE MILLER: being a complete and correct copy of his celebrated jests. *boards, 24mo. Lond., Ridgway, 1800. 2d.ed. (Bound with: The new Joe Miller. Lond., Ridgway, 1800.)*

OLD JOE MILLER, or, Universal jester. *boards, 16mo. Lond., Hughes, 1810. New ed.*

**OLD JOE MILLER REVIVED, or**
London budget of wit. *calf.,*
*24mo. Lond., Hughes, 1822.*

**PICKWICK TREASURY OF WIT,**
or, Joe Miller's jest book.
*leather, 32mo. Lond., Barr,*
*1842.*

**SAM WELLER'S PICKWICK JEST**
**BOOK,** including Joe Miller's
renowned jests. *buckram, 24mo.*
*Lond., Hodgson, n.d.*

**WILLIAM HOGARTH'S OWN JOE**
**MILLER,** or, Quips, cranks,
jokes and squibs, collected
and digested by Toby (Hogarth's
own dog). *boards, 16mo. Lond,*
*Ward & Lock, 1854.*

**YANKEE NOTIONS, or, THE**
**AMERICAN JOE MILLER,** by
Sam Slick (T.C. Haliburton).
*half-calf, 16mo. Lond., Ball,*
*Arnold, 1839.*

**MILLER, MAX.** The town with the
funny name. *buckram, 8vo.*
*N.Y., Dutton, 1948.*

**MILLER, NYLE H.** Some widely
publicized western police
officers. *paper, 8vo. Wichita,*
*Kan., Laugh Book magazine,*
*1958.*

**MILLER, PERRIN** *and* **WILLOCK,**
**RUTH.** Continental cans, etc; a
tourist's guide to European
plumbing. *N.Y., Kanrom, 1960.*

**MILLER, REX.** In search of Santa
Claus. *paper, 16mo. Ankara,*
*Turkish Press, Broadcasting*
*and Tourist Department, 1955.*

**MILLER, WILLIAM C.** Mark Twain
at the Sanitary Ball --- and
elsewhere? *(In: California*
*Historical Society quarterly,*
*March, 1957.)*

**MILLS, G.A.** A saw screams at
midnight; the whodunit-yourself
book. *boards, 8vo. N.Y.,*
*Dutton, 1956.*

**MILNE, A.A.** The man in the
bowler hat. *paper, 12mo. Lond.,*
*French, 1923.*

——————— Methuen's Library of
humour. A. A. Milne. *buckram,*
*16mo. Lond., Methuen, 1933.*

——————— Year in, year out.
*buckram, 8vo. N.Y., Dutton,*
*1952.*

**MILNE, ANGELA.** Jam and genius.
*buckram, 12mo. Lond., Vane,*
*1947.*

**MILNE, F. MURRAY.** The proverbs
of Hocus Pocus; the Omar
Khayyam of the twentieth
century. *boards, 12mo. Lond.,*
*Pearson, n.d.*

**MINGOTE, ANGELO ANTONIO.**
History for beginners. Text by
Jan Read. *buckram, 4to. Lond.,*
*Nelson, 1960.*

——————— Mingote's world.
*paper, 16mo. Madrid, Taurus,*
*1957.*

**MINSTREL GAGS AND END**
**MEN'S JOKES.** *paper, 12mo.*
*Cleveland, Westbrook, n.d.*

**MIR AMMAN OF DIHLI.** *see*
**KHUSRAU, AMIR.**

**MIRROR OF AMUSEMENT.**
*2v. calf., 8vo.*
Contents.-Vicar of Wakefield,
by Oliver Goldsmith.-v2.
History of Rasselas, prince of
Abissinia, by Dr. Johnson.

MIRTH FOR MIDSUMMER, MERRI-
MENT FOR MICHAELMAS,
CHEERFULNESS FOR
CHRISTMAS, LAUGHTER FOR
LADY'DAY; forming a collection of parlour poetry, and
drawing-room drollery... *boards,
12mo. Lond., Baldwin, Cradock
and Joy, 1823.*

MIRTH IN MINIATURE: or, Bursts
of merriment, being a collection of the very best bon mots,
witticisms, smart repartees,
bulls and laughable anecdotes.
*boards, large 16mo. Bost., Hill,
1831.*

MISERIES OF HUMAN LIFE, or,
The groans of Timothy Testy
and Samuel Sensitive. *half-
calf, 16mo. Lond., Miller, 1806.*

MISERIES OF HUMAN LIFE, an
old friend in a new dress.
*buckram, 12mo. N.Y., Putnam,
1853.*

MISHIMA, YUKIO. Twilight sun-
flower. *paper, 12mo. Tokyo,
Hokuseido, 1958.*

MITCHELL, JOSEPH. McSorley's
wonderful saloon. *paper, 8vo.
N.Y., Grosset & Dunlap, 1943.*

MITCHELL, VIRGINIA. The girl
who looks like me; a comedy.
*paper, 12mo. N.Y., French,
1947.*

MIXED PICKLES, from "Funny
Folks" stores. *paper, 12mo.
Lond., "Funny Folks", 1873.*

MOBLEY, MILLY LOU. Me spik
English. *paper, 16mo.
Honolulu, Star-Bulletin, 1938.*

——————*Same, with author's
name as Donnelly, Milly Lou.
1950.*

MODERN HUMOUR: an intire new
collection of tales, allegories,
fables, maxims, remarks and
repartees, instructive and
entertaining. *calf., 16mo.
Lond., Cooper, 1754.*

MOE MILLER'S JOKE BOOK: a
collection of hilarious jokes,
gags & stories. *paper, 12mo.
Wheman, n.d.*

MOLE, G. E. 25 short Chinese
stories, told in simple English.
*paper, 12mo. Shanghai, Com-
mercial Press, 1930.*

MOLEN, SAM. Take 2 and hit to
right; a collection of sports
stories. *buckram, 12mo. Phila.,
Dorrance, 1959.*

——————— They make me laugh;
a collection of stories and
anecdotes about the greats and
also rans in sports. *boards,
12mo. Phila., Dorrance, 1947.*

MOLNAR, GEORGE. Statues.
*buckram, 4to. N.Y., Dutton,
1955.*

MOLONY, JOHN CHARTRES.
Ireland's tragic comedians.
*buckram, 8vo. Edinburgh,
Blackwood, 1934.*

MOMUS IN GOOD HUMOUR, or,
The polite jester. *paper, 16mo.
Lond., Neil, 1805.*

MOMUS'S CABINET OF AMUSE-
MENT. The new encyclopedia
or world of wit, a choice sel-
lection of bons mots, puns,
epigrams and humorous tales
in prose and verse. *boards,
24mo. Lond., Wogan &
Cummings, n.d.*

——————*Same. Lond., Bumpus,
1811, with title transposed.*

MONCREIFF, FREDERICK CHARLES. Wit and wisdom of the bench and bar. *buckram, 16mo. Lond., Cassell, Petter, Galpin, 1882.*

MONCREIFFE, IAIN. Simple custom. *buckram, 4to. Lond., Nelson, 1954.*

MONCRIEFF, WILLIAM T. Tom and Jerry; or, Life in London in 1820. *paper, 12mo. Lond., Lacy, 1821?*

MONETT, NEGLEY. Hair on a cue ball; the hair-raising adventures of a Hollywood writer. *buckram, 8vo. N.Y., Exposition, 1955.*

MONKSHOOD, G. F. Wit and wisdom from Edgar Saltus. *buckram, 16mo. Lond., Greening, 1903.*

_____ Woman and her wits. *buckram, 16mo. N.Y., Caldwell, 1899.*

_____ Woman and the wits; epigrams on woman, love and beauty. *buckram, 12mo. Lond., Greening, 1899.*

_____ Same. *Lond., Cape, 1922.*

MONRO, D. H. Argument of laughter. *buckram, 8vo. Melbourne, University Press, 1951.*

MONSTROUS DROLL JESTER, AND CHEARFUL COMPANION. *paper, 16mo. Lond., Maiden, n.d.*

MONTAGUE, E. R. Tales from the Talmud. *buckram, 12mo. Edinburgh, Blackwood, 1908. 2d.ed.*

MONTEFIORE, CLAUDE. A Rabbinic anthology. *buckram, 8vo. Lond., Macmillan, 1938.*

MONTEZ, LOLA. Anecdotes of love. *buckram, 12mo. N.Y., Dick & Fitzgerald, 1858.*

MONTUCCI, ANTONIO, *ed.* The amusing instructor, or, A key to the Italian classics: *calf., 12mo. Lond., Faulder, 1793.*

MOODY, D.L. Anecdotes and illustrations of D. L. Moody, related by him in his revival work. Compiled by J. B. McClure. *buckram, 8vo. Chic., Rhodes & McClure, 1877.*

_____ Anecdotes, incidents and illustrations. *buckram, 8vo. Lond., Morgan & Scott, n.d.*

_____ Moody's anecdotes and illustrations. *buckram, 12mo. Chic., Rhodes & McClure, 1897.*

_____ Moody's stories; being a second volume of anecdotes, incidents and illustrations. *buckram, 16mo. Chic., Bible Institute Colportage Association, 1899.*

MOORE, F. FRANKFORT. The lighter side of English life. *buckram, 8vo. Lond., Foulis, 1913.*

MOORE, FRANK, *comp.* Anecdotes, poetry and incidents of the war: North and South, 1860-1865. *half-calf, 8vo. N.Y., Bible House, 1867.*

MOORE, GEORGE. Epigrams of George Moore. *paper, 32mo. Girard, Kan., Haldeman-Julius, (Little Blue Books).*

MOORE, GEORGE AUSTIN. Good timin'; over two hundred of the best Negro stories. *paper, 8vo. Hollywood, Boulevard Press, 1935.*

MOORE, GEORGE WASHINGTON.
"Bones" his anecdotes and
goaks. *paper, 12mo. Lond.,
Clarke, 1868.*

MOORE, OLGA. I'll meet you in
the lobby. *buckram, 8vo. Phila.,
Lippincott, 1949.*

MOORE, THOMAS. Thomas Moore
anecdotes. Edited by Wilmot
Harrison. *buckram, 12mo.
Lond., Jarrold, 1899.*

MORANTZ, DAVID. Talmudic
tales. *buckram, 12mo. Kansas
City, Author, 1934.*

MORAVIA, ALBERTO. Roman
tales. *boards, 8vo. N.Y.,
Farrar, Straus & Cudahy, 1956.*

MORE BROAD GRINS, or, Mirth
versus melancholy. *boards,
12mo. Lond., Lowndes, 1819.*

MORE FUN: or, The world of wit.
A selection of characteristic
anecdotes and bon-mots,
repartees, &c, &c. *paper, 24mo.
Dublin, R.Smith, 1810. 4th ed.*

MORE GLEANINGS FROM
GLADSTONE. *pamphlet.
Edinburgh, Blackwood, n.d.*

MORE OVER SEXTEEN. Sequel.
*buckram, 8vo. N.Y., Grayson,
1953.*

MORE SECRETS. *pamphlet.
Milwaukee, Pabst Brewing co.,
n.d.*

MORE WITNESSES. (Reprinted
from Jan 1866 issue of Harper's
New Monthly Magazine.) *7th
annual Christmas production of
Nova Press and William
P. Barlow, jr. 1960.*

MORELAND, A. Humors of
history; 160 drawings in color,
reproduced from the Morning
Leader. *buckram, 12mo. Lond.,
Sully & Ford, 1903?*

MOREY, ALBERT A. Tee-time -
enjoy it and live! *paper, 8vo.
Chic., Franklin, 1952.*

MORGAN, BENJAMIN. Sham, or,
Uncle Ben's experience with
hypocrites. *buckram, 8vo.
Phila., Smith, 1888.*

MORGAN, CLAY, *ed.* Fun en
route; the bon voyage book.
*buckram, 8vo. N.Y., Simon &
Schuster, 1937.*

MORGAN, DAN. The complete
bartender's joke book.
*buckram, 8vo. N.Y., Stravon,
1953.*

MORGAN, HENRY *and* WAGNER,
GARY. And now a word from
our sponsor. *paper, 4to. N.Y.,
Citadel, 1960.*

MORGAN, JOY ELMER. Franklin's
plan of self-improvement.
*paper, 24mo. (Personal Growth
Leaflets.)*

——————— A golden treasury of
beauty and wisdom. *paper,
24mo. (Personal Growth
Leaflets.)*

——————— A golden treasury on
the art of living. *paper, 24mo.
(Personal Growth Leaflets.)*

——————— Your citizenship in
the making. *paper, 24mo.
(Personal Growth Leaflets.)*

——————— Your life in the
making. *paper, 24mo. (Personal
Growth Leaflets.)*

——————— Your mind in the
making. *paper, 24mo. (Personal
Growth Leaflets.)*

——————— Your personality in
the making. *paper, 24mo.
(Personal Growth Leaflets.)*

MORGAN, W.Y. A jayhawker in
Europe. *buckram, 12mo.
Topeka, Crane, 1911.*

MORIER, JAMES. The adventures of Hajji Baba of Ispahan. *buckram, 12mo. Lond., Macmillan, 1895.*

——————— The adventures of Hajji Baba of Ispahan in England. *quarter-morocco, 8vo. Paris, Baudry's European Library, 1835. Rev. corrected ed.*

MORITZEN, JULIUS, *comp.* Proverbs of Germany. *paper, 32mo. Girard, Kan., Haldeman-Julius, n.d. (Little Blue Books)*

MORLEY, CHRISTOPHER, *ed.* A book of days. *buckram, 12mo. N.Y., Day, 1931. 2d.ed.*

MORNINGSIDE, MEE, *ed.* Strange but true. *paper, 12mo. N.Y., Gold Medal Books, 1954.*

MORRAH, DAVE. Cinderalla Hassenpfeffer. *boards, 12mo. N.Y., Rinehart, 1948.*

——————— Fraulein Bo-Peepen. *boards, 12mo. N.Y., Rinehart, 1953.*

——————— Heinrich Schnibble. *boards, 12mo. N.Y., Rinehart, 1955.*

——————— Sillynyms. *boards, 12mo. N.Y., Rinehart, 1956.*

MORRIS, CHARLES, *ed.* Half-hours with the best humorous authors. *2v. buckram, 12mo. Lond., Warne, 1889?*

MORRIS, ERNEST. Legends o' the bells. *buckram, 8vo. Lond., Sampson Low, Marston, n.d.*

MORRIS, FELIX J. Electric love, a farce. *paper, 12mo. N.Y., De Witt, 1883.*

MORRIS, H.H. In and out of court. *paper, 12mo. Cape Town, Central News Agency, 1950.*

MORRIS, J. MALCOLM. The wise bamboo. *paper, 12mo. Rutland, Vt., Tuttle, 1953.*

MORRIS, JOE ALEX. What a year! *buckram, 8vo. N.Y., Harper, 1956.*

MORRIS, PETER. Peter's letters to his kinsfolk. *3v. half-calf, 8vo. Edinburgh, Blackwood, 1819. 3d.ed.*

MORRISON, MORIE. Life with Par. *boards, 8vo. N.Y., Doubleday, 1958.*

MORROW, GENEVIEVE. Colored stories. *cloth, 12mo. Houston, Wetmore, n.d.*

MORROW'S ALMANACK FOR THE YEAR(S) OF OUR LORD, 1928, 1929, 1930. Burton Rascoe and Thayer Hobson, *eds. half-boards, 8vo. N.Y., Morrow, 1928-1930.*

MORTLOCK, GEOFFREY, *and* WILLIAMS, STEPHEN. The flowing bowl; a book of blithe spirits and blue devils. *buckram, 12mo. Lond., Hutchinson, n.d.*

MORTON, ELEANOR *see* STERN, ELIZABETH GERTRUDE.

MORTON, FREDERICK W., *comp.* Love in epigram. *buckram, 16mo. Chic., McClurg, 1903.*

——————— Marriage in epigram. *buckram, 16mo. Chic., McClurg, 1903.*

——————— Men in epigram. *buckram, 16mo. Chic., McClurg, 1901.*

——————— Women in epigram. *buckram, 16mo. Chic., McClurg, 1904.*

MORTON, GEORGE A. *and* MALLOCH, D. MACLEOD. Law and laughter. *buckram, 12mo. Lond., Foulis, 1913.*

MORTON, J.B. The misadventures of Dr. Strabismus. *buckram, 8vo. Lond., Sheed & Ward, 1949.*

——————— Mr. Thake, his life and letters. *buckram, 12mo. Lond., Bles, 1929.*

MORTON, J. MADISON. Betsy Baker; a farce. *paper, 12mo. Chic., Dramatic Publishing Co., n.d.*

——————— Box and Cox; a farce. *paper, 12mo. Phila., Penn Publishing Co., 1891.*

——————— Lend me five shillings. *paper, 12mo. Phila., Penn Publishing Co., 1898.*

——————— Slasher and Crasher; a farce. *paper, 12mo. Chic., Dramatic Publishing Co., n.d.*

——————— Woodcock's little game; a comedy-farce. *paper, 12mo. N.Y., French, 1864.*

MORTON, MICHAEL. "My wife" a comedy. *paper, 12mo. N.Y., French, 1912.*

MORTON, THOMAS *and* MORTON, J.M. All that glitters is not gold. *paper, 12mo. Chic., Dramatic Publishing Co., n.d.*

MOSER, G. *von.* "On 'change" a farce. *paper, 12mo. Lond., French, 1885.*

MOSHER, MARION DIX, *comp.* More toasts, jokes, stories and quotations. *buckram, 12mo. N.Y., Wilson, 1922.*

MOSHER, WILLIAM E. *and* TCHOU, M. THOMAS. World citizenship. *paper, 24mo. (Personal Growth Leaflets.)*

MOTHER BUNCH'S CLOSET NEWLY BROKE OPEN, and The history of Mother Bunch of the west. *boards, 12mo. Lond., Villon Society, 1885.*

MOTHER GOOSE RHYMES. *boards, 16mo. N.Y., Mother Goose, 1929.*

MOTHER GOOSE RHYMES (CENSORED). *boards, 16mo. N.Y., Mother Goose, 1926.*

MOTIVALA, B.N. A dictionary of wisdom. *boards, 12mo. Bombay, Hind Kitabs, 1947.*

MOULTON, POWERS. Best jokes for all occasions. *boards, 16mo. N.Y., Permabooks, 1948.*

——————— 2500 jokes for all occasions. *buckram, 8vo. N.Y., New Home Library, 1942.*

MUDDOCK, J.E., *ed.* The Savage Club papers. *buckram, 12mo. Lond., Hutchinson, 1897.*

MUGGE, MAXIMILIAN A. Serbian folk songs, fairy tales and proverbs. *boards, 12mo. Lond., Drane's, 1916.*

MUIR, DOROTHY ERSKINE. The art of conversation. *buckram, 12mo. Lond., Odhams, 1953.*

MUIR, ELIZABETH MCCREATH. Wee bits o' Scotch humor. *buckram, 12mo. N.Y., Greenberg, 1923.*

MULLER, FREDERICK, *ed.* Here's a good one! over 300 good stories. *paper, 16mo. Lond., Muller, 1946. 5th ed.*

MULLER, HELEN M., *comp.* Still more toasts; jokes, stories and quotations. *buckram, 12mo. N.Y., Wilson, 1935.*

MULLER-CASENOV, HANS. The humour of Germany. *buckram, 12mo. Lond., Scott, 1892?*

MULLER-GUGGENBUHL, FRITZ. Swiss-Alpine folk-tales. *buckram, 8vo. Lond., Oxford University Press, 1958.*

MUMFORD, ETHEL WATTS, HERFORD, OLIVER *and* MIZNER, ADDISON. Complete cynic's calendar of revised wisdom. 1906. *buckram, 24mo. San Francisco, Elder, 1905.*

——————— Joke book note book. *buckram, 12mo. San Francisco, Elder, 1905.* (Pasted in jokes and anecdotes.)

——————— Limerick up to date book. *buckram, 12mo. San Francisco, Elder, 1903.*

MUN *see* LEAF, MUNRO

MUNRO, BRUCE. Groans and grins of one who survived. *buckram, 12mo. Toronto, Warwick, 1889.*

MUN KITTRICK, R.K. The slambangaree, and other stories. *boards, 16mo. N.Y., Russell, 1897.*

MURPHY, EDWARD F. Wise words for richer living. *paper, 12mo. N.Y., Quality Quotes, 1954.*

MURPHY, FITZGERALD. A bit of Blarney. *paper, 12mo. Chic., Dramatic Publishing Co., 1893.*

MURPHY, LU. Maiden effort. *buckram, 12mo. N.Y., Duell, Sloan & Pearce, 1956.*

MURRAY, DAVID. Lawyers' merriments. *boards, 8vo. Glasgow, MacLehose, 1912.*

MURRAY, JOE "MILLER". America's spiciest stories. *paper, 16mo, Hollywood, Americana, n.d.*

——————— Smoker stories. *paper, 24mo. Hollywood, Americana, 1943.Rev.ed.*

——————— Strip tease stories. *paper, 24mo. Hollywood, Americana, n.d.*

MURRAY, KEN. Giant joke book. *paper, 16mo. Ace Books, 1954.*

MURRELL, WILLIAM. A history of American graphic humor (1865-1938). *buckram, 4to. N.Y., Macmillan for the Whitney Museum of American Art, 1938.*

MUSE IN GOOD HUMOUR, THE; a collection of comic tales, by several hands. *2v. tree calf, 12mo. Lond., Noble, 12mo.*

MUSEUM OF MIRTH; or, Humourist's pocket-book. Selected by the editor of the Comic Songster. *half-calf, 24mo. Glasgow, Hamilton, 1846.*

MUSEUM OF WIT: being a choice collection of poetical pieces, instructive and entertaining .. intended as an antidote to care and to promote mirth and hilarity. Selected from various authors. *quarter-calf, 24mo. Lond., Crosby & Letterman, 1801.*

MUSSET, ALFRED *de.* A door must be either open or shut. *boards, 8vo. Lond., Rodale, 1955.*

MUSSEY, J.B., *ed.* Best American humor of today. *buckram, 8vo. N.Y., Boni, 1931.* (Same as Cream of the jesters.)

——————— Best American wit and humor. *buckram, 12mo. N.Y., World, 1931.*

——————— Cream of the Jesters. *buckram, 8vo. N.Y., Boni, 1931.* (Same as Best American humor of today.)

MUSTLAFF, HUGO, *pseud.* see SNODDY, GEORGE WADE.

MY FUNNIEST STORY: a collection of stories chosen by their own authors. *buckram, 12mo. Lond., Faber & Faber, 1932.*

MY NAUGHTIEST STORY; a collection of stories chosen by their own authors. *buckram, 12mo. Lond., Faber & Faber, 1942.*

MYERS, OLIVER H. Little Aden folklore. *pamphlet.* (Reprinted from the Bulletin de l'Institut francais d'Archeologie Orientale.)

MYSTIC ORACLE, or, The complete fortune-teller and dream book. *paper, 8vo. N.Y., Lupton, 1893.*

# N

NAGLE, URBAN. Uncle George and Uncle Malachy. *buckram, 8vo. Milwaukee, Bruce, 1946.*

NAISH, P.LL. Chestnuts hot and cold. *buckram, 12mo. Lond., Heath, Cranton & Ouseley, n.d.*

NAPIER, ROBINA, *ed.* Johnsoniana; anecdotes of the late Samuel Johnson, by Mrs. Piozzi, Richard Cumberland, Bishop Percy and others, together with the diary of Dr. Campbell and extracts from that of Madame D'Arblay. *buckram, 12mo. Lond., Bell, 1889.*

NAPOLEON I, EMPEROR OF THE FRENCH. Maxims of Napoleon. *paper, 32mo. Girard, Kan., Haldeman-Julius, n.d. (Little Blue Books.)*

NASBY, PETROLEUM V. *see* LOCKE, DAVID ROSS.

NASH, J.V. Voltaire's weapon— the smile! *paper, 32mo. Girard, Kan., Haldeman-Julius, n.d. (Little Blue Books.)*

NASH, OGDEN. Good intentions. *buckram, 12mo. Lond., Dent, 1943.*

——————— The primrose path. *buckram, 8vo. N.Y., Simon & Schuster, 1935.*

——————— Selected verse. *buckram, 12mo. N.Y., Modern Library, 1946.*

NASH, RICHARD. The jests of Beau Nash. *calf., 16mo. Lond., Tonson, 1763.* (Bound with: The careless husband, by Colley Cibber.)

NATHAN, GEORGE JEAN. Monks are monks; a diagnostic scherzo. *buckram, 12mo. N.Y., Knopf, 1929.*

NATHAN, ROBERT. The Weans. *boards, 8vo. N.Y., Knopf, 1960.*

NATIONAL COUNCIL ON FREEDOM FROM CENSOR- SHIP. What shocked the censors. *pamphlet, N.Y., National Council on Freedom from Censorship, 1933.*

NATIONAL HUMOURIST, THE; being a choice selection of the most modern jokes, wit, and repartee. The whole compiled by a gentleman many years connected with the Public Press. *buckram, 32mo. Lond., Houstoun, 1836.*

NATIONAL PROVERBS. England. *paper, 16mo. Phila., McKay, n.d.*

NATIONAL PROVERBS. Holland. *boards, 16mo. Lond., Palmer, 1915.*

NATSUME, SOSEKI. I am a cat. *buckram, 8vo. Tokyo, Kenkyusha, 1961.*

NAVY NONSENSE. *boards, 16mo. Chic., Howell, 1918.*

NAYAR, MANAKAMPAT KESAVAN UNNI. My Malabar. *paper, 12mo. Bombay, Hind Kitabs, 1952.*

NEAL, JOSEPH C. Charcoal sketches; or, Scenes in a metropolis. *buckram, 12mo. Phila., Carey & Hart, 1839.*

NEALLY, ANN., *comp. and ed.* Favorite poems from the best authors. Humorous poems. *buckram, 24mo. N.Y., Dutton, 1894.*

NECHES, SOLOMON MICHAEL. Humorous tales of latter day rabbis. *buckram, 12mo. N.Y., Dobsevage, 1938.*

NEIL, JAMES. Riddles and some- thing new about them, by a Literary Clergyman. *buckram, 8vo. Lond., Lang, Neil, n.d.*

NEILSON, G.R., *ed.* The book of bulls. *buckram, 12mo. Lond., Simpkin, Marshall, n.d.*

NEMETY, EMERY. Da kine; pidgin stories. *paper, 8vo. Honolulu, Honolulu Book Shop, 1954.*

NENDICK, BUCKTON. The blackface joker, new from cover to cover. *paper, 12mo. Chic., Denison, 1918.*

NERNEY, PATRICK W. *and* CLEMENS, PAUL. The little black book; a manual for bachelors, by Cadwallader and Nudnick. *buckram, 8vo. Lond., Hutchinson, 1958.*

NEUMEYER, BOB. You speak. *paper, 12mo. Rutland, Vt., Tuttle, 1957.*

NEVILL, RALPH. The merry past. *buckram, 8vo. Lond., Duckworth, 1909.*

NEVILLE, CHARLES B., *ed.* Humorous readings for home and hall. *buckram, 8vo. Lond., Simpkin, Marshall, n.d. 4th ed.*

NEW A.NO.1 TRAMP JOKES. *paper, 32mo. Baltimore, Ottenheimer, 1913.*

NEW AFTER-DINNER STORIES. *paper, 24mo. Baltimore, Ottenheimer, 1908.*

NEW ANECDOTA AMERICANA. *buckram, 8vo. N.Y., Grayson, 1944.*

*see also* ANECDOTA AMERICANA.

NEW BOOK OF A THOUSAND ANECDOTES: wit, humor, odd scraps, tales, legends. *buckram, 12mo. N.Y., Marsh, 1856.*

NEW BOOK OF HEARTY LAUGHS AND LATEST JOKES; a fine collection of the best of fun from here, there and everywhere. *paper, 32mo. Baltimore, Ottenheimer, n.d.*

NEW BOOK OF HUMOR, no. 1. *paper, 12mo. Springfield, Ill., Illinois State Register, 1923.*

NEW BOOK OF MONOLOGUES. *paper, 24mo. Baltimore, Ottenheimer, 1913.*

NEW BOOK OF 1000 CONUNDRUMS, JOKES, RIDDLES AND MONOLOGUES. *paper, 24mo. N.Y., Wehman, 1904.*

NEW BOOK OF "RIDDLES". *paper, 12mo. N.Y., Wehman, n.d.*

NEW BOOK OF SNOBS, by various hands. *buckram, 8vo. Lond., Museum Press, 1959.*

NEW CABINET ALBUM OF ENTERTAINMENT AND INSTRUCTION. *paper, 12mo. Lond., Lacey, n.d.*

NEW COMIC ANNUAL. *quarter-leather, 16mo. Lond., Hurst, Chance, n.d.*

NEW CYCLOPAEDIA OF ILLUSTRATIVE ANECDOTE, RELIGIOUS AND MORAL, ORIGINAL AND SELECTED. With introduction by the Rev. Donald Macleod. *buckram, 8vo. N.Y., Randolph, 1872.*

NEW DRUMMER'S YARNS. *paper, 24mo. Baltimore, Ottenheimer, 1913.*

NEW DUTCH JOKE BOOK. *paper, 24mo. Baltimore, Ottenheimer, 1907.*

NEW ENCYCLOPAEDIA, or World
of wit. Momus's Cabinet of
amusement. *boards, 24mo.
Lond., Bumpus, 1811.*

———————— *Same. Lond., Wogan
& Cummings, n.d. with title
transposed.*

NEW ENTERTAINING HUMORIST,
containing a curious collection
of interesting and diverting
miscellanies, in prose and
verse... *calf., 16mo. Lond.,
Thomlinson & Dalley, 1778.*

NEW FESTIVAL OF WIT, or
Cabinet of humour; a select
collection of anecdotes, bon
mots, &c. including those of
several celebrated characters.
*paper, 12mo. Lond.,
Lackington, Allen, 1814.*

NEW FOUNDLING HOSPITAL
FOR WIT; being a collection
of fugitive pieces, in prose
and verse, not in any other
collection with several pieces
never before published. *6v.
tree calf., 12mo. Lond.,
Debrett, 1771. 3d.ed.*

———————— *Same. New ed. 1786.*

NEW HEBREW JOKE BOOK.
*paper, 24mo. Baltimore,
Ottenheimer, 1907.*

NEW HEBREW JOKES AND
MONOLOGUES. *paper, 12mo.
Baltimore, Ottenheimer, 1905.*

NEW IRISH JOKE BOOK. *paper,
24mo. Baltimore, Ottenheimer,
n.d.*

NEW JOKES AND MONOLOGUES
BY THE BEST JOKERS.
Stage conundrums. *paper, 12mo.
Baltimore, Ottenheimer, 1904.*

NEW JOKES BY OLD JOKERS.
*paper, 12mo. Baltimore,
Ottenheimer, 1901.*

NEW MINSTREL AND BLACK
FACE JOKE BOOK, by leading
footlight favorites. *paper,
12mo. Baltimore, Ottenheimer,
1905.*

NEW PILGRIMAGE, A. *boards,
12mo. Lond., Priv. Print.,
1923.*

NEW POLITE VAUDEVILLE
JOKE BOOK; a collection of
the latest jokes, best stories
and monologues and anecdotes.
*paper, 12mo. Baltimore,
Ottenheimer, 1911.*

NEW STAGE JOKES, with a good
collection of jokes, witty-
sayings, & etc., by the most
prominent actors of the stage.
*paper, 32mo. Baltimore,
Ottenheimer, 1914.*

NEW TRAIN TALES. *paper,
24mo. Baltimore, Ottenheimer,
1911.*

NEW WIT'S MAGAZINE AND
ECCENTRIC CALENDAR,
consisting of original bon mots,
anecdotes, puns &c. of living
public characters. *half calf,
16mo. Lond., Tegg, 1805.*

NEW YORK TIMES. The "Man in
the street" stories. Containing
over six hundred humorous
after-dinner stories about
prominent persons. *buckram,
12mo. N.Y., Ogilvie, 1902.*

NEW YORKER MAGAZINE.
Another HoHum; more news-
breaks. *buckram, 12mo. N.Y.,
Farrar & Rinehart, 1932.*

———————— The fifth New Yorker
album. *boards, 4to. N.Y.,
Harper, 1932.*

———————— HoHum; news breaks
from the New Yorker. *buckram,
12mo. N.Y., Farrar & Rinehart,
1931.*

_____ Short stories from the New Yorker. *buckram, 8vo. N.Y., Simon & Schuster, 1940.*

_____ The sixth New Yorker album. *buckram, 4to. Lond., Lane, 1934.*

_____ The 1942 New Yorker album. *boards, 4to. N.Y., Random, 1942.*

_____ The New Yorker 1950-1955 album. *boards, 4to. N.Y., Harper, 1955.*

_____ The New Yorker twenty-fifth anniversary album. 1925-1950. *boards, folio. N.Y., Harper, 1951.*

_____ The New Yorker war album. *buckram, folio, N.Y., Random, 1942.*

NEWBIGGING, THOMAS. Lancashire humour. *boards, 12mo. Lond., Dent, 1900.*

NEWBY, ERIC. A short walk; a preposterous adventure. *buckram, 8vo. N.Y., Doubleday, 1959.*

NEWCOMB, BOBBY. Tambo, his jokes and funny sayings, with which is incorporated Hints to the amateur minstrel. *paper, 12mo. N.Y., Wehman, 1882.*

NEWCOMB, HARVEY. Anecdotes for boys. *buckram, 16mo. Bost., Gould, Kendall & Lincoln, 1849.*

NEWELL, ROBERT HENRY. The Orpheus C. Kerr papers. *buckram, 12mo. N.Y., Blakeman & Mason, 1862.*

_____ Smoked glass, by Orpheus C. Kerr, *pseud. buckram, 12mo. Lond., Carleton, 1868.*

NEWEST AND MOST COMPLEAT POLITE ENTERTAINING TOWN AND COUNTRY JESTER. Being the smartest, wittiest, and drollest collection ever yet published. *quarter-calf, 12mo. Lond., Millar, Tonson, Dilly, Hodges & Wren, n.d.*

NEWKIRK, NEWTON. Back to nature. *boards, 12mo. N.Y., Funk & Wagnalls, 1911.*

_____ Recollections of a gold cure graduate. *buckram, 24mo. Bost., Caldwell, 1906.*

NEWMAN, JOHN HENRY. Living thoughts of Cardinal Newman. Presented by Henry Tristram. *buckram, 12mo. Lond., Cassell, 1948.*

NEWMAN, LOUIS I. The Hasidic anthology; tales and teachings of the Hasidim. *buckram, 8vo. N.Y., Scribner's, 1935.*

_____ The Talmudic anthology; tales and teachings of the rabbis. *buckram, 8vo. N.Y., Behrman, 1945.*

NEWTON, A. EDWARD. A tourist in spite of himself. *buckram, 8vo. Bost., Little, Brown, 1930.*

NEWTON, DOUGLAS. Clowns. *buckram, 12mo. Lond., Harrap, 1958.*

NEWTON, H. CHANCE. Cues and curtain calls. *buckram, 8vo. Lond., Lane, 1927.*

NEWTON, HARRY L. On a hog train through Kansas. *paper, 12mo. N.Y., Ogilvie, 1906.*

_____ Schwartzbrodt and Pickleman, *paper, 12mo. Chic., Dramatic Pub. Co., n.d.*

NIBLO, GEORGE. B'gosh; a barrel of big ripe snaps shaken from the tree of humor. *paper, 12mo. N.Y., Street & Smith, 1903.*

——————— What's your hurry? a deck full of jokers. *paper, 12mo. N.Y., Street & Smith, 1904.*

NIC-NAC, THE: or, Literary cabinet. *2v. quarter morocco, 8vo. Lond., Wallis, 1823.*

NICHOLSON, FRANK ERNEST. Favorite jokes of famous people. *buckram, 8vo. N.Y., Dutton, 1928.*

NICOLL, W. ROBERTSON *and* WISE, THOMAS J. Literary anecdotes of the 19th century. *buckram, 8vo. N.Y., Dodd, Mead, 1946.*

NICOLSON, HAROLD. The English sense of humour, and other essays. *buckram, 8vo. Lond., Constable, 1956.*

NIEMOELLER, A.F. The funny side of divorce. *paper, 8vo. Girard, Kan., Haldeman-Julius, 1946.*

NIESENWURZEL, PAUL ARTHUR AMADEUS, *pseud.* Doomsday books. *boards, folio. San Francisco, Grabhorn, 1928.*

NIPPON NOODLES. *paper, 32mo. N.Y., Greenberg, 1957.*

NOLAN, PRESTON M. Pertinent and impertinent. *paper, 12mo, Chic., Kabel-Spalding, 1923.*

NOMAD, MAX. A skeptic's political dictionary and handbook for the disenchanted. *buckram, 8vo. N.Y., Bookman Associates, 1953.*

NONPAREIL; or, Harmless feast of wit. Being an entertainment of rational mirth, well seasoned, but entirely divested of every hurtful ingredient, consequently an agreeable parlour companion, and no unworthy acquisition to the library. *half-calf., 24mo. Lond., Vernor, Hood & Sharpe, 1806.*

NONPAREIL:, or, The quintessence of wit and humour; being a choice selection of those pieces that were most admired in the ever-to-be-remembered Midwife; or, The old woman's magazine . . . *half-calf., 12mo. Lond., Carnan, 1757.*

NONSENSE BOOK: a collection of limericks. *boards, 24mo. Bost., Marshall Jones, 1919.*

NOOLAS, RAB. Merry-go-down; a gallery of gorgeous drunkards through the ages. *buckram, 4to. Lond., Mandrake, n.d.*

NORDAU, MAX. Soap bubbles. *buckram, 16mo. N.Y., Neely, 1896.*

NORFOLK, HORATIO EDWARD. Gleanings in graveyards, a collection of curious epitaphs. *buckram, 12mo. Lond., Smith, 1861.*

NORMAN, CHARLES. Mr. Oddity. Samuel Johnson, LL.D. *buckram, 8vo. Lond., Murray, 1951.*

NORTH, STERLING *and* BOUTELL, C.B. *eds.* Speak of the devil. *buckram, 8vo. Garden City, Doubleday, Doran, 1945.*

NORTHCOTE, JAMES. Fables, original and selected. *half-calf., 12mo. Lond., Murray, 1833.*

_____ One hundred fables, original and selected. *half-calf., 12mo. Lond., Lawford, 1828.*

NORTHEND, CHARLES, *comp.,* Churchyard literature; or, Light reading on grave subjects: being a collection of amusing, quaint and curious epitaphs. *buckram, 16mo. Hartford, Dustin, Gilman, 1874.*

_____ Gems of thought. *buckram, 12mo. N.Y., Appleton, 1888.*

NORTON, JAMES SAGER. Addresses and fragments in prose and verse. *buckram, 8vo. Chic., McClurg, 1896.*

NOTHING TO EAT. Not by the author of "Nothing to wear". *buckram, 12mo. N.Y., Dick & Fitzgerald, 1857.*

NOTHING TO WEAR. An episode of city life (from Harper's Weekly). *buckram, 16mo. N.Y., Rudd & Carleton, 1857.*

NOTION-COUNTER, THE, a farrage of foibles; being notes about nothing by Nobody. *buckram, 16mo. Bost., Atlantic, 1922.*

NOW I'LL TELL ONE. *boards, 8vo. N.Y., Celebrities Pub. Co., n.d.*

NUGENT, J.C. *and* NUGENT, ELLIOTT. The poor nut, a comedy. *paper, 12mo. N.Y., French, 1925.*

NUTS AND NUTCRACKERS. *buckram, 16mo. Lond., Orr, 1845. 2d.ed.*

_____ Same. *Chapman & Hall, 1857. 3d.ed.*

NYE, EDGAR WILSON. Baled hay; a drier book than Walt Whitman's "Leaves o'grass" by Bill Nye. *buckram, 12mo. Chic., Donohue, Henneberry, 1890.*

_____ Bill Nye and Boomerang; or, The tale of a meek-eyed mule, and some other literary gems by Bill Nye himself. *buckram, 12mo. Chic., Donohue, Henneberry, 1890.*

_____ Bill Nye's chestnuts old and new, latest gatherings. *buckram, 12mo. Chic., Donohue, Henneberry, 1890.*

_____ Bill Nye's comic history of England. *paper, 12mo. Chic., Thompson & Thomas, 1906.*

_____ Bill Nye's history of the United States. *buckram, 8vo. Chic., Thompson & Thomas, 1906.*

_____ Bill Nye's red book. *buckram, 8vo. Chic., Thompson & Thomas, 1891.*

_____ Bill Nye's remarks. *buckram, 8vo. Chic., Thompson & Thomas, 1900.*

_____ Bill Nye's sparks. *buckram, 12mo. N.Y., Hurst, 1901.*

_____ Forty liars, and other lies. *buckram, 12mo. Chic., Donohue, Henneberry, 1890.*

_____ A guest at the Ludlow. *buckram, 12mo. Indianapolis, Bobbs-Merrill, 1897.*

_____ The humor of "Bill" Nye. *paper, 32mo. Girard, Kan., Haldeman-Julius, n.d. (Little Blue Books.)*

NYE, EDGAR WILSON *and*
RILEY, JAMES WHITCOMB.
Fun, wit and humor. *paper,*
*12mo. Chic., Laird & Lee,*
*1889.*

_____ Nye and Riley's
Railway guide. *paper, 16mo.*
*Chic., Neely, n.d.*

NYE, RUSSEL, *ed.* Modern
essays. *buckram, 12mo. N.Y.,*
*Scott, Foresman, 1953.*

# O

O'BANG, PATSY, comp. 500 epigrams about love. paper, 8vo. Girard, Kan., Haldeman-Julius, 1950.

——————— Witty, wise and wicked maxims. paper, 8vo. Girard, Kan., Haldeman-Julius, 1950.

O'BRIEN, HOWARD VINCENT. Memoirs of a guinea pig; or Eight years in a doctor's waiting room. buckram, 12mo. N.Y., Putnam's, 1942.

O'BRIEN, P.J. Will Rogers, ambassador of good will, prince of wit and wisdom. buckram, 8vo. N.Y., Author, 1935.

O'BRIEN, SEUMAS. Duty and other Irish comedies. buckram, 12mo. Bost., Little, Brown, 1916.

OBSTINATE FAMILY, THE; a farce. paper, 12mo. Chic., Dramatic Pub. Co., n.d.

O'CASEY, SEAN. The green crow. buckram, 8vo. Lond., Allen, 1957.

OCKSIDE, KNIGHT RUSS and THOMSON, MORTIMER (Q.K. Philander Doesticks, pseud.) The history and records of the Elephant Club. buckram, 12mo. N.Y., Livermore & Rudd, 1857.

ODD-FELLOW OF THE OLD SCHOOL, AN. The odd fellow's jest book, or, Repository of oddments. paper, 16mo. Lond., Hughes, ca. 1805.

ODDITIES. calf., 16mo. various publishers. Contents.-The Epping Hunt, by Thomas Hood.-Steamers v. stages, or, Andrew and his spouse.-The Yorkshire Hunt, or, An extraordinary chase of the parson and the cat, by William Cowper.-Monsieur Tonson, by John Taylor.-The devil's walk, by Professor Porson.

O'DONNELL, ELLIOTT. Trees of ghostly dread. buckram, 8vo. Lond., Rider, 1958.

O'DONOGHUE, D.J. The humour of Ireland. buckram, 12mo. Lond., Scott, 1894.

OESTERLEY, W.O.E. The wisdom of Ben-Sira (Ecclesiasticus.) buckram, 12mo. Lond., S.P.C.K. 1931.

OESTLERE, GORDON. Doctor in the house, by Richard Gordon, pseud. buckram, 8vo. N.Y., Harcourt, Brace, 1953.

O'FAOLAIN, EILEEN. Irish sagas and folk-tales. buckram, 8vo. Lond., Oxford Univ. Press, 1957.

OFFICE BOY'S DIGEST: cullings from the American, English and Canadian reports. buckram, 12mo. Charlottesville, Va., Michie, 1904.

OH BOY! a log book of fun. paper, 12mo. N.Y., Ogilvie, 1903.

O'HANLON, REDMOND L. Shakespeare and the hard of hearing. (In: Volta Review, v.56, no.5, May, 1954.)

O'HARA, NEAL. Take it from me. buckram, 8vo. Bost., Waverly, 1939.

O'HIGGINS, BRIAN. Laughter-lighted memories. paper, 16mo. Dublin, Author, n.d.

_____ A tonic in type; sketches grave and gay. *paper, 12mo. Dublin, Author, n.d.*

OKADA, ROKUO. Japanese proverbs and proverbial phrases. *buckram, 12mo. Tokyo, Japan Travel Bureau, 1955.*

_____ Same. 2d.ed., 1958.

OLAV, HANS, *ed.* He who laughs.. LASTS. Anecdotes from Norway's home front. *boards, folio, N.Y., Norwegian News Co., n.d.*

OLD BALLADS. *paper, 32mo. Girard, Kan., Haldeman-Julius, n.d. (Little Blue Books.)*

OLD DOC GAGS "FUNSTER" Number one. *paper, 24mo. N.Y., Ubert, 1924.*

OLD DOC GAGS "FUNSTER" Number two. *paper, 24mo. N.Y., Ubert, 1925.*

OLD DOC GAGS "IDIOTORIALS" Number one. *paper, 24mo. N.Y., Ubert, 1925.*

OLD ENGLISH COFFEE HOUSES. *boards, small 8vo. Lond., Miniature Books, 1954.*

OLD SALT, AN, *pseud.* Jack's kit; or, Saturday night in the forecastle. Being a choice collection of naval songs, nautical jokes, dog watch yarns and galley witticism. The whole revised and arranged by old comic Elton. *buckram, 32mo. N.Y., Marsh, 1955.*

OLD STORIES FROM DENMARK. *boards, 4to. Ebeltoft, Elle, n.d.*

"OLD TRAVELLER, AN". Anecdotes for the steamboat and railroad. *buckram, 12mo. Phila., Lindsay & Blakiston, 1857.*

OLDE TAYLES NEWLYE RELAYTED. Enriched with all ye ancyente embellyshmentes. *buckram, large 4to. Lond., Leadenhall, n.d.*

OLDSTYLE, OLIVER, *pseud.* Every-day characters, or, The Club Worthies. *boards, 12mo. Lond., Longman, Hurst, Rees, Orme, Brown & Green, n.d.*

O'LEAHY, OLEY. Trylongs and perisites. *boards, 8vo. N.Y., Greystone, 1939.*

O'LEARY, C.F. Proverbs and proverbial phrases. *buckram, 12mo. St. Louis, Mo., Harder, 1907.*

OLIVER, HARRY. Desert rat joke book. *paper, 8vo. Ridgecrest, Calif., Harry Oliver, n.d.*

_____ The old mirage salesman, a whimsical desert digest of refreshing nonsense, heralding the life of the Southwest's foremost story-telling Desert Rat, Harry Oliver, 1888-1999. Compiled by his daughters, Amy and Mary. *buckram, 8vo. Palm Springs, The Printery, 1952.*

O'MAHONEY, MICHAEL. Irish humour. *paper, 12mo. Liverpool Daily Post, n.d. 2d.ed.*

O'MALLEY, BILL. Blessed event. *paper, 16mo. N.Y., Perma-books, 1956.*

_____ Feeling no pain. *boards, 8vo. N.Y., Prentice-Hall, 1955.*

_____ Golf fore fun. *boards, 8vo. N.Y., Prentice-Hall, 1953.*

_____ More O'Malley's nuns. *paper, 12mo. N.Y., All Saints, 1960.*

_____ O'Malley's nuns. *paper, 16mo. N.Y., Perma-books, 1958.*

ON A SLOW TRAIN (The original story). *paper, 12mo. Baltimore, Ottenheimer, 1905.*

ON WISDOM; selected from the Sapiental Books. *boards, 8vo. Lond., De La More, n.d.*

ONE HUNDRED CHOICE SELECTIONS, nos. 3,20,37. *paper, 12mo. Phila., Penn, 1871, 1886, 1904.*

ONE HUNDRED MERRIE AND DELIGHTSOME STORIES, right pleasaunte to relate in all goodly companie by way of joyance and jollity. Les Cent Nouvelles Nouvelles now first done in the English tongue by Robert B. Douglas. *2v. buckram, 8vo. Paris, Carrington, n.d.*

100,000,000 "sit down" sitters. *buckram, 12mo. Chic., Action Pub. Co., 1937.*

ONE OF THE OLD SCHOOL *see* WEST, WILLIAM.

ONE THOUSAND LAUGHS FROM VAUDEVILLE, the funny efforts of the leading monologists, comedians, sketch artists and jokers. The best stories told by Fred Niblo, Raymond & Caverly (and others). *paper, 12mo. Baltimore, Ottenheimer, 1908.*

1,000 WITTY SAYINGS, containing the most comical and humorous of all humour. *buckram, 16mo. Lond., Milner, n.d.*

OO-LA-LA; a collection of the naughtiest cartoon post cards ever imported from gay Paree!. *paper, 8vo. N.Y., Skyline, 1957.*

OPEN AT YOUR OWN RISQUE. *buckram, 8vo. N.Y., Scylla, 1955.*

OPIE, EVERETT. Ravioli every morning. *paper, 8vo. Tokyo, Pacific Stars and Stripes, 1957.*

OPIE, IONA *and* OPIE, PETER. The Oxford dictionary of nursery rhymes. *buckram, 8vo. Oxford, Clarendon, 1951.*

OPLER, MORRIS EDWARD. Myths and legends of the Lipan Apache Indians. *buckram, 8vo. N.Y., American Folk-lore Society, 1940.*

OPPER, FREDERICK. Puck's Opper book. *half-calf, 4to. N.Y., Keppler & Schwarzmann, 1888.*

_____ Willie and his papa, and the rest of the family. *boards, 8vo. N.Y., Grosset & Dunlap, 1901.*

ORBEN, ROBERT. Boff bundle. *paper, 8vo. N.Y., Author, 1954.*

_____ Classified comedy. *paper, 8vo. N.Y., Tannen, 1951.*

_____ Comedy caravan. *paper, 8vo. N.Y., Author, 1949.*

_____ Emcee blockbusters. *paper, 8vo. N.Y., Author, 1952.*

_____ The encyclopedia of patter. *paper, 8vo. N.Y., Tannen, 1946. 7th ed.*

_____ M.C. bits. *paper, 8vo. N.Y., Author, 1953.*

_____ *Same. 2d.ed. 1957.*

_____ Patter parade. *paper, 8vo. N.Y., Tannen, 1947.*

_____ Screamline comedy. *paper, 8vo. N.Y., Author, 1953.*

_____ Tag-lines. *paper, 8vo. N.Y., Author, 1954.*

ORCUTT, WILLIAM DANA.
Escape to laughter. *buckram,*
*12mo. Norwood, Mass.,*
*Plimpton, 1942.* (Contains ALS
to Nat Schmulowitz.)

ORDWAY, EDITH B. Handbook of
conundrums. *buckram, 12mo.*
*N.Y., Sully, 1914.*

ORDWAY, SAMUEL H., *jr.* Little
Codfish Cabot at Harvard.
*boards, 16mo. Cambridge,*
*Little, Codfish Cabot Pub. Co.,*
*1924.*

O'REGAN, WILLIAM. Memoirs of
the legal, literary and political
life of the late the Right
Honourable John Philpot
Curran. *half-calf, 8vo. Lond.,*
*Harper, 1817.*

O'REILLY, JOHN *and* KELLY,
WALT. The glob. *buckram, 8vo.*
*N.Y., Viking, 1952.*

O'RELL, MAX, *pseud. see*
BLOUET, PAUL.

ORLANDO, GUIDO *and* MERWIN,
SAMUEL. Confessions of a
scoundrel. *buckram, 8vo.*
*Phila., Winson, 1954.*

ORLEANS, ILO. Laughing up your
sleeve. *paper, 24mo. Newark,*
*Lasky, 1953.*

ORWELL, GEORGE. Animal farm.
*buckram, 12mo. N.Y., Harcourt,*
*Brace, 1946.* (Inserted: Strange
doings at Animal Farm, by
Spencer Brown.)

OSBORN, INNIS G. A taking way;
a farce. *paper, 12mo. Bost.,*
*Baker, 1914.*

OSBORN, NORRIS G. Isaac H.
Bromley. *boards, 8vo. N.Y.,*
*Yale, Univ. Press, 1920.*

OSBORN, ROBERT. Low and
inside. *boards, folio. N.Y.,*
*Farrar, Straus & Young, 1953.*

_____ Osborn on leisure.
*paper, wide 8vo. N.Y., Ridge,*
*1956.*

OSBORNE, MARGHERITA O.
Conundrums. *buckram, 16mo.*
*Phila., Penn, 1930.*

OSBORNE, MARGHERITA, *ed.*
The book of happiness.
*boards, 24mo. N.Y., Algonquin,*
*1928.*

O'SHAMUS, SHAMUS, *pseud.* The
Irish guyed. *buckram, 8vo.*
*Lond., Allen, n.d.*

OSLER, *Sir* WILLIAM. Sir William
Osler - aphorisms from his bed-
side teachings and his writings.
Collected by Robert Bennett
Bean, edited by William Bennett
Bean. *buckram, 16mo. N.Y.,*
*Schuman, 1950.*

OTT, IRV, *ed.* Modern jokes and
monologues, containing a new
collection of the funniest jokes
and monologues told by the
best comedians on the stage.
*paper, 32mo. Baltimore,*
*Ottenheimer, 1915.*

_____ New actors' joke
book, containing a choice collection of the latest and
funniest jokes and monologues,
told and used by great favorites
on the American stage. *paper,*
*32mo. Baltimore, Ottenheimer,*
*1914.*

_____ New black face joke
book. *paper, 32mo. Baltimore,*
*Ottenheimer, 1907.*

_____ New Irish joke book.
*paper, 12mo. Baltimore,*
*Ottenheimer, 1907.*

_____ New Italian joke
book. *paper, 12mo. Baltimore,*
*Ottenheimer, 1909.*

_____ New rube joke book. *paper, 32mo. Baltimore, Otten-heimer, 1908.*

_____ New tramp joke book. *paper, 24mo. Baltimore, Otten-hei mer, 1907.*

_____ New vaudeville joke book. *paper, 32mo. Baltimore, Ottenheimer, 1908.*

_____ On a fast train through Texas. 1,000 miles in 120 minutes. *paper, 32mo. Baltimore, Ottenheimer, 1905.*

OTT, MOE, *ed.* New joke book. *paper, 32mo. Baltimore, Otten-heimer, 1908.*

_____ New kid joke book, no. 1. *paper, 32mo. Baltimore, Ottenheimer, 1907.*

_____ New stage jokes. *paper, 32mo. Baltimore, Otten-heimer, n.d.*

OUR FUNNY FELLOW, *pseud.* Comic holiday book. *buckram, 8vo. Lond., Ward, Lock, n.d. 2d.ed.*

OUTRAM, GEORGE. Legal and other lyrics. *boards, 8vo. Lond, Foulis, 1919.*

OVER SIXTEEN. Prudes won't think it's funny! *buckram, 4to. N.Y., Grayson, 1951.*

OVERSTREET, HARRY A. Seven adventures in pioneering. *paper, 24mo. (Personal Growth Leaflets.)*

OVERTON, GRANT. Cream of the jug, an anthology of humorous stories. *boards, 12mo. N.Y., Harper, 1927.*

OWEN, FRANK. The bedside bonanza; or, A lodestone of love and laughter. *buckram, 8vo. N.Y., Fell, 1944.*

OWENS, PHILIP, *comp.* Bed and sometimes breakfast; an anthology of landladies. *buckram, 8vo. Lond., Sylvan, 1944.*

OXBERRY, W. The actor's budget of wit and merriment. *boards, 12mo. Lond., Simpkin & Marshall, 1820.*

_____ The flowers of litera-ture, or, Encyclopedia of anec-dote. *4v. half-calf, 12mo. Lond, Simpkin & Marshall, 1821-1822.*

OXFORDSHIRE CONTEST, THE; or, The whole controversy between the old and new interest, containing a great variety of wit, humour and argument ... *quarter-calf, small 8vo. Lond., Owen, 1753.*

# P

PAAR, JACK. I kid you not. *paper, 16mo. N.Y., Pocket Books, 1961.*

PACKER, ELEANOR. A day with Charlie McCarthy and Edgar Bergen. *paper, 4to. N.Y., K.K. Publications, 1938.*

PACKET OF PESTILENT PASQUILS, A. *paper, 8vo. Priv. Printed, n.d.*

PAGE, BRETT. Writing for vaudeville. *buckram, 12mo. Springfield, Mass., Home Correspondence School, 1915.*

PAGE, FRANCIS. Confucius comes to Broadway. *buckram, 8vo. N.Y., Wisdom House, 1940.*

PAGET, JOHN. Judicial puzzles gathered from the state trials. *buckram, 16mo. San Francisco, S. Whitney, 1876.*

——————— Paradoxes and puzzles, historical judicial and literary. *buckram, 8vo. Edinburgh, Blackwood, 1874.*

PAGET, R.L., ed. The poetry of American wit and humor. *buckram, 12mo. Bost., Page, 1899.*

PAIN, BARRY. De omnibus, by The Conductor. *buckram, 12mo. Lond., Dent, n.d.*

——————— Humorous stories. *buckram, 12mo. Lond., T.Werner Laurie, 1930.*

——————— Methuen's Library of Humour. Barry Pain. *buckram, 16mo. Lond., Methuen, 1934.*

——————— Stories and interludes. *buckram, 12mo. Lond., Henry, 1892.*

PAINE, ALBERT BIGELOW. Making up with Mr. Dog. *buckram, 12mo. N.Y., Harper, 1900.*

PALEY, F.A. Greek wit; a collection of smart sayings and anecdotes, translated from Greek prose writers. *buckram, 16mo. Lond., Bell, 1888. 2d.ed.*

PALMER, JOHN. Comic characters of Shakespeare. *buckram, 8vo. Lond., Macmillan, 1946.*

PALMER, SAMUEL. Moral essays on some of the most curious and significant English, Scotch and foreign proverbs. *calf, 12mo. Lond., Hodgking, 1710.*

PANORAMA OF WIT, THE; exhibiting at one view the choicest epigrams in the English language. *half-calf, 32mo. Lond., Walker, 1809.*

PARABLE OF THE "WISE" BUYER, THE. *pamphlet.*

PARE, AMBROISE. The apologie and treatise of Ambroise Pare. Edited by G. Keynes. *buckram, 8vo. Chic., Univ. of Chic., 1952.*

PARKER, DOROTHY. Here lies; the collected stories. *buckram, 8vo. N.Y., Literary Guild, 1939.*

——————— Laments for the living. *buckram, 8vo. N.Y., Viking, 1930.*

PARKER, GILBERT. The liar. *buckram, 24mo. Bost., Brown, 1899.*

PARKER, GLADYS. Mopsy. *paper, 12mo. N.Y., Mopsy Pub. Co., 1945.*

PARKER, JAMES REID. The pleasure was mine. *buckram, 8vo. N.Y., Wyn, 1946.*

PARKER, JOHN F. "If elected, I promise ..." 1001 jokes, toasts, stories and gems of wisdom by and about politicians. *buckram, 8vo. Garden City, Doubleday, 1960.*

PARKER, MARION. Thoughts of
the great; a scrapbook of quotations. *paper, 12mo. N.Y.,*
*Philosophical Library, 1960.*

PARKER, MARY MONCURE. Jolly
monologues. *paper, 12mo. Chic,*
*Denison, 1921.*

─────────── Merry monologues.
*buckram, 12mo. Chic., Denison,*
*1916.*

─────────── Mrs. Gadabouts busy
day; a comedy. *paper, 12mo.*
*Chic., Drake, 1908.*

─────────── Snappy monologues.
*buckram, 12mo. N.Y., French,*
*1931.*

PARKINSON, C. NORTHCOTE.
Parkinson's law; and other
studies in administration.
*boards, 8vo. Bost., Houghton,*
*Mifflin 1957.*

PARLOUR PORTFOLIO, THE; or,
Post-chaise companion. *2v.*
*boards, 8vo. Lond., Iley, 1820.*

PARR, SAMUEL. Aphorisms,
opinions and reflections.
*boards, 12mo. Lond., Andrews,*
*1828.*

PARRISH, J.M. *and* CROSSLAND,
JOHN R., *eds.* Great book of
humour. *buckram, 8vo. Lond.,*
*Odhams, 1935.*

PARRY, EDWARD ABBOTT.
Butterscotia, or, A cheap trip
to Fairyland. *buckram, 8vo.*
*Lond., Nutt, 1896.*

PARSON, DENYS, *comp.* It must
be true "It was all in the
papers". *buckram, 16mo.*
*Lond., Macdonald, 1952.*

─────────── All too true. *boards,*
*12mo. Lond., Macdonald, 1954.*

─────────── Can it be true? it
must be true - "It was in all
the papers". *buckram, 12mo.*
*Lond., Macdonald, 1953.*

─────────── Never more true.
*buckram, 12mo. Lond.,*
*Macdonald, 1960.*

─────────── Nothing brightens the
garden like primrose pants.
The life and times of Gobgrey
Shrdlu. *boards, 8vo. N.Y.,*
*Hanover, 1955.*

─────────── True to type.
*boards, 12mo. Lond.,*
*Macdonald, 1955.*

PARSONS, E. BRYHAM. Pot-
pourri parisien, and First
impressions of New York.
*buckram, small 8vo. N.Y.,*
*Author, 1916.*

PARTCH, VIRGIL FRANKLIN
"VIP". Bottle fatigue.
*boards, 8vo. N.Y., Duell,*
*Sloan & Pearce, 1950.*

─────────── Funny cartoons by
VIP. *paper, 12mo. Greenwich,*
*Conn., Gold Medal Books,*
*1960.*

─────────── Here we go again.
*boards, 8vo. N.Y., Duell,*
*Sloan & Pearce, 1951.*

─────────── It's hot in here.
*boards, 12mo. N.Y., McBride,*
*1945.*

─────────── Man the beast.
*boards, 8vo. N.Y., Duell, Sloan*
*& Pearce, 1953.*

─────────── VIP tosses a party.
With tips on party tossing, by
William McIntyre. *buckram,*
*8vo. N.Y., Simon & Schuster,*
*1959.*

─────────── Water on the brain.
*boards, 4to. N.Y., McBride,*
*1945.*

─────────── The wild, wild women.
*boards, 8vo. N.Y., Duell, Sloan*
*& Pearce, 1951.*

PARTON, J., ed. The humorous poetry of the English language. buckram, 12mo. N.Y., Mason, 1857. 4th ed.

——————— Caricature and other comic art in all times and many lands. buckram, 8vo. N.Y., Harper, 1877.

PARTRIDGE, ERIC, ed. A first book of quotations. buckram, 8vo. Lond., Hamilton, 1958.

——————— The 'Shaggy dog' story; its origin, development and nature (with a few seemly examples.) buckram, 12mo. N.Y., Philosophical Library, 1954.

——————— Shakespeare's bawdy; a literary and psychological essay. buckram, 8vo. Lond., Routledge & Kegan Paul, 1956.

PASCAL, BLAISE. Thoughts. paper, 32mo. Girard, Kan., Haldeman-Julius, n.d. (Little Blue Books.)

PASQUINO, pseud. Pasquin and Marforio on the peace: being a discussion, by these celebrated statues at Rome of the general conduct of England, but particularly pending the late war and negotiating the present peace. pamphlet. Lond., Webb, 1736.

PASTMOR, PAUL. The Dorcas society, and other sketches. paper, 16mo. St.Johnsbury, Vt., Walter, 1889.

PATANJALI. Aphorisms of Yoga. Done into English from the original in Sanskrit. boards, 8vo. Lond., Faber & Faber, 1938.

PATRICK, J. MAX. The arrest of Hugh Peters. leaflet. (From Huntington Library Journal)

PATRIOTIC SELECTIONS FOR MEMORIZING. Grades I thru IX. paper, 24mo. (Personal Growth Leaflet)

PATTE, JIM. Two hundred toasts. boards, 16mo. N.Y., 1917.

PATTEN, WILLIAM. Among the humorists and after-dinner speakers, a new collection of humorous stories and anecdotes. 3v. cloth, 12mo. N.Y., Collier, 1909.

PATTON, ROBERT CALDWELL and KING, CHARLES. Roosevelt for king. paper, 4to. N.Y., His Majesty's Ink-Slingers, 1937.

PAUL, ELLIOT. Film flam. buckram, 12mo. Lond., Muller, n.d.

PAUL, HENRY HOWARD. Dashes of American humour. buckram, 8vo. Lond., Piper, 1852.

PAUL, L. Riddles, jokes and stories. paper, 32mo. Baltimore, Ottenheimer, n.d.

PAUL PRY'S JEST BOOK; being a choice collection of comical jests, droll adventures, touches of humour, excellent bon-mots, pleasing short stories, &c, &c. By the author of "Wit and wisdom". buckram, 24mo. Lond., Smith, 1828.

PAULDING, JAMES K. Salmagundi; or, The whim-whams and opinions of Launcelot Langstaff, esq. and others. 2v. tree-calf., 24mo. N.Y., Longworth, 1814.

——————— Same. N.Y., Putnam, 1857.

PAULDING, JAMES KIRKE. The lion of the West. buckram, 8vo. Stanford, Stanford Univ. Press, 1954.

PAULTON, HARRY *and*
PAULTON, EDWARD. Niobe,
all smiles; a farcical comedy.
*paper, 12mo. N.Y., French,
1904.*

PAYNE, JESS WILLIAM. It's a
laugh, by Lord Helpus! *paper,
12mo. San Antonio, Naylor,
1959.*

PAYNE, ROBERT. The great
Charlie. *paper, 16mo. Lond.,
Pan Books, 1957. Rev.ed.*

———————— The great god Pan,
a biography of the tramp played
by Charles Chaplin. *buckram,
8vo. N.Y., Heritage, 1952.*

PAYSON, PRENTISS. Human bail.
*buckram, 12mo. Bost., Meader,
1932.*

PEABODY, LUCY W., *ed.* Fables
in alcohol, by Allsop. *paper,
12mo. Marblehead, Mass.,
Lindsey, 1931. 2d.ed.*

PEAKE, HAROLD. The law and
the prophets. *buckram, 8vo.
Oxford, Clarendon, 1936.*

PEAKE, MERVYN. Figures of
speech. *buckram, 8vo. Lond.,
Gollancz, 1954.*

PEARLE, CYRIL. Bawdy Burns,
the Christian rebel. *buckram,
12mo. Lond., Muller, 1958.*

PEARLS OF THOUGHT,
RELIGIOUS AND PHILO-
SOPHICAL, gathered from old
authors. *buckram, 16mo. N.Y.,
Delisser & Procter, 1859.*

PEARSON, F.S. Compound
fractured French. *boards, 8vo.
Garden City, Doubleday, 1951.*

———————— Fractured French.
(Originally published as two
books: Fractured French and
Compound fractured French.)
*paper, 16mo. N.Y., Permabooks,
1956.*

PEARSON, HESKETH. The Smith
of Smiths, being the life, wit
and humour of Sydney Smith.
*buckram, 8vo. N.Y., Harper,
1934.*

PEARSON'S HUMOROUS RE-
CITER AND READER. *paper,
12mo. Lond., Pearson, n.d.*

PECK, GEORGE W. How private
George W. Peck put down the
rebellion. *buckram, 8vo. Chic.,
Thompson & Thomas, 1900.*

———————— Peck's bad boy and
his pa; complete edition.
*paper, 8vo. N.Y., Dover, 1958.*

———————— Peck's bad boy,
no.2. *buckram, 12mo. Chic.,
Belford-Clarke, 1890.*

———————— Peck's bad boy in an
airship. *buckram, 12mo. Chic.,
Stanton, 1908.*

———————— Peck's bad boy with
the circus. *buckram, 12mo.
Chic., Stanton & Van Vliet,
1905.*

———————— Peck's boss book.
*buckram, 12mo. Chic., Home-
wood, 1884.*

———————— Peck's fun, com-
prising all the choice gems of
wit, humor, sarcasm and
pathos. Edited by Thomas W.
Handford. *buckram, 12mo.
Chic., Donohue, Henneberry,
1890.*

———————— Peck's fun.
Compiled by V.W. Richardson.
*paper, 12mo. Chic., Belford,
Clarke, 1880.*

———————— Peck's sunshine.
*buckram, 12mo. Chic.,
Donohue, Henneberry, 1890.*

———————— Peck's Irish friend,
Phelan Geoheagan. *paper,
12mo. Chic., Morrill, Higgins,
1892.*

_____Peck's Uncle Ike and the red headed boy. Also, Sunbeams; humor, sarcasm and sense. *buckram, 12mo. Chic., Thompson & Thomas, 1900.*

PEELE, CECILY. The encyclopaedia of British bogies. *boards, 8vo. Oxford, Alley Workshops, n.d.*

PEELE, GEORGE. Merrie conceited iests of George Peele, Gentleman, sometimes stvdent in Oxford, wherein is shewed the course of his life, how liued a man very well knowne in the City of London and elsewhere. *boards, 8vo. Lond., Bell, n.d. Reprinted. Lond., Singer & Triphook, 1809.*

PEERY, ROBERT. Small town humour. *paper, 32mo. Girard, Kan., Haldeman-Julius, n.d. (Little Blue Books)*

PEGGE, SAMUEL. Anecdotes of the English language, chiefly regarding the local dialect of London and its environs ... *calf., 8vo. Lond., Nichols & Bentley, 1814.*

_____ Anonymiana; or, Ten centuries of observations on various authors and subjects. *calf., 8vo. Lond., Nichols, & Bentley, 1818. 2d.ed.*

_____ Curialia miscellanea, or, Anecdotes of old times. *half-calf, 8vo. Lond., Nichols & Bentley, 1818.*

PEMBERTON, MORTON H. Reuben, his book. *buckram, 12mo. N.Y., Broadway Pub.Co., 1905.*

PENNINGTON, JEANNE G. "Don't worry" nuggets. *buckram, 24mo. N.Y., Fords, Howard & Hulbert, 1898.*

PEPLE, EDWARD. A night out. *boards, 16mo. N.Y., Moffat, Yard, 1915.*

PEPYS, SAMUEL. Samuel Pepy's diary. *buckram, 4to. N.Y., Illustrated Editions, 1932.*

PEPYS, SAML, jr. see FREEMAN, ROBERT MASSIE.

PERCHERON, MAURICE. Buddha and Buddhism. *paper, 12mo. N.Y., Harper, 1957.*

PERCY, J.C. Bulls ancient and modern. *boards, small 8vo. Dublin, McCready, Percy, 1912.*

_____ More bulls and blunders. *buckram, 8vo. Dublin, McCready, Percy, 1920.*

PERCY, REUBEN and SHOLTO see BYERLY, THOMAS and ROBERTSON, JOSEPH CLINTON.

PERCY, STEPHEN. Robin Hood and his merry foresters. *buckram, 16mo. N.Y., Walker, 1848. New ed.*

PERELMAN, S.J. Acres and pains. *buckram, 12mo. Lond., Heinemann, 1948.*

_____ The best of S.J. Perelman. *buckram, 12mo. N.Y., Modern Library, 1947.*

_____ Bite on the bullet, or, Under the spreading atrophy. *buckram, 8vo. Lond., Heinemann, 1957.*

_____ Crazy like a fox. *buckram, 12mo. Garden City, Garden City Pub.Co., 1945.*

_____ The ill tempered clavichord. *buckram, 8vo. N.Y., Simon & Schuster, 1952.*

_____ Keep it crisp. *buckram, 8vo. N.Y., Random, 1944.*

——————— The Swiss family Perelman. *buckram, 8vo. N.Y., Simon & Schuster, 1950.*

PERIN, FLORENCE HOBART. The optimist's good night. *buckram, 16mo. Bost., Little Brown, 1922.*

PERKINS, ELI *see* LANDON, MELVILLE D.

PERKINS, REUBEN, *comp.* Yankee yarns and American humor, containing original and selected side-splitting dialect stories, witty sayings, comic situations and rare anecdotes. *paper, 8vo. N.Y., Popular Pub. Co., 1902.*

PERRAULT, CHARLES. The fairy tales. *paper, 16mo. Harmondsworth, Middlesex. Penguin, 1957.*

PERTWEE, ERNEST, *comp.* The comic and humorous reciter. *buckram, 8vo. Lond., Routledge, n.d.*

——————— A little book of twentieth-century duologues. *buckram, 12mo. Lond., Routledge, n.d.*

——————— Twentieth-century American humorous reciter. *buckram, 12mo. Lond., Routledge, n.d.*

——————— The very humorous reciter. *buckram, 12mo. Lond., K.Paul, Routledge, 1950.*

PERUGINI, MARK EDWARD. Victorian days and ways. *buckram, 12mo. Lond., Hutchinson, n.d.*

PETER PAUPER'S EPIGRAMS AND APHORISMS. *boards, 12mo. Mount Vernon, N.Y., Peter Pauper, n.d.*

PETER PIPER'S PRACTICAL PRINCIPLES OF PLAIN & PERFECT PRONUNCIATION. *paper, 12mo. Brooklyn, Mergenthaler Linotype Co., 1936.*

PETERS, CHARLES. Autobiography. *paper, 12mo. Sacramento, Calif., LaGrave, 1915.*

PETERS, HARRIET S. "Rocky Mountainania" or, A tenderfoot's dictionary. *paper, 8vo. Denver, Kistler, 1934.*

PETERS, HUGH. The tales and jests of Mr. Hugh Peters. Collected into one volume, published by one that hath formerly been conversant with the author in his lifetime... *calf., 8vo. Lond., Caulfield.* Reprinted from the original edition of 1660 in facsimile. 1807.

PETERS, MADISON C., *ed.* Wit and wisdom of the Talmud. *buckram, 24mo. N.Y., Bloch, 1914.*

PETERSON, ERNST *and* CHAFFIN, GLENN. Sittin' and a-thinkin'. *paper, 12mo. Richmond, Va., Dietz, 1952.*

PETROVICH, WOISLAV M. Hero tales and legends of the Serbians. *buckram, 8vo. Lond., Harrap, 1912.*

PETTIBONE, JAMES, *comp. and ed.* The lodge goat, goat rides, butts and goat hairs gathered from the lodge rooms of every fraternal order. *buckram, 12mo. Cincinnati, Pettibone, 1903.*

PETTIGREW, THOMAS JOSEPH. Chronicles of the tombs, a select collection of epitaphs. *half-calf, 12mo. Lond., Bohn, 1857.*

PETTIWARD, DANIEL. Money for jam; anyone can be a non-artist. *buckram, 8vo. Lond., Perpetua, 1956.*

PETTOELLO, DECIO, *ed.* Great Italian short stories. *buckram, 8vo. Lond., Benn, 1930.*

PEYNET, RAYMOND. The lovers' keepsake. *boards, 8vo. Lond., Perpetua, 1958.*

——————— The lovers' pocket-book. *boards, 8vo. Lond., Perpetua, 1954.*

PHELAN, PAUL J., *comp.* A time to laugh; a risible reader by Catholic writers. *buckram, 8vo. N.Y., Longmans, Green, 1949.*

——————— With a merry heart; a treasury of humor by Catholic authors. *buckram, 8vo. Lond., Longmans, Green,1944.*

"PHELIX" Top sacred. *boards, 12mo. Lond., Merlin, 1960.*

PHELPS, PAULINE *and* SHORT, MARION. Stop! Go! *paper, 12mo. Chic., Denison, 1930.*

PHELPS, WILLIAM LYON. A dash at the pole. *buckram, 12mo. Bost., Ball, 1909.*

PHILISTINA, *pseud.* Alec the great; an account of the curious life and extraordinary opinions of the late Alexander Woollcott. *buckram, 8vo. N.Y., Avolon, 1943.*

PHILIPPE ——————— The strange world of Mr. Mum. *paper, 16mo. N.Y., Pocket Books, 1960.*

PHILLIPS, H.I. The foolish question book. *buckram, 12mo. N.Y., Clode, 1927.*

——————— The private papers of Private Purkey. *buckram, 8vo. N.Y., Harper, 1941.*

——————— Private Purkey in love and war. *buckram, 8vo. N.Y., Harper, 1942.*

——————— Private Purkey's private peace. *buckram, 12mo. N.Y., Putnam's, 1945.*

PHILLIPS, HENRY WALLACE. Mr. Scraggs. *buckram, 12mo. N.Y., Grafton, 1906.*

——————— The pets. *buckram, 16mo. N.Y., Doubleday, Page, 1909.*

PHILLIPS, HUBERT. The Hubert Phillips annual, 1951. *buckram, 12mo. Lond., Hamilton, 1950.*

——————— Question time; an omnibus of problems for a rainy day. *buckram, 8vo. Lond., Dent, 1937.*

PHILLIPS, WATTS. My first day in a quiet street. *buckram, 16mo. Lond., Ackermann-Strand, 1851.*

PHILLPOTTS, EDEN. Curtain raisers. *buckram, 12mo. N.Y., Brentano's, 1914.*

——————— The farmer's wife. *buckram, 16mo. Lond., Duck-worth, 1917.*

PHILOSOPHY OF MODERN HUMBUG, THE. *buckram, 8vo. Lond., Longmans, Green, 1875.*

PHUN FOTOGRAFT. Kewreus konseets komically illustrated by Kweer Feller. *paper, 12mo. N.Y., American News Co., 1865.*

PHUNNY BOOK, THE. published by Dr. Ephraim Muggins, M.D. *paper, 16mo. N.Y., Manhattan Medicine Co., n.d.*

PIAGGI, HENRY REGO. Uncle Schnitz; a collection of Dutch, Irish, coon, rube, dago stories and conundrums. *paper, 12mo. Chic., Donohue, 1907.*

PICARD, BARBARA LEONIE.
French legends, tales and
fairy stories. *buckram,
8vo. Lond., Oxford Univ.
Press, 1957.*

——————— German hero-sagas
and folk-tales. *buckram, 8vo.
Lond., Oxford Univ. Press,
1958.*

PICKARD, WILLIAM BASHYR.
The adventures of Alcassim;
an Iranian entertainment. *buckram, 8vo. Lond., Cape, 1936.*

PICKERING, HY. One thousand
tales worth telling. *buckram,
12mo. Lond., Pickering &
Inglis, n.d.*

PICKLE THE YOUNGER, *pseud.*
Broad grins of the Laughing
Philosopher. *paper, 16mo.
N.Y., Dick & Fitzgerald, 1809?*

PICTURES OF THE FRENCH; a
series of literary and graphic
delineations of French
character by Jules Janin,
Balzac, Cormenin (and others).
*buckram, 8vo. Lond., Tegg,
1841.*

PIDDINGTON, RALPH. The
psychology of laughter; a study
in social adaptation. *buckram,
8vo. Lond., Figurehead, 1933.*

PIERSON, ARTHUR T. Seed
thoughts for public speakers.
*buckram, 8vo. N.Y., Funk &
Wagnalls, 1890.*

PIERSON, LOUISE RANDALL.
Roughly speaking. *buckram,
8vo. N.Y., Simon & Schuster,
1943.*

PIKE, ROBERT E. Granite
laughter and marble tears;
epitaphs of old New England.
*buckram, 4to. Hartford, Conn.
Daye, 1938.*

PILIBIN, AN. Irish ironies; a
collection of short stories.
*buckram, 8vo. Dublin, Talbot,
1930.*

PIM, PAUL. Telling Tommy about
famous people in their youth.
*buckram, 8vo. N.Y., Cupples &
Leon, 1940.*

PIMLYCO, or, Runne Red-cap, tis
a mad world at Hogsdon. Reproduced in facsimile by the
Oxford University Press, with a
preface by A.H. Bullen. *paper,
8vo. Oxford, Printed for Private
circulation, 1891. (Antient
drolleries, no.2.)*

PITKIN, WALTER P. A short
introduction to the history of
human stupidity. *buckram, 8vo.
Lond., Allen & Unwin, 1935.*

PITMAN, NORMAN HISDALE. A
Chinese wonder book. *buckram,
16mo. N.Y., Dutton, 1919.*

PIOZZI, HESTHER LYNCH.
Anecdotes of Samuel Johnson.
Edited by S.C. Roberts. *buck-
ram, 16mo. Cambridge, Univ.
Press, 1932.*

PITT, WILLIAM, *1st earl of
Chatham.* Anecdotes of the
life of the Right Honourable
William Pitt, earl of Chatham.
*3v. tree calf., 8vo. Lond.,
Jordon, 1793. 3d.ed. corrected.*

PITTENGER, WILLIAM. Toasts
and forms of public address for
those who wish to say the
right thing in the right way.
*buckram, 12mo. Phila., Morris,
1907.*

PITZER, F.P. Comical con-
fessions of clever comedians.
*buckram, 16mo. N.Y., Street
& Smith, 1904.*

PLATTEN, JOHN H. *and* BARBIERI, A.M. The laugh's on you. *boards, 4to. Priv.Print., 1938.*

PLAYBOY. The best from Playboy; entertainment for men. *quarter-buckram, 4to. N.Y., Waldorf, 1954.*

——————— The Playboy cartoon album. *buckram, 4to. N.Y., Crown, 1959.*

PLOPPER, CLIFFORD H. Chinese proverbs. *paper, 8vo. Peiping, North China Union Language School, 1932.*

POCKET BOOK OF BONERS: an omnibus of schoolboy howlers and unconscious humor. *paper, 16mo. N.Y., Pocket Books, 1941.*

POCKET-BOOK OF THE EARLY AMERICAN HUMORISTS. *calf, 24mo. Bost., Small, Maynard, 1907.*

POCKET TRIVET: an anthology for optimists. *boards, 16mo. Lond., Morning Post, 1932.*

POCOCK, GUY *and* BOZMAN, M.M., *eds.* Modern humour. *buckram, 16mo. Lond., Dent, 1940.*

POGGIO-BRACCIOLINI. Facetia erotica. *buckram, 8vo. N.Y., Priv.Print., 1930.*

——————— The facetiae, or Jocose tales of Poggio. *2v. half-buckram, 16mo. Paris, Liseux, 1879.*

POINTS OF HUMOUR; illustrated by the designs of George Cruikshank. *half-calf, 8vo. Lond., Baldwin, 1823.*

POLAK, A. LAURENCE. Final legal fictions; a series of cases from folk-lore and opera. *buckram, 12mo. Lond., Stevens, 1948.*

——————— Legal fictions; a series of cases from the classics. *buckram, 12mo. Lond., Stevens, 1946.*

——————— More legal fictions; a series of cases from Shakespeare. *buckram, 12mo. Lond., Stevens, 1946.*

——————— Second thoughts on life, law and letters. *buckram, 12mo. Lond., Stevens, 1949.*

POLEY, IRVIN C. *and* POLEY, RUTH V. Friendly anecdotes. *buckram, 12mo. N.Y., Harper, 1950.*

——————— Quaker anecdotes. *paper, 16mo. Wallingford, Pa., Pendel Hill, 1946.*

POLITE COMPANION, or, Wit-a-la-mode, adapted to the recreation of all rank and degrees ... including a rich variety of comical jests, smart epigrams, diverting riddles &c. &c. *half-roan, 8vo. Lond., Kearsly, 1760.*

——————— *Same. Lond., Serjeant, 1776.*

POLITICAL AND SATIRICAL HISTORY OF THE YEARS 1756 AND 1757, in a series of seventy-five humorous and entertaining prints. *buckram, 24mo. Lond., Morris, 1757?*

POLITICAL APHORISMS, or, The true maxims of government displayed. *buckram, 8vo. Lond., Harrison, 1690.*

POLITICS FOR THE POCKET; being the perfect politicians' complete compendium of fact and fancy, by the Stewards of the Children Hundreds and the Manor of Hempholme. *paper, 8vo. Lond., Putnam's, 1904.*

POLLARD, JNO. GARLAND. A connotary; definitions not found in dictionaries collected from the sayings of the wise and otherwise. *buckram, 12mo. N.Y., Crowell, 1935. 3d.ed. rev. and enl.*

POLLOCK, CHANNING. The adventures of a happy man. *buckram, 8vo. N.Y., Crowell, 1939.*

POLLOCK, ELIZABETH R. Yes, ma'am! the personal papers of a WAAC. *buckram, 12mo. Phila., Lippincott, 1943.*

POLLOCK, LOUIS and ROSE, CARL. Stork bites man; what the expectant father may expect. *buckram, 8vo. Cleveland., World, 1945.*

"POLLUTED PROVERBS" Laughin tissue. roll of toilet tissue imprinted with gags and jokes. *Asbury Park, N.J., Adams, n.d.*

POLWHELE, RICHARD, *ed. and tr.* The idyllia, epigrams and fragments of Theocritus, Bion and Moschus, with the elegies of Tyrtaeus. *2v. half-calf, 8vo. Bath, Cruttwell, 1792.*

POLYANTHEA; or, A collection of interesting fragments. *2v. half-roan, 8vo. Lond., Budd, 1804.*

POMEROY, M.M. Brick-dust; a remedy for the blues, and a something for people to talk about. *buckram, 12mo. N.Y., Carleton, 1871.*

———————— Nonsense, or, Hits and criticisms on the follies of the day. *buckram, 12mo. N.Y., Carleton, 1868.*

POND, J.B. Eccentricities of genius. *buckram, 8vo. N.Y., Dillingham, 1900.*

PONT, *pseud. see* LAIDLER, GRAHAM.

POOLE, JOHN. The comic miscellany. *buckram, 8vo. Lond., Tegg, 1851.*

———————— The comic miscellany for 1845. *buckram, 12mo. Lond., Colburn, 1845.*

———————— Comic sketches and recollections. *2v. half-calf, 12mo. Lond., Colburn, 1843.*

POOLE, T. Deaf as a post; a farce. *paper, 12mo. N.Y., French, n.d.*

POP ANNUAL, THE; engraved and printed for the Daily Sketch & Sunday Graphic. *paper, 8vo. Lond., Daily Sketch and Sunday Graphic, n.d.*

POPULAR JOKE BOOK. *paper, 32mo. Girard, Kan., Haldeman-Julius, n.d. (Little Blue Books.)*

PORSON, PROFESSOR. The devil's walk; a poem. *Lond., Marsh & Millder. In* ODDITIES. *q.v.*

PORTER, ADRIAN. The perfect debutante. *boards, 8vo. Lond., Collins, 1937.*

———————— The perfect pest. *buckram, 8vo. Lond., Collins, 1936.*

PORTER, GRAHAM. Small wonder. wonder. *buckram, 8vo. Lond., Hale, 1958.*

POSNER, GEORGE A. Clever replies. *boards, 12mo. Chic., Denison, 1929.*

_____ Latest Hollywood jokes. *paper, 12mo. Minneapolis, Denison, 1953.*

_____ This good; up-to-date jokes for all occasions. *buckram, 8vo. N.Y., Diehl, Landau & Pettit, 1937.*

_____ The world's spiciest jokes. *paper, 8vo. Los Angeles, Author, 1952.*

POSSELT, ERIC. A merry, merry Christmas book. *buckram, 8vo. Englewood Cliffs, N.J., Prentice-Hall, 1956.*

POSY, ARNOLD. Israeli tales and legends. *buckram, 8vo. N.Y., Bloch, 1948.*

POTTER, STEPHEN. One-upmanship. *buckram, 12mo. N.Y., Holt, 1952.*

_____ Potter on America. *buckram, 12mo. Lond., Hart-Davis, 1956.*

_____ Sense of humour. *buckram, 8vo. Lond., Reinhardt, 1954.*

POURRAT, HENRI. A treasury of French tales. *buckram, 8vo. Lond., Allen & Unwin, 1953.*

POWELL, E.H. Naughty but nice. *buckram, 8vo. N.Y., Red Lantern Books, 1955.*

POWELL, HERBERT PRESTON. The world's best book of minstrelsy. *buckram, 8vo. Phila., Penn., 1926.*

POWELL, LAWRENCE CLARK. The alchemy of books. *boards, 8vo. Los Angeles, Ward Ritchie, 1954.*

POWER, TYRONE. The omnibus: a farce. *paper, 12mo. Chic., Dramatic Pub.Co., n.d.*

POWERS, JAMES T. Twinkle little star. *buckram, 8vo. N.Y., Putnam's, 1939.*

POWERS, T.E. Joys and glooms; a book of drawings. *boards, folio. Chic., Reilly & Britton, 1912.*

POWYS, LLEWELYN. Cup-bearers of wine and hellebore. (a book of intellectual rowdies). *paper, 32mo. Girard, Kan., Haldeman-Julius, n.d. (Little Blue Books)*

POWYS, T.F. Mr. Weston's good wine. *buckram, 12mo. Lond., Chatto & Windus, 1950.*

POYNTZ, ALBANY. A world of wonders, with anecdotes and opinions concerning popular superstitions. *buckram, 8vo. Lond., Bentley, 1845.*

POY'S WAR CARTOONS. *paper, 8vo. Lond., Simpkin, Marshall, Hamilton, Kent, n.d.*

PRATT, FLETCHER *and* DE CAMP. L. SPRAGUE. Tales from Gavagan's bar. *buckram, 8vo. N.Y., Twayne, 1953.*

PREDDY, NORA. Minnie pauses to reflect. *paper, 12mo. San Antonio, Naylor, 1950.*

PRENTICE, GEORGE D. Prenticeana; or, Wit and humor in paragraphs. *buckram, 12mo. Phila., Claxton, Remsen & Haffelfinger, 1871.*

PRESCOTT, LEO. Laff with Leo. *paper, 16mo. Tokyo, Phoenix, 1955.*

PRESIDENT EISENHOWER'S CARTOON BOOK. *buckram, 8vo. N.Y., Fell, 1956.*

PRESTON, CHARLES, *ed.* Bottoms up! *paper, 12mo. N.Y., Dell, 1957*

_____ Funny business. *paper, 12mo. N.Y., Gold Medal Books, 1955.*

_____ Let's go to Bedlam. *buckram, 4to. N.Y., Shelley, 1954.*

_____ Office laffs (Hey, can't you forget busine$$). paper, 12mo. N.Y., Fawcett, 1957.

_____ Oh, doctor! paper, 16mo. N.Y., Berkley, 1955.

_____ The power of negative thinking. paper, 12mo. N.Y., Ballantine, 1955.

_____ The $64,000 answer. paper, 12mo. N.Y., Berkley, 1955.

_____ Thimk. paper, 12mo. Greenwich, Gold Medal Books, 1960.

_____ Zowie! girl meets boy! paper, 12mo. N.Y., Gold Medal Books, 1955.

PRESTON, JACK. The desert batallion. paper, 12mo. Hollywood, Murray & Gee, 1944.

PRETZEL, CARL, pseud. Carl Pretzel's komikal speaker; a new collection. paper, 16mo. N.Y., Ivers, 1873.

PRICE, "DOUGHBELLY." doughbelly's scrap book. paper, 8vo. Taos, N.M., El Crepusculo, 1951.

_____ doughbelly's wisdom & insanity. paper, 8vo. Taos, N.M., El Crepusculo, 1954.

PRICE, GARRETT. Drawing room only. buckram, 4to. N.Y., Coward-McCann, 1946.

PRICE, GEORGE. Cartoons. paper, 16mo. Harrisburg, Pa., Military Service Pub.Co., 1945.

_____ George Price's characters. half-buckram, 4to. N.Y., Simon & Schuster, 1955.

_____ Ice cold war. buckram, 4to. N.Y., Schuman, 1951.

_____ Is it anyone we know? buckram, 4to. N.Y., Murray Hill Books.

_____ It's smart to be people. buckram, 4to. N.Y., Farrar & Rinehart, 1942.

_____ We buy old gold. boards, 4to. N.Y., Schuman, 1951.

_____ Who's in charge here? boards, 4to. N.Y., Farrar & Rinehart, 1943.

PRINCE, GRAHAM. The absolution of Bruce. paper, 24mo. Lond., Gowans & Gray, 1911.

_____ The capture of Wallace. paper, 24mo. Lond., Gowans & Gray, 1911.

_____ Marriages are made in heaven - and elsewhere. paper, 24mo. Lond., Gowans & Gray, 1914.

_____ The song of the seal. paper, 24mo. Lond., Gowans & Gray, 1912.

PRICE, R.G.C. A history of Punch. buckram, 8vo. Lond., Collins, 1957.

PRICE, ROGER. Droodles. paper, 16mo. N.Y., Permabooks, 1953.

_____ I'm for me first; the secret handbook of the Me First Party. paper, 12mo. N.Y., Ballantine, 1956.

_____ The rich sardine. boards, 12mo. N.Y., Simon & Schuster, 1954.

PRIDHAM, HAROLD, comp. Heard this one, Dad? buckram, 16mo. Lond., T.Fisher Unwin, 1926.

PRIESTLEY, J.B. The English comic characters. buckram, 12mo. Lond., Lane, 1928.

———————— English humour. *buckram, 12mo. Lond., Longmans, Green, 1929.*

PRITCHARD, F.H. Humour of to-day. *buckram, 12mo. Lond., Harrap, 1927.*

PRIVATE ANECDOTES OF FOREIGN COURTS. *2v. half-calf, 8vo. Lond., Colburn, 1827.*

PROCEEDINGS OF THE TRIAL OF HON. JAMES BOYD, of Montgomery co., Pa., June 14, 1873, by his colleagues of the Constitutional Convention of Pennsylvania. *buckram, 8vo. Phila., Town, 1874.*

PROCHNOW, HERBERT V. 1001 ways to improve your conversation and speeches. *buckram, 8vo. N.Y., Harper, 1952.*

———————— The public speaker's treasure chest; a compendium of source material to make your speech sparkle. *buckram, 8vo. N.Y., Harper, 1942.*

———————— Speaker's handbook of epigrams and witticisms. *buckram, 8vo. N.Y., Harper, 1954.*

———————— Speaker's treasury of stories for all occasions. *buckram, 8vo. N.Y., Prentice-Hall, 1953.*

PROCTER, RICHARD WRIGHT. The barber's shop. *buckram, 12mo. Manchester, Heywood, 1883. Rev. and enl.ed.*

PROFESSIONAL ANECDOTES OR ANA OF MEDICAL LITERATURE. *3v. half-calf, 16mo. Lond., Knight and Lacey, 1825.*

PROFESSOR IRWIN COREY, THE WORLD'S FOREMOST AUTHORITY. An illustrated lecture. Sex: its origin and application. *paper, 4to. N.Y., Citadel, 1960.*

PROPER, IDA SEDGWICK. Our elusive Willy; a slice of concealed Elizabethan history. *buckram, 8vo. Manchester, Maine, Dirigo, 1953.*

PROPOSAL FOR THE PROHIBITION OF SPEECH, humbly offered to the consideration of Parliament. Photostatic copy in binder. *Dublin, Wilson, 1793.*

PROSSER, WILLIAM L., *ed.* The judicial humorist; a collection of judicial opinions and other frivolities. *buckram, 8vo. Bost., Little, Brown, 1952.*

PROTESTS AND APPEALS. *paper, 24mo. N.Y., Commerce Clearing House, 1955.*

PROUD TOMMY TILT. *paper, 24mo. Kansas City, Faultless Starch Co., n.d.*

PROVERBS; a collection of proverbs of all ages from all countries. *paper, 16mo. Calcutta, Industry Pub.Co., n.d.*

PROVERBS FOR DAILY LIVING. *boards, 12mo. Mount Vernon, N.Y., Peter Pauper, n.d.*

PROVERBS OF ARABIA. *paper, 32mo. Girard, Kan., Haldeman-Julius, n.d. (Little Blue Books.)*

PROVERBS OF CHINA. *paper, 32mo. Girard, Kan., Haldeman-Julius, n.d. (Little Blue Books.)*

PROVERBS OF ENGLAND. *paper, 32mo. Girard, Kan., Haldeman-Julius, n.d. (Little Blue Books.)*

PROVERBS OF FRANCE. *paper, 32mo. Girard, Kan., Haldeman-Julius, n.d. (Little Blue Books.)*

PROVERBS OF IRELAND. *paper, 32mo. Girard, Kan., Haldeman-Julius, n.d. (Little Blue Books.)*

PROVERBS OF ITALY. *paper, 32mo. Girard, Kan., Haldeman-Julius, n.d. (Little Blue Books.)*

PROVERBS OF JAPAN. *paper, 32mo. Girard, Kan., Haldeman-Julius, n.d.(Little Blue Books.)*

PROVERBS OF PERSIA. *paper, 32mo. Girard, Kan., Haldeman-Julius, n.d. (Little Blue Books.)*

PROVERBS OF RUSSIA. *paper, 32mo. Girard, Kan., Haldeman-Julius, n.d. (Little Blue Books.)*

PROVERBS OF SCOTLAND. *paper, 32mo. Girard, Kan., Haldeman-Julius, n.d. (Little Blue Books.)*

PROVERBS OF SOLOMON, THE SON OF DAVID, KING OF ISRAEL. *buckram, 12mo. Lond., Longmans, Green, 1949.*

PROVERBS OF SPAIN. *paper, 32mo. Girard, Kan., Haldeman-Julius, n.d. (Little Blue Books.)*

PRY, PAUL, *the Younger.* Fancy's sketch; or, Gems of poetry and wit. Comprising an entirely new collection of anecdotes, epigrams, jeux d'esprit &c. &c. *boards, 12mo. Lond., Cowie, 1826.*

PUDNEY, JOHN. The smallest room. *buckram, 8vo. Lond., Joseph, 1955.*

PULITZER, WALTER. A cynic's meditations. *cloth, 16mo. N.Y., Dodge, 1904.*

——————— My auto book. *buckram, 12mo. N.Y., Outing, 1908.*

PULLEYN, WILLIAM. Church-yard gleanings, and epigrammatic scraps; being a collection of remarkable epitaphs and epigrams... *boards, 12mo. Lond., Maunder, n.d.*

"PUN-SIBI, TOM." The art of punning: or, The flower of languages in seventy-nine rules. *calf., 16mo. n.p., 1719. 4th ed.*

PUNCH. Benjamin Disraeli, Earl of Beaconsfield, K.G. in upwards of 100 cartoons. *half-leather, 4to. Lond., Punch, 1878.*

——————— Best cartoons from Punch. *buckram, 4to. N.Y., Simon & Schuster, 1952.*

——————— Best humour from Punch, edited by William Cole. *buckram, 12mo. Lond., Spearman, 1955.*

——————— An evening from among the thousand evenings which may be spent with "Punch". *paper, 4to. Lond., Punch, 1900.*

_____ The laughter omnibus, taken from Punch, by Anthony Armstrong. *buckram, 8vo. Lond., Faber & Faber, 1937.*

_____ Mr. Punch on the links. *buckram, 8vo. Lond., Educational Book Co., n.d.*

_____ The pick of Punch; an annual selection. *buckram, 4to. Lond., Chatto and Windus.* Have for years: 1941, 1942, 1944, 1945, 1946-1951, 1957, 1958.

_____ Poems from Punch, 1909-1922. *buckram, 12mo. Lond., Macmillan, 1922.*

_____ Punch almanack. Have for years: 1908-1910, 1914, 1916, 1920-1926.

_____ A "Punch" anthology, compiled by Guy Boas. *buckram, 12mo. Lond., Macmillan, 1932.*

_____ Punch and the war. *paper, 4to. N.Y., Blue Ribbon Books, 1941.*

_____ Punch festival. *paper, 4 to. Lond., Punch, 1951.*

_____ Punch library of humour. Edited by J.A. Hammerton. *25v. buckram, 12mo. Lond., Educational Book Co.,by arrangement with the proprietors of "Punch", n.d.*

_____ Punch's pocket book. Containing a calendar, cash account, diary and memoranda for every day of the year. *leather folders. Lond., Punch.* Have for years, 1858-1877.

_____ The Queen and Mr. Punch; the story of a reign, told by Toby, M.P. *half-calf, folio. Lond., Bradbury, Agnew and Co., 1841.*

_____ The Rt. Hon. John Brith, M.P. Cartoons from the collection of "Mr. Punch". *buckram, 4to. Lond., Punch, 1878.*

_____ A shilling's worth of nonsense. *half-calf, 16mo. Lond., Orr, 1842.*

**PURIFIED PROVERBS AND CENSORED QUOTATIONS.** *boards, 16mo. N.Y., Amour, 1930.*

**PUTNAM, GEORGE HAVEN.** Authors and their public in ancient times. *buckram, 12mo. N.Y., Putnam's, 1894.*

**PUZZLE, THE: being a choice** collection of conundrums. *quarter-calf, 8vo. Lond., Cooper, 1745.*

**PVT. BENNY BUNGLE.** Servicemen's laugh encyclopedia. *paper, 12mo. N.Y., Miller, 1943.*

# Q

QUAD *see* LEWIS, CHARLES BERTRAND.

"QUEX" of the "Evening News". Who told you that? The story-teller's vade-mecum. *boards, 16mo. Lond., Paul, n.d. 3d.ed.*

QUIGG, LEMUEL ELY. Tin-types taken in the streets of New York. *buckram, 12mo. N.Y., Cassell, 1890.*

QUIN, JAMES. Quin's jests; or, The facetious man's pocket-companion. *half-calf, 12mo. Lond., Bladon, 1766.*

QUIPS AND MEMOIRS OF THE CORPS, 1917-1918. *buckram, 8vo. n.p., n.d.*

QUIRKY QUATRAINS: *boards, 32mo. Bost., Carol, 1910.*

QUIVEDO VILLEGAS, FRANCISCO *de.* Fortune in her wits, or, The hour of all men. Translated into English by Capt. John Stevens. *quarter-leather, 16mo. Lond., Sare, Saunders & Bennet, 1697.*

QUOTATIONS OF HUMOR, WIT AND WISDOM. *buckram, 24mo. Bost., Dearbon, 1849.*

QUOTE YEAR BOOK, 1949. *buckram, 8vo. Indianapolis, Droke, 1949.*

# R

RABELAIS, FRANCOIS. Gargantua and Pantagruel. buckram, 8vo. Lond., Westhouse, 1945.

——————Works. buckram, 8vo. N.Y., Tudor, 1930.

RADCLIFFE, ALEXANDER. Ovid travestie; a burlesque upon Ovid's epistles. paper, 8vo. Priv.Print., 1889.

RAEMAKERS, LOUIS. An American in the war. buckram, folio. N.Y., Century, 1918.

——————"Land and Water" edition of Raemakers' cartoons. 2v. half-calf, 4to. Lond., "Land and Water". 1916.

——————Raemakers' cartoon history of the war. Volume 3. buckram, 4to. N.Y., Century, 1919.

——————Raemakers' cartoons. buckram, folio. N.Y., Doubleday, Page, 1917.

RAFF and ARMSTRONG, ANTHONY. Goodbye, nice types! buckram, 12mo. Lond., Methuen, 1946.

RAGGLE TAGGLE: a collection of stories, poems, articles, sketches and drawings compiled from the magazine produced under unusually difficult conditions and inferior and unsuitable materials in the Prisoner of War Camp at Shirakawa, Formosa, during the year 1944. buckram, folio. Aldershott, Gale & Polden, 1947.

RAGTIME RHYMES AND JOYOUS JOKES. paper, 12mo. Chic., Laird & Lee, n.d.

RAIL ODDITIES; odd and interesting facts about the railroads. paper, 8vo. Washington, D.C. Association of American Railroads, 1954.

RAILWAY ANECDOTE BOOK; collection of the best and newest anecdotes and tales to the present day: selected for the reading of railway passengers. buckram, 8vo. Lond., Smith, n.d.

RALEIGH, Sir WALTER. Sir Walter Raleigh's instructions to his son and to posterity. paper, 24mo. Reprinted by The Roanoake Island Historical Association, 1939.

RALLI, PAUL. Nevada lawyer; a story of life and love in Las Vegas. buckram, 12mo. Culver City, Murray & Gee, 1949.

RAMASVAMI RAJU, P.V. Indian fables. buckram, 12mo. Lond., Swan Sonnenschein, 1901.

"RAMESES" Oriental spotlight. buckram, 12mo. Lond., Murray, 1941.

RAMSAY, ALLAN and MCCULLAGH, FRANCIS, comps. Tales from Turkey. buckram, 4to. Lond., Simpkin, Marshall, Hamilton, Kent, 1914.

RAMSAY, E.B. Reminiscences of Scottish life and character. 2v. in 1. buckram, 12mo. Edinburgh, Edmonston & Douglas, 1862.

RAMSAY, GEORGE. A new dictionary of anecdotes, illustrative of character and events. half-calf, 8vo. Lond., Sherwood, Neely and Jones, 1822.

RAMSAY, WILLIAM. A book of toasts. *buckram, 16mo. N.Y., Dodge, 1906.*

RANDOLPH, BORIS. The maxiomatic confuser; a volume of crossword puzzles and games. *buckram, 8vo. N.Y., McKay, 1958.*

RANDOLPH, JOHN, *comp.* The jokes on Texas. *paper, 12mo. Tomball, Tex., Author, 1954.*

——————— Texas brags. *paper, 8vo. Houston, Author, 1949. 4th ed.*

RANDOLPH, VANCE. The devil's pretty daughter, and other Ozark folk tales. *buckram, 8vo. N.Y., Columbia Univ. Press, 1955.*

——————— Funny stories about the hillbillies. *paper, 8vo. Girard, Kan., Haldeman-Julius, 1944.*

——————— Funny stories from Arkansas. *paper, 8vo. Girard, Kan., Haldeman-Julius, 1943.*

——————— Funny stories from the Ozarks. *paper, 32mo. Girard, Kan., Haldeman-Julius, n.d. (Little Blue Books.)*

——————— Sticks in the knapsack. *buckram, 8vo. N.Y., Columbia Univ.Press, 1958.*

——————— The talking turtle, and other Ozark folk tales. *buckram, 8vo. N.Y., Columbia Univ. Press, 1957.*

——————— Tall tales from the Ozarks. *paper, 8vo. Girard, Kan., Haldeman-Julius, 1944.*

——————— We always lie to strangers; tall tales from the Ozarks. *buckram, 8vo. N.Y., Columbia Univ. Press, 1951.*

——————— Who blew up the church house? *buckram, 8vo. N.Y., Columbia Univ. Press, 1952.*

——————— Wild stories from the Ozarks. *paper, 32mo. Girard, Kan., Haldeman-Julius, n.d. (Little Blue Books.)*

RANGEMORE, ROGER. This merrie English. *boards, 12mo. Lond., Epworth, 1954.*

RANGO, ROBERT, *ed.* The good humor book; a treasury of choice jokes and gags, cartoons and comic drawings, puns and patter, limericks and ditties, anecdotes, riddles and repartee, and many other types of humorous prose and verse. *buckram, 4to. N.Y., Harvest House, 1944.*

——————— The marriage joker; a choice collection of jokes and gags satirizing the relations between the sexes, before, during and after marriage. *buckram, 8vo. N.Y., Harvest House, 1945.*

RANSOME, ARTHUR. Russian fairy tales. *boards, 16mo. Mount Vernon, N.Y., Peter Pauper, n.d.*

RAPER, JOHN W. What this world needs. *buckram, 12mo. N.Y., World, 1945.*

RAPP, ALBERT. The ancient Greeks & Joe Miller. *paper, folio. San Francisco, Grabhorn Press for the Roxburghe Club, 1958. (Anecdota Scowah, III.)* Contains also: A prolegomenon, by Nat Schmulowitz.

—————— The Joe Miller of the Near East. *paper, folio. San Francisco, Grabhorn Press for the Roxburghe Club, 1960.* (Anecdota Scowah, IV.) Contains also: Onsoz, by Nat Schmulowitz.

—————— The dawn of humor. *pamphlet.* Reprinted from The Classical Journal, v.43, no.5.

—————— The genealogy of Baron Munchausen. *pamphlet.* Reprinted from The Classical Journal, v.32, no.5.

—————— A Greek "Joe Miller" *pamphlet.* Reprinted from The Classical Journal, v.41, no.6.

—————— The origins of wit and humor. *buckram, 8vo. N.Y., Dutton, 1951.*

—————— A phylogenetic theory of wit and humor. *pamphlet.* Reprinted from the Journal of Social Psychology, 1949.

—————— Tall tales from the Greeks. In: The Classical Weekly, v.44, no.6.

—————— Toward an eclectic and multilateral theory of laughter and humor. *pamphlet.* Reprinted from The Journal of General Psychology, 1947.

RAPPOPORT, MILT. Oh, no! a golf duffer's handbook. *paper, 12mo. N.Y., Simon & Schuster, 1956.*

RARE BITS FROM ALL THE MOST INTERESTING SOURCES. *buckram, folio. Lond., Reynolds, 1884.*

RASPE, RUDOLPH. Adventures of Baron Munchausen. *paper, 12mo. N.Y., Sharlee, n.d.*

—————— Baron Munchausen; his wonderful travels and adventures, retold by Erich Kastner. *buckram, 4to. N.Y., Messner, 1957.*

—————— The original travels of Baron Munchausen. *buckram, 12mo. Chic., Rand McNally, n.d.*

—————— Singular travels, campaigns, and adventures of Baron Munchausen. *buckram, 8vo. Lond., Cresset, 1948.*

—————— The surprising adventures of Baron Munchausen. *buckram, 8vo. Lond., Lawrence & Bullen, 1895.*

—————— The surprising travels and adventures of Baron Munchausen. *buckram, 32mo. Lond., Smith, 1792.*

—————— The travels and surprising adventures of Baron Munchausen. *buckram, 12mo. Phila., Porter & Coates, n.d.*

—————— The travels of Baron Munchausen. Gulliver revived, or, The vice of lying properly exposed. *buckram, 12mo. Lond., Routledge, 1923.*

RATTLING FORD JOKES. *paper, 24mo. Baltimore, Ottenheimer, 1916.*

RAY, BENOY GOPAL. Gandhian ethics. *paper, 12mo. Ahmedabad, Navajivan Pub. House, 1950.*

RAY, CHARLES. Hollywood shorts, compiled from incidents in the everyday life of men and women who entertain in pictures. *boards, 4to. Los Angeles, California Graphic Press, 1935.*

RAY, CYRIL. The compleat imbiber; an entertainment. *buckram, 4to. Lond., Putnam, 1956.*

RAY, J. Complete collection of English proverbs. *half-calf, 12mo. Lond., Allman, Boone & Baldwin, Cradock & Joy, 1817.*

———————— A compleat collection of English proverbs; also the most celebrated proverbs of the Scotch, Italian, French, Spanish and other languages. *calf, 8vo. Lond., Hughs, 1737.*

RAY, JOHN. Conundrums, riddles, puzzles and gags. *paper, 16mo. Chic., Droke, 1902.*

RAY, TED. Raising the laughs. *cloth, 8vo. Lond., Laurie, 1952.*

RAYFORD, JULIAN LEE. The first Christmas dinner. *In: The American Book Collector, v.8, no.3.)*

RAYMOND, HENRY J. The life and public services of Abraham Lincoln. *buckram, 8vo. N.Y., Derby & Miller, 1865.*

REA, GARDNER. Gardner Rea's sideshow. *boards, 4to. N.Y., McBride, 1945.*

———————— The gentleman says its pixies. *boards, 12mo. N.Y., McBride, 1944.*

REACH, ANGUS B. The natural history of "Bores". *paper, 24mo. Lond., Bogue, 1857.*

———————— The natural history of humbugs. *paper, 24mo. Lond, Bogue, 1847.*

READ, OPIE. Glimpses and epigrams. *boards, 12mo. Chic., Hill, 1902.*

———————— Jokes — monologues — funny anecdotes. Flashes of wit, original cartoons, selected from The Arkansaw Traveler. *paper, 12mo. Chic., Stein, 1945.*

———————— The Jucklins. *buckram, 12mo. Chic., Laird & Lee, 1896.*

———————— A Kentucky colonel. *buckram, 12mo. Chic., Laird & Lee, 1893.*

———————— My young master. *buckram, 12mo. Chic., Laird & Lee, 1896.*

———————— Old Ebenezer. *buckram, 12mo. Chic., Laird & Lee, 1897.*

———————— On the Suwanee River. *buckram, 12mo. Chic., Laird & Lee, 1895.*

———————— Opie Read in Arkansas, and what he saw there. *paper, 12mo. N.Y., Ogilvie, 1891.*

———————— A Tennessee Judge. *buckram, 12mo. Chic., Laird & Lee, 1893.*

READERS DIGEST. The best from Life in these United States. *paper, 16mo. Pleasantville, N.Y., Reader's Digest Assoc., 1961.*

———————— Fun fare; a treasury of Reader's Digest wit and humor. *buckram, 16mo. Pleasantville, N.Y., Reader's Digest Assoc., 1949.*

———————— Reader's Digest 40th anniversary treasury. *boards, 12mo. Pleasantville, N.Y., Reader's Digest, 1961.*

———————— Reader's Digest treasury of wit and humor. *buckram, 12mo. N.Y., Reader's Digest Assoc., 1958.*

_____ The Reader's Digest keepsake. *paper, 24mo. Pleasantville, N.Y., Reader's Digest Assoc., 1960.*

REAL PADDY, A, *pseud.* Real life in Ireland, or, The day and night scenes of Brian Boru, esq. and his elegant friend Sir Shawn O'Dogherty. *buckram, 8vo. Lond., Evans, n.d. 4th ed.*

REDDALL, HENRY FREDERIC, *comp. and ed.* Scissors, or The funny side of politics. *buckram, 12mo. Bost., Rand Avery, 1888.*

REDESDALE, ALGERNON BERTRAM FREEMAN-MITFORD, *baron.* Tales of old Japan. *buckram, 12mo. Lond., Macmillan, 1910.*

REDWAY, LAURANCE. The springtime of physick, being a diverting outline of medicine and surgery. *buckram, 12mo. Burlington, Vt., Author, 1928.*

REED, A.W. Maori tales of long ago. *boards, 4to. Lond., Phoenix, n.d.*

REED, E.T. Mr. Punch's pre-historic peeps. *buckram, 8vo. Lond., Bradbury, Agnew, n.d.*

REED, FLO. East meets west. *paper, 12mo. Tokyo, Adams, n.d.*

REED, ISAAC. The repository; a select collection of fugitive pieces of wit and humour in prose and verse. *2v. sheep, 16mo. Lond., Dilly, 1783.*

REED, LANGFORD. A book of nonsense verse. *buckram, 8vo. N.Y., Putnam's, 1926.*

_____ Complete limerick book. *buckram, 8vo. Lond., Jarrolds, 1925.*

_____ The indiscreet limerick book; 200 new examples. *buckram, 12mo. Lond., Jarrolds, n.d.*

_____ My limerick book. *buckram, 12mo. Lond., Nelson, 1937.*

_____ Mr. Punch's limerick book. *buckram, 8vo. Lond., Cobden-Sanderson, 1934.*

_____ The new limerick book. *buckram, 12mo. Lond., Jenkins, 1937.*

_____ Nonsense verses; an anthology. *buckram, 4to. Lond., Jarrolds, n.d.*

_____ Sausages & sundials, a book of nonsense ballads. *boards, 4to. Lond., Jarrolds, n.d.*

REEVE, ISAAC J., *comp. and ed.* The wild garland. v.2: Epigrams. *buckram, 12mo. Lond., Pitman, 1866.*

REEVES, JAMES. English fables and fairy stories. *buckram, 8vo. Lond., Oxford Univ. Press, 1956.*

REFLEXIONS UPON RIDICULE, or, What is that makes a man ridiculous and the means to avoid it. *calf., 8vo. Lond., Newborough, 1707.*

_____ *Same.* Lond., Midwinter, Osborn, Longman, and Motte, 1727. 4th ed.

REGNARD, JEAN FRANCOIS. Satire against husbands. *boards, 8vo. Lond., Rodale, 1954.*

REGNIER, ELIZABETH CHASE. Fruits of the spirit. *buckram, 16mo. Los Angeles, Glass Bookbinding Co., 1911.*

REID, ACE. Cowpokes. *paper, 12mo. Kerrville, Texas, Author, 1958. 2d.ed.*

―――――― More cowpokes. *paper, 12mo. San Antonio, Naylor, 1960.*

REIDER, WILLIAM D. The new tablet of memory; or, Recorder of remarkable events. *buckram, 8vo. Lond., Clements, 1841.*

REIGHTER, FRANK C. "Saws" of Semper Felix, old yet ever new. *paper, 16mo. Chic., Author, 1927.*

REIGN OF HUMBUG: a satire. *boards, 8vo. Lond., Richardson, 1836.*

REISNER, BOB, *comp. and ed.* Best jokes, bop humor and cool cartoons. *paper, 8vo. N.Y., Citadel, 1960.*

REISNER, BOB *and* KAPPLOW, HAL. Captions courageous, or, Comments from the gallery. *buckram, 8vo. Lond., Abelard-Schuman, 1959.*

―――――― More captions courageous. *buckram, 8vo. Lond., Abelard-Schuman, 1959.*

RELICS FOR THE CURIOUS. 2v. in 1. *buckram, 16mo. Lond., Burton, 1824.*

REMEDY FOR SEDITION, A, which rare and witty book is now reprinted for the first time. *boards, 4to. Lond., Golden Hours Press, 1933.*

REMEMBER WILLIAM PENN, 1744-1944. *buckram, 8vo. Phila., William Penn Ter-centenary Committee, 1944.*

RENSHAW, CHARLES BAILEY. The humour club. *buckram, 12mo. Lond., Simpkin, Marshall, etc. 1924.*

REVONS, E.C. *comp.* Sayings of sages; or, Selections from distinguished preachers, poets, philosophers, etc. *buckram, 12mo. N.Y., Carlton & Porter, 1863.*

REYHER, BECKY, *ed.* The stork run; a collection of baby cartoons. *boards, 8vo. N.Y., Hastings, 1944.*

REYNARD―――――― ; The badge of folly, or A humorous illus-tration of the mottos, of the nobility of England, Scotland and Ireland. *half-calf, large 8vo. Lond., Debrett, 1782.*

REYNOLDS, BRUCE. A cocktail continentale. *buckram, 12mo. N.Y., Sully, 1926.*

―――――― Paris with the lid lifted. *buckram, 12mo. N.Y., Burt, 1927.*

REYNOLDS, FRANK. Punch pictures. *boards, folio. Lond., Cassell, 1922.*

REYNOLDS, HARRY B. Such wisdom as men will need. *buckram, 8vo. San Francisco, John Howell, 1951.*

REYNOLDS, JOHN *and* YEATMAN, R.J. Horse nonsense. *buckram, 12mo. Lond., Methuen, 1933. 2d.ed.*

REYNOLDS, REGINALD. A quest for Gandhi. *buckram, 8vo. N.Y., Doubleday, 1952.*

―――――― The wisdom of John Woolman, with a selection of his writings. *buckram, small 8vo. Lond., Allen & Unwin, 1948.*

REZNICK, SIDNEY. How to tell jokes. *leaflet. Author, 1955.*

——————— How to write jokes. *paper, 8vo. N.Y., Townley, 1954.*

REZWIN, MAX, *comp. and ed.* More sick jokes and grimmer cartoons. *paper, 8vo. N.Y., Citadel, 1959.*

——————— Sick jokes, grim cartoons & bloody Marys. *paper, 8vo. N.Y., Citadel, 1958.*

——————— Still more sick jokes and even grimmer cartoons. *paper, 8vo. N.Y., Citadel, 1960.*

RHOADES, JOHN HARSEN. From the crow's nest. *paper, 12mo. N.Y., Priv.Print, 1941.*

——————— Jonathan's apothegms. *2v. paper, 16mo. N.Y., Priv. Print., 1941.*

RHOADS, W.M. Wise and otherwise. *paper (shaped like an owl) Phila., Penn, 1906.*

RHODES, R.S., *ed.* Wit. *buckram, 12mo. Chic., Rhodes & McClure, 1904.*

RHYMING RELICS OF THE LEGAL PAST. *pamphlet.* Reprinted from The Justice of the Peace of 17 December, 1949. *Lond., 1950.*

RICE, WALLACE. Fun and philosophy from the American newspaper humorists. *boards, 12mo. N.Y., Dodge, 1909.*

——————— The little book of Bohemia. *boards, 12mo. Chic., Reilly & Britton, 1910.*

——————— The little book of kisses. *boards, 16mo. Chic., Reilly & Britton, 1910.*

——————— Little book of laughter. *boards, 12mo. Chic., Reilly & Britton, 1910.*

——————— Little book of limericks. *boards, 16mo. Chic., Reilly & Britton, 1910.*

——————— To my friend. *limp leather, 4to. N.Y., Barse & Hopkins, 1914.*

——————— The wealth of friendship. *buckram, 8vo. Chic., Brewer, Barse, 1909.*

RICHARDS, J. Mechanical humour; a collection of original anecdotes connected with engineering and mechanics. *buckram, 12mo. Lond., Richards, 1874.*

RICHARDSON, JUSTIN. Backroom joys. *buckram, 12mo. Lond., Harvill, 1953.*

RICHARDSON, WILLIAM. Anecdotes of the Russian empire in a series of letters written a few years ago from St. Petersburg. *calf, 8vo. Lond., Strahan & Cadell, 1784.*

RICHBERG, DONALD R. My hero. *buckram, 8vo. N.Y., Putnam's, 1954.*

RICHMAN, JACOB. Laughs from Jewish lore. *buckram, 12mo. N.Y., Funk & Wagnalls, 1926.*

RICHMOND, FRANK M. School yarns and howlers. *paper, 16mo. Lond., Universal, 1936.*

RICHTER, HARVEY. Best college humor. *buckram, 4to. Reading, Pa., Handy Book Corp., 1920.*

RICHTER, MISCHA. The man on the couch, and other cartoons. *paper, 16mo. N.Y., Pocket Books, 1958.*

——————— This one's on me! *buckram, 4to. Lond., McGraw-Hill, 1945.*

RIDDLE, NED. Mr. Tweedy. *paper, 16mo. N.Y., Fleet, 1960.*

RIDDLES, CHARADES AND CON-UNDRUMS... with a preface on the antiquity of riddles. *halfcalf, 24mo. Lond., Davis, 1824.*

RILEY, H.H. Puddleford and its people. *buckram, 12mo. N.Y., Hueston, 1854.*

RILEY, JAMES WHITCOMB. Complete works. 6v. *halfmorocco, 12mo. Indianapolis, Bobbs-Merrill, 1913.*

——————— Nye and Riley's wit and humor. *buckram, 12mo. Chic., Thompson & Thomas, 1900.*

RILEY, LAWRENCE. Personal appearance, a new comedy. *paper, 12mo. N.Y., French, 1935.*

RINEHART, MARY ROBERTS. Familiar faces. *buckram, 12mo. Lond., Cassell, 1943.*

——————— "Isn't that just like a man! *boards, 12mo. N.Y., Doran, 1919.* Contains also "Oh well, you know how women are!" by Irvin S. Cobb. Separate title-page, and inverted.

RIPLEY, ROBERT LEROY. 35th anniversary believe it or not! *paper, 8vo. N.Y., Simon & Schuster, 1954.*

RITTER, RED and GADBOIS, BOB. Bet your boots. *paper, 24mo. N.Y., Victoria, 1948.*

——————— Elmore. *paper, 24mo. Richmond, Va., Dietz, 1943.*

RIVERS, DEAN. Conundrums, riddles and puzzles. *buckram, 16mo. Phila., Penn, 1901.*

RIVISE, M.J. Inside Western Union. *buckram, 8vo. N.Y., Sterling, 1950.*

ROBERTS, ARTHUR. Fifty years of spoof. *buckram, 8vo. Lond., Lane, 1927.*

ROBERTS, DAVID. Four fables. *buckram, 8vo. Oxford. Vincent, 1942.*

ROBERTS, DENYS. Beds and roses. *buckram, 12mo. Lond., Methuen, 1956.*

ROBERTS, KENNETH. It must be your tonsils. *buckram, 12mo. Garden City, Doubleday, 1936.*

ROBERTS, MICHAEL. The English joke. *paper, 8vo. Oxford, Johnson, 1941.* (Britain today, Number 56.)

——————— The Faber book of comic verse. *buckram, 12mo. Lond., Faber, 1942.*

ROBERTSON, ANTHONY. How to do and say in England. *buckram, 12mo. Lond., Dickson, 1936.*

ROBERTSON, ARCHIE. Slow train to yesterday, a last glance at the local. *buckram, 12mo. Bost., Houghton, Mifflin, 1945.*

ROBERTSON, GRETA. The book of conundrums. *buckram, 12mo. N.Y., Appleton, 1924.*

ROBERTSON, T.W. Caste; an original comedy. *paper, 12mo. Chic., Dramatic Pub.Co., n.d.*

ROBERTSON-GLASGOW, R.C. I was Himmler's aunt. *buckram, 12mo. Lond., Jenkins, 1940.*

ROBEY, GEORGE. After dinner stories. *buckram, 12mo. Lond., Richards, 1920.*

——————— Bits and spices. *buckram, 12mo. Lond., Jarrolds, n.d.*

_____Family affairs. *buck-ram, 12mo. Lond., Long, 1924.*

_____ In other words; humorous stories. *buckram, 12mo. Lond., Jarrolds, n.d.*

_____ My rest cure. *buck-ram, 12mo. N.Y., Stokes, 1919.*

ROBINSON, JACK. Jack Robinson's yarns. *paper, 12mo. N.Y., Ogilvie, 1899.*

ROBINSON, W.W. Los Angeles from the days of pueblo. *paper, 8vo. San Francisco, California Historical Society, 1959.*

ROBINSON, WILLIAM HEATH. Absurdities; a book of collected drawings. *boards, folio. Lond., Hutchinson, n.d.*

_____ How to be a motorist. *buckram, 12mo. Lond., Hutchinson, n.d.*

_____ How to be a perfect husband. *buckram, 12mo. Lond., Hutchinson, n.d.*

_____ How to live in a flat. *buckram, 12mo. Lond., Hutchinson, n.d.*

_____ How to make the best of things. *buckram, 12mo. Lond., Hutchinson, n.d.*

_____ Railway ribaldry; being 96 pages of railway humour. *paper, 4to. Lond., Great Western Railway, 1935.*

ROCHE, ALEX, *ed.* An anthology of wit. *boards, 12mo. Lond., Lewis, 1935.*

ROE, RICHARD. Straws in my wig. *buckram, 8vo. Lond., Solicitor's Journal, 1954.*

ROGERS, CHARLES. Familiar illustrations of Scottish life, embodying nearly five hundred anecdotes and stories, chiefly original. *buckram, 16mo. Lond., Houlston & Wright, 1866.*

ROGERS, ERNEST. The old Hokum bucket. *buckram, 8vo. Atlanta, Ga., Love, 1949.*

ROGERS, WILL. Autobiography. *buckram, 8vo. Bost., Houghton, Mifflin, 1949.*

_____ Ether and me, or "Just relax". *boards, 12mo. N.Y., Putnam's, 1929.*

_____ How to run a service station. *pamphlet. n.p. Gulf Refining Co., n.d.*

_____ How we elect our presidents. *buckram, 12mo. Bost., Little, Brown, 1952.*

_____ The illiterate digest. *buckram, 8vo. N.Y., Boni, 1935.*

_____ Letters of a self-made diplomat to his president. *buckram, 12mo. N.Y., Boni, 1926.*

_____ Sanity is where you find it. *buckram, 8vo. Bost., Houghton, Mifflin, 1955.*

_____ There's not a bathing suit in Russia, and other bare facts. *buckram, 8vo. N.Y., Boni, 1927.*

_____ Will Rogers wit and wisdom. Compiled by Jack Lait. *buckram, 16mo. N.Y., Stokes, 1936.*

_____ Wit and philosophy from the radio talks of America's humorist, Will Rogers. Broadcast during April, May and June, 1930 through the courtesy of E.R.Squibb and Sons. *paper, 12mo. n.p.*

ROLLICKS, RECTOR. Risibile reading on river, road or railway. *buckram, 16mo. Edinburgh, Author, ca.1870.*

ROONEY, PATRICK. Pat
Rooney's quaint conundrums
and funny gags. *paper, 12mo.
N.Y., Wehman, 1879.*

ROOSEVELT, FRANKLIN
DELANO. Wit and wisdom of
Franklin D. Roosevelt.
*buckram, 8vo. Bost., Beacon,
1950.*

RORICK, ISABEL SCOTT. Mr.
and Mrs. Cugat; the record of a
happy marriage. *buckram, 8vo.
Bost., Houghton, Mifflin, 1942.*

ROSE, A. MCGREGOR, *pseud.
see* GORDON, A.M.R.

ROSE, BILLY. Wine, women and
words. *paper, 4to. N.Y., Simon
& Schuster, 1948.*

ROSE, CARL. One dozen roses.
*boards, 4to. N.Y., Random,
1946.*

ROSE, EDWARD D. Khaki komedy.
*boards, 16mo. Chic., Howell,
1918. 4th ed.*

ROSE, FRANCIS. The white cow,
and other Chinese fairy tales.
*buckram, 4to. Lond.,
Butterworth, 1945.*

ROSELLE, AUBREY C., *ed.* Best
jokes. *paper, 32mo. Girard,
Kan., Haldeman-Julius, n.d.
(Little Blue Books.)*

_____ Famous $12,000
prize-winning tongue-twisters.
*paper, 32mo. Girard, Kan.,
Haldeman-Julius, n.d. (Little
Blue Books.)*

ROSEN, CHARLES F. Use your
own couch; a guide to do it
yourself psychoanalysis.
*buckram, 8vo. N.Y., Julian,
1957.*

ROSENBACH, A.S.W. A book
hunter's holiday. *buckram, 8vo.
Bost., Houghton, Mifflin, 1936.*

_____ Unpublishable
memoirs. *buckram, 12mo. Lond.,
Castle, 1924.*

ROSENFELD, SYDNEY. Her only
fault; a commedietta. *paper,
12mo. Chic., Dramatic Pub.
Co., 1882.*

ROSENFIELD, LOYD. Adam had
a rib. *buckram, 8vo. N.Y.,
Putnam's, 1959.*

ROSENTHAL, FRANZ. Humor in
early Islam. *buckram, 8vo.
Leiden, Brill, 1856.*

ROSS, AL. Sexcapades; the love
life of the modern homo
sapiens. *buckram, 8vo. N.Y.,
Stravon, 1953.*

ROSS, CHARLES H. High tide at
any hour; a book for low water
and low spirits. *paper, 8vo.
Lond., "Judy" 1879.*

ROSS, LEONARD Q *see* ROSTEN,
LEO C.

ROSS, VICTOR. Basic British.
*buckram, 8vo. Lond., Parrish,
1956.*

ROSSITER, HAROLD. How to put
on a minstrel show. *paper,
12mo. Chic., Stein, 1921.*

ROSSO, ROSS. The wit's red
book, or, Calendar of gaiety for
the year 1822. *half-leather,
16mo. Lond., Simpkin &
Marshall, 1822.*

ROSTAND, EDMOND. Cyrano de
Bergerac. *buckram, 12mo. N.Y.,
Lupton, n.d.*

ROSTEN, LEO C. The strangest
places, by Leonard Q. Ross,
*pseud. buckram, 12mo. Lond.,
Constable, 1939.*

ROTHENSTEIN, WILLIAM. Men
and memories. 2v. *buckram,
8vo. Lond., Faber & Faber,
1932.*

ROUGH DIAMONDS, or, Man's nature and actions considered in 950 aphorisms with hints to business men. *paper, 16mo. N.Y., Rice, 1887.*

ROURKE, CONSTANCE. American humor; a study of the national character. *paper, 12mo. N.Y., Doubleday, 1953.*

ROUSON, JOHN HENRY. Boy and girl. *paper, 12mo. N.Y., Fleet, 1959.*

ROUTLEDGE, EDMUND. Riddles and jokes. *boards, 16mo. Lond., Routledge, n.d.*

ROWANS, VIRGINIA. House party. *buckram, 8vo. N.Y., Crowell, 1954.*

ROWDY RHYMES. *boards, 12mo. Mount Vernon, N.Y., Peter Pauper, n.d.*

ROWLAND, HELEN. Reflections of a bachelor girl. *buckram, 12mo. N.Y., Dodge, 1909.*

——————— Sayings of Mrs. Solomon. *buckram, 16mo. N.Y., Dodge, 1913.*

ROWLEY, ANTHONY. The probationer. *paper, 24mo. Lond., Gowans & Gray, 1911.*

——————— A weaver's shuttle. *paper, 24mo. Lond., Gowans & Gray, 1910.*

ROWLEY, HUGH. Gamosagammon; or, Hints on hymen. *buckram, 12mo. Lond., John Camden Hotten, n.d.*

——————— More puniana; or, Thoughts wise and other-why's. A new collection of the best riddles, conundrums, jokes, sells, etc. *buckram, 12mo. Lond., Chatto & Windus, 1875.*

——————— Puniana; or, Thoughts wise and otherwise. A new collection of the best riddles, conundrums, jokes, sells, etc. *buckram, 8vo. Lond., John Camden Hotten, 1867.*

——————— Same. *Lond., Chatto & Windus, 1902. New ed.*

ROY, CHARLES EDWARD. Charlie Roy's book of joy. *paper, 8vo. DeKalb, Ill., Clark, 1951.*

ROYCROFT DICTIONARY, THE, concocted by Ali Baba and the bunch on rainy days. *limpleather, 16mo. East Aurora, N.Y., Roycrofters, 1914.*

RUARK, ROBERT C. One for the road. *buckram, 12mo. N.Y., Doubleday, 1949.*

——————— I didn't know it was loaded. *buckram, 12mo. N.Y., Doubleday, 1948.*

RUBEL, EDITH. The merry muse; the days of music and art. *boards, 4to. N.Y., Schirmer, 1937.*

RUGGLES, ELEANOR. Prince of players, Edwin Booth. *buckram, 8vo. N.Y., Norton, 1953.*

RULAND, WILHELM. Legends of the Rhine. *buckram, 16mo. Cologne, Hoursch & Bechstedy, 1906.*

RULES FOR BEING A WIT. *paper, 12mo. Lond., Lewis, 1740?*

RUNES, DAGOBERT D. Lost legends of Israel. *paper, 12mo. N.Y., Philosophical Library, 1961.*

RUNKLE, MILT. War jokes and others from over the top. *paper, 12mo. Chic., Donohue, 1919.*

RUNYON, DAMON. Furthermore.
*buckram, 12mo. Lond.,
Constable, 1938.*

_____ More guys and dolls.
*buckram, 8vo. Garden City,
Garden City Books, 1951.*

_____ Runyon a la carte.
*buckram, 12mo. Phila., Lip-
pincott, 1944.*

_____ Short takes. *buckram,
12mo. N.Y., Somerset, 1946.*

RURAL LANDMARKS. *boards,
8vo. Chic., Highlights Co.,
1945.*

RUSKIN, JOHN. John Ruskin on
himself and things in general.
*paper, 12mo. Liverpool, At the
Office of Cope's Tobacco
Plant, 1893.*

_____ Precious thoughts,
moral and religious. *calf, 16mo.
N.Y., Crowell, n.d.*

_____ Precious thoughts
moral and religious. *buckram,
12mo. N.Y., Merrill & Baker,
1865. 2d.ed.*

RUSSELL, ANNA. The power of
being a positive stinker.
*paper, 4to. N.Y., Citadel, 1955.*

RUSSELL, BERTRAND. Bertrand
Russell's dictionary of mind,
matter and morals. *buckram,
8vo. N.Y., Philosophical
Library, 1952.*

_____ The good citizen's
alphabet. *buckram, 12mo. N.Y.,
Philosophical Library, 1958.*

_____ An outline of intellectual rubbish; a hilarious
catalogue of organized and
individual stupidity. *paper,
8vo. Girard, Kan., Haldeman-
Julius, 1943.*

RUSSELL, *Sir* EDWARD. That
reminds me_____ *buckram,
8vo. Lond., T.Fisher Unwin,
1899.*

RUSSELL, FRED R. Funny thing
about sports. *buckram, 8vo.
Nashville, McQuiddy, 1948.*

_____ I'll go quietly. *buckram, 12mo. Nashville,
McQuiddy, 1944.*

RUSSELL, LEONARD, ed. The
English comic album. *buckram,
4to. Lond., Joseph, 1948.*

_____ English wits. *buckram, 8vo. Lond., Hutchinson,
1941.*

RUSSELL, M.C. Western sketches.
Indian trail echoes. Straws of
humor. *paper, 8vo. Lake City,
Minn., "The Home Printery"
1904.*

RUSSIAN COURT MEMOIRS, 1914-
1916, with some account of
court, social and political life
in Petrograd before and since
the war. *buckram, 8vo. Lond.,
Jenkins, 1917.*

RUTTER, OWEN. Tiadatha. *buckram, 8vo. Lond., Allan, 1935.*

RYAN, RICHARD N. Spin in,
dumbwhacks. *buckram, 12mo.
Phila., Lippincott, 1943.*

RYAN, THOMAS CURRAN.
O'Hooligan's fine forms.
*boards, 12mo. Indianapolis,
Bobbs-Merrill, 1904.*

RYDER, ROBERT O. The young
lady across the way. *buckram,
12mo. Bost., Luce, 1913.*

RYERSON, FLORENCE *and*
CLEMENTS, COLIN. First
person singular; a book of
monologues. *buckram, 12mo.
N.Y., French, 1937.*

RYLEY, MADELEINE LUCETTE.
An American citizen. *paper,
12mo. Lond., French, 1904.*

RYMES OF THE MINSTRELS,
selected from a manuscript of
the fifteenth century. *boards,
8vo. Shaftesbury, Dorset, High
House Press, 1927.*

# S

S., T.B., *comp.* Illustrated anecdotes, and Pithy pieces of prose and verse. *buckram, 16mo. N.Y., Routledge,n.d. but ca. 1860.*

SACCHETTI, FRANCO. Tales from Sacchetti. *buckram, 8vo. Lond., Dent, 1908.*

SACK, JOHN. From here to Shimbashi. *paper, 16mo. N.Y., Permabooks, 1955.*

SACKVILLE-STONER, WINIFRED. Facts in jingles. *buckram, 12mo. Indianapolis, Bobbs-Merrill, 1915.*

SACKVILLE-WEST, V. Nursery rhymes. *buckram, 4to. Lond., Dropmore Press, 1957.*

SACRED TABLEAUX, THE: or, Remarkable incidents in the old and new Testament. *buckram, 12mo. Bost., Whittemore, 1848.*

SA'DI. Sadi's scroll of wisdom. *paper, 12mo. Lond., Murray, 1913.*

SAGENDORPH, ROBB, *ed.* The old farmer's almanac sampler. *buckram, 8vo. N.Y., Ives Washburn, 1957.*

SAGITTARIUS, *pseud. see* Katzin, Olga.

SAIKAKU, IHARA. Five women who loved love. *paper, 12mo. Rutland, Vt., Tuttle, 1957.*

ST. CLAIRE, EDWARD C. Wind women; poems. *paper, 12mo. Halcyon, Calif., Halcyon Press, 1925.*

ST. FRANCIS LOBBYIST, THE. Edition de luxe. Published at the Hotel St. Francis during the National Democratic Convention, San Francisco, June 23 to July 6, 1920. *boards, folio. San Francisco. Coleman, 1923.*

ST. GEORGE. THOMAS R. c/o Postmaster. *boards, 8vo. N.Y., Crowell, 1943.*

——————— Proceed without delay. *buckram, 12mo. N.Y., Crowell, 1945.*

ST. JACOBS OIL FAMILY CALENDAR, 1886, and book of health and humor for the million. *paper, 8vo. Baltimore, Vogeler, 1886.*

SALE, CHARLES. I'll tell you why. *boards, 24mo. St. Louis, Specialist Pub.Co. 1930.*

———————. The specialist. *boards, 24mo. St. Louis, Specialist Pub.Co., 1929.*

SALE, CHIC. *see* SALE, CHARLES

SALE, WILLIAM M., *ed.* Short stories, tradition and direction. *buckram, 8vo. Norfolk, Conn., New Directions, 1949.*

SALE OF THE HOUSE OF PEERS, THE, or, Ways and means for 1782. *pamphlet. Lond., Kearsley, 1782. 3d.ed.*

SALESMAN, THE. *paper, 8vo. N.Y., Doubleday, 1959.*

SALISBURY, HAROLD. The wrong end of the horse; verse of vice and vice versa. *buckram, 8vo. N.Y., Exposition, 1953.*

SAMPSON, ALISTAIR. The morning after. *boards, 12mo. Lond., Dobson, 1960.*

SAMUEL, *Sir* HERBERT LOUIS SAMUEL, *viscount.* A book of quotations. *buckram, 8vo. Lond., Cresset, 1957.*

SANBORN, KATE. The wit of women. *buckram, 8vo. N.Y., Funk & Wagnalls, 1885. 2d.ed.*

SAND, GEORGE, *pseud.* Aphorisms. *paper, 32mo. Girard, Kan., Haldeman-Julius, n.d. (Little Blue Books.)*

——————— George Sand; thoughts & aphorisms from her works. Arranged by Alfred H. Hyatt. *paper, 24mo. Bost., Phillips, 1911.*

SANDBURG, CARL. Abraham Lincoln: the prairie years. *buckram, 8vo. N.Y., Blue Ribbon Books, 1926.*

SANDER, HAROLD. My Uncle from India; a farcical comedy. *paper, 12mo. N.Y., Dick & Fitzgerald, 1907.*

SANGSTER, MARGARET E. The cheerful convalescent; a bedside anthology. *buckram, 12mo. N.Y., Greenberg, 1931.*

SANGSTER, WILLIAM. Unbrellas and their history. *buckram, 12mo. Lond., Wilson, 1855.*

SANSONE, LEONARD. The wolf. *buckram, 8vo. N.Y., United Pub.Co., 1945.*

SARDOU, VICTORIEN. The black pearl, a comedy. *paper, 12mo. N.Y., French, 1915.*

——————— A scrap of paper, a comedy. *paper, 12mo. Bost., Baker, 1911.*

SARGENT, JOHN WILLIAM. Smoke and bubbles. *buckram, 16mo. N.Y., Saalfield, 1906.*

SARMA, D.S. Tales of ancient India. *paper, 12mo. Bombay, Hind Kitabs, 1948.*

SAROYAN, WILLIAM. Laughing matter. *buckram, 12mo. Lond., Faber & Faber, 1954.*

SARZANO, FRANCES. Sir John Tenniel. *buckram, 8vo. N.Y., Pellegrini & Cudahy, n.d.*

SATURDAY EVENING POST. Best cartoons from the post, 1932 to 1960. (Cut from the magazine and mounted.)

——————— Funny business, edited by Marione Derrickson. *buckram, 4to. N.Y., McGraw-Hill, 1945.*

——————— "Honey, I'm home" a collection of cartoons from the Saturday Evening Post, edited by Marione R. Nickles. *paper, 12mo. N.Y., Bantam, 1954.*

——————— Laugh it off; cartoons from the Saturday Evening Post, edited by Marione R. Derrickson. *buckram, 4to. N.Y., Whittlesey, 1944.*

——————— "One moment, sir!" cartoons, selected by Marione R. Nickles. *buckram, 4to. Lond., Constable, 1958.*

——————— Post scripts, a collection of humor from the Saturday Evening Post, edited by Marione R. Derrickson. *buckram, 8vo. N.Y., Whittlesey House, 1943.*

——————— The Saturday Evening Post carnival of humor, edited by Robert M. Yoder. *buckram, 4to. Englewood Cliffs, N.J., Prentice-Hall, 1958.*

——————— The Saturday Evening Post cartoon festival. 25 years of Post cartoons. *buckram, 4to. N.Y., Dutton, 1958.*

——————— The Saturday Evening Post humor. Edited by John Bailey. *buckram, 8vo. Lond., Elek, 1956.*

—————— The Saturday
Evening Post treasury.
Selected from the complete
files by Roger Butterfield and
the Editors of the Saturday
Evening Post. *boards, 4to.
N.Y., Simon & Schuster, 1954.*

SATURDAY REVIEW OF
LITERATURE. Laughs from
the Saturday Review of
Literature. *boards, 4to. N.Y.,
Vanguard, 1946.*

SAUCY JOKES: the funny sayings
of the leading monologists,
comedians, sketch artists and
jokers; the best stories put
over the footlights. *paper,
32mo. Baltimore, Ottenheimer,
1915.*

SAUERS, DON. The girl watcher's
guide. *boards, 12mo. Lond.,
Deutsch, 1956.*

SAVAGE, HENRY. The Harleian
miscellany. *buckram, 8vo.
Lond., Palmer, 1924.*

SAVO, JIMMY. Little world, hello!
*buckram, 12mo. N.Y., Simon &
Schuster, 1947.*

SAXE, JOHN GODFREY. Fables
and legends of many countries,
rendered in rhyme. *buckram,
12mo. Bost., Osgood, 1872.*

SAXON, LYLE, *comp.* Gumbo
Ya-Ya; a collection of
Louisiana folk tales. *buckram,
8vo. Bost., Houghton Mifflin,
1945.*

SAYINGS OF UNCLE RUFUS.
*paper, 12mo. N.Y., Haney,
1881.*

SAYRE, JOEL. Rackety rax.
*boards, 8vo. N.Y., Knopf,
1932.*

SAZANAMI, IWAYA. Japanese
fairy tales. *cloth, 16mo.
Tokyo, Hokuseido, 1938.*

SCHACHT, AL. Clowning through
baseball. *buckram, 8vo. N.Y.,
Barnes, 1941.*

SCHAFER, BARBARA LOUISE,
*comp.* A book of one-act plays.
*buckram, 12mo. Indianapolis,
Bobbs-Merrill, 1922.*

SCHAFER, KERMIT. Pardon my
blooper. *paper, 12mo.
Greenwich, Conn., Fawcett,
1959.*

—————— Your slip is
showing: a collection of radio
and TV's most hilarious
boners. *buckram, 12mo. N.Y.,
Grayson, 1953.*

SCHEEL, TED. The face is
familiar ... *buckram, 4to. N.Y.,
Beechhurst, 1951.*

SCHERMERHORN, JAMES.
Schermerhorn's stories; 1500
anecdotes from forty years of
after dinner speaking. *buckram, 8vo. N.Y., Sully, 1928.*

—————— *Same. N.Y., Burt,
1934,* with title: 1500 anecdotes and stories for after
dinner speaking.

SCHILLING, BERNARD N. On
Jewish humor. *(Bound with:
The king of schnorrers, by
Israel Zangwill, q.v.)*

SCHIRMER, MATHILDA, *comp.*
The bedside book of humor;
many of the world's funniest
stories. *buckram, 8vo. Chic.,
Peoples Book Club, 1948.*

SCHMULOWITZ, NAT. A crocodile snarls, squawks, and
chuckles! Cartoons about the
United States from the Russian
Soviet magazine KROKODIL,
with a fragment by Nat
Schmulowitz. *paper, 8vo.
San Francisco, Aucune Press
for the Roxburghe Club, 1955.*

_____ Epitaphia. *paper, folio. San Francisco, Grabhorn, Press for the Roxburghe Club, 1956. (Anecdota Scowah, No. I.)*

_____ Jesting among and and about Jews. *(In: Jewish Digest, v.2. no.10. June, 1957.)*

_____ "Liberty, laughter and the law" The power and force of jests. *(In: Vital speeches of the day, August 15, 1947.)*

_____ The Nazi joke courts. *pamphlet. San Francisco, Priv. Print., 1943.*

_____ Onsoz. *(In: Joe Miller of the Near East, by Albert Rapp.)*

_____ A prefatory fragment with Joe Milleriana. *(In: The legend of Joe Miller, by Evan Esar.)*

_____ A prolegomenon. *(In: The Ancient Greeks & Joe Miller, by Albert Rapp.)*

_____ Shun the man who never laughs. *(In: Vital speeches of the Day, January 1, 1951.)*

_____ A tenological thesis. Remarks at the forty-fifth reunion of the class of 1910, University of California. *paper, 8vo. San Francisco, Priv. Print., 1955.*

SCHNUR, HARRY C. Jewish humour. *paper, 24mo. Lond., Allied Book Club, n.d.*

SCHOPENHAUER, ARTHUR. The wisdom of Schopenhauer, as revealed in some of his principal writings. *buckram, 8vo. Lond., Watts, 1911.*

SCHULZ, CHARLES M. But we love you Charlie Brown. *paper, 8vo. N.Y., Rinehart, 1959.*

_____ Go fly a kite, Charlie Brown. *paper, 8vo. N.Y., Holt, Rinehart & Winston, 1960.*

_____ Good grief, more Peanuts! *paper, 24mo. N.Y., Rinehart, 1956.*

_____ A new Peanuts book featuring Snoopy. *paper, 8vo. N.Y., Rinehart, 1958.*

_____ Peanuts. *paper, 8vo. N.Y., Rinehart, 1952.*

_____ Peanuts every Sunday. *paper, wide 24mo. N.Y., Holt, Rinehart & Winston, 1961.*

_____ You're out of your mind, Charlie Brown! *paper, 24mo. N.Y., Rinehart, 1959.*

SCOGGIN, MARGARET C. Chucklebait; funny stories for everyone. *buckram, 8vo. N.Y., Knopf, 1945.*

SCORE, H. BERKELEY. Sparks of light from a fabulist's diamond mine. *buckram, 12mo. Ormskirk, Hutton, 1894.*

SCOTCH HAGGIS; consisting of anecdotes, jests, curious and rare articles of literature: with a collection of epitaphs and inscriptions, original and selected. *half-calf, 12mo. Edinburgh, Webster, 1822.*

SCOTCH HAGGIS; consisting of pieces humorous, witty, droll, ancient and modern, worthy of preservation, connected with Scottish drollery. *half-leather, 16mo. Paisley, Caldwell, 1829. 2d.ed.*

SCOTCH HAGGIS; a selection of choice bon mots, Irish blunders, repartees, anecdotes, &c. *paper, 16mo. Glasgow, Printed for the Booksellers, n.d.*

SCOTCH WIT AND HUMOR. *buckram, 16mo. Phila., Jacobs.*

——————— *Same. Toronto, Musson, n.d.*

SCOTISH PASTIL, A, from "A Miscellaneous manuscript circa 1630". *paper, 12mo. Glasgow, Anderson, n.d.*

SCOT'S WEEK-END, THE: and Caledonian vade-mecum for host, guest and wayfarer. *buckram, 12mo. Lond., Routledge, 1936.*

SCOTT, DUFTON. Humorous Scotch stories and sketches. *paper, 12mo. Inverurie, Scott, 1924.*

SCOTT, EDWARD A. Recess; a pictorial new look at old maxims. *paper, 4to. N.Y., Pandick, 1954.*

SCOTT, W.W. Breaks; unintentional humour by tired newspaper-men and others. *boards, 12mo. Lond., Cape, 1931.*

SCOTT, Sir WALTER. Wit and wisdom of Walter Scott. *paper, 32mo. Girard, Kan., Haldeman-Julius, n.d. (Little Blue Books.)*

SCOTT, WILLIAM. Lessons in elocution; or, A selection of pieces in prose and verse. *calf, 16mo. Plymouth, Collier, 1825.*

SCOTTISH JESTS AND ANECDOTES. To which are added a selection of choice English and Irish jests. *half-calf, 24mo. Edinburgh, Tait, 1838. 2d.ed.*

SCRAP BOOK, THE; choice bits of wit, humor and philosophy. *paper, 12mo. San Leandro, Calif., Seramur, 1937. 3d.ed.*

SCRAP BOOK, THE: or, A selection of interesting and authentic anecdotes. *calf, 24mo. Dublin, Chambers & Hallagan, 1875.*

SCRAPBOOK, A, containing miscellaneous items of poetry, prose and pictures.

SCRAPS OF WIT AND HUMOUR: being an elegant selection of choice good things, calculated to promote innocent mirth and drive away care. *paper, 12mo. Lond., Turner, 1815.*

SCRIBLERUS REDIVIVUS *see* CASWALL, EDWARD.

SCRUGGS, RAY, *comp.* Five hundred laughs; an assortment of after-dinner stories & amusing anecdotes. *paper, 12mo. Houston, Author, 1927.*

——————— Ten hundred laughs. *paper, 12mc. Houston, Author, 1928.*

SCULLY, FRANK, *ed.* Bedside manna; the Third Fun in Bed Book. *buckram, 4to. N.Y., Simon & Schuster, 1936.*

——————— The best of fun in bed. *paper, 8vo. N.Y., Simon & Schuster, 1951.*

——————— Fun in bed. Series four. X just what the doctor ordered. *buckram, 4to. N.Y., Simon & Schuster, 1938.*

SEAGLE, WILLIAM. There ought to be a law; a collection of lunatic legislation. *buckram, 12mo. N.Y., Macaulay, 1933.*

SEAMAN, OWEN. Interludes of an editor. *buckram, 8vo. Lond., Constable, 1929.*

SEARCH, PAMELA, *comp. and ed.* Great true stories of human endurance. *buckram, 8vo. Lond., Arco, 1957.*

SEARLE, RONALD. Back to the slaughterhouse, and other ugly moments. *buckram, 8vo. Lond., Macdonald, 1951.*

————— The female approach. *buckram, 8vo. Lond., Macdonald, 1950.*

————— Hurrah for St. Trinian's, and other lapses. *buckram, 12mo. Lond., Macdonald, 1954.*

————— Paris sketchbook. *buckram, 4to. Lond., Perpetua, 1957.*

————— The Penguin Ronald Searle. *paper, 12mo. Harmondsworth, Middlesex, Penguin, 1960.*

————— The rake's progress. *buckram, 8vo. Lond., Perpetua, 1955.*

SEAVER, EDWIN, *ed.* Pageant of American humor. *buckram, 8vo. Cleveland, World, 1948.*

SECCOMBE, T.S. Comic sketches from English history for children of various ages, with descriptive rhymes. *boards, 8vo. Lond., Allen, n.d.*

SECOND CENTURY OF HUMOUR. *buckram, 8vo. Lond., Hutchinson, n.d.*

SECOND POCKET TRIVET BOOK: sayings of good hope. *boards, 24mo. Lond., Morning Post, 1933.*

SEE, T.J. *see* CAREY, THOMAS J.

SEITZ, DON. Artemas Ward (Charles Farrar Browne) a biography and bibliography. *buckram, 8vo. N.Y., Harper, 1919.*

————— Whistler stories. *calf., 16mo. N.Y., Harper, 1913.*

SELDEN, ELIZABETH, *comp.* The book of friendship; an international anthology. *buckram, 12mo. Bost., Houghton, Mifflin, 1947.*

SELECT COLLECTION OF EPITAPHS AND MONUMENTAL INSCRIPTIONS, A, with anecdotes of distinguished and extraordinary persons. *calf, 16mo. Ipswich, Raw, 1806.*

SELECT EPIGRAMS, *2v. calf, 12mo. Lond., Sampson Low, 1797.*

SELECTED SAYINGS FROM THE PERFECTION OF WISDOM. Chosen, arranged and translated by Edward Conze. *buckram, 8vo. Lond., Buddhist Society, 1955.*

SELECTIONS FOR MEMORIZING. Grades 1 through 16. *pamphlets. (Personal Growth Leaflets.)*

SELECTIONS FROM THE FRENCH ANAS: containing remarks of eminent scholars on men and books. Together with anecdote and apophtegms of illustrious persons interspersed with pieces of poetry. 2v. in 1. *half-calf, 12mo. Lond., Cooke, 1797.*

————— Same in 2v.

SELLAR, R.J.B., *comp.* Over the cocktails; yarns about celebrities and others. *buckram, 12mo. Lond., Rivers, 1931.*

————— Sporting and dramatic yarns. *buckram, 12mo. Lond., T.Fisher Unwin, 1925..*

SELLAR, W.C. *and* YEATMAN, R.J. And now all this. *buckram, 12mo. N.Y., Dutton, 1932.*

_____ 1066 and all that; a memorable history of England. *buckram, 12mo. Lond., Methuen, 1934. 18th ed.*

SELTZER, CHARLES A. Flashes of wit from the Buffalo show, by Hiram Hopkins, *pseud. paper, 12mo. Cleveland, Sparks of Fun Pub.Co., 1901.*

SENTER, A.E. The diddler. *buckram, 12mo. N.Y., Doolady, 1868.*

SERVICE, ROBERT W. Ballads of a Bohemian. *buckram, 12mo. N.Y., Barse & Hopkins, 1921.*

_____ Lyrics of a low brow. *buckram, 8vo. N.Y., Dodd, Mead, 1951.*

_____ Rhymes of a Red Cross man. *leather, 24mo. N.Y., Barse & Hopkins, 1916.*

SETON, GEORGE, *comp. and ed.* A budget of anecdotes relating to the current century. *buckram, 12mo. Edinburgh, Blackwood, 1887. 2d.ed.*

_____ A budget of anecdotes chiefly relating to the nineteenth century. *buckram, 12mo. Lond., Chapman & Hall, 1903. 3d.ed.*

SETTEL, IRVING, *ed.* Best television humor of the year, *paper, 16mo. N.Y., Ace, 1956.*

_____ Best TV humor of 1957. *paper, 12mo. N.Y., Ballantine, 1957.*

SEVENTY TRUE STORIES OF THE SECOND WORLD WAR. *paper, 12mo. Lond., Beacon, 1958.*

SEVIGNE, MARIE, *Marquise de.* Witticism and reflections. *paper, 32mo. Girard, Kan., Haldeman-Julius, n.d. (Little Blue Books.)*

SEWARD, SAMUEL S., *jr.* The paradox of the ludicrous. *buckram, 8vo. Stanford, Calif., Stanford Univ. Press, 1930.*

SEWARD, WILLIAM. Anecdotes of distinguished persons chiefly of the present and two preceding centuries. *4v. calf, 8vo. Lond., Cadell, 1798. 4th ed.*

_____ *Same. 5th ed. 1804.*

SEWELL, ELIZABETH. The field of nonsense. *buckram, 12mo. Lond., Chatto & Windus, 1952.*

SEXSATIONS. *paper, 12mo. Tokyo, Kasuga Boeki, K.K., 1956.*

SEXTRA SPECIAL. *paper, 12mo. Tokyo, Kasuga Boeki, KK., 1955.*

_____ *Same. N.Y., Scylla, 1955.*

SEYMOUR, FREDERICK HENRI. The god Yutzo of B.C. 763, by Lord Gilhooley. *cloth, 8vo. N.Y., Stokes, 1896. 4th ed.*

_____ Son! or, The wisdom of "Uncle Eph" the modern Yutzo. *cloth, 12mo. N.Y., Stokes, 1902.*

SEYMOUR, ROBERT. New readings from old authors. Shakespeare. Romeo and Juliet. *half-calf, 16mo. Lond., Wilson, n.d.*

_____ The odd volume, or Book of variety. *buckram, 16mo. Lond., Kidd, n.d.*

_____ Pictures by Robert Seymour. *paper, 24mo. Lond., Gowans & Gray, 1906. (Humorous masterpieces.)*

_____ Seymour's humorous sketches, comprising eighty-six caricature etchings, illustrated in prose and verse by Alfred Crowquill. *buckram, 8vo. Lond., Bohn, 1866. New ed.*

_____ Seymour's sketches; the book of Cockney sports, whims and oddities. *half-morocco, 4to. Lond., John Camden Hotten, n.d.*

SHAFER, BURR. Louder and funnier; after-dinner speeches and other mistakes. *buckram, 12mo. N.Y., Vanguard, 1951.*

_____ Through history with J. Wesley Smith. *boards, wide 8vo. N.Y., Vanguard, 1950.*

SHAFTESBURY, ANTHONY ASHLEY COOPER, 3d. earl of. Characteristicks. *3v. calf, 32mo. Lond., n.p., 1743-1745.*

SHAH, CHAMPAK C., *comp.* Proverbs of Hindustan. *paper, 32mo. Girard, Kan., Haldeman-Julius, n.d. (Little Blue Books.)*

_____ Proverbs of India. *paper, 32mo. Girard, Kan., Haldeman-Julius, n.d. (Little Blue Books.)*

_____ Sanskrit proverbs. *paper, 32mo. Girard, Kan., Haldeman-Julius, n.d. (Little Blue Books.)*

SHAKESPEARE, WILLIAM. The golden Shakespeare; an anthology compiled by Logan Pearsall Smith. *buckram, 8vo. Lond., Constable, 1949.*

_____ Hey nonny yes; passions and conceits of Shakespeare assembled by Hallam Fordham. *boards, 24mo. Lond., Saturn, 1947.*

_____ An index to Shakespearian thought ... arranged by Cecil Arnold. *buckram, 8vo. Lond., Bickers, 1880.*

_____ Lend me your ears; an anthology of Shakespearian quotations, compiled by Reyner Barton. *buckram, 8vo. Lond., Jarrolds, 1946. Rev. and enl.ed.*

_____ Popular Shakespearian quotations, selected and arranged by Lloyd E. Smith. *paper, 32mo. Girard, Kan., Haldeman-Julius, n.d. (Little Blue Books.)*

_____ Religious and moral sentences culled from the works of Shakespeare, compared with sacred passages drawn from Holy Writ ... dedicated to the Shakespeare Society, by A. Member. *buckram, 8vo. Lond., Calkin & Budd, 1847.*

_____ Shakespeare's merry tales. *boards, 2mo. Lond., Routledge, 1845.*

_____ Shakespeare's Jest book. *half-calf, 12mo. Chiswick, Whittingham, 1814.*

SHAKESPEARE JEST-BOOKS. Reprints of the early and very rare jest-books supposed to have been used by Shakespeare. Edited with introduction and notes by W. Carew Hazlitt. *3v. quarter-calf, 12mo. Lond., Willis & Sotheran, 1864.*

Contents.-v.1: A hundred mery talys, from the only known copy. Mery tales and quicke answeres, from the rare edition of 1567.-v.2: Merie tales of Skelton, Jests of Scogin. Sackfull of Newes. Tarlton's jests. Merrie conceited jests of George Peele. Jacke of

Dover.-v.3. Merie tales of the mad men of Gotham, XII mery jests of the Widow Edyth. Pasquil's Jests with Mother Bunche's Merriments. The pleasant conceits of Old Hobson. Certayne conceyts and feasts. Taylor's wit and mirth. Conceits, clinches, flashes and whimsies.

SHANE NA GAEL *see* WELSH, CHARLES.

SHANKAR, SHYAMA. Wit and wisdom of India; a collection of humorous folk-tales of the court and country side current in India. *boards, 12mo. Lond., Routledge, 1924.*

SHAW, GEORGE. Our relgious humorists. *buckram, 12mo. Lond., Wesleyan Conference Office, n.d.*

SHAW, GEORGE BERNARD. Epigrams of Bernard Shaw. *paper, 32mo. Girard, Kan., Haldeman-Julius, n.d. (Little Blue Books.)*

——————— Nine plays. *buckram, 8vo. N.Y., Dodd, Mead, 1935.*

——————— Saint Joan. *buckram, 12mo. N.Y., Brentano's, 1924.*

——————— Too true to be good. Village wooing. On the rocks. Three plays. *buckram, 8vo. Lond., Constable, 1934.*

SHAW, HENRY WHEELER. Complete works of Josh Billings. *buckram, 12mo. N.Y., Dillingham, 1876. Rev.ed.*

——————— Josh Billings' comical lexicon, and other amusing skits. *32mo. paper, Girard, Kan., Haldeman-Julius, n.d. (Little Blue Books.)*

——————— Josh Billings' farmer's allminax for the year 1871. *pamphlet. Toronto, Canadian News and Pub.Co., 1870.*

——————— Josh Billings' Farmer's Allminax for the year of our lord 1872. *paper, 8vo. N.Y., Carleton, 1872.*

——————— Josh Billings' Farmer's Allmin ax for the year of our lord, 1879. *paper, 8vo. N.Y., Carleton, 1878.*

——————— Josh Billings, his book of sayings, with introduction by E.P. Hingston. *buckram, 16mo. Lond., John Camden Hotten, n.d.*

——————— Josh Billings: his works, complete. *buckram, 8vo. N.Y., Dillingham, 1876.*

——————— Same. *N.Y., Carleton, 1881.*

——————— Josh Billings, hiz sayings. *buckram, 12mo. N.Y., Carleton, 1868..*

——————— Josh Billings' humorous epigrams. *paper, 32mo. Girard, Kan., Haldeman-Julius, n.d. (Little Blue Books)*

——————— Josh Billings' old farmer's allminax. 1870-1879. *buckram, 12mo. N.Y., Dillingham, 1902.*

——————— Josh Billings on ice, and other things. *buckram, 12mo. N.Y., Carleton, 1868.*

——————— Josh Billings' trump kards; blue grass philosophy. *paper, 12mo. N.Y., Carleton, 1877.*

——————— Wit and wisdom of Josh Billings ... carefully collected and revised by H.Montague. *buckram, 12mo. Winston-Salem, N.C. n.p. 1913.*

SHAY, FRANK *and* LOVING,
PIERRE. Fifty contemporary
one-act plays. *buckram, 8vo.
Cincinnati, Stewart & Kidd,
1920.*

SHAY, FRANK *and* HELD, JOHN.
Pious friends and drunken com-
panions. *buckram, 4to. N.Y.,
Macaulay, 1936.*

SHEA, MARGARET. The gals
they left behind. *buckram, 8vo.
N.Y., Ives Washburn, 1944.*

SHEAR NONSENSE: a collection
of mirth-provoking stories for
all occasions. *buckram, 16mo.
Phila., Jacobs, 1914.*

SHEARED CREAM O' WIT; a
classified compilation of the
best wit and humor. *buckram,
12mo. Louisville, Ky.,
Mittler, 1923.*

SHEDLOCK, MARIE L., *ed.* A
collection of eastern stories
and legends. *buckram, 12mo.
Lond., Routledge, 1910.*

SHEELY, AARON. Anecdotes and
humors of school life. *buckram,
12mo. Phila., Claxton, Remsen
& Haffelfinger, 1877.*

SHEEN, FULTON J. God love you.
*buckram, 8vo. Garden City,
Garden City Books, 1955.*

SHEER NONSENSE. *pamphlet,
N.Y., Ceagee Pub.Co., 1944.*

SHEPARD, W.E. Nuts to crack, or,
Mental gymnastics. *paper,
12mo. Pasadena, Art Press,
1930.*

SHEPHARD, ESTHER. Paul
Bunyan. *buckram, 8vo. N.Y.,
Harcourt, Brace, 1924.*

SHEPHERD, C.W. Let's walk
down Fleet Street. *buckram,
8vo. Lond., Swan, 1947.*

SHEPHERD, CHARLES R. One
hundred and one Chinese proverbs. *paper, 12mo. Berkeley,
Calif., Chung Mei Home for
Chinese Boys, n.d.*

SHERIDAN, JOHN D. Bright
intervals. *buckram, 12mo.
Lond., Dent, 1958.*

———————— Funnily enough.
*buckram, 12mo. Lond., Dent,
1956.*

———————— The right time.
*buckram, 12mo. Lond., Dent,
1952.*

———————— While the humour
is on me. *buckram, 12mo. Lond.,
Dent, 1954.*

SHERIDAN, RICHARD BRINSLEY.
The rivals, and The school
for scandal. *paper, 24mo.
Lond., Cassell, 1907.*

———————— The school for
scandal, a comedy. *paper, 12mo.
Chic., Dramatic Pub. Co., 1876.*

———————— Sheridaniana; or,
Anecdotes of the life of
Richard Brinsley Sheridan; his
table-talk and bon-mots.
*quarter-buckram, 8vo. Lond.,
Colburn, 1826.*

SHERWOOD, BOB. Hold everything. *boards, 12mo. N.Y.,
Sherwood, 1929.*

SHERWOOD, JOHN D. The comic
history of the United States.
*buckram, 12mo. Bost., Fields,
Osgood, 1870.*

SHIKES, RALPH E. Cartoon
annual; a selection from the
cream of the year's best
cartoons. *paper, 16mo. N.Y.,
Ace, 1953.*

———————— Slightly out of order;
best cartoons from the continent. *boards, 8vo. Lond.,
Hammond & Hammond, 1959.*

SHILLABER, B.P. Knitting-work;
a web of many textures wrought
by Ruth Partington. *buckram,
12mo. Bost., Brown, Taggard —
& Chase, 1859.*

—————————— Life and sayings of
Mrs. Partington and others of
the family. *buckram, 12mo.
N.Y., Derby, 1854.*

—————————— Mrs. Partington's
knitting-work; and what was
done by her plaguy boy Ike.
*buckram, 12mo. Phila., Potter,
1868.*

——————————Partingtonian patch-
work. Blifkins the martyr. The
modern syntax. Partington
papers. New and old dips.
*buckram, 12mo. Bost., Lee &
Shepard, 1873.*

—————————— Sayings and doings
of Mrs. Partington. *paper,
12mo. Lond., Blackwood, n.d.*

SHIP AHOY: nautical tales and
verse. *paper, 16mo. N.Y.,
Avon, 1954.*

SHIPLEY, MAYNARD. New light
on the ten commandments.
*paper, 32mo. Girard, Kan.,
Haldeman-Julius, n.d. (Little
Blue Books.)*

SHIR-CLIFF, B.W. The wild
reader. *paper, 12mo. N.Y.,
Ballantine, 1956.*

SHOEMAKER, J.W., *ed.* Best
things from best authors. v.1.
*buckram, 12mo. Phila.,
National School of Eluction
and Oratory, 1883.*

SHOLOM ALEICHEM: Inside
Kasrilevke. *buckram, 8vo.
N.Y., Schocken, 1948.*

SHOMER, LOUIS. Bachelor girl
gags. *paper, 12mo. N.Y.,
Larch, 1945.*

—————————— How to make funny
gags. *paper, 12mo. N.Y.,
Larch, 1943.*

—————————— Laughter for the
millions. *buckram, 8vo. N.Y.,
Louellen, 1938.*

—————————— Married life jokes
and gags. *paper, 12mo. N.Y.,
Larch, 1944.*

—————————— Moron jokes and
gags. *paper, 12mo. N.Y.,
Carey, 1943.*

—————————— Movie gags and
jokes; screen and stage
laughs. *paper, 12mo. N.Y.,
Larch, 1944.*

—————————— Pvt. Goldbrick, a
laugh riot for the serviceman.
*paper, 12mo. N.Y., Larch, 1943.*

SHORT STORIES FROM THE
SPANISH. Englished by
Charles B. McMichael. *boards,
12mo. N.Y., Boni & Liveright,
1920.*

SHRIDHARANI, KRISHNALAL.
The adventure of the upside-
down tree. *buckram, 12mo.
Bombay, Asia Pub.House, 1957.*

SHRINER, CHARLES A. Wit,
wisdom and foibles of the
great. *buckram, 4to. N.Y.,
Funk & Wagnalls, 1918.*

SHU CHING. The Shu king, or,
The Chinese historical
classic. Translated by Walter
Gorn Old. *buckram, 12mo.
Lond., Theosophical Pub.Co.,
1904.*

SHULMAN, MAX. Barefoot boy
with cheek. *buckram, 12mo.
Phila., Blakiston, 1943.*

—————————— The feather
merchants. *buckram, 12mo.
Garden City, Sun Dial, 1945.*

―――――― The many loves of Dobie Gillis. *paper, 12mo. N.Y., Bantam, 1960.*

―――――― Max Shulman's guided tour of campus humor. *buckram, 8vo. N.Y., Hanover, 1955.*

―――――― Rally round the flag, boys! *buckram, 12mo. Lond., Heinemann, 1958.*

―――――― Sleep till noon. *buckram, 12mo. Lond., Dobson, 1950.*

―――――― The Zebra derby. *buckram, 8vo. N.Y., Doubleday, Doran, 1946.*

SHURE, ROBERT. Twink. *paper, 24mo. San Francisco, City Lights Books, 1958.*

SHUTE, HENRY A. The real diary of the worst farmer. *boards, 12mo. Bost., Houghton, Mifflin, 1920.*

SIBLEY, ROBERT *and* SIBLEY, CAROL. University of California pilgrimage; a treasury of tradition, lore & laughter. *buckram, 4to. Berkeley, Calif., Lederer, Street & Zeus, 1952.*

SIDDALL, JOHN M. Sid says. *boards, 12mo. N.Y., Century, 1922.*

SIDNEY, FREDERICK W. The Brixton burglary; a farcical comedy. *paper, 12mo. N.Y., French, 1905.*

SIEVEKING, L. DE GIVERNE. Gladstone bags and marmalade. *boards, 4to. Lond., Palmer, 1920.*

SIGOURNEY, L.H. Sayings of little ones. *buckram, 16mo. N.Y., Blakeman & Mason, 1864.*

SILLINCE, W.A. Comic drawing. *buckram, 4to. Lond., Pitman, 1950.*

―――――― We're still all in it. *buckram, 12mo. Lond., Collins, 1942.*

SILVERSTEIN, SHEL. Grab your socks. *paper, 12mo. N.Y., Ballantine, 1956.*

―――――― "Now here's my plan" a book of futilities. *paper, 4to. N.Y., Simon & Schuster, 1960.*

―――――― Take ten. *boards, 12mo. Tokyo, Kyoya, 1955.*

SIMMS, BILL. Too much! cartoons. *paper, 12mo. Tokyo, Tuttle, 1955.*

SIMON, ROBERT A. Bronx ballads. *buckram, 8vo. N.Y., Simon & Schuster, 1927.*

SIMON, SOLOMON. The wise men of Helm, and their merry tales. *buckram, 8vo. N.Y., Behrman, 1945.*

SIMPKINS, JONAS. Reveries of a woodsawyer; or, "Sum" slicings of cord-wood. *buckram, 12mo. N.Y., Lange, Little & Hillman, 1872.*

SIMPSON, J. PALGRAVE. A scrap of paper, a comic drama. *paper, 12mo. Phila., Penn, 1894.*

SIMPSON, JAMES BEASLEY, *comp.* Best quotes of '54, '55, '56. *buckram, 8vo. N.Y., Crowell, 1957.*

SINE *see* SINET, MAURICE.

SINET, MAURICE. Scatty; British cats, French cats and cosmopolitan cats. *paper, 24mo. Lond., Reinhardt, 1958.*

―――――― Sine's proverbs. *paper, 24mo. Lond., Reinhardt, 1959.*

SINGER, HOWARD. Wake me when it's over. *paper, 12mo. N.Y., Bantam, 1959.*

SINGER, JOHN. Quips upon questions. *quarter-morocco, 8vo. Lond., Priv. Print., 1875.*

SINGER, KURT. The Danny Kaye saga. *buckram, 8vo. Lond., Hale, 1957.*

SINGH, KHUSHWANT. The voice of God. *paper, 16mo. Bombay, Jaico, 1957.*

SIRE, GLEN, *and* SIRE, JANE. Something foolish, something gay. *paper, 16mo. N.Y., Berkley, 1959.*

SIS HOPKINS OWN BOOK AND MAGAZINE OF FUN. *paper, 4to. N.Y., Judge, 1901.*

SITWELL, OSBERT. Death of a god. *buckram, 12mo. Lond., Macmillan, 1949.*

——————— Fee fi fo fum! a book of fairy stories. *buckram, 12mo. Lond., Macmillan, 1959.*

SIX PLAYS OF THE YIDDISH THEATRE. *boards, 12mo. Bost., Luce, 1916.*

SIXTY BEST HUMOROUS RECITATIONS. *buckram, 24mo. Lond., Foulsham, n.d.*

SIYAVUSGIL, SABRI ESAT. Karagoz; its history, its characters, its mystic and satiric spirit. *paper, folio. Ankara, Saim Toraman Basimevi, 1955.*

SKEELS, E.R.S. Wag's handbook. *paper, 12mo. Lond., T.Werner Laurie, 1942.*

SKINNER, CORNELIA OTIS. Bottoms up! *buckram, 12mo. Lond., Constable, 1955.*

——————— Dithers and jitters. *buckram, 8vo. N.Y., Dodd, Mead, 1938.*

——————— Excuse it, please! *paper, 16mo. N.Y., Pocket books, 1936.*

——————— Footlights and spotlights. *buckram, 8vo. N.Y., Blue Ribbon, 1924.*

SKOLSKY, SIDNEY. Times Square tintypes. *buckram, 8vo. N.Y., Ives Washburn, 1920.*

SKRENDA, ALFRED *and* JUERGENS, ISABEL. Minute stories from the Bible. *buckram, 4to. N.Y., Grosset & Dunlap, 1932.*

SLADEN, DOUGLAS. My long life; anecdotes and adventures. *buckram, 8vo. Lond., Hutchinson, 1939.*

SLANG DICTIONARY: or, The vulgar words, street phrases, and "fast" expressions of high and low society. Many with their etymology, and a few with their history traced. *buckram, 12mo. Lond., John Camden Hotten, 1864.*

SLATER, W.E. Humour in verse; an anthology. *buckram, 12mo. Cambridge, Univ.Press, 1937.*

SLICK, SAM. *see* HALIBURTON, THOMAS CHANDLER.

SLICK, SAM, *jr. see* AVERY, SAMUEL.

SMALL, GEORGE C. Hon. Sassafras Dodger, or, Joining the Grangers, by Bricktop. *paper, 8vo. N.Y., Ivers, n.d.*

——————— My mother-in-law. *paper, 8vo. N.Y., Collin, 1876.*

——————— Parson Beecher and his horse. *paper, 8vo. N.Y., Ivers, 1885.*

——————— The quiet youth; or, Just like his Uncle. *paper, 4to. N.Y., Collin, 1881.*

SMIFF, P.P.Q. PHILANDER, *pseud. see* DOWTY, A.A.

SMILE AMONG FRIENDS, A, based on "Verdenskarikaturen fra oldtiden til vare dager. *buckram, folio, Oslo, Alb. Cammermeyers forlag, n.d.*

SMILE ON THE FACE OF THE TIGER, THE: a collection of limericks. *boards, 16mo. Bost., Bacon & Brown, 1910.*

SMILES: a book of sunny stories, funny photographs and comic drawings. *paper, wide 24mo. San Francisco, Merry Way Pub. Co., 1918.*

SMILES: side splitting jokes; containing a wonderful selection of jokes, witty sayings, etc. New and original. *paper, 32mo. Baltimore, Ottenheimer, 1915.*

SMITH, ALBERT. Natural history of "stuck-up" people. *paper, 24mo. Long., Bogue, 1897.*

SMITH, ARTHUR H. Proverbs and common sayings from Chinese. *buckram, small 4to. Shanghai, American Presbyterian Mission Press, 1902.*

SMITH, DANIEL. Anecdotes for the fireside; or, A manual for the home. *buckram, 16mo. N.Y., Carlton & Porter, 1850.*

SMITH, EDNA B. The best I know. *buckram, 8vo. Bost., Waverly House, 1941.*

SMITH, EVELYN. Myths and legends of many lands. *buckram, 8vo. Lond., Nelson, 1933.*

SMITH, H. ALLEN. The age of the tail. *buckram, 8vo. Bost., Little, Brown, 1955.*

——————— The compleat practical joker. *paper, 12mo. N.Y., Pocket Books, 1953.*

——————— Desert island decameron. *buckram, 12mo. Phila., Blakiston, 1945.*

——————— Don't get perconel with a chicken. *paper, 16mo. N.Y., Permabooks, 1960.*

——————— Larks in the popcorn. *buckram, 12mo. N.Y., Doubleday, 1948.*

——————— Life in a putty knife factory. *buckram, 12mo. N.Y., Doubleday, Doran, 1945.*

——————— Lo, the former Egyptian. *buckram, 12mo. N.Y., Doubleday, 1947.*

——————— Lost in the horse latitudes. *buckram, 12mo. N.Y., Doubleday, 1945.*

——————— The pig in the barber shop. *buckram, 8vo. Bost., Little, Brown, 1958.*

——————— The rebel yell. *buckram, 8vo. N.Y., Doubleday, 1954.*

——————— Rhubarb. *buckram, 12mo. N.Y., Doubleday, 1946.*

——————— The world, the flesh and H. Allen Smith. *buckram, 8vo. Lond., Barker, 1954.*

——————— Write me a poem, baby. *buckram, 8vo. Bost., Little, Brown, 1956.*

SMITH, HENRY JUSTIN. Deadlines. *boards, 12mo. Chic., Covici-McGee, 1923.*

SMITH, HORATIO. Gaieties and gravities; a series of essays. *3v. half-calf, 12mo. Lond., Colburn, 1825.*

SMITH, J. THORNE. Biltmore Oswald; the diary of a hapless recruit. *boards, 12mo. N.Y., Stokes, 1918.*

SMITH, JAMES. Comic miscellanies in prose and verse. 2v.
buckram, 12mo. Lond.,
Colburn, 1841.

SMITH, JOHN. Irish diamonds, or,
a theory of Irish wit and
blunders. buckram, 16mo.
Lond., Chapman & Hall, 1847.

SMITH, JOHN HENRY. Bill Arp's
peace papers. buckram, 12mo.
N.Y., Carleton, 1873.

SMITH, JOHN THOMAS. The
streets of London; anecdotes
of their more celebrated
residents. buckram, 12mo.
Lond., Bentley, 1861. New ed.

SMITH, LLOYD E., ed. Jokes and
clever sayings about kissing.
paper, 32mo. Girard, Kan.,
Haldeman-Julius, n.d. (Little
Blue Books.)

SMITH, LOGAN PEARSALL. The
English language. half-
morocco, 16mo. Lond., Williams
& Norgate, 1912.

——————— More trivia. boards,
16mo. Lond., Constable, 1922.

——————— On reading Shake-
speare. buckram, 12mo. N.Y.,
Harcourt, Brace, 1933.

——————— Unforgotten years.
buckram, 8vo. Bost., Little,
Brown, 1939.

SMITH, PAMELA COLMAN. Chim-
chim; folk stories from
Jamaica. paper, 12mo. Lond.,
"The Green Sheaf" 1905.

SMITH, RICHARD GORDON.
Ancient tales and folklore of
Japan. buckram, 8vo. Lond.,
Black, 1908.

SMITH, ROBERT PAUL. And
another thing . . . buckram,
8vo. N.Y., Norton, 1959.

——————— How to do nothing
with nobody all alone by
yourself. buckram, 8vo. N.Y.,
Norton, 1958.

——————— "Where did you go?"
"Out." "What did you do?
"Nothing." boards, 8vo.
Kingswood, Surrey, World's
Work, 1958.

SMITH, ROBINSON. English quotations. buckram, 8vo. Lond.,
Routledge, n.d.

SMITH, SEBA. My thirty years out
of the Senate, by Major Jack
Downing, pseud. buckram,
12mo. N.Y., Oaksmith, 1859.

SMITH, STEPHE, ed. Romance
and humor of the rail. buckram,
12mo. N.Y., Carleton, 1873.

——————— Romance and humor
of the road; a book for railway
men and travelers. buckram,
8vo. Chic., Horton & Leonard,
1871.

SMITH, SYDNEY. Bon-mots of
Sydney Smith and R.Brinsley
Sheridan. buckram, 32mo.
Lond., Dent, 1893.

——————— Selected writings of
Sydney Smith. Edited and with
an introduction by W.H. Auden.
buckram, 8vo. N.Y., Farrar,
Straus and Cudahy, 1956.

——————— Wit and wisdom.
leather, 24mo. N.Y., Caldwell,
1901.

——————— The wit and wisdom
of the Rev. Sydney Smith. A
selection of the most memorable passages in his writings
and conversation. buckram,
12mo. Lond., Longman, Green,
Longman & Roberts, 1861.
3d.ed.

——————— Works. calf, 8vo.
Lond., Longman, Brown, Green
and Longmans, 1850. New ed.

SMITH, T. LEDYARD. "Sweet sin". *paper, 12mo. N.Y., Town topics, 1899.*

SMITH, T.V. Abraham Lincoln and the spiritual life. *buckram, 16mo. Bost., Beacon, 1951.*

SMITH, THORNE. Skin and bones. *buckram, 8vo. N.Y., Sun Dial, 1939.*

SMITHERS, LEONARD C., *ed.* The thousand and one quarters of an hour. (Tartarian tales.) *buckram, 8vo. Lond., Nichols, 1893.*

——————The transmigrations of the Mandarin Fum-hoam. (Chinese tales.) *buckram, 8vo. Lond., Nichols, 1894.*

SMOKER'S GARLAND. 3 parts, *paper, 12mo. Liverpool, At the Office of "Cope's Tobacco Plant" 1890.*

SMYTH, MCCAUL. There is a time to laugh. *boards, 8vo. Wien, Hammer, 1946.*

SMYTHE —————— Andy Capp spring tonic. *paper, 8vo. Lond., Daily Mirror, n.d.*

SNAPPY JOKES. *paper, 24mo. Baltimore, Ottenheimer, 1915.*

"SNAPPY SNAPS" Laughin tissue. *roll of toilet tissue, imprinted with gags and jokes, Asbury Park, N.J., Adams, n.d.*

SNEDDON, RICHARD. The golf stream. *buckram, 12mo. Phila., Dorrance, 1941.*

SNIDE LIGHTS ON TEXAS HISTORY. *buckram, 8vo. San Antonio, Naylor, 1959.*

SNIFT, DEAN, OF BRAZEN-NOSE. *see* HILL, BENSON EARLE.

SNODDY, GEORGE WADE. A barrel of jokes, by Hugo Mustlaff, *pseud, paper, 12mo. Chic., Laird & Lee, 1901.*

——————Drummer's yarns (piping hot) mixed by Hugo Mustlaff, *pseud, paper, 12mo. Chic., Laird & Lee, 1900.*

SOBEL, BERNARD. Broadway heartbeat. *buckram, 8vo. N.Y., Heritage, 1953.*

SOCIAL JESTER, or, Merry fellow's companion. A collection of jests, puns and oddities. *paper, 12mo. Lond., Hughes, n.d.*

SOCIO, CLIO CONVIVIUS, *pseud.* The post-chaise companion, and, Magazine of wit. *quarter-leather, 32mo. Baltimore, n.p., 1831.*

SOCIUS. *see* GOOD, RICHARD.

SOLDIER, the British army magazine. Soldier humour, 110 cartoons. *paper, 8vo. n.p. n.d.*

SOLOVYEV, LEONID. The beggar in the harem; impudent adventures in old Bukhara. *buckram, 8vo. N.Y., Harcourt, Brace, 1956.*

SOME AFTER DINNER SPEECHES. *buckram, 12mo. Detroit, Bookkeeper Pub.Co., 1904.*

SOME FUNNY THINGS; a careful selection of funny sketches, from the pens of such well known writers as The Detroit Free Press Man, the Burlington Hawkeye Man, the Danbury News man, the Norristown Herald man, and a number of other funny men. *paper, 16mo. N.Y., Harrison, 1880.*

SOME FUNNY THINGS SAID BY
CLEVER PEOPLE. *paper,*
*12mo. N.Y., Ogilvie, 1886.*

SOME SPICY STORIES FOR YOUR
BIRTHDAY. *birthday card.*

SOME STORIES BY FAMOUS
MEN. *buckram, 16mo. N.Y.,*
*Hearst, 1915.*

SOMETHING TO LAUGH AT.
*boards, 8vo. Lond., Ward &*
*Lock, n.d.*

SOPER, H.M., *ed.* Soper's dialect
readings. *paper, 12mo. Chic.,*
*Denison, n.d.*

_____ Soper's patriotic
speaker. *paper, 12mo. Chic.,*
*Denison, 1890.*

SOPHOCLES. Oedipus, king of
Thebes. Translated by Gilbert
Murray. *buckram, 12mo. N.Y.,*
*Oxford Univ. Press, 1911.*

SOTBENE, OSWOLD. The shrine
of Aesculapius. *half-calf, 8vo.*
*Chic., Saalfield, 1905.*

SOTHERN, EDWARD H. The
melancholy tale of "me".
*buckram, 8vo. N.Y., Scribner's,*
*1916.*

SOUSA, JOHN PHILIP, III. The
psychopathic dog. *buckram,*
*12mo. N.Y., Doubleday, 1946.*

SOUTHGATE, HENRY, *comp.*
Many thoughts of many minds.
*calf, 8vo. Lond., Griffin, 1875.*

_____ Noble thoughts
in noble language. *calf, 8vo.*
*Lond., Ward, Lock & Tyler, n.d.*

SOUTHWICK, ALBERT P. Wisps
of wit and wisdom, or
Knowledge in a nutshell.
*buckram, 16mo. N.Y., Lovell,*
*1892.*

SPADE, MARK *see* BALCHIN,
NIGEL.

SPALDING, J.L. Aphorisms and
reflections. *buckram, 16mo.*
*Chic., McClurg, 1907.*

SPARKS OF LAUGHTER. *7v.*
*buckram, 12mo. Newark, N.Y.,*
*Anderson, 1920-1927. 1st, 2d.*
*4th-8th, eds.*

SPEAKER'S GARLAND AND
LITERARY OUTPUT. *2v.*
*buckram, 12mo. Phila., Garrett,*
*1896.*

SPECTACULAR ANGLER'S
GUIDE BOOK. *pamphlet. N.Y.,*
*Hallmark, n.d.*

SPECTATOR, THE. *calf, 8vo.*
*Lond., Jònes, 1822.*

SPENCE, EDWARD F. Bar and
buskin; being memories of life,
law and the theatre. *buckram,*
*8vo. Lond., Matthews & Marrot,*
*1930.*

SPENCE, JOSEPH. Anecdotes,
observations, and characters of
books and men. Collected from
the conversation of Mr. Pope,
and other eminent persons of
his time. Now first published
from the original papers, with
notes, and a life of the author
by Samuel Weller Singer. *calf,*
*8vo. Lond., Carpenter, 1820.*

_____ Spence's "Anec-
dotes, observations, and
characters of books and men."
A selection, edited with an
introduction and notes by John
Underhill. *buckram, 16mo.*
*Lond., Scott, n.d.*

SPENCE, LEWIS. Myths and
legends of ancient Egypt. *buck-*
*ram, 8vo. Lond., Harrap, 1917.*

_____ Myths and legends
of Babylonia and Assyria.
*buckram, 8vo. Lond., Harrap,*
*1916.*

SPENCER, EDWARD. Cakes & ale; a dissertation on banquets. *buckram, 12mo. Lond., Paul, 1925. 6th ed.*

SPENCER, JOHN. Things new and old, or, A storehouse of illustrations. *half-calf, 4to. Lond., Dickinson, 1872.*

SPENDER, STEPHEN. Learning laughter. *buckram, 8vo. Lond., Weidenfeld & Nicholson, 1952.*

SPERONI, CHARLES. The Italian Wellerism to the end of the Seventeenth century. *paper, 4to. Berkeley, Calif., University of California Press, 1953.* (Folk-lore studies, 1.)

SPHINX, THE: or, Agreeable companion for a winter's evening. *paper, 24mo. Lond., Nowell & Burch, n.d.*

SPICE THAT'S NICE: a book of humor in good taste, offends no one, amuses everyone. *paper, 8vo. N.Y., Key, 1956.*

SPIELMANN, M.H. The history of "Punch". *half-leather, 4to. Lond., Cassell, 1895.*

SPILLER, JAMES. Spiller's jests, or, The humours and pleasant adventures of the comedians. *photostatic copy. Lond., Jackson, 1729.*

SPINNER'S CLUB. Psoti; a book of toasts, by Clotho. *buckram, 12mo. San Francisco, Paul Elder, 1904.*

SPIRIT OF BRITISH WIT: being a collection of anecdotes, bon-mots, epitaphs, &c. &c. selected from the best authorities; including many originals by well known characters. *quarter-calf, 16mo. Leith, Reid, 1813.*

SPIRIT OF ENGLISH WIT, THE: or, Post-chaise companion. *boards, 12mo. Lond., Tegg, 1812. 2d.ed.*

——————— *Same. 3d.ed. n.d.*

——————— *Same. 4th ed. n.d.*

SPIRIT OF THE PUBLIC JOURNALS FOR THE YEARS 1823, 1824, 1825, THE: *3v. half-calf, 8vo. Lond., Sherwood, Jones and co., 1825. v.1: 2d.ed.*

SPOFFORD, A.R. The library of wit and humor, prose and poetry, selected from the literature of all times and nations. *5v. buckram, 8vo. Phila., Gebbie, 1884.*

SPORTING STORIES AND JOKES. *paper, 16mo. Lond., Foulsham, n.d.*

SPORTS ILLUSTRATED. Choice cartoons from Sports Illustrated, selected by Charles Preston. *paper, 16mo. N.Y., Permabooks, 1957.*

——————— Hits, runs and social errors; choice cartoons selected by Charles Preston. *boards, 4to. N.Y., Random, 1956.*

SPRAGUE, WILLIAM C. Flashes of wit from bench and bar. *buckram, 12mo. Detroit, Collector Pub.Co., 1897. 2d.ed.*

SPROD ——————— Chips off a shoulder. *buckram, 8vo. Lond., Reinhardt, 1956.*

SPURGEON, CHARLES H. The salt cellars, being a collection of proverbs. *2v. in 1. paper, 8vo. N.Y., Funk & Wagnalls, n.d.*

——————— Wit and wisdom. *buckram, 16mo. Baltimore, Woodward, 1896.*

SPURR, HARRY A. A cockney in Arcadia. *buckram, 12mo. Lond., Allen, 1899.*

——————— Mel B. Spurr: his life, work, writings and recitations. *buckram, 12mo. Lond., Brown, n.d.*

SQUIER, EMMA LINDSAY. Children of the twilight; folk-tales of Indian tribes. *buckram, 16mo. N.Y., Cosmopolitan, 1926.*

SQUIRE, J.C., *ed.* Apes and parrots; an anthology of parodies. *buckram, 16mo. Cambridge, Washburn & Thomas, 1929.*

——————— The comic muse; an anthology of humorous verse. *buckram, 12mo. Lond., Collins, n.d.*

——————— Imaginary speeches and other parodies in prose and verse. *buckram, 12mo. Lond., Swift, 1912.*

——————— Weepings and wailings. *boards, 8vo. Lond., Cobden-Sanderson, 1935.*

STACKMAN, HOWARD. Bedside humour. *buckram, 12mo. Lond., Elek, 1953.*

——————— Complete bedside joke book. *buckram, 8vo. N.Y., Rainbow Books, 1953.*

STACY, JAMES M. Sage of Waha, the mountain gem humorist on land and on sea. *buckram, 16mo. Portland, Ore., White & Dunham, 1902.*

STAEHLIN VON STORCKSBURG, JAKOB. Original anecdotes of Peter the Great, collected from the conversation of several persons of distinction at Petersburgh and Moscow. *sheep, 8vo. Lond., Murray, 1788.*

STAFFORD, HURLBURT. The orange grove and other poems of the Jamaica peasantry. *boards, 12mo. Jamaica, West Indies, Saint James Press, 1927.*

STANFORD, J.K. Full moon at Sweatenham; a nightmare. *buckram, 8vo. Lond., Faber & Faber, 1953.*

STANLEY, ARTHUR. The bedside book; a miscellany for the quiet hours. *buckram, 12mo. Lond., Gollancz, 1944.*

STANLEY, DAVE, *ed.* A treasury of golf humor. *buckram, 8vo. N.Y., Lantern, 1949.*

——————— A treasury of sports humor. *buckram, 8vo. N.Y., Lantern, 1946.*

STANLEY, HENRY M. My dark companions and their strange stories. *buckram, 8vo. Sampson Low & Marston, 1893.*

STAPLETON, ALFRED. All about the merry tales of Gotham. *paper, 12mo. Nottingham, Pearson, 1900.*

STARK, WALLACE ROLAND. "Don't bust your stitches" a hilarious book of hospital cartoons and Starkrealisms. *paper, 8vo. Hollywood, Calif., S. & S. Pub.Co., 1953.*

STARKE, LESLIE. Starke and unashamed. *buckram, 8vo. Lond., Reinhardt, 1953.*

——————— Starke parade. *buckram, 4to. Lond., Reinhardt, 1958.*

——————— Starke staring. *paper, 12mo. Lond., Reinhardt, 1955.*

STARLING, EDMUND W. Starling of the White House. *buckram, 8vo. Chic., People's Book Club, 1946.*

STARR, LILIAN A. Tales of Tirah and Lesser Tibet. *buckram, 12mo. N.Y., Doran, 1923.*

STARS AND STRIPES. Out of line; a collection of cartoons from the Pacific Stars and Stripes. *boards, 8vo. Tokyo, Stars and Stripes, 1952.*

———————— *Same. Rutland, Vt., Tuttle, 1954. New and enl.ed.*

STEAMERS V. STAGES, or, Andrew and his spouse. Lond., Kidd, 1830. In the volume entitled ODDITIES, *q.v.*

STEARNS, FRANK B. The merchant on the road. *paper, 12mo. Chic., Monarch, 1906, 4th ed.*

STEARNS, J.N., *comp.* Temperance shot and shell. Eight hundred cartridges for the Temperance Army. *buckram, 12mo. N.Y., National Temperance Society, 1892.*

STEBBINS, HAL. The anatomy of laughter, a talk to the children of the Family at the Grove Turning Leaves on the occasion of the 54th Flight of the Stork, Sunday, September 1, 1957. *paper, 12mo. n.p., 1957.*

STEELE, ROBERT. The Russian garland; being Russian folk tales. *buckram, 8vo. Lond., Philpot, 1916.*

STEEP, THOMAS. Chinese fantastics. *buckram, 8vo. Lond., T.Werner Laurie, 1925.*

STEEVENS, G.W. Monologues of the dead. *buckram, 12mo. Lond., Methuen, 1896.*

STEFFENS, LINCOLN. The autobiography of Lincoln Steffens. *buckram, 8vo. N.Y., Literary Guild, 1931.*

STEIG, WILLIAM. The agony in the kindergarten. *buckram, 8vo. N.Y., Duell, Sloan & Pearce, 1950.*

———————— All embarrassed. *buckram, 8vo. N.Y., Duell, Sloan & Pearce, 1944.*

———————— The lonely ones. *boards, 12mo. N.Y., Duell, Sloan & Pearce, 1942.*

———————— Man about town. *buckram, 4to. N.Y., Long & Smith, 1932.*

———————— Persistent faces. *buckram, 12mo. N.Y., Duell, Sloan & Pearce, 1945.*

———————— The rejected lovers. *boards, 4to. N.Y., Knopf, 1951.*

———————— Small fry. *cloth, 24mo. N.Y., Duell, Sloan & Pearce, 1944.*

———————— till death do us part; some ballet notes on marriage. *buckram, 8vo. N.Y., Duell, Sloan & Pearce, 1947.*

STEIN, K.M. Die allerschonste lengevitch. *buckram, 8vo. N.Y., Crown, 1953.*

STEINBECK, JOHN. The short reign of Pippin IV. *buckram, 8vo. N.Y., Viking, 1957.*

STEINBERG, SAUL. All in line. *buckram, folio. N.Y., Duell, Sloan & Pearce, 1945.*

STEINER, PAUL. The bedside bachelor. *paper, 16mo. N.Y., Lion Books, 1957.*

———————— Bedtime laughs. *paper, 12mo. N.Y., Lion, 1956.*

———————— How to be offensive to practically everybody. *paper, 8vo. N.Y., Citadel, 1960.*

_____ Israel laughs; a collection of humor from the Jewish state. *buckram, 8vo. N.Y., Bloch, 1950.*

_____ Sex after six. *paper, 16mo. N.Y., Hillman, 1960.*

_____ Useless information. How to know more and more about less and less. *paper, 8vo. N.Y., Citadel, 1959.*

_____ Women & children first. *paper, 12mo. N.Y., Bantam Books, 1955.*

STEINHAUER, HARRY. German stories. Deutsche novellen. *paper, 12mo. N.Y., Bantam Books, 1961.*

STEINMANN, JEAN. Saint John the Baptist, and the desert tradition. *boards, 12mo. N.Y., Harper, 1957.*

STELLMANN, LOUIS J. Said the observer. *buckram, 12mo. San Francisco, Whitaker & Ray, 1903.*

STEPHENSON, J.D., *ed.* Laughing matter; an anthology of humorous passages. *buckram, 12mo. Lond., Arnold, 1960.*

STERN, BILL. Bill Stern's favorite baseball stories. *buckram, 8vo. N.Y., Blue Ribbon, 1949.*

STERN, DAVID. Francis goes to Washington. *buckram, 12mo. N.Y., Farrar, Straus, 1948.*

STERN, ELIZABETH GERTRUDE. Not all laughter, a mirror to our times, by Eleanor Morton, *pseud. buckram, 8vo. Phila., Winston, 1937.*

STERN, FRIEDEL. In short: Israel. *boards, 16mo. Israel, Hod, 1958.*

STERNE, LAURENCE. Sterne's witticisms; or, Yorick's convivial jester, containing a variety of pleasing bon mots, humorous and sentimental anecdotes &c. &c. *half-calf, 12mo. Lond., Milne, n.d.*

_____ Tristram Shandy. A sentimental journey through France and Italy. *buckram, 12mo. N.Y., Modern Library, 1941.*

_____ Works. v.1,2 and 4. *calf, 8vo. Lond., Johnson, Robinson, Becket, 1803.*

STEVENS, AGNES, *comp.* How men propose; the fateful question and its answer. *buckram, 12mo. Chic., McClurg, 1888.*

STEVENS, C.M. Uncle Jeremiah and his neighbors at the St. Louis exposition. *buckram, 12mo. Chic., Thompson & Thomas, 1904.*

_____ *Same, with title:* Uncle Jeremiah and his neighbors at the great exposition. *Chic., Stanton & Van Vliet, 1904.*

STEVENS, GEORGE ALEXANDER. A lecture on heads... To which is added an Essay on satire. *boards, 12mo. Lond., Kearsley, 1785.*

_____ *Same. Lond., Vernor, Hood & Sharpe, 1806.*

STEVENSON, ADLAI. Adlai's almanac; the wit and wisdom of Stevenson of Illinois. *paper, 8vo. N.Y., Schuman, 1952.*

STEVENSON, JOHN HALL. Crazy tales. *buckram, 8vo. Lond., Priv.Print.,1894.*

_____ Makarony fables; fables for grown gentlemen. *buckram, 8vo. Lond., Priv. Print., 1893.*

STEVENSON, ROBERT LOUIS.
Fables. *buckram, 4to. Lond., Longmans, Green, 1914.*

STEWART, ANDREW. Humorous readings, maistly Scotch. *paper, 12mo. Edinburgh, Menzies, n.d. 19th ed.*

STEWART, AUBREY. English epigrams and epitaphs. *buckram, 16mo. Lond., Chapman & Hall, 1897.*

STEWART, CALVIN. Uncle Josh Weathersby's "Punkin Centre" stories. *buckram, 8vo. Chic., Eckhardt & Stewart, 1903.*

————— Same. *Chic., Thompson and Thomas, 1903.*

————— Same. *Chic., Stanton & Van Vliet, 1903.*

STEWART, DONALD OGDEN. Father William; a comedy of father and son. *buckram, 8vo. N.Y., Harper, 1929.*

————— Aunt Polly's story of mankind. *buckram, 8vo. N.Y., Doran, 1923.*

————— Parody outline of history. *buckram, 8vo. Garden City, Garden City Pub.Co., 1921.*

STEWART, GEORGE. The Stewart simplified method of mimicry. *pamphlet. n.p., n.d.*

STEWART, GEORGE RIPPY. Donner Pass and those who crossed it. *paper, 8vo. San Francisco, California Historical Society, 1960.*

STEWART, JOHN. Collections and recollections. *calf, 12mo. Edinburgh, Oliver & Boyd, 1823.*

STIMPSON, GEORGE. A book about a thousand things. *buckram, 8vo. N.Y., Harper, 1946.*

STINSON, S. SCOTT. Whimlets. *buckram, 16mo. Phila., Coates, 1902.*

STIX, THOMAS L. Slightly overdrawn; a safe depository of cartoons about banks and bankers. *buckram, 12mo. N.Y., Simon & Schuster, 1950.*

————— Slightly underwritten; a collection of cartoons about insurance. *boards, 8vo. N.Y., Simon & Schuster, 1951.*

STODDARD, RICHARD HENRY, *ed.* Anecdote biographies of Thackeray and Dickens. *buckram, 16mo. N.Y., Scribner, Armstrong, 1875.*

————— Anecdote biography of Percy Bysshe Shelley. *buckram, 16mo. N.Y., Scribner, Armstrong, 1877.*

STOKER, BRAM. Personal reminiscences of Henry Irving. *buckram, 8vo. Lond., Heinemann, 1907.*

STONE, STUART B. Nonsensical U.S.A. *buckram, 12mo. N.Y., Caldwell, 1912.*

STONER, W. BURTON. Splinters. *paper, 8vo. Akron, O., Anderson Novelty Pub. Co., 1912.*

STONIER, G.W., *ed.* New Statesman competitions. *buckram, 8vo. Lond., Faber & Faber, 1956.*

STOOPNAGLE, COLONEL LEMUEL. *see* TAYLOR, F. CHASE.

STOP, LOOK AND LAUGH! *paper, 32mo. Girard, Kan., Haldeman-Julius, n.d. (Little Blue Books.)*

STORIES FOR THE SMOKING ROOM; humorous and grotesque. *buckram, 12mo. Lond., White, n.d.*

STORIES, JOKES AND RIDDLES; a gloom destroyer and a mental tonic. *paper, 12mo. Baltimore, Ottenheimer, n.d.*

STORIES OF HUMOR. *buckram,
12mo. N.Y., Doubleday, 1908.*

STORIES OF OLD CHINA. Translated by W.W. Yen. *boards,
8vo. Shanghai, New Art and
Literature Pub. Co., n.d.*

STORY OF A GANGSTER NAMED
MUGGSY. *pamphlet. San Diego,
Calif., Anti-prohibition Committee, California State
Council of Culinary Workers,
Bartenders and Hotel Service
Employees, n.d.*

STORY OF NELL GWYN AND
THE SAYINGS OF CHARLES
II, THE. Related and collected by Peter Cunningham.
*buckram, 12mo. Lond.,
Gibbins, 1903.*

STORY OF SIR WALTER
RALEIGH, THE, and A day in
a tobacco factory. *paper, 12mo.
Liverpool, At the Office of
"Cope's Tobacco Plant" 1893.*

STRACHAN, R. Humour in the
schoolroom. *buckram, 12mo.
Lond., Stockwell, n.d.*

STRACK, LILIAN HOLMES.
Winning monologues. *paper,
12mo. Chic., Denison, 1923.*

STRANGE STORIES FROM A
CHINESE STUDIO, translated
and annotated by Herbert A.
Giles. *buckram, 12mo.
Shanghai, Kelly & Walsh,
1936. 4th ed. rev.*

STRANGE SURPRISING
ADVENTURES OF THE
VENERABLE GOOROO
SIMPLE AND HIS FIVE
DISCIPLES, NOODLE,
DOODLE, WISEACRE,
ZANY AND TOOZLE.
Adorned with fifty illustrations drawn on wood by
Alfred Crowquill. *buckram,
12mo. Lond., Trubner, 1861.*

STRANGER, THE. *buckram,
24mo. Savannah, n.p., 1823.*

STRAPAROLA, GIOVANNI
FRANCESCO. The facetious
nights of Straparola, now first
translated into English by
W.G. Waters. *4v. buckram, 8vo.
Bost., Priv. Print. for Members
of the Burton Ethnological
Society, n.d.*

STRAUSBERG, JACK. "Now I'll
tell one" favorite yarns from
the world of sports. *paper, 4to.
N.Y., Wilcox & Follett, 1951.*

STREAMER, D. Perverted proverbs; a manual of immorals for
the many. *buckram, 12mo.
N.Y., Russell, 1903.*

STREET, JULIAN. The need of
change. *buckram, 12mo. N.Y.,
Lane, 1910.*

——————— Ship-bored. *buckram, 16mo. N.Y., Lane, 1912.*

——————— Sunbeams, inc.
*boards, 12mo. N.Y., Doubleday,
Page, 1920.*

STREETER, EDWARD. "As you
were, Bill!" *boards, 12mo.
N.Y., Stokes, 1920.*

——————— Daily except
Sundays. *buckram, 12mo. N.Y.,
Simon & Schuster, 1938.*

——————— Dere Mable — love
letters of a rookie. *boards,
12mo. N.Y., Stokes, 1918.*

——————— Mr. Hobbs' vacation.
*buckram, 8vo. N.Y., Harper,
1954.*

——————— "That's me all
over, Mable". *boards, 12mo.
N.Y., Stokes, 1919.*

STREETER, ROBERT A. *and*
HOEHN, R.G., *eds.* Are you a
genius? Second series. *buckram, 12mo. N.Y., Stokes, 1933.*

STRETTELL, ALMA. Lullabies of many lands, collected and rendered into English. *buckram, 8vo. Lond., Allen, 1896. 2d.ed.*

STRETZER, THOMAS. Merryland. *boards, 4to. N.Y., Robin Hood House, 1932.*

STRINDBERG, GERT. Norwegian fairy tales. *buckram, 12mo. Lond., Muller, 1959.*

STROUSE, FRANK EWING. Mule-osophy; the mule thinks and kicks. *buckram, 12mo. St. Louis, Blackwell Wielandy, 1940.*

STUART, JESSE. Taps for Private Tussie. *buckram, 8vo. N.Y., Dutton, 1943.*

STUART, RUTH MCENERY. George Washington Jones. *buckram, 12mo. Phila., Altemus,*

STYX _____ Holiday fun book. *paper, small 4to. Lond., Associated Newspapers, n.d.*

_____ Over 180 Styx cartoons. Bumper fun book. *paper, 8vo. England, n.p., n.d.*

_____ Styx Christmas fun book. *paper, 8vo. Lond., McCorquodale, n.d.*

SUFFLING, ERNEST R. Epitaphia; being a collection of 1300 British epitaphs. *buckram, 8vo. Lond., Gill, 1909.*

SULAIMAN AL KRETLI, *sheikh.* Legends of the Bait al-Kretliya put into English by R.G. "John" Gayer-Anderson. *boards, 4to. Ipswich, East Anglian Daily Times, 1951.*

SULLIVAN, FRANK. A rock in every snowball. *buckram, 8vo. Bost., Little, Brown, 1946.*

_____ Sullivan bites news; perverse news items. *boards, 8vo. Bost., Little, Brown, 1954.*

SULLY, JAMES. An essay on laughter; its forms, its causes, its development and its value. *buckram, 8vo. Lond., Longmans, Green, 1907.*

SUMMERS, FLORENCE ELIZABETH. Dere Bill: Mable's love letters to her rookie. *boards, 12mo. N.Y., Stokes, 1918.*

SUMMERS, MONTAGUE, *ed.* Covent Garden drollery. *quarter-buckram, 12mo. Lond., Fortune Press, 1927.*

SUNDAY AMERICAN'S JEST BOOK. *paper, 12mo. N.Y., American-Journal-Examiner, 1911.*

SURTEES, R.S. Jorrocks jaunts and jollities. *buckram, 12mo. N.Y., Appleton, 1903. New ed.*

SUTER, WILLIAM E. "Brother Bill and me" an original farce. *paper, 12mo. Bost., Baker, n.d.*

SUTRO, ALFRED. Freedom. *buckram, 16mo. N.Y., Brentano's, 1916.*

_____ A maker of men. *paper, 12mo. N.Y., French, 1902.*

_____ Mr. Steinmann's corner. *paper, 12mo. N.Y., French, 1902.*

_____ The two virtues. *buckram, 16mo. N.Y., Brentano's, 1916.*

SUTTAPITAKA. Buddhist birth stories (Jataka tales). Translated from Prof. V.Fuasboll's edition of the Pali text, by T.W.Rhys Davids. *buckram, 12mo. Lond., Routledge, n.d. New rev.ed.*

_____ Buddha's words of wisdom; the Buddhist's companion book .. compiled from the Pali canonical writings, by G.F. Allen. *buckram, 12mo. Lond., Allen & Unwin, 1959.*

_____ The essence of Buddhism, compiled by E.M. Bowden. *paper, 32mo. Girard, Kan., Haldeman-Julius, n.d. (Little Blue Books.)*

_____ The quest of enlightenment; a selection of the Buddhist scriptures, translated from the Sanskrit, by E.J. Thomas. *buckram, 12mo. Lond, Murray, 1950.*

_____ Sayings of Buddha. *boards, 12mo. Mt. Vernon, N.Y., Peter Pauper, 1957.*

_____ Some sayings of the Buddha according to the Pali canon. *buckram, 16mo. Lond., Oxford Univ. Press, 1945.*

SVENNINGSEN, PAUL F. Little nuisance. *boards, 12mo. Lond., Putnam, 1952.*

_____ Little stranger. *boards, 12mo. Lond., Putnam, 1951.*

_____ Snooze. *buckram, 12mo. Lond., Putnam, 1954.*

SWAIN, JOHN. The pleasures of the torture chamber. *buckram, 8vo. Lond., Douglas, 1931.*

SWANN, FRANCIS. Out of the frying pan; a comedy. *paper, 12mo. N.Y., French, 1941.*

SWEDENBORG, EMMANUEL. The living thoughts of Swedenborg, presented by Eric Sutton. *buckram, 12mo. Lond., Cassell, 1947. 2d.ed.*

SWEETNESS AND LIGHT; a collection of cartoons from the California Pelican, 1903-1943, and photographs of the University of California, 1868-1943. 40th anniversary, The California Pelican. 75th anniversary, University of California. *paper, 4to. Berkeley, Calif., Lederer, Street & Zeus, 1943.*

SWETCHINE, SOPHIE. The maxims of Madame Swetchine. *buckram, 16mo. Lond., Burns & Oates, 1908.*

SWIFT, JONATHAN. Gulliver's travels in Lilliput and Brobdingnag. *buckram, 8vo. Lond., Dakes, n.d.*

SWINBURNE, CHARLES ALFRED. Sacred and Shakespearian affinities. *half-calf, 8vo. Lond., Bickers, 1890.*

SWINGLEHURST, EDMUND. All abroad! *buckram, 8vo. Lond., Parrish, 1958.*

_____ French lovers are lovely. *buckram, 8vo. Lond., Arco, 1957.*

_____ How! the whole truth about the wild west. *buckram, 8vo. Lond., Parrish, 1957.*

SWITZER, MAURICE. Letters of a self-made failure. *buckram, 12mo. Bost., Small, Maynard, 1914.*

_____ Richard's poor almanack, containing the days weeks & months of the year 1909 ... by Richard Fuller Proones. *boards, 24mo. N.Y., Strauss, 1909.*

_____ Satire and song. *boards, 8vo. N.Y., Brunswick, 1917.*

SYKES, M'CREADY. Poe's run
and other poems. *buckram,
12mo. Princeton, Cannon, 1904.*

SYLVA: or, The wood; being a
collection of anecdotes, dissertations, characters,
apophthegms, original letters,
bons mots and other little
things. By a Society of the
Learned. *half-calf, 8vo. Lond.,
Payne, 1786.*

—————— *Same. 2d. ed. corrected and enlarged, 1788.*

SYMONDS, JOHN and HOFFNUNG,
GERARD. The isle of cats.
*buckram, 8vo. Lond., T.Werner
Laurie, 1955.*

SYNGE, JOHN MIDDLETON.
Riders to the sea. *In: Three
Irish plays, q.v.*

SYNTAX, DOCTOR, *pseud.* The
tour of Doctor Syntax in search
of the picturesque. *buckram,
12mo. Lond., Whittaker, 1878.*

—————— The three tours of
Doctor Syntax in search of 1.
The picturesque. 2. Of Conso-
lation. 3. Of a wife. *buckram,
12mo. Lond., Murray, 1869.*

SYVERSON, HENRY. Lovingly
yours; cartoons. *buckram, 4to.
N.Y., Dutton, 1957.*

SZYK, ARTHUR. The new order.
*buckram, 4to. N.Y., Putnam's,
1941.*

# T

T.B.S. *see* S., T.B.

TABLE TALK FROM BEN
JONSON TO LEIGH HUNT.
*buckram, 12mo. Lond., Dent,
1934.*

TABORI, PAUL. The art of folly.
*buckram, 8vo. Phila., Chilton,
1961.*

TABOUROT, ESTIENNE.
Bigarrures, or, The pleasant
and witlesse and simple
speeches of Lord Gaulard of
Burgundy. From a manuscript
circa 1660. *paper, 8vo.
Glasgow, Robert Anderson for
Private Circulation, 1884.*

TAFT, HARRY. All boloney.
*buckram, 12mo. Lond., Uni-
versal, n.d.*

TAGGART, *Sir* JAMES. Stories
told by Sir James Taggart.
*paper, 8vo. Dundee,
Valentine, 1927.*

TAGORE, RABINDRANATH. The
gardener. *buckram, 12mo.
N.Y., Macmillan, 1923.*

TALES AND LEGENDS OF
NATIONAL ORIGIN OR
WIDELY CURRENT IN
ENGLAND FROM EARLY
TIMES. *buckram, 8vo. Lond.,
Sonnenschein, 1892.*

TALES OF MIRTH, ORIGINAL
AND SELECT. Containing The
Irish Wedding; Fat widow of
Worthing; A bachelor's remi-
niscences; My aunt and her
diary; Letter from an
emigrant; Rip Van Winkle;
Sorrows of an undertaker; The
uncle's will; Will Wizard & Tom
Straddle; The Cit's journal;
Mr. and Mrs. Higgs; The
Headless Hessian, &c. & c.
Lond., Dean & Munday, 1833.

TALES OF THE GENII: or, The
delightful lessons of Horam,
the son of Asmir. Translated
from the Persian ... by Sir
Charles Morell. *2v. calf, 8vo.
Lond., Wilkie, 1764.*

—————— *Same. New edition.
Lond., Bohn 1857.*

TALK-TACTICS: or, How to win
with speech; a handbook for
public speakers. *simulated
leather, 12mo. Washington,
D.C. Williams, 1936.*

TALKING TURKEY. *paper, 8vo.
N.Y., Turkish Information
Office, n.d.*

TALMAGE, T. DE WITT. Around
the tea-table. *buckram, 8vo.
Phila., Cowperthwait, 1874.*

—————— Crumbs swept up.
*buckram, 12mo. N.Y., Street
& Smith, 1877.*

TALMUD. The essence of the
Talmud. *paper, 32mo. Girard,
Kan., Haldeman-Julius, n.d.
(Little Blue Books.)*

TALMUD OF JERUSALEM, THE.
*paper, 12mo. N.Y., Philosophi-
cal Library, 1956.*

TARRANT, FRED J. A Texan's
antic-dotes. *boards, 8vo.
San Antonio, Naylor, 1953.*

"TATLER, THE." Bubble and
squeak; a collection of
humorous satires. *buckram,
12mo. Lond., Sphere and
Tatler, n.d.*

TATLER, THE, *and* THE
GUARDIAN. Complete in 1
volume. *calf., 8vo. Lond.,
Wilson, 1814.*

TAYLOR, ARCHER. "Audi, vide,
tace" and The Three monkeys.
*leaflet, reprinted from
Fabula.*

_____ English riddles from oral tradition. *buckram, 8vo. Berkeley, Calif., Univ. of Calif. Press, 1951.*

_____ Proverbial comparisons and similes from California. *paper, 4to. Berkeley, Calif., Univ. of Calif. Press, 1954.* (Folklore studies, 3)

_____ The riddle. *In: Studies in Cheremis folklore, v.1. Bloomington, Indiana, Indiana Univ. Press, 1952.*

TAYLOR, BERT LESTON *and* GIBSON, W.C. The log of the Water Wagon; or, The cruise of the good ship "Lithia". *buckram, 24mo. Bost., Caldwell, 1905.*

_____ The so-called human race. *buckram, 16mo. N.Y., Knopf, 1922.*

_____ Extra dry; being further adventures of the Water Wagon. *buckram, 24mo. N.Y., Dillingham, 1906.*

TAYLOR, F. CHASE. My tale is twisted! by Colonel Stoopnagle, *pseud. buckram, 12mo. N.Y., Mill, 1946.*

_____ You wouldn't know me from Adam. *buckram, 8vo. N.Y., McGraw-Hill, 1944.*

TAYLOR, J. Antiquitates curiosae, the etymology of many remarkable old sayings, proverbs and singular customs explained. *calf., 16mo. Lond., Allman, 1818.* (Bound with: Joe Miller's Jest-book, with additions. Lond., Mason, 1836.)

TAYLOR, J.M. A telegram from Dad; a farce. *paper, 12mo. Bost., Baker, 1911.*

TAYLOR, JOHN. Iacke a Lent; his beginning and entertainment. *paper, 8vo. Reprinted from Collected works of John Taylor. Lond., Boler, 1630.*

_____ Mad fashions; odd fashions, all out of fashions, or, The emblems of these troubled times. *paper, small 4to. Lond., Priv.Print., 1871.* (Facsimile reprint of the rare original printed in London in 1642.)

TAYLOR, JOHN. Monsieur Tonson. *Lond., Marsh & Taylor, 1830.* (Bound in the volume entitled ODDITIES. q.v.)

TAYLOR, JOHN, *ed.* The pocket lacon; comprising nearly one thousand extracts from the best authors. *half-buckram, 24mo. Lond., Cox, 1837.*

TAYLOR, JOSEPH. A cabinet of curiosities or repository of entertainment. *half-calf, 24mo. Lond., Allen, 1807.*

_____ Eccentric and humorous letters of eminent men and women. *boards, 16mo. Lond., Burton & Smith, 1824.*

_____ The pocket volume of humour; being a choice collection of epigrams, repartees, and jeux d'esprits. *half-calf, 24mo. Lond., Hughes, 1807.*

TAYLOR, MARY TERRI. Snapshots from life. *paper, 16mo. Minneapolis, Denison, 1951.*

TAYLOR, RICHARD. The better Taylors. *boards, folio. N.Y., Random, 1944.*

_____ By the dawn's ugly light; a pictorial study of the hang-over. *boards, 4to. N.Y., Holt, 1953.*

TAYLOR, ROBERT LEWIS.
Center ring. *buckram, 8vo.
N.Y., Doubleday, 1956.*

——————— W.C.Fields; his
follies and fortunes. *buckram,
8vo. N.Y., Doubleday, 1949.*

——————— Winston Churchill;
an informal study of greatness.
*buckram, 12mo. N.Y.,
Doubleday, 1952.*

TAYLOR, ROSEMARY. Chicken
every Sunday; my life with
mother's boarders. *buckram,
8vo. N.Y., Whittlesey, 1943.*

TAYLOR, SUSETTE M., *comp.*
The humour of Spain. *buckram,
12mo. Lond., Scott, 1894.*

TAYLOR, T. Irish Jem's three
trials. *buckram, 16mo. N.Y.,
Hunt & Eaton, n.d.*

TAYLOR, TOM. To oblige Benson;
a comedietta. *paper, 12mo.
Chic., Dramatic Pub.Co., n,d.*

TAYLOR, WILFRED. Scot easy;
travels of a roads scholar.
*buckram, 8vo. Lond., Rein-
hardt, 1955.*

——————— Scot free; a book of
Gael warnings. *buckram, 8vo.
Lond., Reinhardt, 1954.*

TEASER, TOM. Muldoons' Base
Ball Club in Philadelphia.
*paper, 4to. N.Y., Wide Awake
Library, 1890.*

TEGG, WILLIAM, *comp.* Epitaphs
witty, grotesque, elegant &c.
&c. *buckram, 16mo. Lond.,
Author, 1875.*

——————— The last act; being
the funeral rites of nations and
individuals. *buckram, 16mo.
Lond., Author, 1878.*

——————— The mixture for low
spirits; being a compound of
witty sayings of many people,
in many climes, both humorous
and pathetic. *buckram, 16mo.
Lond., Author, 1875. 2d.ed.*

——————— Proverbs from far
and near. *buckram, 16mo.
Lond., Tegg, 1875.*

TEITELBAUM, ELSA, *comp. and
trans.* An anthology of Jewish
humor and maxims. *buckram,
8vo. N.Y., Pardes, 1945.*

TELEPHONE ALMANAC FOR
1958. *paper, 8vo. N.Y., Bell
Telephone Co., 1958.*

TELL-TALE, THE; an original
collection of moral and amusing
stories. *half-calf, 16mo. Lond.,
Harris, 1823.*

TELL-TALE, THE; or, Anecdotes
expressive of the characters of
persons eminent for rank,
learning, wit or humor. *2v.
calf., small 24mo. Lond.,
Baldwin, 1856.*

TELLEZ, GABRIEL. Three
husbands hoaxed, by Tirso de
Molina. *buckram, 8vo. Lond.,
Rodale, 1955.*

THACKERAY, WILLIAM MAKE-
PEACE. The book of snobs;
by one of themselves. *paper,
8vo. Girard, Kan., Haldeman-
Julius, 1945.*

——————— The English
humourists of the eighteenth
century. *boards, 12mo. Lond.,
Smith, Elder, 1853.*

——————— Extracts from the
writings of W.M. Thackeray.
*buckram, 16mo. Lond., Smith,
Elder, 1886.*

——————— Thackerayana, notes and anecdotes, illustrated by hundreds of sketches by William Makepeace Thackeray, depicting humorous incidents in his school life, and favorite scenes and characters in the books of his every-day reading. *buckram, 8vo. Lond., Chatto & Windus, 1901. New ed.*

——————— Wisdom of Thackeray. *paper, 32mo. Girard, Kan., Haldeman-Julius, n.d. (Little Blue Books.)*

THADDEUS, VICTOR. Voltaire; genius of mockery. *buckram, 8vo. N.Y., Brentano's, 1928.*

"THAT REMINDS ME" a new crop of drummer's yarns. *paper, 8vo. N.Y., Excelsior, 1894.*

THAT REMINDS ME: a collection of tales worth telling. *buckram, 16mo. Phila., Jacobs, 1905.*

THAT REMINDS ME AGAIN; a second collection of tales worth telling. *buckram, 16mo. Phila., Jacobs, 1912.*

THAYER, CHARLES. Hands across the caviar. *buckram, 8vo. Lond., Joseph, 1953.*

THEALL, GEORGE MCCALL. Kaffir folk-lore. *buckram, 12mo. Lond., Sonnenschein, Le Bas & Lowrey, 1886. 2d.ed.*

THEOPHRASTUS. The characters of Theophrastus. Translated from the Greek by Eustace Budgell. *calf., 16mo. Lond., Tonson, 1718. 3d.ed.*

"THERE IS A TIME TO LAUGH" Dedication of room for housing of Schmulowitz jest book collection at the San Francisco Public Library, November 30, 1950. Remarks by John Cuddy, Nat Schmulowitz and Paul Speegle. *paper, 8vo. San Francisco, Priv.Print., 1951.*

THESAURUS AENIGMATICUS; or, A collection of the most ingenious and diverting aenigmas or riddles; the whole being design'd for universal entertainment; and in particular for the exercise of the f fancies of the curious. To which is prefixed a discourse of aenigmas in general. *half-calf., 12mo. Lond., Wilford, 1725-1726.*

THIEBAULT, DIEUDONNE. Original anecdotes of Frederic the Second, king of Prussia and of his family, his court, his ministers, his academis, and his literary friends. *2v. calf., 8vo. Lond., Johnson, 1805.*

THINGS I SHOULDN'T TELL. By the author of "Uncensored recollections." *buckram, 8vo. Lond., Nash & Grayson, 1924. 4th ed.*

THINKER'S DIGEST, THE. The spoiled priest, and other satires. *buckram, 8vo. N.Y., Kenedy, 1950.*

THIS WEEK. What's funny about that? *buckram, 4to. N.Y., Dutton, 1954.*

THOMAS, BENJAMIN P. Abraham Lincoln, a biography. *buckram, 8vo. N.Y., Knopf, 1952.*

THOMAS, BRANDON. The Lancashire sailor. *paper, 12mo. N.Y., French, 1898.*

THOMAS, CHARLES J. Half wit
and humor. paper, 12mo.
San Antonio, Naylor, 1961.

THOMAS, F.W. Extra turns.
buckram, 12mo. Lond.,
Putnam's, 1923.

THOMAS, FREDERICK. Humorous
and other poetic pictures;
legends and stories of Devon.
buckram, 12mo. Lond., Kent,
n.d.

THOMAS, JOHN. Dry martini; a
gentleman turns to love. buckram, 12mo. N.Y., Doran, 1926.

THOMAS, JOHN B. Selected
stories, quotations and aphorisms; a compilation of
humorous stories, quotations
and aphorisms. buckram, 8vo.
Kingsport, Tenn. Southern
Publishers, 1936.

THOMAS, LOWELL. Fan mail.
buckram, 12mo. N.Y., Dodge,
1935.

—————————— Tall stories; the
rise and triumph of the great
American whopper. buckram,
8vo. N.Y., Blue Ribbon, 1931.

THOMAS, ROBERT B. The (old)
farmer's almanack, calculated
on a new and improved plan for
the year of our lord 1961.
paper, 12mo. Dublin, N.H.,
Yankee, inc., 1961.

THOMAS, S. EVELYN, comp.
Cricket fanfare, and Laughs
around the wicket. paper,
12mo. Lond., Author, n.d.

—————————— Football fanfare.
paper, 12mo. Lond., Author,
n.d.

—————————— Good Humour, nos.
1,3,4,5. paper, 12mo. Lond.,
Author, n.d.

—————————— Happy Xmas to you.
paper, 12mo. Lond., Doran,
Hart, n.d.

—————————— Happy birthday to
you. paper, 12mo. Lond.,
Author, n.d.

—————————— Laugh and live
longer. paper, 12mo. Lond.,
Author, n.d.

—————————— Laugh while you
travel, Nos. 1 and 2. paper,
12mo. Lond., Author, n.d.

—————————— Laugh your blues
away. paper, 12mo. Lond.,
Author, n.d.

—————————— Laughs along the
line. Nos. 1 and 2. paper,
12mo. Lond., Author, n.d.

—————————— Laughs around the
heartstrings. paper, 12mo.
Lond., Author, n.d.

—————————— Laughs around the
home. paper, 12mo. Lond.,
Author, n.d.

—————————— Laughs around the
land. paper, 12mo. Lond.,
Author, n.d.

—————————— Laughs at the local.
paper, 12mo. Lond., Author,
n.d.

—————————— Laughs for light
moments. paper, 12mo. Lond.,
Author, n.d.

—————————— Laughs for your
holiday. paper, 12mo. Lond.,
Author, n.d.

—————————— Laughs for your
leisure. Nos. 1 and 2. paper,
12mo. Lond., Author, n.d.

—————————— Laughs in short
pants. No. 2. paper, 12mo.
Lond., Author, n.d.

—————————— Laughs of mystery
and crime. paper, 12mo. Lond.,
Author, n.d.

_____ Laughs on the home front. *paper, 12mo. Lond., Author, n.d.*

_____ Laughs with all the lovers. *paper, 12mo. Lond., Author, n.d.*

_____ Laughs with the forces. No. 3. *paper, 12mo. Lond., Author, n.d.*

_____ Laughs with the busy bodies. *paper, 12mo. Lond., Author, n.d.*

_____ Laughs with the law. *paper, 12mo. Lond., Author, n.d.*

_____ Laughs with the lovelies. Nos. 2 and 3. *paper, 12mo. Lond., Author, n.d.*

_____ Laughs with the medicos. *paper, 12mo. Lond., Author, n.d.*

_____ Laughs with the navy, No. 2. *paper, 12mo. Lond., Author, n.d.*

_____ Laughs with the R.A.F. *paper, 12mo. Lond., Author, n.d.*

_____ Laughs with the workers. *paper, 12mo. Lond., Author, n.d.*

_____ Laughs with the Yanks. *paper, 12mo. Lond., Author, n.d.*

_____ Laughs with the youngsters. *paper, 12mo. Lond., Author, n.d.*

_____ Laughter ahoy. *paper, 12mo. Lond., Author, n.d.*

_____ Laughter awheel. *paper, 12mo. Lond., Author, n.d.*

_____ Laughter on holiday. *paper, 12mo. Lond., Author, n.d.*

_____ Many happy returns! *paper, 12mo. Lond., Author, n.d.*

_____ Married mirth. Nos. 1 and 3. *paper, 12mo. Lond., Author, n.d.*

_____ More laughs with the forces. *paper, 12mo. Lond., Author, n.d.*

THOMPSON, D.D. Abraham Lincoln, the first American. *buckram, 12mo. Cincinnati, Cranston & Curts, 1894.*

THOMPSON, HARRY. The cynic's dictionary. *boards, 24mo. Phila., Altemus, 1905.*

THOMPSON, JAMES WESTFALL. Ancient libraries. *buckram, 12mo. Berkeley, Calif., Univ. of Calif. Press, 1940.*

THOMPSON, KAY. Eloise. *boards, 4to. N.Y., Simon & Schuster, 1955.*

_____ Eloise at Christmastime. *boards, 4to. N.Y., Random, 1958.*

_____ Eloise in Moscow. *boards, 4to. N.Y., Simon & Schuster, 1959.*

_____ Eloise in Paris. *boards, 4to. N.Y., Simon & Schuster, 1957.*

THOMPSON, M. AGNES. The hay in my hair; blithesome essays. *buckram, 12mo. Dallas, Van Nort, 1944.*

THOMPSON, MORTON. How to be a civilian. *buckram, 12mo. N.Y., Doubleday, 1946.*

———————— Joe, the wounded tennis player. *buckram, 16mo. N.Y., Doubleday, Doran, 1945.*

THOMPSON, W.H. Sixty minutes with Winston Churchill. *boards, 12mo. Lond., Johnson, 1953.*

THOMPSON, W.T. Major Jones's courtship. *buckram, 12mo. Phila., Peterson, 1879. Rev. and en1.*

THOMSON, A.A. Written humour. *buckram, 12mo. Lond., Black, 1936.*

THOMSON, BASIL. Queer people. *buckram, 8vo. Lond., Hodder & Stoughton, 1922.*

THOMSON, CHAS. W. Scottish school humour. *buckram, 12mo. Glasgow, Gibson, 1936.*

THOMSON, H. UNDERWOOD *and* YEOMAN, ANTONIA. Anton's amusement arcade. *buckram, 12mo. Lond., Collins, 1947.*

THOMSON, JAMES. The seasons. *calf., 24mo. Lond., Wenman, 1790.*

THOMSON, JAMES. Selections from original contributions to Cope's Tobacco Plant. *paper, 12mo. Liverpool, At the Office of "Cope's Tobacco Plant" 1889.*

THOMSON, MORTIMER. Doesticks' letters, and what he says. By Q.K. Philander Doesticks, *pseud. buckram, 12mo. Phila., Peterson, 1855.*

———————— Doesticks, what he says. *buckram, 12mo. N.Y., Livermore & Rudd, 1856.*

———————— Nothing to say: a slight slap at mobocratic snobbery. *buckram, 12mo. N.Y., Rudd & Carleton, 1853.*

———————— Plu-ri-bus-tah; a song that's by no author. *buckram, 12mo. N.Y., Livermore & Rudd, 1856.*

———————— The witches of New York, a faithful revelation and exposition of the doings of all the principal astrologists, sorceresses, prophets, clairvoyants, witches, planet readers and other votaries of the black art in the City of New York. *buckram, 12mo. Phila., Peterson, 1858.*

THOMSON, S.J. The silent India, being Tales and sketches of the masses. *buckram, 8vo. Edinburgh, Blackwood, 1913.*

THOREAU, DAVID HENRY. Epigrams of Thoreau. *paper, 32mo. Girard, Kan., Haldeman-Julius, n.d. (Little Blue Books.)*

THORNTON, WILLIS. Fable, fact and history. *buckram, 8vo. Phila., Chilton, 1957.*

THORPE, BENJAMIN. Yule-tide stories; a collection of Scandinavian and North German popular tales and traditions. *half-calf, 12mo. Lond., Bohn, 1853.*

THOUSAND AND ONE RIDDLES, A, WITH A FEW THROWN IN. *paper, 12mo. Phila., McKay, n.d.*

———————— Same. *Lond., Routledge, n.d.*

THREE IRISH PLAYS. The land of heart's desire, by W.B. Yeats.-Twisting of the rope, by Douglas Hyde.-Riders to the sea, by J.M. Synge. *paper, 16mo. Bost., International ·Pocket Library, n.d.*

THROUGH NEW HAMPSIRE ON A
BUCKBOARD. *paper, 12mo.
Chic., Donohue, 1901.*

THROWER, J. THURSTON. Wit
and wisdom; a medley of life
and laughter. *boards, 12mo.
Lond., Burke, 1946.*

THURBER, JAMES. Alarms and
diversions. *buckram, 8vo.
Lond., Hamilton, 1957.*

———————— The beast in me,
and other animals. *buckram,
8vo. N.Y., Harcourt, Brace,
1948.*

———————— Fables for our time,
and Famous poems illus-
trated. *buckram, 4to. Blue
Ribbon, 1943.*

———————— Further fables for
our time. *buckram, 8vo. Lond.,
Hamilton, 1956.*

———————— Is sex necessary?
or, Why you feel the way you
do. *boards, 8vo. N.Y., Harper,
1929.*

———————— Men, women and
dogs. *buckram, 4to. N.Y.,
Harcourt, Brace, 1943.*

———————— The owl in the
attic, and other perplexities.
*buckram, 8vo. N.Y., Harper,
1931.*

———————— The seal in the
bedroom, and other predica-
ments. *boards, 4to. N.Y.,
Harper, 1932.*

———————— The Thurber
carnival. *buckram, 8vo. N.Y.,
Harper, 1945.*

———————— Thurber country; a
new collection of pieces. *buckram, 8vo. N.Y., Simon &
Schuster, 1953.*

———————— A Thurber garland.
*boards, 32mo. Lond., Hamilton,
1955.*

———————— The wonderful O.
*buckram, 8vo. Lond., Hamilton,
1958.*

———————— The years with
Ross. *buckram, 8vo. Bost.,
Little, Brown, 1958.*

TICHENOR, H.M., *ed.* Irish fairy
tales. *paper, 32mo. Girard,
Kan., Haldeman-Julius, n.d.
(Little Blue Books.)*

———————— Irish folk songs
and tales. *paper, 32mo. Girard,
Kan., Haldeman-Julius, n.d.
(Little Blue Books.)*

TICKELL, JERRARD, *ed.*
Gentlewomen aim to please.
*buckram, 12mo. Lond.,
Routledge, 1938.*

TIDWELL, JAMES N. A treasury
of American folk humor. *buckram, 8vo. N.Y., Crown, 1956.*

TIFFANY, ESTHER B. Anita's
trail; a comedy. *paper, 12mo.
Bost., Baker, 1889.*

TILLIE THE TOILER AND THE
MASQUERADING DUCHESS.
Based on the famous newspaper
strip by Russ Westover.
*buckram, 8vo. Racine, Wis.,
Whitman, 1943.*

TIMBS, JOHN. Anecdote lives of
wits and humourists. *2v. buckram, 12mo. Lond., Bentley,
1872.*

———————— Book of modern
legal anecdotes; the bar, bench
and woolsack. *buckram, 16mo.
Lond., Routledge, n.d.*

———————— A century of anecdote from 1760 to 1860. *buckram, 12mo. Lond., Warne, n.d.*

———————— Clubs and club life
in London, with anecdotes of
its famous coffee-houses,
hostelries, and taverns, from
the seventeenth century to the
present time. *buckram, 12mo.
Lond., Chatto & Windus, 1882.*

_____ Doctors and
patients; or, Anecdotes of the
medical world and curiosities
of medicine. *boards, 12mo.
Lond., Bentley, 1876. New
and rev.ed.*

_____ Notabilia; or,
Curious and amusing facts about
many things, explained and
illustrated. *buckram, 12mo.
Lond., Griffith & Farran, 1872.*

TIMES, THE, *London.* Fourth
leaders from the Times, 1950.
*buckram, 8vo. Lond., Times,*

TIMES BROADSHEETS, THE.
*buckram, 12mo. Lond., Hodder
& Stoughton, 1948.*

TIN TRUMPET, THE: or, Heads
and tails for the wise and
waggish. *buckram, 8vo. N.Y.,
Appleton, 1859. New American
ed.*

TIOMKIN, DIMITRI *and*
BURANELLI, PROSPER.
Please don't hate me.
*buckram, 8vo. Garden City,
Doubleday, 1959.*

TIRSO DE MOLINA *see*
TELLEZ, GABRIEL.

TIT-BITS OF AMERICAN
HUMOUR. *buckram, 24mo. N.Y.,
White & Allen, n.d.*

TIT-BITS OF ENGLISH HUMOUR.
*boards, 24mo. N.Y., White &
Allen, n.d.*

TIT-BITS OF IRISH HUMOUR.
*leather, 24mo. N.Y., White &
Allen, n.d.*

TIT-BITS OF SCOTTISH
HUMOUR. *buckram, 24mo.
N.Y., White & Allen, n.d.*

TITTLE, WALTER. The first
Nantucket tea party. *buckram,
8vo. N.Y., Doubleday, Page,
1907.*

TOASTMASTER'S GUIDE: or,
President's companion. being a
new collection of toasts and
sentiments. *buckram, 16mo.
Lond., Hughes, n.d.*

TOASTS AND AFTER-DINNER
STORIES. *buckram, 16mo.
Chic., Brewer, Barse, 1907.*

TOASTS AND SPEECHES: how
to prepare and deliver them.
*paper, 12mo. Baltimore,
Ottenheimer, n.d.*

TOASTS, RAKES AND CITS,
being portraits of maids, men
& matrons fashionable and
unfashionable 'about town' in
the eighteenth century.
*boards, 12mo. Lond., Allan,
1920.*

TOBACCO TALK AND
SMOKERS' GOSSIP. *buckram,
16mo. Lond., Redway, 1896.*

TOLD OUT OF COURT: personal
experiences of members of the
Chicago Bench and Bar. *buckram, 12mo. Chic., Smyth, 1909.*

TOLSTOI, LEV NIKHAILOVICH.
Lyof Tolstoy, an anthology.
*buckram, 8vo. Bost., Beacon,
1958.*

TOMFOOL, *pseud.* Tomfooleries.
*paper, 12mo. Lond., Daily
Herald, 1920.*

TON OF FUN, A, or, 2,000 square
laughs. *paper, 12mo. N.Y.,
Ogilvie, n.d.*

TONG, HOLLINGTON K. Japanese
sense of humour. *paper, 12mo.
n.p., n.d.*

TOOGOOD, HECTOR B. The
outline of everything. *buckram,
8vo. Bost., Little, Brown,
1923.*

TORGA, MIGUEL. Farrusco the
blackbird, and other stories
from the Portuguese. *buckram,
4to. N.Y., Arts, 1951.*

TORSON, GLADYS. How to be a hero to your secretary. *buckram, 8vo. N.Y., Greenberg, 1941.*

TORTORA, VINCENT R. The Amish folk of Pennsylvania Dutch country. *paper, 4to. Lancaster, Pa., Photoarts, 1958.*

TOUCHSTONE————— Legends of the leading cases; or, Law and laughter. *half-calf, 12mo. Lond., Reeves & Turner, 1881.*

TOVEY, CHARLES. Wit, wisdom and morals, distilled from Bacchus. *buckram, 12mo. Lond., Whittaker, 1878.*

TOWN AND COUNTRY JESTER: or, Wit's best companion, being mostly an original collection of jests, puns, bons mots, repartees, quibbles, bulls, &c. *boards, 12mo. Lond., Roson, 1745.*

TOWN AND COUNTRY JOKER; being a choice selection of jests and witticisms. *paper, 16mo. Lond., Harrild, n.d.*

TOWN AND COUNTRY NUT-CRACKER; or, Jack Sharp's compleat jests. Being a choice collection of funny jokes, merry stories, droll adventures, &c. &c. *paper, 12mo. Lond., Printed for the Author and sold by Sabine, 1740.*

TOWN TATTLER AND CHEERING SECTION. *pages cut from newspapers and mounted in folder.*

TOWNE, CHARLES WAYLAND. The altogether new foolish dictionary; perpetrated for the second time, after ten years of national peace and good will, by Gideon Wurdz, *pseud. buckram, 12mo. Bost., Luce, 1914.*

————— Eediotic etiquette, by Gideon Wurdz, *pseud. buckram, 16mo. N.Y., Stokes, 1906.*

————— The foolish dictionary, executed by Gideon Wurdz, *pseud. buckram, 12mo. Bost., Luce. 1904.*

————— Foolish etiquette, written by O.B. Hayve, *pseud. buckram, 12mo. Bost., Luce, 1906.*

————— Foolish finance, compiled by Gideon Wurdz., *pseud. buckram, 12mo. Bost., Luce, 1905.*

TOWNLEY, JAMES. Biblical anecdotes, illustrative of the history of the sacred scriptures and of the early translations of them into various languages. *calf, 16mo. Lond., Blanshard, 1813.*

TOWNSEND, CHARLES. Finnigan's fortune; an original comic Irish play. *paper, 12mo. Chic., Dramatic Pub.Co., 1893.*

————— Shaun Aroon; an original Irish drama. *paper, 12mo. Chic., Dramatic Pub. Co., 1893.*

TOWNSEND, E.D. Anecdotes of the Civil War in the United States. *buckram, 12mo. N.Y., Appleton, 1884.*

TOWNSEND, EDWARD W. Chimmie Fadden explains; Major Max expounds. *buckram, 12mo. N.Y., United States Book Co., 1895.*

————— Chimmie Fadden; Major Max, and other stories. *buckram, 12mo. N.Y., Lovell, Coryell, 1895.*

TOZER, BASIL. Life's lighter side. *buckram, 8vo. Lond., Grayson & Grayson, 1952.*

TRADITIONARY ANECDOTES
OF SHAKESPEARE, collected
in Warwickshire in the year
MDCXCIII. *paper, 8vo. Lond.,
Rodd, 1838.*

TRAGICAL COMEDY OR COMI-
CAL TRAGEDY OF PUNCH
AND JUDY. *boards, 12mo.
Lond., Allen & Unwin, 1928.*

TRAILL, PETER. No farthing
richer. *buckram, 8vo. Lond.,
Jenkins, n.d.*

TRAVERS, BEN. Vale of laughter;
an autobiography. *buckram,
8vo. Lond., Bles, 1957.*

TREANOR, TOM. One damn thing
after another. *buckram, 8vo.
N.Y., Doubleday, Doran, 1944.*

TREASURES FROM THE PIER-
PONT MORGAN LIBRARY.
50th anniversary exhibition,
1957. *paper, 4to. N.Y.,
Thistle Press, 1957.*

TREASURY OF WIT. *buckram,
24mo. Lond., Allman, 1837.*

TREDEGAR, GODFREY
CHARLES MORGAN, *1st
viscount.* Wit and wisdom. *half-
buckram, 8vo. Lond., Western
Mail, 1911.*

TREE, HERBERT BEERBOHM.
Six and eightpence. *paper,
12mo. N.Y., French, 1900.*

_____ Thoughts and after-
thoughts. *buckram, 8vo. N.Y.,
Funk & Wagnalls, 1913.*

TREFFRY, ELFORD EVELEIGH,
*comp.* Stokes' cyclopedia of
familiar quotations. *buckram,
8vo. Lond., Chambers, 1907.*

TREFUSIS, VIOLET. Don't look
around. *buckram, 12mo. Lond.,
Hutchinson, 1952.*

TREMAYNE, SYDNEY. Tatlings.
*boards,12mo. Lond., Lane,
1922.*

TRENCH, RICHARD CHENEVIX.
On the lessons in proverbs.
*buckram, 12mo. N.Y.,
Redfield, 1855.*

TRESMONTANT, CLAUDE. Saint
Paul and the mystery of Christ.
*boards, 12mo. N.Y., Harper,
1957.*

TRESSLER, IRVING D. Horse and
buggy daze. *buckram, 12mo.
N.Y., Howell, Soskin, 1940.*

_____ How to lose friends
and alienate people. *buckram,
12mo. N.Y., Stackpole, 1937.*

TREVELYN, G.M. The seven
years of William IV; a reign
cartooned by John Doyle. *buckram, 8vo. Lond., Avalon Press,
1952.*

TREWIN, J.C. The night has been
unruly. *buckram, 8vo. Lond.,
Hale, 1957.*

TRISTRAM, WILLIAM OUTRAM.
Comedies from a country-side.
*buckram, 12mo. Lond., Ward &
Downey, 1887. New ed.*

TROLLEY JOKES. *paper, 24mo.
Baltimore, Ottenheimer, 1913.*

TROMBONERS, or, Musical anecdotage. *buckram, 12mo. N.Y.,
Knopf, 1932.*

TROWBRIDGE, ROBERTSON.
Forty-eight years. Anecdotes
and other oddments collected
from original sources 1884-
1932. *buckram, 8vo. N.Y.,
Priv. Print., 1937.*

TRUE, THE MAN'S MAGAZINE.
Best cartoons. *paper, 16mo.
N.Y., Fawcett, 1955.*

_____ Cartoon laffs. The
pick of the best by Clyde
Carley. *paper, 12mo. N.Y.,
Gold Medal books, 1952.*
_____ Gags for guys; a
bonus booklet of belly boffs.
*pamphlet. N.Y., True, n.d.*

TRUMBULL, ROBERT and CHONG, JERRY. Sol Pluvius' Hawaiian commoniques. paper, 12mo. Honolulu, Armitage, 1942.

TRUTHS ILLUSTRATED BY GREAT AUTHORS, a dictionary of nearly four thousand aids to reflection, quotations of maxims, metaphors, counsels, cautions, aphorisms, proverbs, &c. &c. buckram, 16mo. Lond., Lockwood, 1867.

TSK! — TSK! The sick-a-bed book. buckram, 12mo. Indianapolis, Droke, 1936.

TUCKER, SOPHIE. Some of these days; the autobiography of Sophie Tucker. buckram, 8vo. N.Y., Doubleday, Doran, 1945.

TUER, ANDREW W. Old London street cries, and the cries of today. boards, 24mo. Lond., Field & Tuer, 1885.

_____ Quads for authors, editors and devils. vellum, 24mo. Lond., Field & Tuer, Simpkin, Hamilton, 1884.

TUFT-HUNTERS AND TOADIES. paper, 24mo. Lond., Kent, 1849?

TUITE, HUGH. Iris plays better bridge. buckram, 16mo. Lond., Bles, 1928.

TUPPER, MARTIN FARQUHAR. Proverbial philosophy. buckram, 12mo. Lond., Moxon, n.d.

_____ Same. Lond., Hatchard, 1849. 9th ed.

_____ Rides and referies of the late Mr. Aesop Smith. Edited by Peter Query. buckram, 12mo. Lond., Hurst & Blackett, 1858.

TURNER, E.S. A history of courting. paper, 12mo. Lond., Pan, 1954.

TURNER, JUSTIN G. Betsy Ross. pamphlet. (Reprinted from Manuscripts, Fall, 1956.)

_____ A note on Solomon Nunes Carvalho, and his portrait of Abraham Lincoln. paper, 8vo. Los Angeles, Plantin, 1960.

TURNER, SHARON. The sacred history of the world, attempted to be philosophically considered in a series of letters to a son. 3v. calf, 8vo. Lond., Longman, Orme, Brown, Green and Longmans, 1840.

TUT! TUT! The birthday book. buckram, 12mo. Indianapolis, Droke, 1936.

TUTTLE, CHARLES E. Japan unbuttoned. paper, 12mo. Rutland, Vt., Tuttle, 1954.

TWAIN, MARK, pseud. The American claimant. buckram, 12mo. Lond., Chatto & Windus, 1892.

_____ Amusing answers to correspondents, and other pieces. paper, 32mo. Girard, Kan., Haldeman-Julius, n.d. (Little Blue Books.)

_____ Extracts from Adam's diary. buckram, 8vo. N.Y., Harper, 1904.

_____ Humorous fables. paper, 32mo. Girard, Kan., Haldeman-Julius, n.d. (Little Blue Books.)

_____ Humorous sketches. paper, 32mo. Girard, Kan., Haldeman-Julius, n.d. (Little Blue Books.)

_____ The innocents abroad, a book of travel in pursuit of pleasure. half-morocco, 16mo. Lond., John Camden Hotten, n.d.

_____ Journalism in Tennessee. paper, 32mo. Girard, Kan., Haldeman-Julius, n.d. (Little Blue Books.)

_____ The jumping frog. buckram, 8vo. N.Y., Harper, 1903.

_____ The letters of Quintus Curtius Snodgrass. buckram, 8vo. Dallas, Southern Methodist Univ. Press, 1946.

_____ Mark Twain at your fingertips. Edited by Caroline Thomas Harmsberger. buckram, 8vo. N.Y., Cloud, 1948.

_____ Mark Twain in India. Edited by B.J. Vaswani. paper, 12mo. Karachi, "Sind Observer," n.d. 3d.ed.

_____ Mark Twain in three moods. boards, 8vo. San Marino, Huntington Library, 1948.

_____ Mark Twain to Mrs. Fairbanks. Edited by Dixon Wecter. buckram, 8vo. San Marino, Huntington Library, 1949.

_____ Mark Twain's burlesque autobiography. buckram, 8vo. Larchmont, Peter Pauper, 1930.

_____ Mark Twain's Date, 1601. Conversation as it was by the social fireside in the time of the Tudors. buckram, 8vo. Chic., Mark Twain Society, 1939.

_____ Mark Twain's library of humor. buckram, 8vo. N.Y., Webster, 1888.

_____ Same. Lond., Chatto & Windus, 1899.

_____ Mark Twain's note-book. buckram, 12mo. N.Y., Harper, 1935.

_____ Mark Twain's speeches. buckram, 12mo. N.Y., Harper, 1923.

_____ My dear bro; a letter from Samuel Clemens to his brother Orion. paper, 4to. Berkeley, Calif., The Berkeley Albion, 1961.

_____ San Francisco Virginia City Territorial Enter-prise correspondent. Selections from his letters to the Terri-torial Enterprise, 1865-1866. boards, 4to. San Francisco, Allen Press for the Book Club of California, 1957.

_____ 1601. paper, 12mo. N.Y., Earth Pub.Co., 1955.

_____ What is man? buck-ram, 12mo. Lond., Watts, 1910.

TWELFTH U.S. INFANTRY, 1789-1919. Its story - by its men. buckram, 8vo. N.Y., Knicker-bocker, 1919.

XXTH CENTURY GRIDIRON PRIMER. buckram, 12mo. Washington, D.C., Roberts, 1901.

TWO HUNDRED AFTER DINNER
STORIES, as told by many
American humorists. *paper*,
*12mo. N.Y., Ogilvie, 1902.*

275 SELECT AUTOGRAPH
ALBUM MOTTOES. broadside
in plastic case. On verso: The
joker's budget; 200 riddles
and conundrums.

TWO OF THE JONESES. The
hand-book of joking; or, What
to say, do and avoid. *buckram*,
*24mo. Lond., Grant &
Griffith, 1847.*

2,000 JOKES AND JESTS. Wit,
humor and anecdote. *buckram*,
*12mo. Chic., Rhodes &
McClure, 1895.*

TYNDALL, HENRY M. Illus-
trative anecdotes for preachers,
Sunday school teachers and
the family circle. *buckram*, *4to.
N.Y., Author, 1925.*

TYRRELL-GILL, FRANCES,
*comp. and ed.* Wit and wisdom
of modern women writers. *buckram, 12mo. Lond., Richards,
1902.*

# U

UBERT, CHARLES H. Old Doc Minstrels gags. *loose leaf in binder. N.Y., Author, various dates from 1923 to 1930.*

ULLMAN, JOE. What's the odds? Funny, true and clean stories of the turf. *buckram, 12mo. N.Y., Metropolitan, 1903.*

ULLYETT, ROY. Sports cartoons by Roy Ullyett of the Daily Express. Fifth series. *paper, 12mo. Lond., Daily Express, n.d.*

U.S. WORKS PROJECTS ADMINIS-TRATION. *Tennessee writers' project.* God bless the devil! Liars' bench tales. *buckram, 8vo. Chapel Hill, N.C. North Carolina Univ.Press, 1940.*

UNIVERSAL JESTER, THE, or, The constellation of living geniuses, containing all good things, lively stories, sprightly repartees, smart observations, ingenious flights, and brilliant ebullitions of all the wits, male and female of the present age. *calf., 16mo. Lond., Robinson & Roberts, 1770.*

——————— *Same. Dublin, Ingham, 1770.*

UNTERMEYER, LOUIS and SHIKES, RALPH E., eds. The best humor annual. *buckram, 8vo. N.Y., Holt, 1952.*

——————— Best humor of 1949-1950. *buckram, 8vo. N.Y., Holt, 1950.*

UNTERMEYER, LOUIS. The lowest form of wit. *boards, folio. N.Y., For the Friends of the Author, Christmas, 1947.*

——————— A treasury of laughter, consisting of humor-ous stories, poems, essays, tall tales, jokes, boners, epigrams, memorable quips, and devastating crushers. *buckram, 8vo. N.Y., Simon & Schuster, 1946.* (Contains ALS to Nat Schmulowitz.)

——————— A treasury of ribaldy. *buckram, 8vo. Lond., Elek, 1957.*

UPANISHADS. The spirit of the Upanishads. *buckram, 12mo. Chic., Yogi Pub. Co., 1907.*

UPSON, WILLIAM HAZLITT. Earthworms through the ages. *buckram, 8vo. N.Y., Rinehart, 1947.*

——————— "Hello, Mr. Henderson". *buckram, 8vo. N.Y., Rinehart, 1949.*

URQUHART, FRED., ed. and comp. Men at war. *buckram, 8vo. Lond., Arco, 1957.*

——————— W.S.C., a cartoon biography. *buckram, 4to. Lond., Cassell, 1955.*

# V

VAGABOND VENDER, ZEP HAWKER, THE. *buckram, 12mo. Ontario, Dominion Bureau of Circulation, 1929. 2d.ed.*

VAJRACHCHEDIKA. Buddhist wisdom books, containing the Diamond Sutra and the Heart Sutra. Translated and explained by Edward Conze. *buckram, 8vo. Lond., Allen & Unwin, 1958.*

VALENTINE, W. Comic metamorphoses. *buckram, 12mo. N.Y., Dick & Fitzgerald, 1855.*

VAN, BILLY B. "Snap out of it!" *buckram, 16mo. Bost., Stratford, 1933.*

VAN AMBURGH, F.D. Just common sense. *buckram, 12mo. N.Y., Silent Partner, 1920.*

—————— The silent partner scrapbook. *buckram, 12mo. N.Y., Silent Partner, 1915.*

VAN BUITENEN, J.A.B., *tr.* Tales of ancient India. *paper, 12mo. N.Y., Bantam Books, 1961.*

VAN-TI, THE CHINESE MAGISTRATE, and other tales of other countries. *buckram, 16mo. Lond., Parker, 1844.*

VAN ZELLER, HUBERT. Cracks in the cloister, by Brother Choleric, *pseud. buckram, 8vo. N.Y., Sheed & Ward, 1954.*

—————— Last cracks in legendary cloisters, by Brother Choleric, *pseud. buckram, 8vo. Lond., Sheed & Ward, 1960.*

VARE, DANIELE. Laughing diplomat. *buckram, 8vo. Lond., Murray, 1938.*

VASEY, GEORGE. Philosophy of laughter and smiling. *buckram, 12mo. Lond., Burns, 1877. 2d.ed.*

VASWANI, B.J., *comp.* Laugh, soldiers, laugh! A collection of funny stories, jokes, howlers and other laughs for the war-weary soldiers and civilians of the United Nations. *paper, 16mo. Karachi, Modern Pub. Soc., n.d.*

VAUGHN, STANTON. Limerick lyrics. *buckram, 12mo. N.Y., Sully & Kleinteich, 1906.*

—————— 700 limerick lyrics; a collection of choice humorous versifications. *buckram, 12mo. N.Y., Carey-Stafford, 1906.*

VEDDER, ELIHU. The digressions of V., written for his own fun and that of his friends. *buckram, 8vo. Lond., Constable, 1910.*

VEILLER, BAYARD. The fun I've had. *buckram, 8vo. N.Y., Reynal & Hitchcock, 1941.*

VERNEY, JOHN. Verney abroad. *boards, 8vo. Lond., Collins, 1954.*

VERTES, MARCEL. It's all mental. *boards, 8vo. N.Y., Tudor, 1952.*

VICES IN VIRTUES AND OTHER VAGARIES. *buckram, 8vo. Lond., Longmans, Green, 1914.*

VICKY, pseud. *see* WEISS, VICTOR.

VICTOR, METTA VICTORIA. The blunders of a bashful man, by the author of "A bad boy's diary". *paper, 8vo. Lond., Ward, Lock, n.d.*

—————— Miss Slimmens' boarding house, and Miss Slimmens' window. *paper, 8vo. Lond., Routledge, n.d.*

VICTOR, ORVILLE J., *ed.*
Incidents and anecdotes of the
war. *buckram, 8vo. N.Y.,
Torrey, 1862.*

VICTORY JOKE BOOK. 4 books
in 1v. *paper, 8vo. Brisbane,
Australia, Bevan, 1945.*

"VIGILANS" Chamber of horrors;
a glossary of official jargon,
both English and American.
*buckram, 8vo. N.Y., British
Book Centre, 1952.*

VINCENZ, STANISLAW. On the
high uplands; sagas, songs,
tales and legends of the
Carpathians. *buckram, 8vo.
Lond., Hutchinson, 1955.*

VLADISLAV, JAN. Persian
fables. *boards, 8vo. Lond.,
Spring Books, n.d.*

VOICE OF THE SILENCE, THE,
and other chosen fragments
from the Book of the Golden
Precepts. *morocco, 24mo. N.Y.,
Theosophical Pub.Co., 1889.*

VOLTAIRE, FRANCOIS MARIE
AROUET *de.* Alphabet of wit.
*boards, 12mo. Mount Vernon,
N.Y., Peter Pauper, n.d.*

—————————Wit and wisdom.
*paper, 32mo. Girard, Kan.,
Haldeman-Julius, n.d. (Little
Blue Books.)*

VON RHAU, HENRY. The hell of
loneliness. *boards, 8vo. N.Y.,
Inwood, 1929.*

VOORHIES, FRANK C. The
knocker. *buckram, 12mo. Bost.,
Mutual, 1903.*

—————————Reflections of
Bridget McNulty. *paper, 12mo.
Bost., Dickerman, 1903.*

VOWLES, REGINALD. Logical
nonsense. *buckram, 8vo. N.Y.,
Vantage, 1954.*

VOYNICH, E.L., *ed.* The humour
of Russia. *buckram, 12mo. Lond
Lond., Scott, 1895.*

VULLIAMY, C.E., *ed.* The
anatomy of satire. *buckram,
8vo. Lond., Joseph, 1950.*

—————————An exhibition of
satirical writing. *buckram,
8vo. Lond., Joseph, 1950.*

—————————Little Arthur's
guide to humbug. *buckram,
8vo. Lond., Joseph, 1960.*

—————————Prodwit's guide to
writing. *buckram, 8vo. Lond.,
Joseph, 1949.*

VYNNE, HAROLD R. Tales from
Town Topics. *paper, 12mo.
N.Y., Town Topics, 1897.*

# W

W., F.G. *see* WELCH, F.G.

W.,P. Reflections of a bachelor. *buckram, 12mo. N.Y., Ogilvie, 1897.*

W., W., *gent. see* WRIGHT, W.

WAG, THE; or, Life of humour, and the soul of whim. *calf, 16mo. Dublin, Hoey, 1773.*

WAGNER, HENRY R. Sixty years of book collecting. *boards, 8vo. San Francisco, Ward Ritchie for the Roxburghe Club, 1952.*

WAGNER, W. Asgard and the gods; tales and traditions of our Northern ancestors told for boys and girls. *buckram, 8vo. Lond., Sonnenschein & Allen, 1880.*

WAGONTONGUE, ALEX, *pseud.* A book of modern jokes. *paper, 16mo. Fort Sill, Okla., n.p., 1933.*

WAKELEY, J.B. The American temperance cyclopedia of history, biography, anecdote and illustration. *buckram, 8vo. N.Y., National Temperance Society, 1875.*

———————— Anecdotes of the Wesleys. *buckram, 12mo. Toronto, Briggs, n.d.*

WALE, WILLIAM. What great men have said of great men. *buckram, 8vo. Lond., Sonnenschein, 1902.*

WALEY, ARTHUR. Ballads and stories from Tun-Huang. *buckram, 8vo. Lond., Allen & Unwin, 1960.*

WALKER, DANTON. Spooks deluxe; some excursions into the supernatural. *buckram, 4to. N.Y., Watts, 1956.*

WALKER, JOAN. Pardon my parka. *buckram, 8vo. Lond., Barker, 1954.*

WALKER, MORT *and* BROWNE, DIK. Trixie. *paper, 16mo. N.Y., Avon, 1960.*

WALKER, STANLEY. City editor. *buckram, 8vo. N.Y., Stokes, 1934.*

———————— Home to Texas. *buckram, 8vo. N.Y., Harper, 1956.*

———————— Mrs. Astor's horse. *boards, 8vo. Lond., Lane, 1936.*

———————— Same. *N.Y., Stokes, 1936.*

WALL, JOSEPH FRAZIER. Henry Watterson; reconstructed rebel. *buckram, 8vo. N.Y., Oxford Univ.Press, 1956.*

WALL STREET JOURNAL. "Care for a merger?" Cartoons from the Wall Street Journal. *buckram, 4to. N.Y., Dutton, 1958.*

———————— "Hey, can't you forget busine$$? Wall Street Journal cartoons, edited by Charles Preston. *buckram, 4to. N.Y., Dutton, 1953.*

WALLACE, IRVING. The fabulous originals. *buckram, 8vo. Lond., Longmans, Green, 1956.*

WALLACE, MIKE. Mike Wallace asks; highlights from 46 controversial interviews. *paper, folio. N.Y., Simon & Schuster, 1958.*

WALLACH, IRA. How to pick a wedlock; a pocket guide to bliss. *buckram, 12mo. N.Y., McGraw-Hill, 1956.*

———————— "Farmer, have you a daughter fair?" *buckram, 8vo. N.Y., Vanguard, 1929.*

WALLBRIDGE, ARTHUR. Bizarre fables. *buckram, 12mo. Lond., Orr, 1843. 2d.ed.*

WALLETT, F.W. The public life of W.F. Wallett, the queen's jester; an autobiography. *paper, 12mo. Lond., Pemrose, 1870.*

WALLIS, CHARLES L. Stories on stone; a book of American epitaphs. *quarter-buckram, 4to. N.Y., Oxford Univ.Press, 1954.*

WALLIS, KEENE, *tr. and ed.* French cartoons of the twentieth century. *paper, small 8vo. N.Y., International Humor Pub., 1945.*

WALSH, JAMES J. Laughter and health. *buckram, 12mo. N.Y., Appleton, 1928.*

WANG, CHI-CHEN. Traditional Chinese tales. *buckram, 8vo. N.Y., Columbia Univ., 1944.*

WANG, I-TING. Fifty popular Chinese folk-stories with Chinese notes. *paper, 12mo. Shanghai, World Book Co., 1929.*

WARD, ANNA L., *ed.* A dictionary of quotations from English and American poets. *buckram, 8vo. N.Y., Crowell, 1883.*

WARD, ARCH. In the wake of the news. *paper, 8vo. Chic., Chicago Tribune, 1939.*

WARD, ARTEMAS, *pseud. see* BROWNE, CHARLES FARRAR.

WARD, CHRISTOPHER. Gentleman into Goose. *half-calf, 12mo. Lond., T.Werner Laurie, 1924.*

WARD, JOSEPH O. My grandpa went west. *buckram, 8vo. Caldwell, Caxton, 1956.*

WARNER, SYLVIA TOWNSEND. Lolly Willowes, or, The loving huntsman. *buckram, 12mo. Lond., Chatto & Windus, 1951.*

WARREN, LOUIS A. Address before Joint Convention of the Michigan Legislature, Feb. 8, 1956. *Leaflet.*

WARTER, JOHN WOOD. "Wise saws and modern instances" or Pithy sentences in many languages. Scraps for the rail. *buckram, 16mo. Lond., Saunders, Otley, 1861.*

WARWICK, EDEN, *pseud. see* JABET, GEORGE.

WASHBURN'S ENTERTAINER: a choice collection of up-to-date toasts. *paper, 16mo. N.Y., Washburn, 1904.*

WASHINGTON, BOOKER T. Booker T. Washington at Tuskegee Institute. *paper, 24mo. (Personal Growth Leaflets.)*

WASHINGTON, GEORGE. Letters and recollections of George Washington, being letters to Tobias Lear and others, between 1790 and 1799. *buckram, 8vo. N.Y., Doubleday, Doran, 1932.*

—————— Maxims of Washington: political, social, moral and religious. *boards, 8vo. Mount Vernon, Mount Vernon Ladies' Association, 1942.*

WASKA, FRANK E. Frïed knot-holes from Yuba dam. *paper, 12mo. Chic., Thompson, 1909.*

WASON, SANDYS. Magenta minutes; nonsense verses. *buckram, 12mo. Lond., Goschen, 1913.*

WATERS, ROBERT. Flashes of wit and humor, or, A brief study of the best things of the brightest minds. *buckram, 12mo. N.Y., Werner, 1900.*

—————— William Shakespeare as portrayed by himself. *buckram, 12mo. N.Y., Worthington, 1888.*

**WATKINS, ERNEST.** According to plan. *buckram, 12mo. Lond., Architectural Press, 1945.*

**WATKINS, J.B.** Anecdotes & tales for young people, moral & entertaining. *2v. v.1: half-calf, v.2: paper, 24mo. Lond., Kelly, n.d.*

**WATKINS, SYLVESTRE C.** The pleasures of smoking as expressed by those poets, wits and tellers of tales who have drawn their inspiration from the fragrant weed. *buckram, 8vo. N.Y., Schuman, 1948.*

**WATSON, HELEN ORR.** Shavetail Sam, U.S. Army mule. *buckram, 12mo. Bost., Houghton, Mifflin, 1944.*

**WATSON, JAMES.** Paramythia; or, Mental pastimes, being original anecdotes, historical, descriptive, humorous and witty; collected chiefly during a long residence at the court of Russia. *half-calf, 12mo. Lond., Lawler & Quick, 1821.*

**WATSON, ROWLAND.** Merry gentleman; a Bacchanalian scrapbook. *buckram, 4to. Lond., T.Werner Laurie, 1951.*

**WATT, FRANCIS.** The book of Edinburgh anecdote. *boards, 8vo. Lond., Foulis, 1913.*

**WATT, JOHN,** *ed.* Radio variety. *buckram, 8vo. Lond., Dent, 1939.*

**WATTS, ISAAC.** The improvement of the mind. *leather, 32mo. N.Y., Waugh & Mason, for the M.E.Church, 1832.*

**WATTS, W.** An Irish engagement; a farce. *paper, 12mo. N.Y., Roorbach, n.d.*

**WATWOOD, WARREN.** Lady Loverley's chatter. *paper, 8vo. N.Y., Macaulay, 1960.*

**WE JAPANESE:** being descriptions of many of the customs, manners, ceremonies, etc. *buckram, 8vo. Yokahama, Fujiya Hotel, 1949.*

**WEAVER, DANNY.** Mother Goose-step, and other nertzery rhymes. *boards, 8vo. Los Angeles, Lymanhouse, 1940.*

**WEBB, C.H.** Liffith Lank; or, Lunacy. *buckram, 12mo. N.Y., Carleton, 1876.*

**WEBB, PAUL.** The mountain boys. *paper, 12mo. N.Y., Signet, 1957.*

**WEBB, T.** A new select collection of epitaphs. *2v. sheep, 12mo. Lond., Bladon, 1775.*

**WEBER, JOSEPH M.** *and* **FIELDS, LEW.** Weber and Field's funny sayings. *paper, 12mo. N.Y., Ogilvie, n.d.*

**WEBSTER, DORIS** *and* **HOPKINS, MARY.** I've got your number! a book of self-analysis. *buckram, 12mo. Lond., Hamilton, 1930.*

**WEBSTER, HAROLD TUCKER.** The best of H.T.Webster; a memorial collection. *buckram, 4to. N.Y., Simon & Schuster, 1953.*

_____ How to torture your husband. *buckram, 8vo. Phila., Winston, 1948.*

_____ How to torture your wife. *buckram, 8vo. Phila., Winston, 1948.*

_____ To hell with fishing; or, How to tell fish from fishermen. *buckram, 4to. N.Y., Appleton-Century, 1945.*

_____ Who dealt this mess? *boards, 8vo. N.Y., Doubleday, 1948.*

WEBSTER, JEAN. Dear enemy.
*buckram, 12mo. N.Y., Grosset &
Dunlap, 1915.*

WEBSTER, WENTWORTH. Basque
legends; collected chiefly in
the Labour. *buckram, 8vo.
Lond., Griffith & Farran, 1879.
2d.ed.*

WECHSBERG, JOSEPH. Looking
for a bluebird. *paper, 12mo.
Lond., Penguin, •1948.*

———————— Sweet and sour.
*buckram, 12mo. Lond., Joseph,
1949.*

WEEGEE. *see* FELLER, ARTHUR.

WEEKEND MAIL. Weekend Mail
book of jokes. *paper, 12mo.
Lond., Associated Newspapers,
n.d.*

WEHMAN BROS' BOOK OF FUNNY
RHYMES; a choice collection
of merry jingles, jokes and
verses. *paper, 32mo. N.Y.,
Wehman, 1907.*

WEHMAN BROS' COON JOKES,
Number 1. *paper, 24mo. N.Y.,
Wehman, 1907.*

WEHMAN BROS' TRAMP JOKES,
Number 1. *paper, 32mo. N.Y.,
Wehman, 1908.*

WEHMAN BROS' WITTY SAYINGS:
a choice collection of humorous,
snappy and crisp jokes.
*paper, 32mo. N.Y., Wehman,
1907.*

WEHMAN'S BUDGET OF JOKES.
*paper, 12mo. N.Y., Wehman,
n.d.*

WEHMAN'S BLACK JOKES FOR
"BLUE DEVILS". *paper,
12mo. N.Y., Wehman, 1887.*

WEHMAN'S COMIC SPEECHES
AND RECITATIONS. *paper,
12mo. N.Y., Wehman, 1891.*

WEHMAN'S SELECTION OF
POPULAR DIALOGUES,
Number 3. *paper, 12mo. N.Y.,
Wehman, n.d.*

WEIGALL, ARTHUR. Laura was
my camel. *buckram, 8vo. N.Y.,
Stokes, 1933.*

WEISFELD, ISRAEL H. The
pulpit treasury of wit and
humor. *buckram, 12mo. N.Y.,
Prentice-Hall, 1950.*

WEISS, HARRY B. American
chapbooks, 1822-1842.
*paper, 4to. N.Y., New York
Public Library, 1945.*

———————— Oeneirocritica
Americana; the story of
American dream books.
*paper, 4to. N.Y., New York
Public Library, 1944.*

WEISS, JOHN. Wit, humor and
Shakespeare; twelve essays.
*buckram, 12mo. Bost.,
Roberts, 1876.*

WEISS, VICTOR. A selection of
Evening Standard cartoons
by Vicky. *paper, wide 12mo.
Lond., Evening Standard,
1960.*

———————— Vicky's world.
*paper, 8vo. Lond., Secker &
Warburg, 1959.*

WELCH, F.G. That convention;
or, Five days a politician.
*buckram, 12mo. N.Y., Author,
1872.*

WELCH, JOE. Diamonds; up-to-
the-minute Hebrew jokes.
*paper, 12mo. Chic., Donohue,
1910.*

WELCH, PHILIP H. Said in fun.
*boards, 8vo. N.Y., Scribner's,
1889.*

WELCKER, ADAIR. For people who laugh; showing how, through woman, came laughter into the world. *buckram, 8vo. San Francisco, Author, 1904.*

WELLS, CAROLYN, *ed.* The book of humorous verse. *buckram, 8vo. N.Y., Doran, 1920.*

——————— *Same. Revised and amplified. N.Y., Garden City Pub.Co., 1947.*

——————— The jingle book. *buckram, 12mo. N.Y., Macmillan, 1906.*

——————— A nonsense anthology. *buckram, 12mo. N.Y., Scribner's, 1903.*

——————— An outline of humor. *buckram, 8vo. N,Y., Putnam's, 1923.*

——————— A satire anthology. *buckram, 12mo. N.Y., Scribner's, 1905.*

——————— Such nonsense! an anthology. *buckram, 8vo. N.Y., Doran, 1918.*

——————— A whimsey anthology. *buckram, 12mo. N.Y., Scribner's, 1906.*

——————— The world's best humor. *buckram, 8vo. N.Y., Boni, 1923.*

WELLS, ERNEST. "Chestnuts". *buckram, 12mo. Lond., Sands, 1900. 3d.ed.*

WELSFORD, ENID. The fool; his social and literary history. *buckram, 8vo. N.Y., Farrar & Rinehart, 1937?*

WELSH, CHARLES. Irish toasts, by Shane Na Gael, *pseud. boards, 24mo. N.Y., Caldwell, 1908.*

WEMBRIDGE, ELEANOR ROWLAND. Life among the lowbrows. *buckram, 12mo. Bost., Houghton, Mifflin, 1931.*

WENDT, HERBERT. In search of Adam. *buckram, 8vo. Bost., Houghton, Mifflin, 1956.*

WENZEL, BILL, *ed.* The Flimsey report, or, Sex is here to stay. *paper, 4to. N.Y., Farrell, 1953.*

WERNER, A., *comp. and tr.* The humour of Holland. *paper, 12mo. Lond., Scott, 1894.*

——————— The humour of Italy. *buckram, 12mo. Lond., Scott, 1893.*

WERNER, ALICE. Myths and legends of the Bantu. *buckram, 8vo. Lond., Harrap, 1933.*

WERNER, E.T.C. Myths and legends of China. *buckram, 8vo. Lond., Harrap, 1922.*

WEST, MAE. Goodness had nothing to do with it. *buckram, 8vo. Englewood Cliffs, N.J., Prentice-Hall, 1959.*

WEST, REBECCA *and* LOW, DAVID. The modern "Rake's Progress". *boards, 4to. Lond., Hutchinson, 1934.*

WEST, WILLIAM. Tavern anecdotes and reminiscences of the origin of signs, clubs, coffee-houses, streets, city companies, wards, &c. By One of the Old School. *boards, 16mo. Lond., Cole, 1825.*

WESTERMARCK, EDWARD. Wit and wisdom in Morocco; a study of native proverbs. *buckram, 8vo. Lond., Routledge, 1930.*

WESTMINSTER HALL; or, Professional relics and anecdotes of the bar, bench and woolsack. *3v. calf, 16mo. Lond., Knight & Lacey, 1825.*

WESTON, S. Persian recreations, or, New tales. *half-calf, 12mo. Lond., Rousseau, 1812.*

WESTWOOD, H.R. Modern caricaturists. *buckram, 4to. Lond., Dickson, 1932.*

WETTACH, ADRIEN. Grock, life's a lark, by Grock. *buckram, 8vo. Lond., Heinemann, 1931.*

WEWITZER, RALPH. The school for wits; containing a choice collection of bons-mots, anecdotes, epigrams &c. &c. *calf., 16mo. Lond., Sherwood, Neely & Jones, 1815.*

WHAT COMES DOWN OUR CREEK. *pamphlet. n.p. 1935.*

WHAT FAMOUS MEN HAVE SAID; excerpts from stenographic records of the State Law Reporting company. *paper, 4to. N.Y., State Law Reporting Co., 1935.*

WHAT GREAT MEN HAVE SAID ABOUT WOMEN. *paper, 32mo. Girard, Kan., Haldeman-Julius, n.d. (Little Blue Books.)*

WHAT GREAT WOMEN HAVE SAID ABOUT MEN. *paper, 32mo. Girard, Kan., Haldeman-Julius, n.d. (Little Blue Books.)*

WHEATLEY, HENRY B. Literary blunders. *half-buckram, 12mo. Lond., Stock, 1893.*

WHEELER, ELMER. Tested telegrams and how to write them. *boards, 12mo. N.Y., Prentice-Hall, 1941.*

WHEELER, GERALD CAMDEN. Mono-alu folklore. (Bougainville Strait, Western Solomon Islands.) *buckram, 8vo. Lond., Routledge, 1926.*

WHEELER, H.H., *comp.* Up-to-date minstrel jokes. *paper, 12mo. Bost., Up-to-date Pub. Co., n.d.*

WHEELER, ROGER. A puzzle a day; an almanac of puzzles. *buckram, 12mo. N.Y., Fitzgerald, 1936.*

WHIBLEY, CHARLES, *ed.* In cap and gown; three centuries of Cambridge wit. *buckram, 12mo. Lond., Kegan Paul, Trench, 1889.*

WHICHCOTE, BENJAMIN. Moral and religious aphorisms. *buckram, 8vo. Lond., Mathews & Marrot, 1930.*

WHIPPLE, WAYNE. The story life of Lincoln; a biography composed of five hundred true stories ... *buckram, 8vo. Phila., Winston, 1908.*

WHISTLER, JAMES MCNEIL. The gentle art of making enemies. *paper, 32mo. Girard, Kan., Haldeman-Julius, n.d. (Little Blue Books.)*

——————— The humor of Whistler. *paper, 32mo. Girard, Kan., Haldeman-Julius, n.d. (Little Blue Books.)*

——————— "Ten o'clock". *paper, 32mo. Girard, Kan., Haldeman-Julius, n.d. (Little Blue Books.)*

WHISTLER, REX. !OH! *boards, 4to. Lond., Bodley Head, 1946.*

WHISTON, DON. Cowhand. *buckram, 12mo. Monrovia, Calif., Donlen, 1946.*

WHITCHER, FRANCES MIRIAM BERRY. The Widow Bedott. *papers, buckram, 12mo. N.Y., Blakeman & Mason, 1863.*

WHITE, E.B. Quo vadimus? or, The case for the bicycle. *buckram, 12mo. Garden City, Garden City Pub. Co., 1946.*

_____ The second tree from the corner. *buckram, 8vo. N.Y., Harper, 1954.*

_____ A subtreasury of American humor. *buckram, 8vo. N.Y., Coward-McCann, 1941.*

WHITE, E.V. Chocolate drops from the south; a book of negro humor and philosophy. *buckram, 16mo. Austin, Steck, 1932.*

WHITE, J.J. Funabout Fords. *boards, 16mo. Chic., Howell, 1915.*

_____ More funabout Fords. *boards, 16mo. Chic., Howell, 1915.*

WHITE, LEE STROUT. Farewell to Model T. *buckram, 12mo. N.Y., Putnam's, 1936.*

WHITE, TERENCE HANBURY. The age of scandal. *buckram, 8vo. N.Y., Putnam's, 1950.*

_____ The Godstone and the blackymor. *buckram, 8vo. N.Y., Putnam's, 1959.*

_____ The scandalmonger. *buckram, 8vo. N.Y., Putnam's, 1952.*

WHITE, WILLIAM ALLEN. Autobiography. *buckram, 12mo. N.Y., Macmillan, 1946.*

WHITEAR, WALTER H. More Pepysiana; notes on the diary of Samuel Pepys. *buckram, 8vo. Lond., Simpkin, Marshall, 1927.*

WHITECROSS, JOHN. Anecdotes illustrative of select passages in each chapter of the New Testament. *paper, 24mo. Phila., Presbyterian Board of Publication, 1838.*

WHITEHEAD, ALFRED NORTH. The wit and wisdom of Alfred North Whitehead. *buckram, 4to. Bost., Beacon, 1947.*

WHITING, BARTLETT JERE. Chaucer's use of proverbs. *buckram, 8vo. Cambridge, Harvard Univ.Press, 1934.*

WHITING, ROBERT RUDD. A ball of yarn. *boards, 12mo. San Francisco, Elder, 1907.*

_____ Four hundred good stories. *buckram, 12mo. N.Y., Doubleday, Page, 1926.*

WHO ALTERS SHAKESPEARE, a Hamlet query. *paper, 16mo. Saint Joseph, Twilight Pub. Co., n.d.*

WHORE'S RHETORICK, THE, calculated to the meridian of London and conformed to the rules of art, in two dialogues. *boards, 12mo. Lond., Holland, 1960.*

WIBBERLEY, LEONARD. The mouse that roared. *paper, 16mo. N.Y., Bantam, 1959.*

WICKSTEED, BERNARD. It's fun finding out. *buckram, 8vo. Lond., Daily Express, 1947.*

WIELAND, CHRISTOPHER MARTIN. The republic of fools. *2v. half-calf, 12mo. Lond., Allen, 1861.*

WIGGIN, KATE DOUGLAS *and* SMITH, NORA ARCHIBALD. Tales of laughter. *buckram, 8vo. N.Y., Doubleday, Page, 1926.*

WIGGIN, MAURICE. My court casebook. *buckram, 12mo. Lond., Sylvan, 1948.*

WILCOX, FREDERICK B. Little book of aphorisms. *buckram, 16mo. N.Y., Scribners, 1947.*

WILCOX, HENRY S. Foibles of the bar. *buckram, 12mo. Chic., Legal Literature Co., 1906.*

——————— Foibles of the bench. *buckram, 12mo. Chic., Legal Literature Co., 1906.*

——————— Frailties of the jury. *buckram, 12mo. Chic., Legal Literature Co., 1906.*

——————— Trials of a stump-speaker. *buckram, 12mo. Chic., Legal Literature Co., 1906.*

WILD ASSES. *pamphlet.*

WILDE, OSCAR. Collected works of Oscar Wilde, including the poems, novels, plays, essays and fairy tales. *boards, 8vo. N.Y., Greystone, n.d.*

——————— Epigrams. *boards, 12mo. Mount Vernon, N.Y., Peter Pauper, n.d.*

——————— Epigrams of Oscar Wilde; an anthology by Alvin Redman. *buckram, 8vo. N.Y., Day, 1952.*

——————— Epigrams of Oscar Wilde. *paper, 32mo. Girard, Kan., Haldeman-Julius, n.d. (Little Blue Books.)*

——————— The importance of being earnest. *paper, 12mo. N.Y., French, n.d.*

——————— Oscariana. *paper, 24mo. Lond., Humphreys, 1910.*

——————— Wit and wisdom of Oscar Wilde, collected by Cecil Hewetson. *boards, 16mo. Lond., Duckworth, 1960.*

——————— Wit and humor of Oscar Wilde. *paper, 8vo. N.Y., Dover, 1959.*

——————— Three-minute plays. Innocentia. Musicalia. Immoralia. *buckram, 12mo. N.Y., Greenberg, 1927.*

WILDE, W. The reservoir of wit and fancy; being a selection of stories, bon-mots, anecdotes, &c. *half-calf, 12mo. Lond., Sutton, 1803.*

WILDER, MARSHALL P. The people I've smiled with; recollections of a merry little life. *buckram, 12mo. N.Y., Cassell, 1889.*

——————— Smiling 'round the world. *buckram, 12mo. N.Y., Funk & Wagnalls, 1908.*

——————— The sunny side of the street. *buckram, 12mo. N.Y., Funk & Wagnalls, 1905.*

——————— The wit and humor of America. *10v. simulated leather, 8vo. N.Y., Funk & Wagnalls, 1911.*

WILEY, ALEXANDER. Laughing with Congress. *buckram, 8vo. N.Y., Crown, 1947.*

WILKES, GEORGE. Shakespeare, from an American point of view. *buckram, 8vo. Lond., Low, Marston, Searle & Rivington, 1877.*

WILKIE, ANDREW. The diorama of life, or, The macrocosm and microcosm displayed; characteristic sketches and anecdotes, of men and things. *boards, 24mo. Bath, Barrett, 1824.*

WILKINSON, OSBORN *and* WILKINSON, JOHNSON. The memoirs of the Gemini Generals: personal anecdotes, sporting adventures and sketches of distinguished officers. *buckram, 8vo. Lond., Innes, 1896.*

WILLANS, GEOFFREY. Admiral on horseback. *buckram, 12mo. Lond., Joseph, 1954.*

——————— Fasten your lap-straps! *buckram, 8vo. N.Y., Vanguard, 1956.*

WILLANS, GEOFFREY and
ROETTER, CHARLES. The
wit of Winston Churchill.
*buckram, 12mo. Lond.,
Parrish, 1955.*

WILLANS, GEOFFREY and
SEARLE, RONALD. The
dog's ear book. *buckram, 8vo.
Lond., Parrish, 1958.*

—————— How to be topp.
*buckram, 8vo. Lond.,
Parrish, 1954.*

—————— Whizz for atomms.
*buckram, 12mo. Lond.,
Parrish, 1956.*

WILLARD, JOSEPH A. half a
century with judges and
lawyers. *buckram, 12mo.
Bost., Houghton, Mifflin,
1895.*

WILLIAMS, GAAR. Among the
folks in history. *buckram,
8vo. N.Y., Rand, McNally,
1947.*

—————— How to keep from
growing old. *buckram, 8vo.
N.Y., Rand, McNally, 1948.*

WILLIAMS, GLUYAS. The
Gluyas Williams book.
*boards, 4to. N.Y., Doubleday,
Doran, 1929.*

—————— The Gluyas Williams
gallery. *buckram, 4to. N.Y.,
Harper, 1957.*

WILLIAMS, GURNEY. I meet such
people! A careful collection of
more than 200 carefree
cartoons. *boards, 4to. N.Y.,
Farrar, Straus, 1946.*

WILLIAMS, GUS. Fireside recitations, no.2. *paper, 16mo.
N.Y., Wehman, n.d.*

—————— Gus Williams'
standard recitations. *paper,
16mo. N.Y., DeWitt, 1882.*

—————— Gus Williams' world
of humor. *paper, 12mo. N.Y.,
Wehman, 1880.*

WILLIAMS, HENRY L. Fun burst.
*boards, 12mo. Lond., Maxwell,
n.d.*

WILLIAMS, J.R. Kids out our way.
*boards, 8vo. N.Y., Scribner's,
1946.*

—————— The bull of the
woods. *boards, 8vo. N.Y.,
Scribner's, 1944.*

WILLIAMS, LARRY. Bombshells
of laughter. *buckram, 12mo.
Chic., Author, 1936.*

WILLIAMS, LEEWIN B., comp.
Master book of humorous illustrations. *buckram, 12mo.
N.Y., Abingdon-Cokesbury,
1938.*

—————— Pungent paragraphs;
a handbook of humorous illustrations, wit and wisdom. *buckram, 12mo. Washington, D.C.
Author, 1926.*

WILLIAMS, NEIL WYNN. Greek
peasant stories; or, Gleams
and glooms of Grecian colour.
*buckram, 12mo. Lond., Digby,
Long, 1899.*

WILLIAMS, ROY. How's the
back view coming along?
*buckram, 4to. N.Y., Dutton,
1949.*

WILLIAMS, T., comp. and ed.
Political wit and humour in our
own times. *paper, 16mo. Lond.,
Field & Tyler, 1889.*

WILLIAMS, THOMAS J. Ici on
parle francaise; a farce. *paper,
12mo. Phila., Penn Pub.Co.,
1908.*

—————— Race for a widow, a
farce. *paper, 12mo. Bost.,
Baker, n.d.*

—————— Turn him out, a farce. *paper, 12mo. Chic., Denison, n.d.*

WILLIAMS, URSULA MORAY. The pettabomination. *buckram, 4to. Lond., Archer, 1933.*

WILLIAMS, VICTOR W. "Hello, Bill" toasts. *buckram, 12mo. N.Y., Author, 1905.*

WILLIAMS, W.H., *comp.* Memory gems for school and home. *buckram, 12mo. N.Y., Barnes, 1907.*

WILLIS, MRS. AMBROSE MADISON. The social ruba 'iyat of a bud. *paper, 8vo. San Francisco, Elder, 1913.*

WILLIS, N. PARKER. Funjottings; or, Laughs I have taken a pen to. *half-calf, 12mo. N.Y., Scribner's, n.d.*

WILLOCK, JOHN. Legal facetiae, satirical and humorous. *buckram, 8vo. Lond., London Literary Society, 1887.*

WILLS, NAT M. A son of rest. *paper, 12mo. Chic., Donohue, 1903.*

—————— A son of rest who? *paper, 12mo. Chic., Donohue, 1908.*

WILLS, ROYAL BARRY. Houses have funny bones. *buckram, 8vo. N.Y., Wheelwright, 1951.*

WILLS, W.H., *comp.* Poets' wit and humour. *buckram, 8vo. Lond., Bell & Daldy, 1861.*

WILLSON, MEREDITH. And there I stood with my piccolo. *buckram, 12mo. N.Y., Doubleday, 1948.*

—————— Eggs I have laid. *buckram, 8vo. N.Y., Holt, 1955.*

—————— Who did what to Fedalia? *buckram, 12mo. N.Y., Doubleday, 1952.*

WILSON, A.E. Prime minister of mirth; the biography of Sir George Robey. *buckram, 8vo. Lond., Odhams, 1956.*

WILSON, ANGUS *and* JULIAN, PHILIPPE. For whom the cloche tolls; a scrapbook of the twenties. *boards, 16mo. Lond., Methuen, 1953.*

WILSON, BARBARA KER. Scottish folk-tales and legends. *buckram, 8vo. Lond., Oxford Univ. Press, 1957.*

WILSON, DANIEL MUNRO. Tutor Flynt, New England's earliest humorist. *(In: New England Magazine, 1901.)*

WILSON, EARL. I am gazing into my 8-ball. *paper, 24mo. N.Y., Pocket Books, 1948.*

—————— Let'em eat cheesecake. *buckram, 8vo. N.Y., Doubleday, 1950.*

—————— Look who's abroad now. *buckram, 8vo. N.Y., Doubleday, 1953.*

WILSON, FRANCIS. Francis Wilson's Life of himself. *buckram, 8vo. Bost., Houghton, Mifflin, 1924.*

WILSON, HENRY. The book of wonderful characters; memoirs and anecdotes of remarkable and eccentric persons in all ages and countries. *half-calf, 12mo. Lond., Reeves & Turner, n.d.*

WILSON, JOHN HAROLD. The court wits of the Restoration. *buckram, 12mo. Princeton, Princeton Univ. Press, 1948.*

WILSON, LAWRENCE W. Around
the Dublin bookshops. *(In:
American Book Collector, Nov.
1956.)*

_____ The Canadian
member of Parliament.
*pamphlet. Quebec, Momus,
1958.*

_____ Chibougamau
venture. *buckram, 12mo.
Montreal, Chibougamau Pub.
Co., 1952.*

_____ The richest man on
earth; the story of a book-
seller; a buffoonery. *(In: The
Amateur Book Collector,
Sep. 1955.)*

_____ Stories in the
Montrealer Magazine. *buckram,
4to. Montreal, Montrealer,
1953-1955.*

_____ This was Montreal
in 1814, 1815, 1816, and
1817. *buckram, 8vo. Montreal.
Priv.Print. for the Chateau de
Ramezay, 1960.*

_____ The world's greatest
book collector. *(In: The
Amateur Book Collector, Sep.
1953.)*

WILSON, MARGERY. How to live
beyond your means. *buckram,
8vo. Phila., Lippincott, 1945.*

WILSON, RICHARD ALBERT.
The miraculous birth of
language. *paper, 12mo. Lond.,
British Pub. Guild, 1937.*

WILSON, RUFUS ROCKWELL.
Caricature in America. *(In:
New England Magazine, 1904.)*

WILSON, WOODROW. Wit and
wisdom. *buckram, 12mo.
Garden City, Doubleday,
Page, 1916.*

WILSON'S WONDERFUL CHARAC-
TERS; being a history of
persons remarkable for their
extraordinary abilities,
eccentricities and personal
peculiarities. *buckram, 24mo.
Halifax, Milner & Sowerby,
1860.*

WING, FRANK. "The fambly
album" another "Fotygraft
album" shown to the new
preacher by Rebecca Sparks
Peters aged eleven. *boards,
8vo. Chic., Reilly & Britton,
1917.*

_____ "The fotygraft
album" shown to the new
neighbor by Rebecca Sparks
Peters, aged eleven. *boards,
8vo. Chic., Reilly & Britton,
1915.*

WINKLE, WILLIAM. A great
success; a comedy. *paper,
12mo. N.Y., De Witt, 1882.*

WINSTEDT, RICHARD. Malay
proverbs. *buckram, 12mo.
Lond., Murray, 1950.*

WINSTEN, STEPHEN. Jesting
apostle; the private life of
Bernard Shaw. *buckram, 12mo.
N.Y., Dutton, 1957.*

_____ Days with Bernard
Shaw. *buckram, 8vo. Lond.,
Hutchinson, 1933.*

WINTER, BEVIS. Sad laughter;
stories of the inimitable
Sebastian Riffkin. *buckram,
12mo. Lond., Mortimer, 1947.*

WINTERS, JONATHAN *and*
CAMMARATA, PHILIP. Did
anyone bring an opener?
*paper, wide 16mo. Lond.,
Cassell, 1960.*

WISDOM OF SOLOMON, THE;
certain views as conceived
and expressed by Mr. Solomon
Baker, storekeeper, Hatch's
Harbor. *boards, 8vo. Bost.,
Priv. Print., 1919.*

WISDOM WHILE YOU WAIT: being
a foretaste of the glories of the
"Insidecompletuar Brittania-
ware". *paper, 8vo. Lond.,
Isbister, 1903.*

WISE CRACKS. *paper, 12mo.
N.Y., Minoan Pub.Co., 1955.*

WISECRACKS OF THE YEAR.
*paper, 24mo. Indianapolis,
Droke, 1949.*

WISEMAN, F. Cyclopedia of wit
and wisdom; being a selection
of choice anecdotes. *buckram,
24mo. Lond., Johnson, 1842.*

WIT AND HUMOR OF AMERICAN
STATESMEN, a collection from
various sources. *buckram,
16mo. Phila., Jacobs, 1902.*

WIT AND HUMOR OF THE AGE;
comprising wit, humor, pathos,
ridicule, satires, dialects,
puns, conundrums, riddles,
charades, jokes and magic, by
Mark Twain, Robt. J. Burdette,
Alex. Sweet, Eli Perkins. With
The philosophy of wit and
humor, by Melville D. Landon.
*calf, 8vo. Chic., Cline, 1889.*

WIT AND HUMOR OF THE
AMERICAN BAR. *buckram,
24mo. Phila., Jacobs, 1905.*

WIT AND HUMOR OF THE
AMERICAN PULPIT. *buckram,
16mo. Phila., Lippincott, 1904.*

WIT AND HUMOR OF THE
PHYSICIAN. *buckram, 16mo.
Phila., Jacobs, 1906.*

WIT AND HUMOR OF THE
WORLD. *paper, 4to. n.p. n.d.*

WIT AND HUMOR OF WOMEN.
*buckram, 16mo. Phila.,
Jacobs, 1907.*

WIT AND HUMOUR; an amusing
collection of good things, both
in prose and verse. *buckram,
16mo. Lond., Cox, 1867.
2d.ed.*

WIT AND MIRTH; or, Pills to
purge melancholy. *calf, 16mo.
Lond., Tonson, 1719.*

WIT AND WISDOM, or, The world's
jest book. *quarter-calf, 24mo.
Lond., Smith, 1835.*

——————— *Same. Lond., Allman,
1844.*

WIT AND WISDOM "The best of
all good company". *2v. buckram, folio. Lond., "Wit and
Wisdom" Office, 1886.*

WIT OF THE WORLD, consisting
of an endless variety of Yankee
jokes, witty sayings, jests,
bon mots, repartees, &c. &c.
*buckram, 24mo. Halifax, Milner
& Sowerby, 1856.*

WIT OF THE WORLD, or, Jests
and sayings of the present
day. *buckram, 24mo. Lond.,
n.p., 1851.*

WITHERSPOON, HALLIDAY.
Liverpool Jarge. *buckram,
12mo. Bost., Author, 1933.*

WITS MUSEUM, or, The New
London Jester; a collection by
the choice spirits of the
present age. *calf., 16mo.
Lond., Lane, n.d. New ed.*

WIT'S VADE-MECUM; being a
selection of humorous pieces,
curious anecdotes, repartees,
&c. &c. *paper, 32mo.
Doncaster, Thomas & Hunsley,
n.d.*

WITT, PETER. Abraham Lincoln,
the man of sorrow. *paper, 16mo.
Cleveland, Feather, 1938.*

WITTY AND ENTERTAINING
EXPLOITS OF GEORGE
BUCHANAN, COMMONLY
CALLED THE KING'S FOOL.
From the original manuscript
dated 1725. *half-calf, 12mo.
Lond., n.p., 1900.*

WITTY APOPHTHEGMS, delivered
at severall times and upon
severall occasions, by King
James, King Charles, the
Marquess of Worcester,
Francis, Lord Bacon and Sir
Thomas Moore. *calf, 24mo.
Lond., Farnham, 1658.*

WITTY, WISE AND WICKED
MAXIMS, with a preface by
Henri Pene du Bois. *buckram,
16mo. N.Y., Brentano's, 1897.*

WITWER, H. C. The classics in
slang. *buckram, 12mo. N.Y.,
Grosset & Dunlap, 1927.*

WODEHOUSE, PELHAM
GRENVILLE *and* MEREDITH,
SCOTT. The best of modern
humor. *buckram, 12mo. N.Y.,
Metcalf, 1952.*

—————— A century of humour.
*buckram, 8vo. Lond.,
Hutchinson, n.d.*

—————— Divots. *buckram,
8vo. N.Y., Doran, 1927.*

—————— A few quick ones.
*buckram, 8vo. N.Y., Simon &
Schuster, 1959.*

—————— Fish preferred.
*buckram, 12mo. Garden City,
Doubleday, Doran, 1929.*

—————— Methuen's Library
of humour: P.G. Wodehouse.
*buckram, 16mo. Lond.,
Methuen, 1934.*

—————— Week-end book of
humour. *buckram, 12mo.
Lond., Jenkins, 1954.*

WOHL, JACK. The conformers.
*paper, 8vo. N.Y., Pocket
Books, n.d.*

WOLFF, ED. Why we do it. *buckram, 8vo. N.Y., Macaulay,
1929.*

WOMAN'S OWN BOOK OF TOILET
SECRETS ... *paper, 8vo.
Bost., Arakelyan, n.d.*

WOMEN AND WISDOM OF JAPAN.
*buckram, 12mo. Lond., Murray,
1914.*

WONS, TONY. 'R' you listenin'?
*buckram, 8vo. Chic., Reilly &
Lee, 1931.*

—————— Three famous Tony's
Scrap books in one volume.
*buckram, 8vo. Chic., Reilly &
Lee, 1933.*

—————— Tony's scrap book,
1941-42 edition. *buckram,
8vo. Chic., Reilly & Lee,
1941.*

WOO, Y.T., *trans.* Chinese merry
tales. *paper, 8vo. Shanghai,
American Presbyterian
Mission Press, 1909.*

WOOD, BONNY T., *ed.* The mirth
of a nation. *paper, 8vo. Girard,
Kan., Haldeman-Julius, 1948.*

—————— Quotable quotes.
*paper, 8vo. Girard, Kan.,
Haldeman-Julius, 1948.*

WOOD, CLEMENT. *ed.* Best
American Jokes. *paper, 32mo.
Girard, Kan., Haldeman-Julius,
n.d. (Little Blue Books.)*

—————— Best Irish jokes.
*paper, 32mo. Girard, Kan.,
Haldeman-Julius, n.d. (Little
Blue Books.)*

——————— Best Negro jokes. *paper, 32mo. Girard, Kan., Haldeman-Julius, n.d. (Little Blue Books.)*

——————— A book of Broadway wisecracks. *paper, 32mo. Girard, Kan., Haldeman-Julius, n.d. (Little Blue Books.)*

——————— A book of comic dialect poems. *paper, 32mo. Girard, Kan., Haldeman-Julius, n.d. (Little Blue Books.)*

——————— A book of humorous limericks. *paper, 32mo. Girard, Kan., Haldeman-Julius, n.d. (Little Blue Books.)*

——————— The Greenwich Village blues. *buckram, 8vo. N.Y., Harrison, 1926.*

WOOD, HENRY FIRTH. Jokes, a fresh crop. *paper, 24mo. Phila., Penn., 1913.*

WOOD, J. HICKORY. Merry-thoughts for recitation or reading. *buckram, 12mo. Lond., Ward, Lock, 1912.*

——————— Recitations, comic and otherwise. *buckram, 12mo. Lond., Ward, Lock, 1901.*

WOOD, JOHN SEYMOUR. Yale yarns; sketches of life at Yale University. *paper, 16mo. N.Y., Putnam's 1899.*

WOOD, RAY. Fun in American folk rhymes. *buckram, 8vo. Phila., Lippincott, 1952.*

——————— Mother Goose in the Ozarks. *boards, 12mo. Raywood, Texas, Author, 1938.*

WOOD, ROBERT WILLIAMS. Animal analogues. *boards, 12mo. San Francisco, Elder, 1908.*

——————— How to tell the birds from the flowers, and other wood cuts. A revised manual of flornithology for beginners. *paper, 12mo. N.Y., Dover, 1959.*

WOOD AND STONE: or, A dialogue between a wooden duke and a stone lion. *pamphlet. Lond., Wilks & Taylor, n.d.*

WOODENSCONCE, PAPERNOSE, *pseud.* Wonderful drama of Punch and Judy. *boards, 4to. n.p., n.d.*

WOODFIN, JANE. Of mikes and men. *buckram, 8vo. N.Y., McGraw-Hill, 1951.*

WOODRUFF, DOUGLAS. Plato's American republic. *buckram, 16mo. N.Y., Dutton, 1926.*

WOODRUFF, PRESS. A backwoods philosopher from Arkansas. An avalanche of mirth. *buckram, 8vo. Chic., Thompson & Thomas, 1901.*

——————— A bundle of sunshine. An avalanche of mirth. *paper, 12mo. Chic., Monarch, 1901.*

WOODS, HENRY F. American sayings, famous phrases, slogans and aphorisms. *boards, 8vo. N.Y., Perma Giants, 1950. Rev. and enl.ed.*

WOODS, RALPH L., *comp. and ed.* A treasury of friendship; sentiment, philosophy, humor, inspiration, observation, counsel, analysis, idealism, and friendship in action. *buckram, 8vo. N.Y., McKay, 1957.*

WOODWARD, JOSIAH. Fair warnings to a careless world; or, The serious practice of religion recommended by the admonitions of dying men. *paper, 16mo. Lond., Longman, 1736.*

WOOLLCOTT, ALEXANDER, *ed.* As you were; a portable library of American prose and poetry. *buckram, 16mo. N.Y., Viking, 1944.*

_____ Long, long ago. *buckram, 8vo. N.Y., Viking, 1943.*

_____ The portable Woollcott. *buckram, 16mo. N.Y., Viking, 1946.*

_____ While Rome burns. *buckram, 4to. N.Y., Viking, 1934.*

_____ The Woollcott reader; bypaths in the realms of gold. *buckram, 8vo. N.Y., Viking, 1935.*

WORK FOR CHIMNY-SWEEPERS, or, A warning for tobacconists. Facsimile of the 1601 ed. *boards, 8vo. Lond., Pub. for the Shakespeare Association by H. Milford, 1936.*

WORLD OF WIT, A, containing characteristic anecdotes and bon-mots of eminent living persons. *quarter-calf, 24mo. Lond., Hurst & Chapple, 1804. 3d.ed.*

WORLD'S BEST LIMERICKS. Illustrated by Richard Floethe. *boards, 12mo. Mount Vernon, N.Y., Peter Pauper, 1951.*

WORLD'S GREATEST COMIC READINGS AND POPULAR RECITATIONS, by favorite master writers. *paper, 12mo. n.p., n.d.*

WORLD'S WIT AND HUMOR. *15v. buckram, 8vo. N.Y., Rev. of Rev., 1905.*

WORTABET, JOHN, *ed.* Arabian wisdom. *boards, 16mo. Lond., Murray, 1907.*

WRENWICK, CHARLIE. Hound dog joke book. *paper, 16mo. Pasadena, Author, n.d.*

WRIGHT, C. KENT, *pseud.* A.R.P. and all that (and other wartime stories). *boards, 12mo. Lond., Allen & Unwin, 1940.*

_____ Nectar in a nutshell; an anthology of wit and wisdom. *boards, 24mo. Lond., Allen & Unwin, 1944.*

_____ Relax with a smile; an anthology designed mainly for after-dinner speakers. *boards, 12mo. Lond., Allen & Unwin, 1960.*

_____ Speaking after dinner. *buckram, 12mo. Lond., Allen & Unwin, 1936.*

_____ Unaccustomed as I am ... an anthology designed for the after-dinner speaker. *buckram, 12mo. Lond., Allen & Unwin, 1956.*

WRIGHT, CONSTANCE HAGBERG. Tales of Chinese magic. *buckram, 4to. Lond., Dulau, 1925.*

WRIGHT, MILTON. What's funny — and why, an outline of humor. *buckram, 12mo. N.Y., Harvest House, 1939.*

WRIGHT, RICHARDSON. The bed-book of eating and drinking. *buckram, 12mo. N.Y., Lippincott, 1943.*

WRIGHT, THOMAS. A history of caricature and grotesque in literature and art. *buckram, 8vo. Lond., Virtue, 1865.*

_____ Caricature history of the Georges. *buckram, 12mo. Lond., Chatto & Windus, 1876.*

WRIGHT, W. The new help to discourse, or, Wit and mirth intermixt with more serious matters. By W.W., gent. *half-calf, 24mo. Lond., Parker, 1672?*

WRIGHT, W.H.K. The Blue Friars; their sayings and doings. *buckram, 12mo. Lond., Simpkin, Marshall, 1889.*

_____ Pleasantries from the "Blue Box" being a selection of papers ... by Ye Brothers Blue. *buckram, 12mo. Lond., Stock, 1891.*

WU CH'ENG-EN, *supposed author.* Monkey. Translated from the Chinese by Arthur Waley. *buckram, 8vo. Lond., Allen & Unwin, 1942.*

WURDZ, GIDEON, *pseud, see* TOWNE, CHARLES WAYLAND.

WYATT, HORACE. Malice in kulturland. *boards, 8vo. Lond., The Car Illustrated, 1915.*

WYKES, ALAN. A sex by themselves. *buckram, 4to. Lond, Barker, 1958.*

WYLIE, PHILIP. The innocent ambassadors. *paper, 16mo. N.Y., Pocket Books, 1958.*

WYNDHAM, HORACE. Feminine frailty. *buckram, 8vo. Lond., Benn, 1929.*

WYNDHAM LEWIS, DOMINIC BEVAN. Francois Villon. *buckram, 8vo. N.Y., Literary Guild, 1928.*

_____ I couldn't help laughing! an anthology of wartime humour. *buckram, 4to. Lond., Drummond, 1942.*

WYNN, MAKIN, *pseud.* Of pots and privies. *boards, 8vo. Middlesburg, Va., Denlinger's, 1959.*

WYNNE-TYSON, JON. Accomodation wanted; a short guide to the 'bed-sitter'. *boards, 12mo. Lond., Britannicus Liber, 1951.*

# Y

YALE RECORD. Yale wit and humor, being selections of prose, poetry and drawings from the Yale Record of the years eighteen hundred and eighty-nine—ninety-three. Edited by E.R. Lamson. *buckram, folio. Cambridge, Yale University, 1894.*

YANAGITA, KUNIO. Japanese folk-tales. *boards, 12mo. Tokyo, Tokyo News Service, 1954.*

YANK, THE ARMY WEEKLY. The best from Yank. *buckram, 4to. Cleveland, World Pub.Co., 1945.*

——————— Highlights from Yank. *paper, 12mo. N.Y., Royal, 1953.*

YANKEE DROLLERIES. the most celebrated works of the best American humourists. *buckram, 12mo. Lond., Routledge, n.d.*

YANKEE DROLLERIES, or, Sketches of Down-Easters. *paper, 12mo. N.Y., Wehman, n.d.*

YANKEE HUMOUR, and Uncle Sam's fun. *half-calf, 12mo. Lond., Cooke, 1853.*

YASUDA, YURI. Old tales of Japan. *boards, 12mo. Rutland, Vt., Tuttle, 1956.*

YATES, BILL, *ed.* Forever funny. *paper, 12mo. N.Y., Dell, 1956.*

——————— Too funny for words; a book for people who can't read. *paper, 16mo. N.Y., Dell, 1954.*

YATES, DORA E. A book of gypsy folk-tales. *buckram, 8vo. Lond., Phoenix, 1948.*

YEATS, WILLIAM BUTLER. The land of heart's desire. *In: Three Irish plays, q.v.*

YELDHAM, WALTER. Lays of Ind, by Aliph Cheem, *pseud. buckram, 12mo. Calcutta, Thacker, Spink, 1883.*

YELLOTT, GEORGE. The funny philosophers, or, Wags and sweethearts. *buckram, 12mo. Phila., Lippincott, 1872.*

YODER, ROBERT M. There's no front like home. *buckram, 12mo. Bost., Houghton, Mifflin, 1944.*

YORICK'S BUDGET; or, Repository of wit, humour, and sentiment. *half-calf, Lond., Vernor, Hood & Sharpe, etc. 1810.*

YORK, S.A., *ed.* Yale humor; a collection of humorous selections from the University publications. *buckram, 4to. N.Y., Author, 1890.*

YOSELOFF, THOMAS. A fellow of infinite jest. *buckram, 8vo. N.Y., Prentice-Hall, 1945.*

YOU TELL 'EM; funny sayings. *paper, 24mo. Baltimore, Ottenheimer, n.d.*

YOUNG, ALFRED W. False alarm, a farce. *paper, 12mo. Lond., French, 1872.*

YOUNG, B.A. Tooth and claw; a new bestiary. *buckram, 8vo. Lond., Elek, n.d.*

YOUNG, CHIC. 25 years with Blondie. *paper, 12mo. N.Y., Simon & Schuster, 1958.*

YOUNG, MIRIAM. Mother wore tights. *buckram, 8vo. Lond., Whittlesey, 1944.*

YOUNG, VINNE. It's fun to be fat. *buckram, 8vo. N.Y., Wyn, 1953.*

YOUTH'S COMPANION, THE,
edited by Lovell Thompson,
M.A. De Wolfe Howe, Arthur
Stanwood Pier and Harford
Powel. *buckram, 8vo. Bost.,
Houghton Mifflin, 1954.*

YU HSIU SEN, *ed.* Ancient
Chinese parables. *paper,
12mo. Shanghai, Commercial
Press, 1927.*

# Z

ZABARA, JOSEPH BEN MEIR.
The book of delight. *paper,
8vo. N.Y., Columbia Univ.
Press, 1932.*

ZANGWILL, ISRAEL. The king
of Schnorrers. To which is
added an Essay on Jewish
Humor, by Bernard N.
Schilling. *buckram, 12mo.
Hamden, Shoe String Press,
1953.*

ZERN, ED. How to catch
fishermen. *buckram, 8vo.
N.Y., Appleton, 1951.*

——————— How to tell fish
from fishermen, or, A plague
on both your houses. *buckram,
8vo. N.Y., Appleton-Century,
1947.*

——————— To hell with hunting.
*buckram, 8vo. N.Y., Appleton-
Century-Crofts, 1946.*

"ZETA" The diagnosis of the
acute abdomen in rhyme. *buckram, 12mo. Lond., Lewis, 1947.*

ZILLER, ROBERT. We make
history. *boards, 8vo. Lond.,
Allen & Unwin, 1940.*

ZIMMERMAN, EUGENE. Cartoons
and caricatures, or, Making the
world laugh. *half-calf, 12mo.
Scranton, Pa., Correspondence
Institute of America, 1910.*

ZIMMERMAN, GERTRUDE, *comp.*
The golden treasury of popular
quotations from Genesis to
Winchell. *paper, 4to. Chic.,
Consolidated Book Pub., 1944.*

ZIPSER, ARTHUR *and* NOVACK,
GEORGE. Who's hooey; nit-
witticisms of the notable.
*boards, 16mo. N.Y., Dutton,
1932.*

ZINGARI——————— The paradise
of posers. *paper, 12mo. Lond.,
Humphreys, 1919.*

ZLOTOGORSKI, SALVI G. Laugh,
man, laugh. Five hundred
jokes, episodes and anecdotes
for the amusement of sick and
healthy people. *buckram, 8vo.
N.Y., Pegasus, n.d.*

ZMEE, X. Q., *pseud.* The excuse
book, or, Pocket life preserver.
*boards, 12mo. Bost., Luce,
1911.*

ZOLOTOW, MAURICE. It takes all
kinds. *buckram, 8vo. Lond.,
Allen, 1953.*

ZONG IN-SOB, *ed. and trans.* Folk
tales from Korea. *buckram, 8vo.
Lond., Routledge & Kegan
Paul, 1952.*

ZVONAREVOI, V. Let's have a
rest. *paper, 12mo. Moskva,
1959. (Title-page in Russian.)*

ZWEIG, STEFAN. Balzac. *buckram, 8vo. N.Y., Viking, 1946.*

AMERICAN BOOK COLLECTOR.
*June, 1960, Feb. 1961-to date.
Chicago.*

AMERICAN JEWISH HISTORICAL
SOCIETY. Publication. *v.43,
no.2-to date. New York.*

BLAGUES: bi-mensuel. *1956 - to
date. Paris. (French)*

BUNGEI-SHUNJU *see* MANGA-
DOKUHON.

CALIFORNIA HISTORICAL
SOCIETY QUARTERLY. *Dec.
1957 - to date. San Francisco.*

CALIFORNIA PELICAN. *April,
1908, November 1909,
February, 1950. 1960 - to date.
Berkeley.*

CANDIDO; settimanale del sabato.
*1956 - to date. Milano. (Italian)*

CHAI KRUNG. *- to date. (Thai)*

CHISTES Y PASATIEMPOS. *1954
- to date. Madrid. (Spanish)*

DESERT RAT SCRAP BOOK.
*n.d. Packet one of pouch two -
to date. 1000 Palms, Calif.*

DUBLIN OPINION; the national
humorous journal of Ireland.
*August 1959 - to date. Dublin.*

FABULA; zeitschrift fur
erzahforschung. *1957 - to date.
Berlin. In German, English
and French.*

FOR LAUGHING OUT LOUD.
*1958 - to date. New York.*

FOU-RIRE. *1955 - to date. Paris.
(French)*

GAMAD LILLIPUT. *1957 - to date.
Tel Aviv. (Hebrew)*

HUMOR-REVUE. *1956 - to date.
Bern. (German)*

HUMOUR: selection des meil-
lieures blagues. *1957 - to date.
Belgique-Luxembourg. (French)*

HUMOUR VARIETY (incorporating
Laughter Variety, Happy
Variety, Passing and Barrack
Variety). *n.d. No. 28 - to date.
London.*

HUNTINGTON LIBRARY
QUARTERLY. *February 1960 -
to date. San Marino, California.*

KEREMPUH: knijizevni casopis
za satiru i humor. *1957 - to
date. Zagreb. (Yugoslavian)*

KROKODIL. *1951 - to date (some
numbers lacking) Moskva.
(Russian)*

LAUGH BOOK MAGAZINE. *1944,
Jan. 1946, Dec. 1947, May,
Aug. Nov., 1948, Feb., Sept-
Dec. 1949, 1950 - to date.
Wichita, Kansas.*

LAUGH MAGAZINE. *n.d. Nos.
8,9,11 - to date. London.*

LINCOLN LORE; bulletin of the
Lincoln National Life
Foundation. *1935 - to date.
Fort Wayne, Indiana.*

LUDAS MATYI HUMOROS,
SZATIRIKUS HETILAP. *1957 -
to date. Budapest (Hungarian)*

MAD, *January 1959 - to date.
New York.*

MANGA-DOKUHON (formerly
Bungei-Shunju). *May 1956,
July, 1956, Sep. 1956 - to date.
Tokyo. (Japanese)*

## FOOTNOTE

*The following are regular subscription magazines. At the end of this file
are listed single copies, irregulars, etc. All languages are included.*

MISSOURI HISTORICAL REVIEW.
*April, 1960 - to date. Kirksville, Mo.*

NEW YORK FOLKLORE QUARTERLY. *Winter, 1960 - to date. Cooperstown, New York.*

NEW YORKER MAGAZINE. *April, 1955 - to date. New York.*

1000 JOKES MAGAZINE. *Winter, 1948-49, Winter 1951-52, Spring, 1952 - to date. New York.*

POURQUOI PAS? *1958 - to date. Bruxelles. (French)*

PUNCH. *1841-1891, 1951 - to date. London.*

QUOTE, the weekly digest. *1944 - to date. Indianapolis, Indiana.*

RECORDER. *December 1955 - to date. San Francisco.*

RIRE, journal satirique. *Mai, 1953 - to date. Paris. (French)*

SCOOP; the official publication of the Press and Union League Club of San Francisco. *1954 - to date.*

SHANKAR'S WEEKLY. *Aug. 19, 1956 - to date. New Delhi.*

SIMPLICISSIMUS. *May 7, 1955 - to date. Munchen. (German)*

SZPILKI; prawdziwa cnota krytyk sie nie boi. (Krasicki) *1957 - to date. Warszawa. (Polish)*

TARANTEL; satirische monatsschrift der sowjetzone. *May 1953 - to date. Leipzig. (German)*

TIT-BITS. *bound volumes 1882-1895, 1921, 1922, 1923. Scattered numbers for 1926-1936, April 18, 1953 - to date. London.*

TRAVERSO; organo ufficiale dell persone intelligenti. *1956 - to date. Milano. (Italian)*

USSR illustrated monthly. *Aug. 1956 - to date. Washington, D.C.*

WESTERN FOLK-LORE. *1957 - to date. Berkeley, California.*

WISDOM; the magazine of knowledge for all America. *v.1, no. 12, 1946 - to date. Beverly Hills, Hills, California.*

YANKEE. *Dec. 1960 - to date. Dublin, New Hampshire.*

## Singles and Irregulars

AKBABA. *1958. Ankara. (Turkish)*

ALLY SLOPER'S HALF HOLIDAY. *1908-1909. London.*

AMERIKANISCHE RUNDSCHAU. *v.2, no.5. 1946. Information Control, U.S. Army. (German)*

ANEKDOTE. Ballfest. *Jan. 29, 1927. Berlin. (German)*

ANPFIFF; zeitschrift fur den massensportarbeiter. *Aug. 1956. Berlin. (German)*

ANSWERS, the popular journal for home and train. *Nov. 12, 1932-Dec.2, 1933. London.*

BALLYHOO. *1931-1933. New York.*

BASSETT'S SCRAPBOOK; a magazine for riders of the wheel. *v.2, no.6. August, 1913. Newtonville, Massachusetts.*

BAWL STREET JOURNAL. *June 6, 1958. New York.*

BORINOT. *33 issues between
Sep.1924 and April, 1925.
26 issues between Jan.1926
and July 1926 and 40 issues
between Jan.1924 and Aug.
1924. Barcelona. (Catalonian)*

CALEJADES: revue humoristique.
mensuelle. *no.12, 1959. Givors
(Rhone) (French)*

CANEBIERE HUMOUR MAGAZINE.
*Nos. 49, 82. 1956, 1959. Paris.
(French)*

CAPTAIN BILLY'S WHIZ BANG.
*Scattered numbers 1922 through
1929. Robbinsdale, Minnesota.*

CARTOONS MAGAZINE. *Scattered
numbers 1914-1924. New York.*

CENT BLAGUES: *pour mourir
de rire 1956-1957. Lyon.
(French)*

CHARIVARI. *1860, 1869, 1875.
Paris. (French)*

CHAUTAUQUAN; a monthly
magazine. *1890-1898, 1904.
Meadville, Pennsylvania.*

CHISTES; revista de humor
mensual. *1953. Madrid.
(Spanish)*

COLLEGE HUMOR. *Scattered
numbers from 1924-1926.
Cleveland.*

COLNER CARNEVALS ULK.
*v.17: 1889. Koln. (German)*

COMEDIAN. *Numbers 1 and 2.
New York.*

COMEDY WORLD: trade journal
of the humor field. *Scattered
numbers 1954-1956. New York.*

COMIC PAPERS. Contains
numbers of the following.
Tit-Bits. Once A Week.
Rare Bits. Illustrated Bits.
Wit and Humor. Gems.
*London.*

CRAPOUILLOT; magasin
parisien. *1955. Paris. (French)*

DEUTSCHE ARBEIT. *v.34, no.9.
1934. Berlin. (German)*

DOLMUS. *9-Nisan, 1958. Ankara?
(Turkish)*

EMCEE; the entertainer's
magazine. *Scattered numbers
1950-1955.*

EULENSPIEGEL; zeitschrift fur
satire und humor. *October 1955,
September 1956. Berlin.
(German)*

FAME AND FORTUNE WEEKLY.
*1920, 1923. New York.*

EUROPEO; settimanale politico
de attualita. *Nov. 1938.
Milano. (Italian)*

FUN; old series. *1861. London.*

FUN; new series. *Incomplete file,
1862-1892. London.*

FUNNY FOLKS; the comic
companion to the newspaper.
*Jan. 2, 1886. London.*

GAIETY; a magazine of humor.
*1921, 1922, 1924. London.*

GLOBUS; internationale jugend-
zeitschrift. *1959. Berlin,
(German)*

HAYAT. *1959. Ankara? (Turkish)*

HOOEY. *May, 1931. New York.*

HUMOR DIJEST. Single sheet of
jokes and cartoons published
at irregular intervals. *New
York.*

HUMOR NEWSLETTER. *Nov.
1959, Mar. 1960. New York.*

HUMORIST IN VARIOUS MOODS.
*July, 1922. London.*

HUMORISTISCHES ECHO. *1926-
1929. Berlin. (German)*

JIM JAM JEMS. *Scattered numbers,
1914-1924. Bismarck, North
Dakota.*

JESTER. *Jan. 1958. New York.*

JOKER. *1891, 1892. London.*

JONES, published fortnightly.
*1849. Liverpool.*

JOSH. *Sep-Nov. 1896.
San Francisco.*

JUDGE. *Scattered numbers 1923-
1931. New York.*

KLADDERADATSCH; organ fur
und von bummler. *1848-1863.
Berlin. (German)*

LACH. *July 1959. Amsterdam.
(Dutch)*

LARK. *May 1896 - April, 1897.
San Francisco.*

LAUGH IT OFF! *Sep.1961.
New York.*

LAUGHTER. *1927, 1931.
New York.*

LIFE. *Aug. 1904, Sep. 1908, Jan.
1924, Mar. 1933. New York.*

LLOYD'S WEEKLY VOLUME OF
AMUSING AND INSTRUCTIVE
LITERATURE. *1869? London.*

LONDON OPINION. *Christmas
numbers, 1951, 1953. London.*

LONDON SOCIETY. *Christmas
number, 1873. London.*

MADRID COMICO: periodico
semanal, literario, festivo,
ilustrado. *1889. Madrid.
(Spanish)*

MEDLEY; a magazine for odd
moments. *1934-1939. London.*

MENESTREL; partir litteraire.
*June, 1844. Quebec. (French)*

MIND! *Special illustrated
Christmas number, 1901.
London.*

MOONSHINE; the best topical
comic paper. *Jan.-June, 1884.
London.*

MUNDO COMICO; semanario
humoristico. *1873. Madrid.
(Spanish)*

NACHRUF: zeitung fur die
trauernden hinter-bliessenen.
*1956. Berlin. (German)*

NATIONAL JOKER; a laugh riot!
*August, 1961. New York.*

NEUE ILLUSTRIERTE. Die
grosse karnevals-nummer aus
Koln. *Feb. 27, 1954. (German)*

NEW YORK LIFE (English
edition) *1887-1888. London.*

OLD DOC GAGS: a monthly
magazine of twice told tales
and witticisms. *Scattered
numbers, 1920-1922. New York.*

PLUCK AND LUCK. *16 copies of
1928. New York.*

PICK-ME-UP. *1889-1897. London.*

QUIP; the magazine of modern
humor. *Jan-April, 1957.
Indianapolis.*

RADIO HUMORIST. *April-July,
1936. San Francisco.*

RECORD. *v.78, no.5. May 1956.
San Francisco.*

REVUE COMIQUE A L'USAGE
DES GENS SERIEUX. *Nov.
1848-Avril, 1849. Paris.
(French)*

RICO TIPO; revista semanal
humoristica. *v.5, no.217. 1948.
(Spanish)*

SNAPS; a comic weekly of comic
stories by comic authors.
*July 1900. (Facsimile reprint
made by the Dime Novel Club,
1945.)*

TOMAHAWK. *1867-1869. London.*

UNGARN. *Dec.5, 1956. Berlin.
(German)*

WAR IN CARTOONS MAGAZINE.
*Nov. 1914. New York.*

WAYSIDE TALES AND
CARTOONS MAGAZINE. *Nov.
1921. New York.*

WEDNESDAY JOURNAL. *1890.*
*London.*

WEEKEND; Wednesday to Sunday.
*Jan. 12, 1958. London.*

WHIM: a periodical without a
tendency. *1900-1902. Newark,
New Jersey.*

WILL-O-THE-WISP. *1869. London.*

## ARABIC

DALUL, SA'UD. Majmu'a nawadir Juha wa-bnihi wa-himarihi. *paper, 8vo. Damascus, 1953.*

FUTUH AL YAMAN, ALMA RUF BI RA'S AL-GHUL. *paper, 8vo. Tunis, n.d.*

JOUHA, HIS SON AND HIS DONKEY, jokes. *paper, 8vo. Tunis, n.d.*

NAWADIR AL-KHWAJA NASR AD-DIN AL MUGLAQQAB BI-JUA AR RUMI. *paper, 8vo. Tunis n.d.*

AS-SINDABAD AL-BARRI. *paper, 12mo. Tunis, n.d.*

## CHINESE

BOW SHECK FAR. *paper, 12mo.*

CHING NEW. *paper, 12mo.*

CHIUN PING YOW SHEW WAH. *paper, 16mo. Hong Kong, 1954.*

CHUNG KWOCK SEN WA. *paper, 12mo.*

COO POI SHEW WA SIEN. *paper, 12mo.*

DOOK WON GEE. *paper, 12mo.*

EDWARDS, EVANGELINE D., *ed.* A collection of Chinese proverbs (In Mandarin). *paper, 8vo. Shanghai, Kwang Hsueh, 1926.*

EGYPT COO SEE. *paper, 12mo.*

FEE WAT YEE SING KEE. *paper, 12mo.*

FONG GEE HOY. Mon wah Ah Q. Jangin. *paper, 16mo. Shanghai, 1949. 13th ed.*

HEE LIB SEN WA. *paper, 12mo.*

HO YUEN YEE. The magic scroll. *boards, 8vo. Hong Kong, South China Morning Post, 1954.*

HOO GEE DI COO SEE. *paper, 12mo.*

HSIAO LIN KUANG CHI. *4 fascicules in blue cloth case.*

KIANG KEN CHUNG KWOCK DI COO SEE. *paper, 12mo.*

KEWI YU, *ed. and tr.* Tales of different nations. *paper, 12mo. Hong Kong, Commercial Press, n.d. Text in Chinese and English.*

LOW CHAN YOW KEE. *paper, 12mo.*

LUM SI CHEIN. What Kai di coo se. *paper, 16mo. Hong Kong, 1955. 2d. ed.*

MON HOCK GAR COO SEE. *paper, 12mo.*

RELATIONS OF OLD HUMOUR OF THE MING DYNASTY. *paper, 12mo.*

SHEW HEE HOP. *paper, 12mo.*

TONG CHOKE MON JOE SEE SHEW GIT. *paper, 12mo.*

TSENG KWANG HSIEN WEN; a collection of Chinese proverbs, with English translation by R.H. Mathews. *paper, 12mo. Shanghai, China Inland Mission, 1932.*

YARD REAP KEE TOM. *paper, 12mo.*

YEE TOON CHUNG KWOCK DIN PIN SHEW SEI. *paper, 12mo.*

YEE TOON SAE GAI DIN PIN SHEW SEI. *paper, 12mo.*

YEE TOON SOO YOUNG COO SEE. *paper, 12mo.*

# DANISH

AERBØDIGST UDVALGET VISER OG VERS, 1919-1949. *paper, 4to. København, Navers, 1949.*

AGGEBO, ANKER. Aforismer om Laeger og Laegekunst fra oldtid til nutid. *paper, 8vo. København, Levin & Munksgaard, 1934.*

ALMQVIST, K.J. Tanker til eftertanke et reformatorisk evangelium. *paper, 8vo. København, Author, 1944.*

ALVERDEN'S ANEKDOTER. *2v. boards, 16mo. København, Politikens Forlag, 1956-1957.*

ANDERSEN, HANS CHRISTIAN. Anekdoter og historier. *paper, 8vo. København, Erichsen, 1945.*

BADEN, GUSTAV LUDVIG. Skamt og alvor, eller fortid og rutid. *paper, 16mo. Odense, Hempel, 1816.*

BJØRN, L.N. Dumriana. *paper, 16mo. Kjøbenhavn, Biøpping, 1829.*

BLAEKSPRUTTEN. Anno 94. *paper, 8vo. København, Bojesen, 1895.*

BLICHER-HANSEN, INGVAR. Mellem journalister; journalisthistorier. *paper, 16mo. København, Reitzel, 1946.*

—————— Pastoren er morsom; praestehistorier. *paper, 24mo. København, Reitzel, 1942.*

—————— Vore egne mandariner; politiker-anekdoten. *paper, 24mo. København, Reitzel, 1943.*

BLIX. *1933-1939, 1947, 1950. paper, wide 4to. København, Hasselbach.*

BO, LARS. Julens tolv dage. *paper, 8vo. København, Olsen, 1955.*

BOJESEN, BO. Dagligt liv i Danmark. Danskere her og der. Nyt dagligliv. *paper, 8vo. København, Reitzel, 1959. Captions in Danish and English.*

—————— Nyt dagligliv. *paper, 12mo. København, Reitzel, 1953. Captions in Danish and English.*

—————— Parade. *paper, 4to. København, Reitzel, 1958. Captions in Danish and English.*

BRANDT, FRITHIOF. Maximer & sentenser. *paper, 12mo. København, Gyldendal, n.d.*

BREIDAHL, AXEL. (Taeppet) hundrede skuespillerhistorier. *paper, 8vo. København, Pios, 1925.*

CHRISTENSEN, ARTHUR. Dumme folk. *paper, 4to. København, Munskgaard, 1941.*

—————— Synspunkter og synsvinkler; aforismer. *boards, 32mo. København, Guldenalske Boghandel Norsk Forlag, 1929.*

CHRISTENSEN, LAJ *og* GJEDDE, GEORG. En teskefuld 3 gange daglig. *paper, 12mo. København, Andersen & Pedersen, 1939.*

COLD, JØRGEN. Juristhistorier. *paper, 12mo. København, Navers, 1955.*

DANSKE ORDSPROG. *paper, 16mo. København, Foreningen Fremtiden, 1944.*

ENGMAN, HARALD. Billeder fra besaettelsestiden. *paper, 4to. København, Petersen, 1945.*

EULENSPIEGEL. Andersig og
historie om Til Uglespil.
*boards, 16mo. Kjøbenhavn,
Woldikes Forlag, n.d.*

EWALD, JESPER. Poetisske
skrifter, 1912-1948. *paper, 8vo.
København, Gyldendal, 1948.*

FOERSOM, PETER.
Anekdotsamleren,eller Samling
af anekdotre, indfald,
karaktertreef og tanker.
*quarter-calf, 16mo. Kisbenhavn,
Brummer, 1812.*

FOLKEHOJSKOLENS SANGBOG:
uidgivet af foreningen for
hojskoler og landbrugsskoler.
*buckram, 16mo. Odense,
Foreningens Forlag, 1933.*

GYLDENBLONDE, DEN.
Aegtefaelden; en kvindes
dagbog. *paper, 12mo.
København, Navers, 1954.*

HALLAGER, C.B. Studenter-
pudser eller komiske fortal-
linger. *half-calf, 12mo.
Kiøbenhavn, Breinholm, 1817.*

HANSEN, H.P. Jyske originaler
i gamle dage. *paper, 24mo.
København, Rosenkilde &
Bagger, 1948.*

HENNINGSEN, POUL. Kort sagt.
*paper, 8vo. København,
Erichsen, 1955.*

HØFFDING, HARALD. Den store
humor; en psykologisk studie.
*paper, 8vo. København, Nordisk
Forlag, 1916.*

HOLBERG, LUDVIG.
Holberganekdoter. *paper, 12mo.
København, Berlingske Forlag,
1936.*

HOLM, SOREN. Eet hundrede og
sytten aphorismer. *paper, 8vo.
København, Privattryk, 1952.*

HOST, J.H. Anekdoter og moer-
somme indfold. *boards, 12mo.
Maribo, n.p. 1807.*

HOUMARK, CHRISTIAN. Han
spurgte - de sagde. *boards,
16mo. København, Pedersen,
n.d.*

HOVMAND, AAGE V. Den kendte
fusentast Fridolin Hulkefrids,
liv og vaerker. *paper, 12mo.
København, Branner, 1952.*

JENSENIUS, HERLUF. Af en
lille mands dagbog. *paper, 8vo.
København, Rasmus Navers,*

JURGENSENS, FRITZ. Fritz
Jurgensens tegniner. *paper,
4to. København, Gyldendal,
1919.*

KABUS'S BOG, indeholdende en
samling af persiske historiere
og anekdoter. *quarter-calf,
12mo. Kiøbenhavn, Steen, n.d.*

KAPEL, HOLGER. Alvorlig talt.
*paper, 12mo. Helsinge, Author,
n.d.*

KEHLER, HENNING.
Blaeksprutten gennem 50 aar.
*paper, 8vo. København,
Gyldendal, 1938.*

KETCHAM, HANK. Jern Henrik.
*paper, 8vo. København,
Schonberg, 1960.*

KIERKEGAARD, SØREN.
Aforismer. *paper, 12mo.
Fredensborg, Kongstad, 1946.*

_____ Kerneord. *paper,
8vo. København, De Unges
Forlag, 1955.*

KIRCHOFF-LARSEN, CHR. Ave
Eva, en buket anekdoter om
kvinden. *paper, 8vo. København,
Nyt Nordisck Forlag, 1941.*

KJØLSEN, FRITZ HAMMER.
Orlogsliv og lune. *paper, 8vo.
København, Jóst, 1960.*

KNUDSEN, MOGENS, LUNDBO,
ORLA, og SCHWARTZ,
WALTER. Satire og humor i
dansk tegnekunst. *half-
morocco, 4to. København,
Andersen, n.d.*

KORCH, MORTEN. Fynsk humør.
*paper, 8vo. København,
Branner og Korch, 1956.*

KRISTENSEN, J.E.T. og
MORTENSEN, N.T. Dansk
lune; fortaellinger fra
folkemunde. *paper, 8vo.
Aalborg, Lauritzen, 1947.*

─────────── Hysk lune. *paper,
8vo. Aalborg, Lauritzen, 1951.*

LIND, MOGENS og FULFORD,
MARY. Danskerne set gennem
tre Par Briller. *paper, 8vo.
Københaven, Naver, 1941.*

─────────── Tabacbrinos; hvad
de sagde, digtede tegnede og
fortalte om tobak. *paper, 8vo.
København, Haase, 1941.*

MADSEN, LUND. Apotekeren og
doktoren. *paper, 8vo.
København, Skandinavisk
Bogforlag, n.d.*

MADSEN, KAI BERG. Ord om
Kaelighed. *boards, 24mo.
København, Reitzel, 1945.*

MØLLER, POUL. Folkestyret i
dansk humor, 1849-1949. *half-
morocco, 4to. København,
Hagerup, 1949.*

NATURLIG HEKSERI: gamle
laegeraad, kuriøse kunstys-
tikker og pudserlige løger.
*paper, 8vo. København, Naver,
1955.*

NOURI, ALI. Abdul-Hamid i
karikatur; interiorer fra
yildiz-kiosk. *paper, 8vo.
København, Pio, 1903.*

NYGAARD, GEORG. Humor og
satire i Dansk tegnekunst.
*boards, 12mo. København,
Høst, 1937.*

NYHETER, DAGENS. Salon
Gahlin I. *pamphlet. København,
n.p., n.d.*

ODDFUX. Humoristisk kalendar
for 1881. *half-calf, 4to.
Kiobenhavn, Bojesen, 1881.*

OLSEN, FREJLIF. Det menne-
skelige menneske; en samling
aforismer. *buckram, 12mo.
København, Jespersen & Pios,
1929.*

OPPENHEJM, RALPH. Litteratur
i det bla. *paper, 12mo.
København, Hertz, 1953.*

PALUDAN, JACOB. Sagt i
korthed, 1929-1954. *paper,
12mo. København, Hasselbalch,
1954.*

PETERSEN, EIGIL. Tegninger.
*paper, 8vo. København, Navers,
1947.*

PETERSEN, ROBERT STORM see
STORM PETERSEN, ROBERT.

PINDSVINET: politikens muntre
aarbog. 1930-1934. *paper,
wide 4to. København.*

PLETSKUD OG KRANIEBRUD.
*paper, 16mo. Aarhus, Aros,
1946.*

RASMUSSEN, H.V. Danske
ordsprog. *paper, 12mo.
København, Gad, 1920.*

SABROE, SEVN. Saadan er Børn.
*paper, 12mo. København,
Reitzel, 1947.*

SCHWARTZ, WALTER. Satire og
humor i verdenskunsten.
*boards, 8vo. København,
Andersen, n.d.*

SKIEMT OG ALVOR: forteellinger
og billeder af den store
nordiske almanak. *paper, 12mo.
København, Pio, n.d.*

SOYA_____Lomme uld, 300
indfald og udfald. *paper, 12mo.
København, Borgens, 1955.*

DE STAR EN EVINDE BAGVAD
ALT. *boards, 16mo. København.
Branner & Korch, 1954.*

STEINCKE, K.K. Braendenaelder
strøtanker. *paper, 8vo.
København, Gyldendal, 1945.*

_____Kaktus. *paper, 12mo.
København, Gyldendal, 1960.*

_____Myggestik; strøtanker.
*paper, 12mo. København,
Gyldendal, 1943.*

_____ Svovlstikker;
strøtanker. *paper, 12mo.
København, Gyldendal, 1941.*

_____Vid-tjøtn; strøtanker.
*paper, 12mo. København,
Gyldendal, 1941.*

_____Vid-tjorn; strøtanker.
*paper, 12mo. København,
Gyldendal, 1952.*

STORM PETERSEN, ROBERT.
And er magt. *paper, 12mo.
Frederikshavn, Venelkaer, n.d.*

_____ Bilisten. *paper,
8vo. København, Dansk Esso,
1952.*

_____100 fluer. *paper,
16mo. København, Fischer,
n.d.*

_____ 102 fluer. *paper,
16mo. København, Fischer,
1945.*

_____ 103 fluer. *paper,
16mo. København, Fischer,
1946.*

_____ 107 fluer. *paper,
16mo. København, Fischer,
1950.*

_____ 108 fluer. *paper,
16mo. København, Fischer,
1951.*

_____Jyde-og skotte
historier. *paper, 8vo. København. Andersen, n.d.*

_____De kaere bøger.
*paper, 12mo. København,
Selskabet, 1952.*

_____ Og tobakken. *paper,
8vo. København, Hirschprung,
1955.*

_____ Op med humøret.
*buckram, 4to. København,
Andersen, n.d.*

_____ Proppen I, og
andre historier. *paper, 12mo.
København, Branner & Korch,
1960.*

_____ Respekt for retten.
*paper, 8vo. København,
Andersen, 1955.*

_____ Sa Ruller VI.
*paper, 8vo. København,
Andersen, n.d.*

_____ Skotte historier.
*paper, 8vo. København,
Andersen, n.d.*

_____620 Danske
ordsprog. *boards, 12mo.
København, Branner, 1948.*

_____ Storm Petersens
mindelalbum, 1958. *paper,
4to. København, Branner &
Korch, 1958.*

_____De traenger til
noget styrkende. *paper, 12mo.
København, Benzon, 1953.*

_____Det var den gang.
*paper, 12mo. København,
Branners, 1944.*

_____ Ved lukketid.
*boards, 12mo. København,
Branner & Korch, 1950.*

TANKETORSKE,OG ANDRE
SMAAFISH FRA
LØRDAGSLYNTOGET.
*paper, 8vo. Køpenhavn,
Helios, n.d.*

TOGEBY, SIGURD. Kongen morer
sig. 100 historier om kongen.
*paper, 8vo. København,
Thorkild, 1945.*

TRANBERG, MOGENS. Smedens
Vitsebog en hvile-og smilebog
for smede. *paper, 8vo.
København, Bording Bogtryk,
1956.*

VIA DOLOROSA PER STUDIUM
MEDICINAE, illuminata et
descripta ad usum Societatis
Boserupinae. *paper, 8vo. n.p.,
1947. (Captions in Danish.)*

VORSLUND-KIAER———————
Epigrammer og vers. *paper,
8vo. København, Nationale
Forfatteres, Forlag, n.d.*

WERNER, HANS. Fogelberg,og
andre atoiner. *paper, 4to.
København, Kunsforlaget
Samleren, 1936.*

WIINBLAD, FLEMMING. Kloge
jurister; aforismer og citater.
*paper, 12mo. København,
Gad, n.d.*

WIWEL, N. Julegave til Sorensen
og Skroder pennetegninger.
*paper, 4to. Kjobenhavn,
Thaning & Appel, 1878.*

WULFF, GEORG. Kunsten udvalget
aforismer. *paper, 24mo.
Holsterbo, Thomsen, 1944.*

ZIELER, MOGENS. 40 sider.
*paper, 4to. København, Nodisck
Forlag, 1934.*

# DUTCH

ALMANAK VOOR
BLIJGEESTIGEN JAAR 1829-
1830,1833. *3v. paper, 24mo.
Brussel, Sacre, 1829-1830.
Amsterdam, Diederichs, 1833.*

BEUGEL INA *van der.* Een man
over vrouwen. *paper, 12mo.
Baarn, De Boekerij, 1946.*

———————— Een vrouw over
mannen. *paper, 12mo. Baarn,
De Boekerij, 1946.*

BOTSCHUIJER, HARRY. "Om te
gillen". *paper, 8vo. Amsterdam,
Toneel, n.d.*

CARMIGGELT, S. Omnibus.
*buckram, 8vo. Amsterdam, N.V.
de Arbeiderspers, 1961.*

DAAN, JOHA. C. Hij zeit wat;
grepen uit de Amsterdamse
volkstaal. *paper, 12mo.
Amsterdam, Jacob van Campen,
1949.*

DALEN, PUCK *van* . Moppen
automat. *paper, 8vo. Rotterdam. Appeldoorn-Moret, n.d.*

———————— Moppentapper.
*paper, 8vo. Rotterdam, Appel-
doorn-Moret, n.d.*

DE DEMOCRIET; anecdoten-
album voor het jaar 1848.
*paper, 16mo. Tiel, Campagne,
1848.*

HAVERKAMP, OKKE. ... en
Nederland lacht. *boards, 12mo.
Doesburg, Rutgers, 1946.*

————————*Same. Elfde deeltje,
1946.*

————————*Same. Achtste
deeltje, 1947.*

HEERMAN, FRANCISCUS. De
guldene annotatien. *vellum,
16mo. Leeuwarden, Allart,
1660.*

HUMOR, onontbeerlijk in het leven ... *sheet, reprinted from Albemen Handelsblad van Zaterdag, 30 November, 1957.*

KEN-JE-DIE? *boards, 8vo. Amsterdam, Drucken Aenvallen, 1944.*

KEUR VAN ANEKDOTEN, luimige invallen, snedige gezegden, enz. tot uitspanning. *paper, 16mo. Delft, Van Alphaen, n.d.*

KNOLLEN EN CITROENEN. *paper, 24mo. Amsterdam, De Grebber, n.d.*

LAAN, K. *ter.* Humor in Grunnegerlaand. *buckram, 8vo. Amsterdam, Strengholt, 1947.*

LAMMERTINK, HARRY. Dies yrrah; tekeningen. *boards, 16mo. Amsterdam, De Arbeiderspers, 1959.*

LENNEP, J. *van.* Vermakelijke anekdoten, en historische herinneringen. *boards, 12mo. Amsterdam, Kraay, 1870.*

——————— Vermakelijke anekdoten en alledaagsche bokken. *paper, 12mo. Leiden Sijthoff, 1882. 3de druk.*

LINKS, KAREL. Moffenspiegel; een boekje over Adolf de Ferste (en de Laatste). *boards, 12mo. n.p., Bezige Bij, 1945.*

MALHERBE, F.E.J. Afrikaanse humor verhale. *buckram, 8vo. Pretoria, Van Schaik, 1953.*

MULLER, FRITS. Hang de beest uit. *paper, 24mo. Amsterdam, Bezige Bij, 1960.*

NEDERLANDSCHE ANEKDOTEN ALMANAK VOOR 1834, 1835. *quarter-calf, 32mo. Franeker, Ypma, 1834, 1835.*

NIEUWEN WOORDEN-BOEK VAN ANECDOTEN, ofte vermaekelyk tydverdrff. *2v. in 1. quarter-calf, 16mo. Gend, Vernand, 1792.*

REENS, A.M. Ghetto-ghijntjes; amsterdamsche schetsen. *paper, 12mo. Amsterdam, Boon, n.d.*

——————— Ghetto-ghijntes; humoristische schetsen. *paper, 12mo. Amsterdam, Boon, n.d.*

RIDDER, FRANZ. Historisch A.B.C.; tot een besige ledigheid ... *vellum, 16mo. Leyden, Van Damme, 1699.*

ROODNAT, BAS. Amsterdam is een beetje gek. *paper, 8vo. Amsterdam, Bezige Bij, 1960.*

ROOIJ, JAN *de.* Lollige bakken. *paper, 8vo. Gouda, Jongeneel, n.d.*

VANDENBERGHE, BRUONO H. Aisopeia. *paper, 8vo. Brussel, Uitgeverij Electa, 1950.*

VERHOEVEN, BERNARD. Over de lach. *boards, 12mo. Utrecht Uitgeverij het Spectrum, 1958.*

VRIES, JULES *de.* Ghettoschetsen en verhalen. *boards, 8vo. Utrecht, Bruna, 1906.*

ZINCGRAVEN, JULIUS WILHELM. Duytsche apophthegmata. *calf, 24mo. Amsterdam, Johannes van Ravesteyn, 1669.*

——————— Teutscher nation klug-aussgesprochene weiszheit. *calf, 32mo. Leyden, Franz Hegern, 1644.*

# ESTONIAN

EESTI RAHVA-NALJANDID; mois ja kirik. *boards, 8vo. Tallinn, Eesti Riiklik Kirjastus, 1957.*

# FRENCH

ABELARD ——————— Histoires de cures. *paper, 12mo. Paris, Les Belles Editions, 1927.*

ACADEMIE DE L'HUMOUR FRANCAIS. Dictionnaire humoristique de la gastronomie. *paper, 16mo. Paris, Le Francois, 1941.*

ACANTHOLOGIE, ou, Dictionnaire epigrammatique. *paper, 16mo. Paris, Marchands de Nouveautes, 1817.*

ACHARD, MARCEL. Rions avec eux; les grands auteurs comiques. *paper, 12mo. Paris, Fayard, 1957.*

ACQUES, D. Les contes du rabbin; les meilleures histoires juives. *paper, 12mo. Paris, Quignon, 1927.*

ADAM, VICTOR J.M. An par an; maximes, paradoxes. *paper, 12mo. Lausanne, Du Grand-Chene, 1955.*

ADES, ALBERT, *et* JOSPIPOVICI, ALBERT. Le livre de Goha le simple. *paper, 12mo. Paris, Calmann-Levy, 1919.*

AESOPUS. Esope en belle humeur, ou, Derniere traduction, et augmentation de ses fables. *2v. calf, 16mo. Brusselle, Foppens, 1700.*

ALBERT GUILLAUME (les maitres humoristes). *quarter-calf, 8vo. Paris, Juven, 1905.*

ALEXANDRE, ARSENE. L'art du rire et de la caricature. *buckram, 4to. Paris, Reunies, n.d.*

ALLAIS, ALPHONSE. Autour du Chat Noir "Francisque Sarcey" et contes inedits du Chat Noir. *paper, 12mo. France, Les Quatre Jeudis, 1955.*

——————— Avec le sourire. *paper, 12mo. Paris, Le Quatre Jeudis, 1955.*

ALLEM, MAURICE. Epigrammes francaises (XVI au XIX siecle). *paper, 12mo. Paris, Fayard, n.d.*

ALMANACH COMIQUE, PITTORESQUE, DROLATIQUE, CRITIQUE, ET CHARIVARIQUE POUR 1896. *paper, 24mo. Paris, Au Depot Central des Almanachs, 1896.*

ALMANACH DE L'HUMOUR. *boards, 8vo. Paris, Lang, Blanchon et Cie, n.d.*

ALMANACH DU CHARIVARI. *paper, 12mo. Paris, Librairie Pagnerre, 1871-1872.*

ALMANACH PITTORESQUE, 1898. *paper, 32mo. Tournai, Belgique, 1898.*

ALMANAQUE POUR RIRE, 1862, 1876. *paper, 12mo. Paris, Pagnerre, 1862, 1876.*

ALMORAN ET HAMET, anecdote orientale. *calf, 16mo. Lond., n.p., 1763.*

AMORY DE LANGERBACK, Mlle. Histoires anecdotiqe des fetes et jeux populaires au moyen-age. *buckram, 4to. Lille, Lefort, 1870.*

AMUSEMENS SERIEUX ET COMIQUES. *calf, 24mo. Luxembourg, Chevalier, 1731. 5me edition.*

AMUSEMENS SERIEUX ET COMIQUES, ou, Les delassemens de l'esprit et du coeur. *calf, 24mo. Amsterdam, Francois l'Honore, 1747.*

AMUSEMENS SERIEUX ET COMIQUES, ou, Nouveau recueil. *calf, 16mo. La Haye, Vaillant, 1719.*

AMUSEMENT CURIEUX ET
DIVERTISSANT, PROPRE A
EGAYER L'ESPRIT, ou,
Fleurs de bons mots, contes a
rirer, valeur heroique, &c.
Recueilli par D***. *calf, 16mo.*
*Florence, Mossy, 1770.*

AMUSEMENT DE LA RAISON.
*calf, 16mo. Paris, Duran, 1747.*

AMUSETTE DES GRASSES ET
DES MAIGRES. *paper (boxed)*
*16mo. Paris, Au Cap de Bonne-*
*Esperance, 1867.*

ANA, *ou.* Collection de bons mots,
contes, pensees detachees,
traits d'histoire et anecdotes
des hommes celebres. *10v.*
*half-calf, 12mo. Amsterdam,*
*Visse, 1789.*

ANECDOTES AMERICAINES,
ou, Histoire abregee des
principaux evenements.
*calf, 16mo. Paris, Vincent,*
*1776.*

ANECDOTES DE SUEDE, LES,
ou, Histoire secrete des
changemens arrives dans ce
royaume, sous le regne de
Charles XI. *calf, 16mo. Cassel,*
*Hesse, 1718.*

ANECDOTES DES REPUBLIQUES,
auxquelles jointe La Savoye,
La Hongrie, et La Boheme.
*3v. in 1. half-calf, 16mo.*
*Paris, Vincent, 1771.*

ANECDOTES FRANCOISES,
depuis l'establishement de la
monarchie jusqu' au regne de
Louis XV. *calf, 16mo. Paris,*
*Vincent, 1768. 2me edition.*

——————— *Same. 3me edition,*
*1774.*

ANECDOTES GERMANIQUES,
depuis l'an de la fondation de
Rome 648, et avant l'ere
chretienne 106, jusqu'a nos
jours. *calf, 16mo. Paris,*
*Vincent, 1769.*

ANECDOTES GRECQUES, ou,
Avantures secretes d'Aridee.
*boards, 2mo. Amsterdam,*
*Francois L'Honore, 1732.*

ANECDOTES INTERESSANTES
ET HISTORIQUES DE
L'ILLUSTRE VOYAGEUR,
pendant son sejour a Paris.
*vellum, 16mo. Paris, 1777.*

ANECDOTES ITALIENNES
depuis la destruction de
l'empire romain en occident
jusqu'a nos jours. *calf, 16mo.*
*Paris, Vincent, 1769.*

ANERIES REVOLUTIONNAIRES,
ou, Balourdisiana, Betisiana,
etc. Anecdotes de nos jours.
*paper, 24mo. Paris, Capelle*
*An X. 2me edition.*

APOPHTEGMES, LES, ou, Bons
mots des anciens, tirez de
Plutarque, de Diogenne
Laerce, d'Elien d'Athenee,
de Stobee, de Macrobe, & de
quelques autres. De la
traduction de Nicolas Perrot.
*calf, 16mo. Paris, Delaulne,*
*1694.*

——————— *Same. Amsterdam,*
*Gallet, 1695.*

APHORISMES DU "PROGRES
CIVIQUE," LES. *paper, 12mo.*
*Paris, "Progres Civique,"*
*1921.*

ARLIQUINIANA, ou, Les bons
mots, les histoires plaisantes &
agreables. Recueilles des conversation d'Arlequin. *calf,*
*24mo. Paris, De Laulne, 1694.*

ARNAC, MARCEL. Le brelan de
joie. *paper, 12mo. Paris,*
*Grasset, 1924.*

AROUET ——————— Voyage en
absurdie. *paper, 24mo.*
*Bruxelles, Editions du Soleil,*
*1946.*

ART ET HUMOUR AUX XXe SIECLE. *paper, folio. Paris, Cahiers d'Art, 1957.*

ASCAR-NAHAS, J. Les reflexions d'Ebn Goha. *paper, 12mo. Cairo, Editions de La Revue Du Caire, 1945.*

ASIANA, ou, Recueil de naivetes et d'aneries. Paris, Martin du Pre, n.d. *(Bound with: Arlequiniana, q.v.)*

AYCARD, ALBERT. Le realite depasse la fiction, ou, L'humour en liberte. *paper, 8vo. Paris, Gallimard, 1955.*

BACKER, GEORGE *de., comp.* Dictionnaire des proverbes francais. *calf, 16mo. Brusselle, de Backer, 1710.*

BEAUMARCHAISIANA, ou, Recueil d'anecdotes, bons mots, plaisanteries, maximes, &c. &c. *Paris, Davi et Locard, 1812. (Bound with: d'Alembertiana, q.v.)*

BEUNIER, ANDRE. Eloge de la frivolite. *paper, 12mo. Paris, Hachette, 1925.*

BEAUREPAIRE, EDMOND. Causeries anecdotiques sur les monuments de Paris. Le Louvre et Les Tuileries. *paper, 8vo. Paris, Seven & Rey, 1901.*

BEAUSACQ, MARIE JOSEPHINE DE SUIN, *comtesse de.* Maximes de la vie, par Comtesse Diane. *calf, 24mo. Paris, Ollendorff, 1892.*

BEAUVAIS, JEAN *de.* Histoires de cures. *paper, 12mo. Paris, Bibliotheque Du Bon Vivant, 1926.*

——————— Histoires de commis-voyageurs. *paper, 12mo. Paris, Editions Amusantes, n.d.*

BENAYOUN, ROBERT. Anthologie du nonsense. *buckram, 12mo. Paris, Pauvert, 1957.*

BERESFORD, JAMES, *ed.* Les miseres de la vie humaine, ou, Les gemissemens et souphirs. *2v. in 1. half-calf, 16mo. Paris, Roux, 1817.*

BERGSON, HENRI. Le rire; essai sur la signification du comique. *paper, 12mo. Paris, Alcan, 1922.*

——————— *Same. Paris, Presses Universitaires de France, 1950.*

BERNARD, TRISTAN. Auteurs, acteurs, spectateurs. *paper, 12mo. Paris, Lafitte, 1909.*

BERTIN, T.P. Les rieurs anglais, ou, Supplement a l'encyclopedie comique. *2v. in 1., calf, 16mo. Paris, Chez l'Editeur, n.d.*

BESSAT, JEAN. Au vent dis ouro; au gre du temps; pensees. *paper, 8vo. Uzes, Peladan, 1946.*

BEYLE, HENRI. Melanges d'art et de litterature, par De Stendhal, *pseud. buckram, 12mo. Paris, Levy, 1867.*

BIBLIOTHEQUE AMUSANTE, ou, Recueil choisi de jolis romans, anecdotes interessantes & contes moraux. *quarter-calf, 16mo. Paris, Grange, 1776.*

BIBLIOTHEQUE FACETIEUSE, HISTORIQUE ET SINGULIERE. *half-calf, 16mo. Paris, Claudin, 1858.*

BIENVENU, CHARLES LEON. L'homme qui rit, par Touchatout, *pseud. quarter-calf, 8vo. Paris, Chez Tous les Libraires, n.d.*

BIEVRE, _____ Bievriana, ou,
Jeux de mots de M. de Bievre.
paper, 24mo. Paris, Maradan,
1814. 3^me edition.

BLISMON, ANA-GRAMME,
pseud. see BLOCQUEL,
SIMON.

BLOCQUEL, SIMON. Tresor des
anecdotes comiques, remede
contre l'ennui.Histoire de
Camouflet, par Ana-Gramme
Blismon, pseud. quarter-
morocco, 32mo. Paris, Delarue,
n.d.

_____ Le tresor des bons
mots, pensees, traits remar-
quables, etc. des personnages
celebres, par Ana-Gramme
Blismon, pseud, quarter-
morocco, 32mo. Paris, Delarue,
n.d.

_____ Varietes litterairies,
anecdotiques et morales, par
Ana-Gramme Blismon, pseud.
quarter-morocco, 32mo. Paris,
Delarue, n.d.

BOBECHE see SAILLAND,
MAURICE EDMOND.

BOILLOT, FELIX. Repertoire des
metaphores et mots francais
tires des noms de villes et de
pays etrangers. paper, 8vo.
Paris, Universitaires de
France, 1926.

BONNES HISTOIRES. paper,
12mo. Paris, Editions de
France, 1932.

BONOT, JEAN. Dictionnaire
humoristique des lettres et
des arts. paper, 12mo. Paris,
De La Tournelle, 1947.

BOSC. Mort au tyran. paper, 32mo.
Paris, Pauvert, 1959.

_____ petite riens.
boards, 12mo. Paris. Fernand
Hazan, 1956.

BOSC, LAUZIER, MAURICE
HENRY, MOSE, TREZ. Fri-
volites. boards, 12mo. Paris,
Fernand Hazan, 1955.

_____ Liberte cherie.
boards, 12mo. Paris, Fernand
Hazan, 1955.

BOUCHET, GUILLAUME. Les
serees. 6v., paper, 16mo.
Paris, Lemerre, 1873-1882.

BOUHOURS, P. Pensees
ingenieuses des anciens et
des modernes. calf, 16mo.
Paris, Mabre-Cramoisy, 1693.

_____ Same. Nouvelle
edition augmentee.

BOVFON DE LA COUR, LE, ou,
Remede preservatif contre la
melancholie. quarter-calf,
24mo. Paris, Barbin, 1695.

BOYER, ABEL. Le compagnon
sage & ingenieux, anglois &
francois. calf, 16mo. Lond.,
Midwinter, 1742. (French and
English on opposite pages.)

BREFFORT, A. Les contes du
grand-pere Zig. paper, 8vo.
Paris, Les Quatre Jeudis,
1955.

BRISSON, ADOLPHE. Nos
humoristes: Caran d'Ache -
J.-L. Forain - Hermann-Paul -
Leandre - Robida - Steinlen -
Willette. buckram, folio.
Paris, Over-label of
Librairie Georges Baranger,
n.d.

BRUN, HENRY. Poivre et sel.
paper, 12mo. Paris, Deux
Rives, 1950.

BUONAPARTE, SA FAMILLE ET SA COUR. Anecdotes secretes sur quelques personnages qui ont marque au commencement du dixneuvieme siecle. Par un Chambellan force a l'etre. *2v. paper, 8vo. Paris, Menard et Desenne, 1816.*

BURNAT, JEAN. Histoires des Romains. *paper, 12mo. Paris, Editions de Paris, 1957.*

BUSSY, DH. *de see* MARCHAL, CHARLES.

CALEMBOURG EN ACTION, LE; anecdote tiree des annales secretes des chevalieres de l'opera. *paper, 16mo. Neuchatel, Societe des Bibliophiles Cosmopolites, 1874.*

CALEMBOURGS DE MADAME ANGOT. *paper, 24mo. Paris, Barba, 1800. 2de edition.*

CALLIERES, FRANCOIS. Des bons mots et des bons conte... *calf, 16mo. Paris, Barbin, 1692.*

CARACCIOLI, LOUIS ANTOINE, *marquis de.* De la gaiete. *calf, 16mo. Paris, Nyon, 1767.*

CARTIER DE SAINT-PHILIP. Le je ne scai quoi, ou, Melanages curieux historiques & critiques de bons mots & pensees choisies. Par M. C** D**S**P**. *2v. in 1. calf, 16mo. La Haye, 1724.*

CAZES, E. Pensees et maximes pour la pratique de la vie. *paper, 16mo. Paris, Delagrave, 1901.*

CECIL, HENRI. Coincidences. *paper, 8vo. Paris, Hachette, 1959.*

CENT NOUVELLES, LES. *2v. buckram, 16mo. Paris, Jannet, 1858.*

CHAM, *pseud. see* NOE, AMEDEE de.

CHAMFORT, SEBASTIAN ROCH NICHOLAS. Chamfortiana, ou, Recueil choisi d'anecdotes piquantes et de traits d'esprit. *paper, 16mo. Paris, Marchands de Nouveautes, n.d.*

_____ Maximes et pensees, anecdotes et caracteres. *buckram, 12mo. Paris, Larousse, 1928.*

_____ Oeuvres choisies. *2v. paper, 12mo. Paris, Flammarion, 1892.*

_____ Oeuvres completes. *half-calf, 8vo. Paris, Maradan, 1812. 3me edition.*

_____ Oeuvres principales. *paper, 8vo. Paris, Pauvert, 1960.*

CHAMPI, *pseud. see* VIEVILLE, LUCIEN.

CHARRON, PIERRE. Les epigrammes du siecle; anthologie. *paper, 12mo. Paris, Editions du Siecle, 1934.*

CHAZOT, JACQUES. Les carnets de Marie-Chantal. *paper, 12mo. Paris, Hachette, 1956.*

CHEGHLON, KHATI. Histoires Arabes. *paper, 12mo. Paris, Quignon, 1927.*

CHOFFIN, D.E. Amusemens litterairies, ou, Magazin de la belle litterature tant en prose et qu'en vers. *calf, 12mo. Barndebourg, Les Freres Halle, 1772.*

CHOIX D'ANECDOTES, ANCIENNES ET MODERNES, ou, Recueil choise de traits d'histoires. *4v. in 2. quartercalf, 32mo. Paris, Poncelin, 1803-1804.*

CHOLIERES, NICOLAS de.
Oeuvres du Seigneur de
Cholieres. 2v. half-morocco,
4to. Paris, Librairie des
Bibliophiles, 1879.

CHOMEL, JEAN. Amenites litteraires et recueil d'anecdotes.
2v. in 1. calf, 16mo. Amsterdam, Vincent, 1773.

CHRESTIEN, MICHEL. Esprit,
es-tu la? De Rabelais a Sacha
Guitry 1200 histoires droles.
paper, 8vo. Paris, Gallimard,
1957.

_____ Humour quand tu
nous tiens; de Christophe
Colomb a Winston Churchill;
mille histoires droles anglo-
saxonnes. paper, 8vo. Paris,
Gallimard, 1959.

CICERO, MARCUS TULLIUS.
Ciceroniana, ou, Recueil des
bons mots et apophthegmes
de Ciceron. quarter-calf, 8vo.
Lyon, Ballanche, 1812.

_____ Pensees, traduites
par M. l'Abbe D'Olivet. calf,
16mo. Paris, Davidts, 1761.

CIM, ALBERT. Nouvelles recreations litteraires et gustoriques.
paper, 8vo. Paris, Hachette,
1921.

CLAREL, PIERRE. Le club des
400 coups. paper, 12mo. Paris,
Martel, 1953.

CLARETIE, LEO. Sourires litteraires. paper, 12mo. Paris,
Societe Francaise d'Imprimerie
et de Librairie, 1909.

CLAUDE _____ Interferences.
paper, 24mo. Paris, Jean-
Jacques Pauvert, 1959.

CLEMENT, ANDRE, ed. Les 100
meilleures histoires de l'occupation. paper, 16mo. Paris,
Lesourd, 1945.

COLLECTION DES MORALISTES
ANCIENS. 14v. calf, 24mo.
Paris, Didot l'Aine, 1782.

COLLEVILLE, F. de. Contes
grotesques du Danemark.
paper, 12mo. Paris, Chamuel,
1896.

COLLIN DE PLANCY, JACQUES
ALBIN SIMON. Anecdotes du
dix neuvieme siecle. 2v.
quarter-calf, 8vo. Paris,
Author, 1822.

COLOMBEY, EMILE. Histoire
anecdotique du duel dans tous
les temps et dans tous les
pays. paper, 12mo. Leipzig,
Hetzel, n.d.

COMEDIES, PROVERBES,
PARADES (Tome second).
quarter-calf, 12mo. n.p., 1825.

COMTESSE DIANE see
BEAUSACQ, MARIE JOSEPHINE
DE SUIN, comtesse de.

CONSTANT, BENJAMIN. Adolphe.
paper, 4to. Paris, Le Livre
Francais, 1923.

CONSTANTIN, YVES de. Points
de vue. paper, 8vo. Copenhague,
Berlin'ske Bogtrykkeri, 1934.

CONTES A RIRE, ou, Recueil
amusant d'aventures joyeuses
et divertissantes, d'historiettes plaisantes et recrea-
tives, &c. paper, 16mo. Paris,
Delarue, n.d.

CONTES A RIRE ET AVENTU-
RES PLAISANTES, ou,
Recreations francaises. half-
calf, 12mo. Paris, Belin, 1881.

CONTES AUX HEURES PER-
DUES DU SIEUR D'OVVILLE,
LES. vellum, 16mo. n.p. 1643?

COQ _____ Man'zelle Souris;
100 histoires sans paroles.
paper, 12mo. Paris, Editions
Presses Mondiales, n.d.

CORNEILLE, PIERRE. Anecdotes litteraires. *paper, 4to. Rouen, Peron, 1846.*

CORRESPONDENCE POLITI-QUE ET ANECDOTIQUE SUR LES AFFAIRES DE L'EUROPE. *5v. quarter-calf, 16mo. n.p., 1789.*

COURTIN, ANT. de. Nouveau traite de la civilite qui se pratique en France, parmi les honnestes gens. *calf, 16mo. Paris, Helie Josset, 1671.*

COUSIN D'AVALLON, CHARLES YVES. Diderotiana, ou, Recueil d'anecdotes, bons mots, plaisanteries, reflexions et pensees de Denis Diderot. *boards, 24mo. Paris, Lebel et Guitel, 1811.*

——————Molieriana; ou, Recueil d'aventures, anecdotes, bons mots et traits plaisans de Pocqueilin de Moliere. *boards, 24mo. Paris, Marchang, 1801.*

——————Pironiana, ou, Recueil des aventures, plaisantes, bons mots, sailles ingenieuses, etc. d'Alexis Piron. *boards, 24mo. Paris, Vata-Jouannet, 1800.*

——————Rivaroliana, ou,. Recueil d'anecdotes, bons mots, sarcasmes, reparties, satires, epigrammes, et autres pieces. *boards, 24mo. Paris, Davi & Locard, 1812.*

——————*Same. Bound with: d'Almbertiana, q.v.*

CROCE, GIULIO CESARE. Histoire de Bertolde, contenant ses avantures, sentences, bons-mots, reparties ingenieuses. *quarter-leather, 8vo. La Haye, n.p., 1750.*

CURNONSKY. *see* SAILLAND, MAURICE EDMOND.

D'ALEMBERTIANA, ou, Recueil d'anecdotes, bons mots, plaisanteries, maximes, re-flecions, sentences et pensees. *quarter-morovoo, 24mo. Paris, Davi & Locard, 1813. (Bound with: Beau-marchaisiana et Rivaroliana.)*

DANINOS, PIERRE. Les carnets du Major W. Marma-duke Thompson. *paper, 8vo. Paris, Hachette, 1954.*

——————Un certain Monsieur Blot. *paper, 8vo. Paris, Hachette, 1960.*

——————Le tour du monde du rire. *paper, 12mo. Paris, Hachette, 1953.*

——————Tout l'humour du monde. *buckram, 8vo. Paris, Hachette, 1958.*

——————Vacances a tous prix. *paper, 8vo. Paris, Hachette, 1958.*

D'AVAL, C ——————. Gasconi-ana, ou, Recueil des hauts faits et jeux d'esprit des engans de la Garonne. *boards, 24mo. Paris, Marchand, 1802.*

DEAK, ETIENNE. Dictionnaire d'americanismes. *buckram, 8vo. Paris, Dauphin, 1956.*

DEBERDT, RAOUL. La caricature et l'humour francaise au XIX$^{me}$ siecle. *buckram, 8vo. Paris, Larousse, n.d.*

DE BUSSY, M.CH. *see* MARCHAL, CHARLES.

DEKOBRA, MAURICE. Les meil-leurs contes. *paper, 12mo. Paris, Nouvelles Editions de Paris, 1951.*

DELACOUR DAMONVILLE.
Fables moralisees en
quatrains; a la usage des
enfans. *calf, 16mo. Paris,*
*Barbou, 1756.*

DES ACCORDS, *Seigneur see*
TABOUROT, ESTIENNE.

DESCISEAUX_____ Recueil
de calembours, jeux de mots,
etc. *paper, 32mo. Paris,*
*Delarue, 1854?*

_____ Recueil de contes a
rire. *paper, 32mo. Paris,*
*Delarue, 1850?*

DESPERIERS, BONAVENTURE.
Contes et nouvelles, et joyeux
devis ... *2v. calf, 24mo.*
*Amsterdam, Bernard, 1711.*

_____ Le cymbalum
minud; precede des nouvelles
recreations et joyeux devis.
Nouvelle ed., revue et cor-
rigee par P.K. Jacob, pseud.
de Paul Lacroix. *quarter-calf,*
*16mo. Paris, Delahaye, 1858.*

_____ Nouvelles recre-
ations et joyeux devis. *2v.*
*half-morocco, 4to. Paris,*
*Librairie des Bibliphiles,*
*1874.*

200 HISTOIRES POUR RIRE.
*paper, 12mo. Paris, Paris-*
*Gai-Magazine, 1959.*

DIANE, *Comtesse. see*
BEAUSACQ, MARIE
JOSEPHINE DE SUIN,
*comtesse de.*

DICTIONNAIRE CONTENANT
LES ANECDOTES HISTORI-
QUES DE L'AMOUR, despuis
le commencement du monde
jusqu'a ce jour. *5v. quarter-*
*calf, 8vo. Troyes, Govelet,*
*1811. 2^{me} edition.*

DICTIONNAIRE D'ANECDOTES,
de traits singuliers et
caracteristiques historiettes,
bons mots, &c. &c. *calf, 16mo.*
*Paris, LaCombe, 1766.*

_____ Same. *Paris,*
*Ledoux, 1817.*

DICTIONNAIRE DE L'ACADE-
MIE DE L'HUMOUR FRAN-
CAIS. *paper, 12mo. Paris,*
*Editions de la Tournelle,*
*1946.*

DICTIONNAIRE HUMORISTIQUE
DE LA MEDICINE, par
l'Academie de L'Humour
francais. *paper, 16mo. Paris,*
*Editions de laTournelle,*
*1939.*

DICTIONNAIRE DES
PROVERBES FRANCAIS.
*quarter-calf, 8vo. Paris,*
*Treuttel & Wurtz, 1821.*
*2me edition.*

DONVILLE, F. *ed.* Mille et un
calembours, bons mots, anecdotes, etc., precedes d'une
histoire du calembour.
*quarter-calf, 16mo. Paris,*
*Garnier, n.d.*

DOUMEL_____ Les
meilleures histoires de Marius.
*paper, 12mo. Paris, Nouvelles*
*Editions, 1951.*

DUCHE, JEAN. On s'aimera toute
la vie. *buckram, 8vo. Paris,*
*Des Imprimeries Reunies de*
*Chambery, 1956.*

DUCLOS, CHARLES PINOT.
Morceaux choisis de Duclos.
*2v. tree calf, 8vo. Paris,*
*Nicolle, 1810.*

DUCOUDRAY, ALEXANDRE
JACQUES LOUIS, *chevalier.*
Anecdotes interessantes et
historiques de l'illustre
voyageur pendant sen sejour a
Paris. *calf, 16mo. Paris,*
*Ruault, 1777. 2me edition.*

DU FAIL, NOEL. Contes et
discours d'Eutrapel. *2v. half-
morocco, 4to. Paris, Librairie
des Bibliophiles, 1875.*

DUFRESNY, CHARLES. Amuse-
ments serieux et comiques.
*paper, 12mo. Paris, Bossard,
1921.*

DULAC, EDOUARD. Histoires
gasconnes; Gasconnades,
contes, legendes et proverbes
de Gascogne. *paper, 12mo.
Paris, Editions de France,
1925.*

DU LORENS, JACQUES. Satires.
Edition de 1646, publiee par
D. Jouaust. *buckram, 16mo.
Paris, Jouaust, 1869.*

DUMANI, GEORGES. Goha et son
ane, ou, Le conformiste et le
non-conformiste. *paper, 12mo.
Cairo, Editions de la Revue
du Caire, 1950.*

DUMONT, LEON. Des causes du
rire. *paper, 8vo. Paris, Durand,
1862.*

DUVERNET, THEOPHILE
IMARIGEON. Les devotions de
Madame de Bethzamoeth et Les
pieuses faceties de Monsieur de
Saint-Ognon. *boards, 16mo.
Paris, Gay, 1871.*

ENCYCLOPEDIANA. Recueil
d'anecdotes anciennes,
modernes et contemporaines...
*buckram, 8vo. Paris, Laisne,
1857. Nouvelle edition.*

ENCYCLOPEDIE COMIQUE, ou,
Recueil francais d'anecdotes,
traits d'esprit, bons mots,
originalities, aventures,
meprises, rebus, naivetes,
sailles, epigrammes,
calembours, etc. *3v. boards,
16mo. Paris, Barba, 1803.*

ENCYCLOPEDIE MORALE, ou,
Choix des essais du Spectateur,
du Babillard et du Tuteur. *2v.
quarter-calf, 8vo. Paris,
Maurice, 1826.*

ESPRIT DE M. DE TALLEYRAND,
L'; anecdotes et bons mots.
*boards, 8vo. Paris, Bibliophiles
Fantaisistes, 1909.*

ESPRIT DE PARIS, L' *paper,
12mo. Paris, Editions de
France, 1927.*

ETUDIANTS ET LES FEMMES
DU QUARTIER LATIN EN
1860, LES. *paper, 24mo.
Paris, Marpon, 1860.*

FABRE, SATURNIN. Douche
ecossaise. *paper, 12mo.
Fontenay-aux-Roses, Fournier
Valdes, 1948.*

FACECIEUX REVEILLE-MATIN
DES ESPRITS MELAN-
CHOLIQUES, LES, ou, Le
remede preservatis contre les
tristes. *half-calf, 24mo.
Utrecht, Gisbert de Zyll, 1662.*

FAREWELL, NINA. Du cote des
jeunes filles en flirt. *paper,
12mo. Paris, Fasquelle, 1955.*

FILON, AUGUSTIN. La caricature
en Angleterre. *paper, 12mo.
Paris, Hachette, 1902.*

FINBERT, ELIAN-J. Les contes
de Goha. *paper, 8vo. Paris,
Attinger, 1929.*

_____ La livre de la
sagesse arabe. *paper, 16mo.
Paris, Laffont, 1948.*

FLEURI, JULES. Histoire de la
caricature antique, par
Champfleury. *paper, 12mo.
Paris, Dentu, 1879.*

_____Histoire de la
caricature sous la republique,
l'empire et la restauration.
*half-morocco, 12mo. Paris,
Dentu, 1875?*

FLORIAN, JEAN PIERRE
CLARIS *de.* Fables choisies.
*half-calf, 24mo. Lille,
Castiaux, 1810?*

FOREST, BOBY. Blagues dans
le coin, et nouvelles fables en
argot. *paper, 12mo. Paris,
Beuscher, 1954.*

FURETIERE, ANTOINE.
Furetieriana, ou, Les bons
mots, et les remarques
d'histoire, de morale, de
critique, de plaisanterie &
d'erudition. *calf, 24mo.
Brussel, Francois Foppens,
1686.*

GADEN,HENRI. Proverbes et
maximes Peuls et Toucouleurs.
*buckram, 4to. Paris,
Institute d'Ethnologie, 1931.*

GARNIER, JEAN-PAUL.
Nasreddin Hodja et ses
histoires turques. *paper, 12mo.
Paris, Julliard, 1958.*

GARON, LOUIS. La chasse ennuy.
*calf., 24mo. Paris, 1645?*

GARRULUS, *Dr.* Les gaites de la
medecine. *buckram, 12mo.
Paris, Societe d'Editions
Scientifiques, n.d.*

GASCOGNIANA, ou, Recueil des
bons mots des habitans des
bords de la Caronne et de
tous les Gascons du monde.
Bordeaux, De Crac, n.d.
*(Bound with: Le Nouvel
Arlequiniana, q.v.)*

GAULARD, *Lord see* TABOUROT,
ESTIENNE.

GAULTIER, PAUL. Le rire et la
caricature. *buckram, 12mo.
Paris, Hachette, 1906.*

GAY, SOPHIE. Physiologie du
ridicule. *buckram, 12mo. Paris,
Levy, 1864.*

GAYOT DE PITAVAL, FRANCOIS.
Anecdotes du dix-huitieme
siecle. *2v. calf, 12mo. Lond.,
n.p., 1783.*

_____ Sailles d'esprit, ou,
Choix curieux de traits utiles...
*2v. calf, 16mo. Paris,
Briasson, 1732.*

GEIGER, RAYMOND. Histoires
juives. *paper, 12mo. Paris,
Nouvelle Revue Francaise,
1923. 5me edition.*

_____ Nouvelles histoires
juives. *buckram, 12mo. Paris,
Gallimard, 1925. Trente-
septieme edition.*

_____ Same. *Quarante et
unieme edition.*

GENLIS, STEPHANIE FELICITE
DUCREST DE SAINT-AUBIN,
*comtesse de.* Genlisiana, ou,
Recueil d'anecdotes, bons
mots, plaisanteries, pensees
et maximes. *tree calf, 24mo.
Paris, La Librairie Politique,
1820.*

GERALDY, PAUL. L'amour.
*paper, 16mo. Paris, Hachette,
1929.*

GIANNONE, PIETRO. Anecdotes
ecclesiastiques, contenant la
police & la discipline de
l'eglise chretienne. Tirees de
l'historie du Royaume de
Naples, 1726. *calf, 16mo.
Amsterdam, Catuffe, 1738.*

GICEY, ROBERT *de.* Pour
adultes seulement. *paper, 12mo.
Paris, Editions Rabelais,
1955.*

GOETHE, JOHANN WOLFGANG.
Werther. Hermann & Dorothee.
Maximes & pensees. *buckram,
16mo. Paris, Dentu, 1884.*

GOMEZ, MADELEINE ANGELI-
QUE POISSON *de.* Anecdotes
persanes. *2v. 16mo. calf,
Paris, Le Clerc, 1727.*

GOUNOUILHOU, GUSTAVE.
Les meilleures histoires
bordelaises. *paper, 12mo.
Paris, Nouvelles Editions de
Paris, 1951.*

GRAND-CARTERET, JOHN. Les
caricatures sur l'Alliance
franco-russe. *quarter-morocco,
8vo. Paris, Librairies-
Imprimeries Reunies, 1893.*

GREGOIRE—————*docteur.*
Turlutaines; dictionnaire
humoristique, satirique et
antinaturaliste. *buckram, 12mo.
Paris, Ches Tous les
Libraires, 1893.*

GREVIN, A. *et* HUART, A.
Almanach des Parisiennes
1881, 1882. *paper, 8vo. Paris,
Plon, 1881-2.*

GRIMM, FRIEDRICH MELCHIOR,
*freiherr von.* Memoires
historiques, litteraires et
anecdotiques. *4v. half-calf,
8vo. Londres, Colburn, 1813.*

GUEMADEUC, BAUDOUIN *de.*
L'espion devalise, ou, Recueil
des anecdotes les plus
interessantes de personnes
illustres. *half-calf, 12mo.
Londres, 1784.*

GUERARD, EDMOND. Diction-
naire encyclopedique d'anecdotes modernes et anciennes,
francaises et etrangeres. *2v.
buckram, 8vo. Paris, Dorbon-
Aine, n.d.*

—————— *Same. Paris, Firmin-
Didot, 1879.*

GUERLAC, OTHON. Les
citations francaises. *buckram,
8vo. Paris, Colin, 1931.*

GUS.————La machine du
Professeur Douille. *paper,
12mo. Paris, Segur, 1951.*

GUTH, PAUL. Le naif sous les
drapeaux; roman. *paper, 12mo.
Paris, Michel, 1954.*

HALEVY, LUDOVIC. La famille
cardinal. *paper, 4to. Paris,
Calmann-Levy, n.d.*

HANSI. *see* WALTZ, JEAN
JACQUES.

HENRI GERBAULT. Les maitres
humoristes les meilleurs
dessins, les meilleures
legendes. *half-morocco, 8vo.
Paris, Felix Juven, 1907.*

HENRY, MAURICE. A bout
portant. *paper, 8vo. Paris,
Gallimard, 1958.*

HERY, RENE, d'. Le fou rire
partout et pour tous. *paper,
16mo. Paris, Rire Parisien,
n.d.*

HISTOIRES DE FUMOIR; mots et
anecdotes. *paper, 12mo. Paris,
Editions de France, 1931.*

HISTOIRES DE VACANCES.
*paper, 16mo. Paris, Gallimard,
1925.*

HISTOIRES D'HOMMES ET DE
DAMES. *buckram, 16mo. n.p.,
1913.*

HISTOIRES GRIVOISES. *paper,
12mo. Paris, Editions de Paris,
1947.*

HISTOIRES ITALIENNES. *paper,
12mo. Paris, Editions de Paris,
1956.*

HISTOIRES PLAISANTES ET
INGENIEUSES. *calf, 12mo.
Paris, Helie Josset, 1673.*

HISTOIRES POUR LIRE ENTRE
HOMMES (Collection d'anas).
*paper, 16mo. Paris, Gallimard,
1926.*

HUISMAN, MARCELLE *et* HUISMAN, GEORGES. Contes et legendes du moyen age francais. *boards, 12mo. Paris, Nathan, 1933.*

HUMOUR CONTEMPORAIN, L': souvenirs, anecdotes-interviews. Premier fascicule: Albert Guillaume, par Hugues Delorme. Deuxieme fascicule; Raoul Gueir, par lui-meme. Troiseme fascicule; Abel Faivre, par Hugues Delorme. Quatrieme fascicule; Dubout, par Philippe Soupault. Cinquieme fascicule; Poulbot, par Hugues Delorme. Sixieme fascicule; H.P. Gassier, par lui-meme. Paris, Laboratoire le Brun, n.d.

HUMOUR LIBERE. *paper, 4to. Paris, Delmas, n.d.*

ILLUSTRES PROVERBES HISTORIQUES, ou, Recueil de deverses questions... *calf, 24mo. Paris, Pierre David, 1655.*

—————————— *Same. 1659.*

IMBERT, M. Lecture du matin, ou, Nouvelles historiettes en prose. *calf, 8vo. Paris, Bastien, 1782.*

INTRODUCTION A L'ETUDE SCIENTIFIQUE DU RIRE, PHENOMENE HUMAIN. *paper, 12mo. Paris, Flammarion, 1959.*

ISAAC, JACOB. Les joyeuses histoires juives. *paper, 12mo. Paris, Belles Editions, n.d.*

JACOB, P.L. Recueil de farces soties et moralities. *quarter-calf, 12mo. Paris, Garnier, 1876.*

JEAN-CHARLES. Les nouvelles perles du facteur. *paper, 12mo. Paris, Calmann-Levy, 1960.*

—————————— Les perles du facteur. *paper, 12mo. Paris, Calmann-Levy, 1959.*

JEANSON, FRANCIS. Signification humaine du rire. *paper, 8vo. Paris, Du Seuil, 1950.*

JOUBERT —————*docteur.* Traite du ris. *calf, 16mo. Paris, 1579.*

JULLIAN, PHILIPPE, *ed.* Dictionnaire du snobisme. *paper, 8vo. Paris, Plon, 1958.*

LACROIX, JEAN-PAUL. Comment ne pas reussir; manuel du petit immobiliste. *paper, 8vo. Paris, Les Quatre Jeudis, 1956.*

LA FONTAINE, JEAN *de.* Fables de La Fontaine. Suivies d'Adonis, poeme. *2v. half-calf, 24mo. Paris, Forin Masson, n.d.*

LA MESANGERE, PIERRE *de.* Dictionnaire des proverbes francais. *half-calf, 8vo. Paris, Treuttel & Wurtz, 1823.*

LA ROCHEFOUCAULD, FRANCOIS *de.* Maximes et reflexions morales. *boards, 8vo. Paris, Didot, 1815.*

LATOUR, MARIUS. Le probleme du rire et du reel. *paper, 8vo. Paris, Presses Universitaires de France, 1956.*

LAUWICK, HERVE. Le merveilleux humour de Lucien et Sacha Guitry. *paper, 12mo. Paris, Fayard, 1959.*

LEBER, C. Plaisantes recherches d'un homme grave sur un farceur, ou, Prologue Babarinque a la histoire litteraire et boufonne de Tabarin. *boards, 16mo. Paris, Techener, 1856.*

LECLERCQ, MICHEL THEODORE.
Proverbes dramatiques. 5v.
boards, 16mo. Bruxelles, Hayez,
1827.

LEFUTE, JACQUES. La mystifi-
cation, ou L'art de faire aller
les gens. buckram, 32mo.
Paris, Marchands de
Nouveautes, 1838.

LE METEL D'OUVILLE,
ANTOINE. L'elite des contes.
2v. half-morocco, 4to. Paris,
Libraire Des Bibliophiles,
1883.

LENIENT, C. La satire en France
au moyen age. quarter-calf,
12mo. Paris, Hachette, 1883.

LE ROUX, PHILIBERT JOSEPH.
Dictionaire comique,
satyrique, critique, burlesque,
libre & proverbial. calf, 8vo.
Lion, Beringo, 1735.

LEROY, CHARLES. La foire aux
conseils. boards, 12mo. Paris,
Marpon & Flammarion, 1886.

LEVRAULT, LEON. La satire des
origines a nos jours. paper,
12mo. Paris, Librairie
Mellottee, n.d.

LOIRE, LOUIS. Anecdotes, bons
mots, faceties, contes,
epigrammes. buckram, 12mo.
Paris, Dentu, 1875.

LOLIEE, FREDERIC. Le
paradoxe; essai sur les
excentricites de l'esprit
humain dans tous les siecles.
paper, 16mo. Paris, Nouvelle
Libraire Pariesienne, 1888.

LUDOVICIANA, ou, Recueil
d'anecdotes, traits historiques,
et reponses de Louis XVI.
buckram, 24mo. Paris,
Pillot, 1801.

MAITRES HUMORISTES, LES.
quarter-calf, 8vo. (Title-page
missing)

MANGUIN, ANDRE. L'Humour
chez les Vikings d'apres les
sagas. paper, 12mo. Paris,
Peyronnet, 1947.

MARCHAL, CHARLES. Dictionnaire amusant recueil d'anecdotes drolatiques, par M.Ch de
Bussy, pseud. paper, 12mo.
Paris, Delahay, 1859.

MARCHAND, J.-S. Le sac a
malices. paper, 12mo. Paris,
Editions Montaigne, 1925.

MARIOT DE BEAUVOISIN,
AUGUSTE. (A collection of
anecdotes and stories in
French, with epigrams,
repartees, maxims, &c. in
prose and verse.) boards,
16mo. Lond., Marlborough,
1866. (Title-page in English.)

MAROTTES A VENDRE, ou,
Triboulet tabletier. calf, 16mo.
Lond., Harding & Wright, 1812.

MARTEL, L. Petit recueil des
proverbes francais. paper,
12mo. Paris, Garnier, n.d.
10me edition.

MARTIN, EMAN. Origine et
explications de 200 locutions
et proverbes. quarter-calf, 8vo.
Paris, Delagrave, 1888.

MASQUE DE FER, LE; echoes
illustres du Figaro. buckram,
folio. Paris, Bureau du
Figaro, 1878.

MAUGUIN, GEORGES. La gaiete,
l'esprit et l'humour de
Napoleon. paper, 8vo. Paris,
Peyronnet, 1957. 2me edition.

MEDECINE ANECDOTIQUE
HISTORIQUE LITTERAIRE,
LA. paper, 8vo. Paris, Jules
Rousset, 1901.

MEDICIANA, ou, Recueil d'anecdotes medici-chirurgico-
pharmacopoles. *Paris, Blocquel,
n.d. (Bound with: Le nouvel
Arlequiniana, q.v.)*

MEILLEURES HISTOIRES CON-
TEMPORAINES, LES;
histoires gaies de chanson-
niers. *paper, 12mo. Paris,
Nouvelles Editions de Paris,
1951.*

MEILLEURES HISTOIRES
PARISIENNES, LES. *paper,
12mo. Paris, Nouvelles
Editions de Paris, 1951.*

MELANGES, DRAMATIQUES,
COMEDIES, VAUDEVILLES.
*quarter-calf, 12mo. Paris,
Various pub., ca. 1850.*

MENAGE, GILLES. Menagiana, ou
bon mots, recontres agreeables,
pensees judicieuses et
observations curieuses. *half-
calf, 32mo. Paris, Delaulne,
1694.*

——————— *Same. Paris,
Delaulne, 1715. 3me edition.*

——————— *Same. 4v. calf,
16mo. Paris, Delaulne, 1729.
Nouvelle edition.*

MERCED, RALPH *et* LAWRENCE,
GEORGE. Bonnes histoires
americaines. *paper, 12mo.
Paris, Editions de Paris, 1953.*

MEYRAN, JACQUES. Qu'y dit le
Gars! histoires et blagues.
*paper, 12mo. Paris, Editions
Daverdain, 1951.*

MIKES, GEORGE. A bas tout le
monde. *paper, 12mo. Paris,
Hachette, 1954.*

——————— Drole d'Europe.
*paper, 12mo. Paris, Hachette,
1957.*

——————— Droles de gens.
*paper, 12mo. Paris, Hachette,
n.d.*

——————— Droles de pays.
*paper, 12mo. Paris, Hachette,
1951.*

MILLE ET UNE ANECDOTES
COMIQUES CALEMBOURS,
JEUX DE MOTS, ENIGMES ...
*half-calf, 24mo. Paris,
Passard, 1854.*

MILLION DE PLAISANTERIES,
CALEMBOURS, NAIVITES,
JEUX DE MOTS, FACETIES,
REPARTEES, SAILLES ...
*paper, 32mo. Paris, Passard,
1853.*

MIRABEAU, HONORE GABRIEL
RIQUETTE, *comte de.*
Faceties.. *2v. boards, 16mo.
A-Cote-Rotie, Boivin, 1790.*

MOLIERE, JEAN BAPTISTE
POQUELIN. Maximes.
*boards, 12mo. La Haye,
Nijhoff, 1959.*

MONTESQUIEU, CHARLES LOUIS
DE SECONDAT. Considerations
sur les causes de la grandeur
des Romains et de leur
decadence. *boards, 24mo.
Munster, Imprimerie et
Librairie de Theissing, n.d.*

MONTET, EDOUARD. Choix de
proverbes, dictons, maximes,
et pensees de l'Islam. *paper,
12mo. Paris, Librairie
Orientale et Americaines, 1933.*

MORALE EN ACTION, LA, ou,
Elite de faits memorables et
d'anecdotes instructives...
*calf, 12mo. Paris, Garnier,
1830.*

MOREAU, PAUL. Fous et bouf-
fons; etude physiologique,
psychologique et historique.
*paper, 12mo. Paris, Bailliere,
1885.*

MOSE ——————— Noirs desseins.
*boards, 12mo. Paris, Hazan,
1956.*

MOURGUES, MICHEL. Recueil d'apophtegmes, ou, Bons mots anciens et modernes mis en vers francois. *paper, 24mo. Toulouse, Boude, 1695.*

MURCIER, ARTHUR. Mosaique. Amusettes vieilles et nouvelles. *buckram, 12mo. Paris, Gaume, 1870. 3me edition.*

MUSEE, ou, Magasin comique de Philipon ... *buckram, folio. Paris, Aubert, 1842.*

MUSEE-HOMME, LE. *morocco, folio. n.p., n.d.*

MUSSET, ALFRED *de.* Oeuvres. Comedies et proverbes. *paper, 16mo. Paris, Lemerre, n.d.*

NEGIS, ANDRE. Les vraies histoires marseillaises et les fausses. *paper, 12mo. Paris, Regard, 1954.*

NEUHAUS, GUSTAVE. Breviaire de l'antifeministe. *paper, 12mo. Neuchatel, Cassardes, n.d.*

NICOLAS, ROGER. Blagues a part; nouvelles histoires et fables. *paper, 12mo. Paris, Dumont, 1955.*

—————— Ecoute ... mon pote! *paper, 12mo. Paris, Beuscher, 1956.*

—————— Mes nouvelles histoires. *paper, 12mo. Paris, Dumont, 1954.*

—————— Pochades. *paper, 12mo. Paris, Beuscher, 1956?*

NOE, AMEDEE *de.* Douze annes comiques par Cham, 1868-1879. *buckram, folio. Paris, Levy, 1880.*

—————— Album du siege, par Cham et Daumier. Recueil de caricatures publiees pendant le siege dans Le Charivari. *calf, folio. Paris, Bureaux du Charivari, 1870.*

—————— Paris aux courses; album par Cham. *paper, 4to. Paris, Martinet, n.d.*

NOUSSANNE, HENRI *de.* Anatole France, philosophe sceptique. *paper, 12mo. Paris, Peyronnet, 1925.*

NOUVEAU DICTIONNAIRE D'ANECDOTES. *quarter-calf, 16mo. Paris, Corbet Aine, 1825.*

NOUVEAUX CONTES A RIRE, ET AVENTURES PLAISANTES DE CE TEMPS. Ou, Recreations francoises. *calf, 16mo. Cologne, Bontemps, 1702. 3me edition.*

NOUVEL ARLEQUINIANA, LE, ou, Recueil de bons mots. *quarter-calf, 32mo. Lille, Blocquel, n.d. (Bound with:* Pironiana. Vie d'Alexis Piron.- Gascogniana, ou, Recueil des bons mots des habitans des bords de la Garonne ... - Asiana, ou, Recueil de naivetes et d'aneries.-Mediciana, ou, Recueil d'anecdotes medici - chirurgico - pharmacopoles.)

NOUVELLES HISTOIRES MARSEILLAISES. *paper, 12mo. Paris, Editions de Paris, 1950.*

OCHSENBEIN, HERMANN. Bapteme de l'air. *boards, 16mo. Zurich, Sanssouci, 1958.*

OMNIA HUMOUR, no.13. *paper, 12mo. Givors, Martel, n.d.*

OMNIA HUMOUR BLAGUES. *paper, 12mo. Givors, Martel, 1954.*

OWEN, JOHN. Les epigrammes d'Owen; traduties en vers francois, par M. Le Brun. *paper, 24mo. Bruxelles, Leonard, 1719.*

OXENSTIERNE, JOHAN, grefve.
Pensees de Monsieur le comte
d'Oxenstirn sur divers sujets.
2v. calf, 16mo. La Haye, Jean
van Duren, 1744.

PAGNOL, MARCEL. Notes sur le
rire. paper, 12mo. Paris, Nagel,
1947.

PAILLARD, AUGUSTE. Pina-
poisse. paper, 12mo. Paris,
Segur, 1951.

PANNETIER, ODETTE.
Histoires poivrees. paper,
12mo. Paris, Editions de Paris,
1957.

——————— Histoires salees.
paper, 12mo. Paris, Editions
de Paris, 1956.

PASSE-TEMS AGREABLE, LE,
ou, Nouveaux choix de bons
mots. 2v. quarter-calf, 16mo.
Amsterdam, Aux de' Pens de
la Compagnie, 1753.

——————— Same. 2v. in 1.
calf. Rotterdam, Jean Hofhout,
1760? Nouvelle edition.

PATIN, JACQUES. Du tac au tac.
paper, 12mo. Paris, Lugunum,
1945. 2me edition.

PEACOCK, LUCY. La petite
emigree, conte mele d'anecdotes amusantes et de conversations instructives; traduit
de l'anglais, sur la 4e edition.
calf, 24mo. Paris, Le Tellier,
1836. 2me edition.

PENSEES, FACETIEUSES ET
BONS MOTS DE BRUSCAM-
BILLE, COMEDIEN
ORIGINAL. calf, 16mo.
Cologne, Savoret, 1709.

PERCEAU, LOUIS. La redoute des
contrepeteries. paper, 16mo.
Paris, Briffault, 1952.

PEYTEL, ADRIEN. L'Humour au
palais; anecdotes, repliques,
naivetes. paper, 12mo. Paris,
Michel, 1925.

PERMISION DE RIGOLER ...
paper, 12mo. Lausanne, Spes,
n.d. 2me edition.

PHAEDRUS. Fables esopiques.
boards, 8vo. Paris, Hachette,
n.d. (French translations of
Latin.)

PHILBERT, LOUIS. De l'esprit
du comique du rire. paper, 8vo.
Paris, Claye, 1876.

PHILOMNESTE, G.P. Predica-
toriana, ou, Revelations
singulieres et amusantes sur
les predicateurs. buckram,
8vo. Dijon, Lagier, 1841.

PHYSIOLOGIE DE CALEMBOURG,
par un Nain Connu. boards,
24mo. Paris, Raymond-Bocquet,
1841.

PIERRE, ROGER. On rigole - on
rigole - on rigole - on rigole.
Les histoires de Roger Pierre.
paper, 12mo. Paris, Beuscher,
1956.

PIERRE-GOSSET, RENE. Mes
quatre coins du monde. paper,
12mo. Paris, Julliard, 1954.

PIGAULT, MAX. Nouvelles
histoires fines et savoureuses.
paper, 12mo. Toulon, Editions
Mediterranee, 1952.

PIRONIANA, ou, Recueil des
aventures plaisantes, bons
mots et saillies ingenieuses
d'Alexis Piron. Lille, Bloquel,
n.d. (Bound with: Le Nouvel
Arlequiniana, q.v.)

PLAISANTERIES DE NASR-
EDDIN HODJA, LES;
traduites du Turc par J.-A.
Decourdemanche. boards,
12mo. Paris, Leroux, 1876.

PLAUTUS. Comedies de Plaute. traduites en francois. *3v. in 1. calf, 16mo. Paris, Thierry & Barbin, 1691.*

POGGIO-BRACCIOLINI. Les facecies de Poge, Florentin, traitant de plusiers nouvelles choses morales. *buckram, 12mo. Paris, Willem, 1878.*

─────────── Les faceties de Pogge. *2v. paper, 16mo. Paris, Liseux, 1878.*

─────────── Poggiana, ou, La vie, le caractere, les sentences, et les bons mots de Pogge Florentin. Avec son histoire de la republique de Florence. *2v. paper, 12mo. Amsterdam, Humbert, 1720.*

POUR CHASSER LE CAFARD. *paper, 12mo. Paris, Editions de Paris, 1952.*

RABELAIS, FRANCOIS. Histoire fantastique du celebre Pierrot ecrite par le magicien Alcofribas. *half-morocco, 4to. Paris, Furne, 1875.*

─────────── Oeuvres de F. Rabelais, precedees d'une notice sur sa vie et ses ouvrages, avec glossaire, tables, erotica verba. Rabeloesiana, &c. *quarter-calf, 4to. Paris, Desrez, 1838.*

RAGON, MICHEL. Le dessin d'humour; histoire de la caricature et du dessin humoristique en France. *paper, 12mo. Paris, Fayard, 1960.*

RAMOND, EDOUARD. Marius et cie; nouvelles histoires Marseillaises. *paper, 12mo. Paris, Baudinere, 1925.*

─────────── Les veritables histoires Marseillaises. Galejades et proverbes de Provence. *paper, 12mo. Paris, Editions de Paris, 1925.*

RASSIM, AHMED. Chez le marchand de musc. (Proverbes populaires arabes.) *paper, 16mo. n.p., n.d.*

RAULIN, J.-M. Le rire et les exhilarants. *paper, 4to. Paris, Bailliere, 1900.*

RAVIZZOTTI, GAETANO. Viridarium latinum, ou, Recueil des pensees et bonsmots. *half-calf, 8vo. Londres, Spilsbury, 1801.*

RAVON, GEORGES. Des yeux pour voir. *paper, 12mo. Paris, Flammarion, 1953.*

RECUEIL CHOISI DES PLUS BEAUX TRAITS D'HISTOIRE PRIS DES ANCIENS ET DES MODERNES. *calf, 16mo. Paris, Bobin, 1694.*

RECUEIL D'APOPHTEGMES, ou, Bons mots anciens et modernes, mis en vers francois. *calf, 24mo. Toulouse, Boude, 1694.*

RECUEIL DES BONS CONTES ET DES BONS MOTS. De leur usage, de la raillerie des anciens, de la raillerie & des railleurs notre temps. *paper, 32mo. Paris, Mabre-Cramoisy, 1693.*

RECUEIL DES BONS MOTS DES ANCIENS ET DES MODERNES. *calf, 16mo. Paris, Brunet, 1710. Nouvelle edition augmentee.*

RECUEIL DES ENIGMES LES PLUS CURIEUSES DE CE TEMPS. *calf, 16mo. Paris, Legras, 1717.*

REFLEXIONS MORALES
SATIRIQUES ET COMIQUES
SUR LES MOEURS DE NOTE
SIECLE. *calf, 16mo.*
*Amsterdam, Bernard, 1713.*
*Nouvelle edition.*

REMY, TRISTAN. La cirque de
Moscou. *boards, 4to. Paris,*
*Editions Cercle d'Art, 1966.*

RICANNERIES, LES, ou, Le sabat
des lurons. *boards, 24mo.*
*Paris, L'Escrivain, 1817.*

RIRE, LE. Album du journal Le
Rire. *boards, folio. Paris, Le*
*Rire, 1948.*

ROBERT, JULES. Guide des
amants; dictionnaire dans mots,
expressions et maximes usites
dans le langage de l'amour.
*quarter-calf, 16mo. Paris,*
*Bechet, n.d.*

ROGER BONTEMS EN BELLE
HUMEUR. *2v. paper, 16mo.*
*Cologne, Marteau, n.d.*
*Nouvelle edition.*

ROUSSELIANA, ou, Recueil de
tous les bons mots, vers,
calembourgs, lazzis et
faceties des Cadet-Roussel,
ou l'en a reuni toutes les
M.Brunet. *half-calf, 32mo.*
*Paris, Cavanagh, n.d.*
*2^{me} edition.*

RUPIED, JEAN. Elysee, 1928-
1934; anecdotes et souvenirs.
*paper, 12mo. Paris, Peyronnet,*
*1952.*

SADE, DONATIEN ALPHONSE
FRANCOIS. Historiettes
contes et fabliaux. Dorci.
*paper, 16mo. Paris, Pauvert,*
*1957.*

SAILLAND, MAURICE EDMOND.
Bobechiana, ou, Recueil
choisi des bons mots du sieur
Bobeche, *pseud. tree calf,*
*24mo. Paris, Tiger, n.d.*

———————— Le bonheur du jour;
1,000 joyeusetes et faceties
recueillies. *paper, 12mo.*
*Paris, Nouvelles Editions*
*Excelsior, 1938.*

———————— Le compartiment
des dames seules; nouvelle
histoires de femmes. *paper,*
*12mo. Paris, Quignon, 1928.*

———————— Histoires de tous
et de personne, par Curnonsky,
*pseud.* et Bienstock. *paper,*
*lamo. Paris, Grasset, 1934.*

———————— Le musee des
erreurs, ou, Le francais tel
qu'on l'ecrit. *paper, 12mo.*
*Paris, Albin Michel, 1928.*

———————— Le train de
plaisir. *paper, 12mo. Paris,*
*Quignon, 1926.*

———————— Le wagon des
fumeurs. *paper, 12mo. Paris,*
*Cres, 1931.*

SAINT-ARMAND, JACQUES.
Pour rire follement en
societe. *paper, 12mo. Paris,*
*Editions Rire Parisien, 1908.*

SAINT-HILAIR, MARCO *de.* Anecdotes du temps de Napoleon
I^{er}. *buckram, 12mo. Paris,*
*Hachette, 1859. Nouvelle*
*edition.*

SANTEUL, JEAN *de.* Santeuil-
liana, ou, Les bons mots de
Monsieur de Santeuil avec un
abrege de sa vie. *calf, 12mo.*
*La Haye, Crispin, 1708.*
(Library of Congress states
imprint fictitious. Probably
printed in Paris or Rouen.)

———————— La vie et les
bons mons de M. de Santeuil.
*2v. in 1. calf, 16mo. Cologne,*
*L'Enclume, 1738.*

SAULNIER, CLAUDE. Le sens
du comique; essai sur le
caractere esthetique du rire.
paper, 8vo. Paris, Vrin,
1940.

SCALIGER, JOSEPH JUSTE.
Scaligerana, ou, Bons mots,
rencontres agreeables et
remarques judicieusee &
scavantes. calf, 16mo.
Cologne chez*** (Amsterdam,
Ches les Huguetans) 1695.
(French and Latin)

SCHAAD, H.P. et SCHRADER,
OTTO C.H. Chacun a son
gout. boards, 16mo. Zurich,
Diogenes, 1957.

SEGUR, LOUIS PHILIPPE,
comte de. Oeuvres completes.
3v. half-calf, 8vo. Paris,
Eymery, 1824.

SEGUR, SOPHIE, comtesse de.
Comedies et proverbes. boards,
16mo. Paris, Hachette, 1933.

SEVIGNE, MARIE, marquise de.
Histoires amusantes, scandal-
euses, facetieuses, piquantes.
quarter-morocco, 32mo. Paris,
Delarue, n.d.

——————— Recueil de caquets,
bon mots et anecdotes
historiques. quarter-morocco,
32mo. Paris, Delarue, n.d.

——————— Sevigniana; ou,
Recueil de pensees ingenieuses.
calf, 24mo. Paris, Grignan,
1768.

SEYPPÉL, KARL MARIA. Roi -
reine - prince; recit humoristique egyptien, peint et ecrit
d'apres nature, l'an 1302 avant
la naissance de J.C. burlap,
4to. Dusseldorf, Bagel, 1888?

SINE. see SINET, MAURICE.

SINET, MAURICE. A bons chats,
bons rats. paper, 24mo. Paris,
Pauvert, 1960.

——————— Complaintes sans
paroles. paper, 12mo. Paris,
Pauvert, 1959.

——————— Paporama. paper,
24mo. Paris, Pauvert, 1959.

——————— Portee de chats.
paper, 24mo. Paris, Pauvert,
1957.

——————— Les proverbes de
Sine. paper, 24mo. Paris,
Pauvert, 1958.

SIYAVUSGIL, SABRI ESAT.
L'ame turque a travers les
nouvelles. paper, 12mo.
Istanbul, Zellic & Basimevi,
1953.

SONGES D'UN HERMITE.
Nouvelle biblotheque de
Campagne, ou, Les amusemens
du coeur et de l'esprit. boards,
12mo. Paris, Duchesne, n.d.

SORBIERE, SAMUEL. Sorberiana,
ou, Bons mots, rencontres
agreables, pense'es judicieuses et observations
curieuses. calf, 24mo. Paris,
Cramoisy, 1694.

STERN, ALFRED. Philosophie du
rire et des pleurs. paper, 8vo.
Paris, Presses Universitaires
de France, 1949.

STERNBERG, JACQUES, ed. Un
siecle d'humour francais.
buckram, 8vo. Paris, Les
Productions de Paris, 1961.

SZYK, ARTHUR. Le juif qui rit.
paper, 12mo. Paris, Michel,
1927.

TABOUROT, ESTIENNE. Les
bigarrvres dv Seignevr Des
Accords. vellum, 32mo. Roven,
Jean Bavchv, 1591.

_____ Les bigarrves et tovches dv Seignevr Des Accords, auec les apophtegmes du Sieur Gaulard, et les escraignes dijonnoises. *boards, 24mo. Rouen, David Geuffroy, 1525.*

TERENTIUS AFER, PUBLIUS. Les comedies de Terence, avec la trduction et les remarques de Madame Dacier. *3v. calf, 16mo. Hambourg, Vanden-Hoeck, 1732. Nouvelle edition.*

TESSIER, CARMEN. Bibliotheque rosse. *paper, 8vo. Paris, Gallimard, 1953.*

_____ Histoires de Marie-Chantal et de beaucoup d'autres. *paper, 8vo. Paris, Gallimard, 1955.*

TOUCHATOUT. *see.* BIENVENU, CHARLES LEON.

TOUSSAINT, FRANCOIS-VINCENT. Anecdotes curieuses de la cour de France sous le regne de Louis XV. *quarter-buckram, 8vo. Paris, Plon, 1908.*

TRAIT DES CAUSES PHYSIQUES ET MORALES DU RIRE, relativement a l'art de l'exciter. *paper, 16mo. Amsterdam, Rey, 1768.*

TRESOR DES DAMES, ou, Choix de pensees, maximes et reflexions. *calf, 24mo. Paris, Le Roy, 1826.*

TREZ. Des pieds et des mains. *paper, 16mo. Paris, Pauvert, 1960.*

TRICOCHE, G.N. Recueil gradue de bons mots et anecdotes courtes. *buckram, 12mo. Lond., Hachette, 1916.*

TROGAN, E. Les mots historiques du pays de France. *boards, folio. Tours, Meme, 1915?*

VADE. Oeuvres choisies de Vade et de ses imitateurs. *paper, 24mo. Paris, Marchands de Nouveautes, 1825.*

VALBERT, LEON. Histoires d'autos. *paper, 12mo. Paris, Montaigne, 1931.*

VALERY, ANTOINE. Curiosites et anecdotes italiennes. *quarter-calf, 8vo. Paris, Amyot, 1842.*

VALLEE, LEON. La sarabande. *2v. paper, 12mo. Paris, Welter, 1903.*

VALOIS, ADRIEN *de.* Valesiana, ou, Les pensees, critiques, historiques et morales. *vellum, 16mo. Paris, Florentin & Delzulne, 1695.*

VARILLAS, ANTOINE. Les anecdotes de Florence, ou L'histoire secrete de la maison de Medicis. *calf, 16mo. La Haye, Leers, 1685.*

VASCONIA, ou, Recueil des bons mots, des pensees les plus plaisantes, et des rencontres les plus vives des Gascons. *calf, 12mo. Paris, Brunet, 1708.*

VATELLE, ALCIBIADE *et* VATELLE, YOLANDE. Grammaire de gastronomie sentimentale. *paper, 12mo. Toulon, Editions Provencia, 1951.*

VEBER, JEAN. L'assiette au beurre; les camps de reconcentration au Transvaal. *paper, folio. (Edition speciale du La Satire, Sept. 1915.)*

VELDE, ERNEST *van de.* Anecdotes musicales. *paper, 12mo. Tours, Author, 1926.*

VICTOR, JEAN-LOUIS. Histoires
snobs. paper, 12mo. Paris,
Editions de Paris, 1956.

VICTOROFF, DAVID. Le rire et
le risible; introduction a la
psycho-sociologie du rire.
paper, 8vo. Paris, Presses
Universitaires de France, 1953.

VIE PRIVEE DE LOUIS XV; ou,
Principaux evenemens, parti-
cularities et anecdotes de son
regne. 4v. calf, 16mo. Londres,
Lyton, 1781.

VIERE, MAX. Les dernieres de la
canebiere. paper, 12mo. Paris,
Beuscher, 1952.

VIEVILLE, LUCIEN. Et Champi
raconte, par Champi, pseud.
paper, 12mo. Paris, Editions
de Paris, 1955.

——————— Et Champi raconte
encore. paper, 12mo. Paris,
Editions de Paris, 1955.

——————— Histoires gauloises
de Champi. paper, 12mo. Paris,
Editions de Paris, 1939.

——————— Nouvelles histoires
gauloises. paper, 12mo. Paris,
Editions de Paris, 1948.

——————— Rions ensemble
avec Champi. paper, 12mo.
Paris, Daverdain, n.d.

——————— Les toutes derni-
eres blagues. paper, 12mo.
Paris, Daverdain, 1957?

VILLIERS, PIERRE. Souvenirs
d'un deporte. vellum, 16mo.
Paris, l'Auteur, 1802.

VOLTAIRE, FRANCOIS. Le
sottisier. quarter-leather, 8vo.
Paris, Libraire des Bibliophiles, 1880.

WALTZ, JEAN JACQUES. Madame
Bissinger prend un bain. paper,
8vo. Mulhouse, Imprimerie de
l'Alsace, n.d.

——————— Le premier phono-
graphe. paper, 8vo. Mulhouse,
Imprimerie de l'Alsace, 1951.

——————— Professor Knat-
schke; oeuvres choisies du
grand savant allemand et de
sa fille Elsa. paper, 4to.
Paris, Floury, 1947.

WILLY, pseud. Contes san feuil-
le de vigne. paper, 12mo.
Paris, Querelle, 1928.

——————— Les histoires les
plus spirituelles de Willy.
paper, 12mo. Paris, Le Livre
de l'Avenir, n.d.

WITKOWSKI, G.-J. Anecdotes
medicales, bons mots,
pensees et maxims, chansons,
epigrammes, &c. paper, 16mo.
Paris, Steinheil, n.d.

——————— Les droleries
medicales. paper, 16mo. Paris,
Steinheil, n.d. 3me edition.

——————— Les joyeusetes de
la medecine. paper, 16mo.
Paris, Steinheil, n.d.

ZECZECZEB; anecdotes
indostanes. 4v. in 2. calf,
16mo. Berlin, n.p., 1751.


# GAELIC

MACDONALD, T.D. Gaelic proverbs and proverbial sayings,
with English translations.
buckram, 12mo. Stirling,
Mackay, n.d.


# GERMAN

18-20-PASSE; ein skatbuch mit
contra und regimischt und
ausgespielt. boards, 16mo.
Frankfurt am Main, Barmeier
u. Nikel, 1957.

ADOLPH, RUDOLF, hrsg. Heitere
bucherwelt. *boards, 12mo.*
*Heidelberg, Kemper, 1960.*

AHRENS, W. Gelehrten-anekdoten.
*buckram, 12mo. Berlin, Sack,*
*1911.*

_____ Mathematiker-
anekdoten. *paper, 12mo.*
*Leipzig, Teubner, 1920.*

ALBERTI_____ Das dicke
witzbuch. *paper, 12mo. Berlin,*
*Edenbucherei, n.d.*

ALBRECHT, GUNTER. Welthumor.
*buckram, 12mo. Berlin,*
*Eulenspiegel, 1960.*

ALBUM EINER FRAU. *buckram,*
*12mo. Hannover, Rumpler,*
*1860. 2te. auflage.*

ALBUM UNFREIWILLIGER
KOMIK: sammlung humorist-
ischer annoncen, druckfehler un
auspruche mit angabe der
quellen. *2v. in 1. buckram,*
*16mo. Berlin, Nachfolger, 1884.*

ALLERLEI ULK AUS DEN
BERLINER GERICHTSSALEN.
*paper, 12mo. Berlin, Steinitz,*
*n.d. 5te auflage.*

ALLOTRIA: ungeflugelte worte
aus dem jocosen citaten-
schake des gymnasialdirektors.
*half-boards, 16mo. Leipzig,*
*Brehse, 1888.*

_____ *Same. Zweite auflage.*

ALTDEUTSCHER SCHWANK UND
SCHERZ. *boards, 12mo. Biel-*
*efeld, Velhagen & Klasing,*
*1878.*

ALTEDEUTSCHE SCHWANKE.
*paper, 12mo. Munchen, Lengen,*
*n.d.*

ALTSCHWEIZERISCHE SPUCHE
UND SCHWANKE: aus einer
handschrift des Schwizerischen
idiotikons. *boards, 12mo.*
*Frauenfeld, Huber, 1941.*

ALVERDES, PAUL. Deutsches
anekdotenbuch; eine sammlung
von kurzgeschichten aus vier
jahrhunderten. *buckram, 8vo.*
*Munchen, Callwey, 1936.*

AMOR UND KOMUS. *boards, 24mo.*
*Padua, Tarone, 1790?*

ANEKDOTEN-BIBLIOTHEK...
ein humoristischer haus-
schatz fur haus und familie,
fur jung und alt. *buckram, 8vo.*
*Wien, Hartleben, n.d. Zweite*
*auflage.*

ANGELA. Autonarrisches skizzenbuch. *boards, wide 32mo.*
*Zurich, Classen, n.d.*

_____ Pfedernarrisches
skizzenbuch. *boards, wide*
*32mo. Zurich, Classen, n.d.*

ANGERER, RUDOLF. Helden und
andere menschen. *boards,*
*12mo. Munchen, Langen &*
*Muller, 1960.*

ANTI-GRILLENFANGER, oder.
Neueste anekdoten-sammlung
zur heilung des trubsinns und
starfung des frohsinns.
*boards, 24mo. Nurenberg,*
*Zeh'schen, 1819.*

ARCHER, JUDAS. Der Juden-
freudn, oder. Auserlesene
anekdoten, schwanke und
einfalle von den kindern
Israels. *quarter-calf, 12mo.*
*Leipzig, Baumgartnerschen,*
*n.d.*

ARLOTTO, ALESSANDRO. Die
schwanke und schnurren des
pfarrers Arlotto; gesammelt und
herausgegeben von Albert
Wesselski. *2v. in 1. half-*
*leather, Berlin, Duncker, n.d.*

ARNOLD, KARL. Arnolds kriegs-
flugblatter der Liller-Kriegszeitung. *boards, folio. Lille,*
*Liller-Kriegszeitung, n.d.*

—————— Hoopla, wir leben! *buckram, 8vo. Hannover, Fackeltrager, 1956.*

AUERBACH, ALFRED. Schwabische miniaturen; schnurren und schwanke. *boards, 16mo. Hannover, Steegemann, 1925.*

AUERBACH, BERTHOLD. Schatzkastlein des gevatters-manns. *2v. in 1. buckram, 16mo. Stuttgart, Cott'scher, 1862.*

AUS EINES NARREN TAGEBUCH VON ROLAND VON BERLIN. *boards, 16mo. Berlin, Harmonie, n.d.*

AUSSCHLIEBLICH LIEBE: ein bilderbuch mit rezepten und mahnungen. *boards, 17mo. Frankfurt a. Main, Barmeier u. Nikel, 1960.*

AYME, MARCEL. Die verlobung; oder. Oskar und Erik.. *boards, 16mo. Zurich, Diogenes, 1956.*

BABERADT, KARL FRIEDRICH. Das Frankfurter anekdoten-buchlein. *boards, 12mo. Frankfurt a. Main, Kramer, 1940.*

BACHEM, BELLE. Lacheln aber lila. *boards, 24mo. Hannover, Fackeltrager, 1958.*

BACHWITZ, HANS. Wettensie lachen! *paper, 12mo. Munchen, Bergmann, 1956.*

BALDER, EGON *von, hrsg.* Kleine geschichten aus Rus-sland. *buckram, 12mo. Stutt-gart, Klett, 1949.*

BALZAC, HONORE *de.* Der intime Balzac anekdoten. *boards, 12mo. Hannover, Steegemann, 1922.*

BANZHAF, JOHANNES. Lachendes leben; ein buch voll herzhaften humors. *paper, 16mo. Amsterdam, Bertels-mann Gutersloh, 1942.*

BARANSKI, ADALBERT. Das Kasperlebuch fur grosse und kleine leute. *paper, 12mo. Munchen, Gassler, 1958.*

BARBERIS—————— Berberis deutschschweizerische sprichworter. *boards, 16mo. Rorschach. Nebelsplater, n.d.*

BARON MIKOSCH DER UNGARISCHE WITZBOLD: lustige anekdoten aus seinem leben. *buckram, 16mo. Berlin, Neufeld & Henius, n.d. Zweiundzwanzigste auflage.*

BARTEL, ALFRED. Berliner humor in wort und bild. *boards, 12mo. Berlin, Weise, 1943.*

BARTHLME, ANTON. Von alten hellmesberger; komische aus-spruche und anekdoten. *paper, 16mo. Wien, Konegen, 109.*

BAUER, ROLF PETER. "Es wird besser" sagt Weiss Ferdl; das neue lustige Weiss-Ferdl-buch. *boards, 12mo. Munchen, Hugendubel, 1940.*

—————— Das grosse spiel. *boards, 12mo. Munchen, Braun & Schneider, 1953.*

BAUM, GEORGINA. Humor und satire in der Burgerlichen asthetik. *boards, 12mo. Berlin, Rutten & Leening, 1959.*

BAUMANN, GUIDO *und* STEGER, H.U. In kino veritas. *boards, 16mo. Zurich, Diogenes, 1956.*

BAUMBACH, RUDOLF. Abenteuer und schwanke, alten meistern nacherzahlt. *buckram, 4to. Leipzig, Liebeskind, 1884.*

BAUSE, EWALD, *hrsg.* Kleine geschichten aus Asien. *buckram, 16mo. Stuttgart, Klett, 1949.*

BEBEL, HEINRICH. Heinrich Bebels schwanke. *2v. boards, 8vo. Munchen, Muller, 1907.*

——————— Die schwanke des Rheinlandischen hausfreundes. *boards, 4to. Berlin, Mauritius, 1922.*

BEHRENDT, F. Spass beiseite. *boards, 16mo. Rorschach, Nebelspalter, n.d.*

BELLUS, JEAN. Humour verboten! *paper, 4to. Paris, Artheme Fayaard, 1945.*

BEN-GAVRIEL, M.Y. Frieden und krieg des Burgers Mahaschavi. *paper, 12mo. Berlin, Burger, 1952.*

BERLINER PFLANZEN: ein humoristisches bilderbuch fur erwachsene. *buckram, 12mo. Berlin, Schlingmann, 1859.*

BERN, MAXIMILIAN. Die zehnte muse. *boards, 12mo. Darmstadt, Elsner, 1955.*

BERNHARDT, HANNS. Lexikon vor verliebte. *boards, 16mo. Frankfurt a. Main, Barmeier & Nikel, n.d.*

BERTINA, M. Aber Klarchen! *boards, 12mo. Munchen, Heimeran, 1941.*

——————— Poldi. *boards, 12mo. Munchen, Heimeran, 1949.*

BETHGE, HANS, *hrsg.* Der kanzler; hundert kleine geschichten um Otto von Bismarck. *boards, 12mo. Berlin, Frundsberg, 1941.*

BETHLI ——————— Eine handvoll confetti; gesammelt aus dem Nebelspalter. *boards, 16mo. Rorschach, Nebelspalter, n.d.*

BEUGEL, INA *van der.* Was Adam uber Eva denkt. *boards, 16mo. Zurich, Sanssouci, 1955.*

——————— Was Eva uber Adam denkt. *boards, 16mo. Zurich, Sanssouci, 1955.*

BIBLIOTHEK DES WITZES, HUMORS UND DER SATYRE. *3v. boards, 12mo. Hamburg, Verlags-Bureau, 1880.*

BIDSTRUP, HERLUF. Ausgelacht und angelacht; humoristische und satirische bildserien. *boards, folio. Berlin, Eulenspiegel, 1955.*

BILEKS, FRANZISKA. Heitere welt. *buckram, 4to. Hannover, Fackeltrager, 1956.*

BINDER, WILHELM. Sprichworterschatz der deutschen nation, *half-calf, 12mo. Stuttgart, Schaber'schen Buchhandlung, 1873.*

BLANK, HERBERT. Preussische anekdoten I. *boards, 12mo. Oldenburg, Stalling, n.d.*

BLAUKOPF, KURT. Hohes C zu vermieten; nebigerausche aus dem musikleben der gegenwart fur lachelnde leser. *boards, 12mo. Rorschach, Nebelsplater, 1956.*

BLESCH, JOSEPHINE. Studien uber Johannes Wit, venannt v. Dorring, und seine denkwurdigkeiten nebst einem exhurs uber die liberalen stromungen von 1815-1819. *paper, 8vo. Berlin, Rothschild, 1917.*

BLOCH, CHAJIM. Das judische
volk in seiner anekdote.
*buckram, 12mo. Berlin, Verlag
fur Kulturpolitik, 1931.*

BLUFF; worter und taten des
ehrenwerten Mister Wilson,
prasident der Ver.Staaten von
Amerika. *paper, 4to. Berlin,
Lustigen Blatter, n.d.*

BLUMML, E.K. Schnurren und
schwanke des franzosischen
bauernvolkes. *buckram, 8vo.
Leipzig, Deutscher Verlag-
sactiengesellschaft, 1906.*

BO *see* BOCKLI, KARL.

BOBERTAG, FELIZ, *hrsg.*
Narrenbuch. *quarter-leather,
12mo. Berlin, Spemann, 1884.*

BOCK, ALFRED. Artiges;
GUTartiges - BOSartiges -
EIGENartiges - UN-artiges und
SEHR UNartiges; ein fideler
irrgarten des witzes. *boards,
12mo. Munchen, Lama-verlag,
1961.*

BOCKLI, KARL. Abseits vom
heldentum; zeichnungen und
sers, vom Bo. *boards, 8vo.
Rorschach, Lopfe-Benz, 1946.*

——————— Bo figurli aus dem
Nebelspalter. *boards, 8vo.
Rorschach, Nebelspalter, 1951.*

——————— Euserein; 84
zeichnungen und vers aus dem
Nebelspalter, vom Bo. *boards,
8vo. Rorschach, Nebelspalter,
1955.*

——————— Ich und andere
schweizer. *boards, 8vo.
Rorschach, Nebelspalter,
1957.*

——————— Ich bin ein
schweizer knabe. *boards,
16mo. Zurich, Sanssouci,
1953.*

——————— Seldwylereien.
*boards, 8vo. Rorschach,
Lopfe-Benz, 1949.*

——————— So simmer, 84
zeichnungen und verse
vom Bo. Rorschach,
Nebelspalter, 1955.

BODENSIEK, K.H. Wer lacht is
ein besserer mensch! *paper,
12mo. Offenbach a. Main,
Kumm, 1954.*

BOLL, HEINRICH. Doktor Murkes
gesammeltes schweigen, und
anderer satiren. *buckram,
16mo. Koln, Kiepenheuer &
Witsch, n.d.*

BONGARTZ, JOSEPH. Schel-
mische Justitia; anekdoten.
*buckram, 12mo. Ratingen,
Henn, 1953.*

BONSCH, ALFRED. Kleine
geschichten aus Italien.
*buckram, 12mo. Stuttgart,
Klett, 1949.*

BOREV,JURJI. Uber das
komische. *buckram, 12mo.
Berlin, Aufbau-verlag, 1960.*

BORSIANA: ergotzliches aus
alter, neuer und neuster zeit.
*paper, 12mo. Berlin,
Alterthum, n.d.*

BOSC ——————— Homo sapiens.
*boards, wife 32mo. Zurich,
Diogenes, 1957.*

BOSC, CHAVAL, COBEAN,
*u.a.* Cherchez la femme!
*boards, 12mo. Zurich,
Diogenes, 1954.*

BOSC, CHAVAL, DUBOUT,
KIRAZ, *u.a.* Wird einge-
fahren! autos und ihre
besitzer. *boards, 16mo.
Zurich, Diogenes, 1954.*

BOSC, CHAVAL *und*
VANDERBORN. Kleine
nachtmusik. *boards, 16mo.
Zurich, Diogenes, 1954.*

BRANDL, WILLY. Scherzo; heiteres aus der welt der musik. *boards, 12mo. Esslingen, Bechtle, 1951.*

BRANT, SEBASTIAN. Das narrenschiff; faksimile der erstausgabe vom 1494. *buckram, 8vo. Strassburg, Trubner, 1913.*

_____ Narrenschiff. *paper, 16mo. Leipzig, Reclam, 1877.*

BREINHOLST, WILLY. Handbuch fur vater. *boards, 12mo. Frankfurt a. Main, Barmeier & Nikel, 1960.*

BRENNET, HANS. Der wiehernde amtsschimmel; Berliner geschichten. *boards, 8vo. Berlin, Eysler, 1926.*

BRIE, ALFRED. Der theaterteufel. *boards, 8vo. Berlin, "Lustigen Blatter" 1911.*

BROCKELMANN, C. Geschichte der Arabischen litteratur. *buckram, 8vo. Leipzig, Amelangs, 1909.*

BROCKMANN, H.M. Das deutsche wunder; ein ABC in Karikaturen. *paper, 4to. Munchen, Prangen, 1955.*

BRODTBECK, KARL ADOLF. Geistesblitze grosser manner. *half-morocco, 8vo. Leipzig, Naumann, n.d.*

BROICHSTETTEN, HORST. Eheleute und kirchenleute. *vellum, 12mo. Berlin, Borngraber, n.d.*

BRUDER RAUSCH: faksimile des Strassburger druckes von 1515. *boards, 8vo. Wien, Gesellschaft der Bibliophilen, 1912.*

BRUGG, ELMAR. Vom tod ins leben; ein hymnus. *paper, 12mo. Munchen, Gassler, 1958.*

BRUHL, FRITZ. Ollenhauer in der karikatur. *buckram, 4to. Berlin, Dietz, 1957.*

BRUNS, MAX. Uber den humor seine wege und sein ziel. *boards, 8vo. Minden in Westfalen, Bruns, 1921.*

BUBER, MARTIN. Hundert chassidische geschichten. *boards, 12mo. Berlin, Schocken, 1935.*

_____ Das verborgene licht. *buckram, 12mo. Frankfurt a. Main, Rutten & Loening, 1924.*

BUCH DER ANEKDOTEN VON HOMUNKULUS, DAS. *paper, 8vo. Wien, Nestroy, 1920.*

BUCH DER GUTEN WUNSCHE, DAS; ein gluckwunschsammel surium fur passende und unpassende gelegenheiten. *boards, 16mo. Frankfurt a. Main. Barmeier & Nickel, 1956.*

BUCH DER WEISHEIT; dumme blatter. *paper, 12mo. Wien, Markgraf & Comp, 1862.*

BURGEL, BRUNO H. Vom taglichen arger; eine lesebuch. *boards, folio. Minden in Westphalen, Kohler, 1954.*

BURGER, GOTTFRIED AUGUST. Des freiherrn von Munchausen wunderbare reisen und abenteuer zu wasser und zu lande. *boards, folio. Winklerverlag, 1947.*

BURKLE, VEIT. Der schelmensack; alte deutsche schelmerei. *boards, 12mo. Berlin, Deutsche Kulturbuchreihe, 1941.*

BUSCH, WILHELM. Abenteuer eines junggesellen. *boards, 8vo. Munchen, Bassermann, 1899.*

—————— Balduin Bahlamm; der verhinderte dichter. *buckram, 8vo. Munchen, Bessermann, 1909.*

—————— Bilderpossen. *boards, 32mo. Leipzig, Insel-verlag, 1940.*

—————— Dideldum! *buckram, 8vo. Munchen, Bassermann, 1923.*

—————— Der geburtstag; oder, Die partikularisten. *buckram, 8vo. Munchen, Bassermann, 1908.*

—————— Hans Huckebein, der unglucksrabe. Das pusterohr. Das bad am samstag abend. *paper, 8vo. Berlin, Deutsche Verlags-Anstalg, n.d.*

—————— Herr und Frau Knopp. *buckram, 8vo. Munchen, Bassermann, 1909.*

—————— Lustige kleinigzeiten. *boards, 8vo. Munchen, Delphin-verlag, 1919.*

—————— Maler Klecksel. *buckram, 8vo. Munchen, Bassermann, 1909.*

—————— Trost bei Wilhelm Busch; ein froliches brevier. *buckram, 12mo. Zurich, Classen, n.d.*

—————— Wilhelm Busch-album; humoristischer hauschatz. *buckram, folio. Munich, Bassermann, 1954.*

BUTTNER, HENRY. Humor aus linker hand. *boards, 12mo. Berlin, Eulenspiegel, n.d.*

CANZLER, GUNTER. Die Schmunzelinsel. *boards, 12mo. Berlin, Buchheim Feldafing, n.d.*

—————— Wer will unter die soldaten. *boards, 8vo. Berlin, Buchheim Feldafing, 1955.*

CARTOON 56. *boards, 16mo. Zurich, Diogenes, 1956.*

CARTOON 59. *boards, 16mo. Zurich, Diogenes, 1958.*

CARTOON 60. *boards, 16mo. Zurich, Diogenes, 1959.*

CARTOON 61. *boards, 16mo. Zurich, Diogenes, 1960.*

CASPARY, HANNS. 115 jahre humor aus Munchen; das beste aus den "Fliegenden Blatter." *buckram, 4to. Munchen, Braun & Schneider, n.d.*

CHAVAL —————— Diesseits von gut und bose. *boards, 8vo. Zurich, Diogenes, 1955.*

—————— Mein name ist hase. *boards, 12mo. Zurich, Diogenes, 1958.*

—————— Zum heulen; franzosischer galgenhumor. *boards, 16mo. Zurich, Diogenes, 1955.*

CHAVAL *und* STRICH, CHRISTIAN. Autofahren kann jeder! *boards, 32mo. Zurich, Diogenes, 1959.*

CHEKOV, ANTON. Der roman mit dem kontrabass, und anderer erzahlungen. *buckram, 12mo. Munchen, Braun & Schneider, n.d.*

CHIAVACCI, VINZENZ. Aus kleinen fenstern. *buckram, 24mo. Wien, Mohr, 1914.*

—————— Die frau Sopherl vom Naschmarkt. *buckram, 24mo. Wien, Mohr, 1911.*

CHRISTOPHE, E.C. Die welt geht under; ein buch zum totlachen. *boards, 8vo. Berlin, Kasper, 1942.*

CONADAM, A. (u.a.) Bilder aus dem modernen leben. *buckram, folio. Munchen, Braun & Schneider, 1920.*

CONRADT, ALBERT. Lustigen
geschichten aus Ostpreussen.
*boards, 8vo. Konigsberg,
Reichsnahrstand, 1938.*

CORTI, EGON CESARE; *conte.*
Beethoven anekdoten. *boards,
12mo. Berlin, Frundsberg,
1943.*

——————— *Same. Wien, Amandus,
1947.*

——————— Der edle ritter;
anekdoten un den Prinzen
Eugen. *boards, 12mo. Berlin,
Frundsberg, 1941.*

——————— Die Kaiserin;
anekdoten um Maria Theresia.
*buckram, 12mo. Graz, Verlag
Styria, 1953.*

DA CAPO HUMORE; gelachter
aus den Suden. *boards, 12mo.
Berlin, Eulenspiegel, 1959.*

DAHL, HEINZ, *hrsg.* Lachen der
jugend. Heft 1. *paper, 23mo.
Kassel, Buchdienst der
Jugend, 1956.*

DANINOS, PIERRE. Woruber die
welt lacht, eine kurzweilige
geographie des humors.
*buckram, 12mo. Dusseldorf,
Droste, 1956.*

DARIMONT, REINHARD. Lach
mit. *boards, 16mo. Lubeck,
Norddeutsche Verlags-
gesellschaft, MBD, n.d.*

DAUMIER, HONORE. Karikaturen
der justiz, lithographien.
Ausgewahlt und eingeleitet
von Gustav Radbruch. *paper,
8vo. Gottingen, Vandenhoeck
& Ruprecht, 1957.*

DAZUMAL, ANNO. Aus der guten
alten zeit; lustiger bilder u.
scherzo. *paper, 4to. Munchen,
Braun & Schneider, n.d.*

DECSEY, ERNST. Die spieldose;
musiker-anekdoten. *boards,
24mo. Leipzig, Tal, 1922.*

DEMIMONDE; kulturbilder aus
dem Simplicissimus. *boards,
16mo. Munchen, Langen, 1905.*

DEMOKRITISCHES TASCHEN-
BUCH, oder, Scherz nach dem
ernste fur das jahr 1800.
*boards, 16mo. Erfurt, Henning-
schen Buchhandlung, n.d.*

DENK, OTTO. Alter deutscher
humor. *buckram, 4to. Bonn,
Wahlband der Buchgemeinde,
1928.*

DEPOUD, MOISE. Hande hoch -
es brennt! ein bilderbuch, von
Mose. *boards, 8vo. Berlin,
Buchheim Feldafing, 1955.*

D'ESTER, KARL. Journalisten;
kleine geschichten von der
presse und ihren leuten.
*boards, 12mo. Berlin,
Frundsberg, n.d.*

——————— *Same. Berlin,
Winkler, 1949.*

DICHTER-UND SCHRIFTSELLER
ANEKDOTEN. *buckram, 12mo.
Stuttgart, Lutz, n.d. 4te
auflage.*

DIECKMANN, HEINZ, *hrsg.*
Achtung vor dem hund!
Heitere kulturgeschichte des
vierbeiners. *boards, 16mo.
Frankfurt a. Main, Barmeier
& Nikel, 1958.*

DIEHL, EDGAR. Sterbliches von
unsterblichen; 116 deutsche
anekdoten. *paper, 12mo. Essen,
Bildgut-verlag, 1943.*

DOMINO——————— Party spiele
fur erwachsens. *paper, 12mo.
Zurich, Classen, 1960.*

DORN, WILHELM, *hrsg.* Humor in
der technik. *2v. buckram, 8vo.
Essen, Vulkan-verlag, 1949,
1953.*

DOUAY, MICHEL. Cowboys und
korsaren. *boards, 8vo. Stuttgart,
Buchheim Feldafing, 1955.*

DREXLER, ALBERT. An der
angel hangt das gluck. *paper,
12mo. Zurich, Classen, 1956.*

DREI BUCHER DES LACHENS.
*3v. buckram, 12mo. Berlin,
Ullstein, 1928.*

DROBISCH, THEODOR. Humor-
istischer musik-und theater-
kalendar aus das jahr 1855.
*buckram, lemo. Leipzig,
Wengler, 1855.*

DUBOUT, ALBERT. Widersehen
mit Jonathan; eine
geschichte mit bildern.
*boards, 16mo. Zurich,
Sanssouci, 1953.*

DUNBIER, OTTO. Der kumpel;
schnurren und schwanke aus
dem Bergmannsleben. *boards,
8vo. Essen, Vulkan-verlag,
1956.*

EBELER, GERHARD. Lachende
butt. *paper, 8vo. Koln,
Bergwald, n.d.*

EBNER-ESCHENBACH, MARIA
*von.* Aphorismen. *buckram,
12mo. Bern, Scherz, n.d.*

EFFELS, JEAN. Bilderbuch der
estern liebe. *boards, 16mo.
Zurich, Sanssouci, 1957.*

EHRLICH, MAX, *und* MORGAN,
PAUL. Heulen und zahnek-
lappern. *paper, 12mo. Berlin,
Eden-Verlag, 1927.*

EHRSAM, EDUARD. Weltgeschichte in versen. *2v. boards,
12mo. Basel, Birkhauser, 1956.*

EICHBAUM, PERCY. Kranken-
viste. *boards, 12mo. Zurich,
Sanssouci, 1956.*

EICHHOLZ, ARMIN. In flagranti;
parodien. *boards, 12mo.
Munchen, Pohl, 1954.*

EIFFE, PETER ERNST. Splissen
und knoten; heiteres aus der
alten Kaiserlichen Marine.
*boards, 12mo. Wilhelmshaven,
Hera, 1951.*

EIS, GERHARD. Kleine geschichten alter weisheit aus dem
altdeutschen. *paper, 8vo.
Munchen, Beck, n.d.*

ELBINGER, CARL. Witz und
satire anno 1848. *boards,
12mo. Wien, Wiener, 1848.*

ENDRIKAT, FRED. Der froliche
Diogenes; verse in kurze zur
lebenswurze. *boards, 12mo.
Berlin, Blanvalet, 1952.*

_____ Liederliches und
lyrisches. *boards, 12mo.
Berlin, Blanvalet, 1952.*

ENGEL, ALEXANDER, *hrsg.*
Vorhang auf! 250 witze und
anekdoten vom theater. *paper,
12mo. Wien, Moritz Perles,
1910.*

ERNST, OTTO. Sankt Yoricks
glockenspiel. *buckram, 16mo.
Leipzig, Staackmann, 1914.*

_____ Vom geruhigen leben;
humoristische plaudereien.
*paper, 12mo. Leipzig, Staack-
mann, 1917.*

ERNY, KARL. Adam klagt Eva an;
ein buchlein uber und fur
unsere lieben frauen. *buckram,
12mo. Rorschach, Nebelspalter,
1957.*

_____ In einem gewissen
alter. *buckram, 12mo.
Rorschach, Nebelspalter, 1956.*

ESCHER, KARL, *hrsg.* Die lustigen von Weimar. Goethe-
anekdoten. *buckram, 8vo.
Berlin, Runge, 1925.*

ESKUKE, GUSTAV. Hellenisches
lachen; lustige lieder und
geschichten der alten Griechen.
*buckram, 8vo. Hannover,*
*Norddeutsche Verlagsanstalt*
*O.Hoedel, 1911.*

ETTLINGER, KARL. Marquis
Bonvivant. *boards, 12mo.*
*Munchen, Muller, 1913.*

FALK, J.D., *hrsg.* Grotesken,
satyren und navitaten fur das
jahr 1806-1807. *2v. half-*
*calf, 32mo. Tubingen, Cotta'*
*schen Buchhandlung, 1806,*
*1807.*

FALK, NORBERT. Meisterbuch
des humors. *buckram, 8vo.*
*Berlin, Ullstein, n.d.*

FEHSE, WILLI. Der bluhende
lorbeer. *buckram, 12mo.*
*Munchen, Langewiesche-*
*Brandt, 1953.*

_____ Frauenspiegel.
*boards, 12mo. Esslingen,*
*Bechtle, 1956.*

_____ Lachelnde justitia;
Solomonische entscheidungen
in anekdoten und geschichten.
*boards, 12mo. Esslingen,*
*Bechtle, 1955.*

FEICHTEN, PAUL. Das paradies
der witze; gute alte und neue
witze in rauhen mengen. *paper,*
*12mo. Berlin, Weiss, n.d.*

FELKEL, ERWIN. Lesefruchten
aus antiquariatskatalogen.
(In: "Borsenblatt fur den
Deutschen Buchhandel,
nr.26, 13 jahrgang. 29 Marz,
1957.)

FERNANDEZ FLOREZ,
WENCESLAO. Ein mann kauft
ein auto. *boards, 16mo. Zurich,*
*Sanssouci, 1957.*

FERNAU, JOACHIM. "Deutschland, Deutschland, uber alles.."
*buckram, 8vo. Oldenberg,*
*Stalling, 1952.*

FISCHER, HANS W. Lachende
heimat. *half-boards, 12mo.*
*Berlin, Deutschen Buch-*
*gemeinschaft, 1933.*

_____ Nur sum spass.
*boards, 4to. Augsburg,*
*Bucheim Feldafing, 1957.*

FISCHER, KUNO. Ueber die
entstehung und die entwick-
klungsformen des witzes.
*paper, 12mo. Heidelberg,*
*Vassermann, 1871.*

FLOGEL, KARL FRIEDERICH.
Geschichte des burlesken.
*half-calf, 8vo. Leipzig,*
*Schwickertschen, 1794.*

FLORA, PAUL. Menschen und
andere tiere. *boards, 24mo.*
*Munchen, Piper, 1957.*

_____ Das musenross;
ein buch von dichtern.
*boards, 24mo. Zurich,*
*Diogenes, 1955.*

_____ Das schlachtross;
ein buch von kriegern.
*boards, 32mo. Zurich,*
*Diogenes, 1957.*

_____ Trauerflora; idyl-
len. *boards, 32mo. Zurich,*
*Diogenes, 1958.*

_____ Viva vamp! ein
photobuch zum lob des vamps
von Mae West bis Marylyn
Monroe, von Marlene Dietrich
bis Brigitte Bardot. *boards,*
*8vo. Zurich, Diogenes, 1959.*

FOITZICK, WALTER. Ich gruss
euch, ihr lieben. *boards, 12mo.*
*Munchen, Heimeran, 1956.*

FRAENGER, WILHELM, *hrsg.*
Deutscher humor aus funf
jahrhunderten. *2v. buckram,*
*8vo. Munchen, Piper, 1925.*

———————— Humor der nationen; aus funf jahrhunderten Europascher dichtung. *buckram, 4to. Berlin, Verlag der Nation, 1957.*

FRANCISCEISCHE CURIOSA: oder, Ganz besondere denkwurdigkeiten aus der lebens- und regierungsperiode des Kaisers Franz II. *buckram, 12mo. Wien, Klang, 1849.*

FRANCK, SEBASTIAN. Sprichworter schone weise klugreden. *calf, 16mo. Frankfort am Meyne, Christian Egenolffs Erben, 1560.*

FRANCOIS, ANDRE, CHAVAL, MOSE. Frivolitaten; meister des franzosischen humors. *boards, 4to. Buchheim Verlag Feldafing, 1953.*

FRANKENFELD, PETER. 1000 albernheiten zum frohlichen zeitvertreib; spiele, scherze, witze und anekdoten. *paper, 8vo. Berlin, Blanvalet, 1956.*

FRANZ, HERMANN. Munchner schnurren; lustige geschichten aus Munchen und dem Oberland. *paper, 12mo. Munchen, Hubendubel, n.d.*

FREISBURGER, WALTHER. Konrad sprach die frau mama. Adenauer in der karikatur. *buckram, 4to. Oldenburg, Stalling, 1955.*

FREUD, SIGMUND. Der witz und seine beziehung zum unbewssten. *paper, 8vo. Leipzig, Deuticke, 1925.*

FREUD UND LEID DES EHESTANDES, sowie allerlei verwandtes. *boards, 12mo. Zurich, Classen, 1956.*

FRIEDRICH II, *der grosse.* Anekdoten von Friedrich der Grossen. *boards, 12mo. Leipzig, Inselverlag, n.d.*

FRISCHLIN, LEONHART. Deutsche schwanke. *boards, 8vo. Leipzig, Zeitler, 1906.*

FUCHS-HARTMANN, WERNER. Die Berliner anekdote im 19. jahrhundert. *cloth, 12mo. Berlin, Schlieffen, 1931.*

FUNZEHN KLEINE SCHMUNZEL-BUCHER. *see also* DIE KLEINEN SCHMUNZEL-BUCHER.

FUNFZEHN KLEINE SCHMUN-ZELBUCHER. *15 small paper books. Frankfurt a. Main. Barmeier & Nikel, 1957.* Contents.-Alles gute!.-Auf einem besseren stern.-Blaue dunst.-Brevier der zartlichkeit.-Canzlers curiostaten cabinett.-Gaumenfruden.-Glucklich auf den leim gegangen.-Ein kusschen in ehren.-Ins lesen vernarrt.-Maskottchen am stauer.-Das tier in dir.-Unentbehrlicher ratgeber fur das benehmen in seiner gesellschaft.-Verliebte zeiten.-Verzauberte welt.-Zwischen 12 und 1.

FURSTENWERTH, LUDWIG. Vom kostlichen humor. *buckram, 16mo. Leipzig, Hesse & Banker, n.d.*

GALLETTIS, J.G.A. Der klassiker der Katherblute. *buckram, 12mo. Munchen, Piper, n.d.*

GANZ UND DER FUCHS, DIE: drei dutzend fabeln von La Fontaine, Goethe, Heine und andern schulern des Aesop. *boards, 16mo. Zurich, Diogenes, 1957.*

GANZE SCHWEIZ: sonnig und heiter. 25 froliche geschichten aus dem Nebelspalter. *boards, 8vo. Rorschach, Nebelspalter, n.d.*

GARVENS, ERWIN. Der froliche
jungfernstieg; Hamburger anekdoten. *boards, 16mo. Berlin,
Kiepenheuer, 1940.*

GASS, FRANZ ULRICH. Mit humor
ins ehejoch. *buckram, 12mo.
Wien, Wancura, 1959.*

GAUDITORIUM MARIMUM; eine
lasterschule fur akademiker.
*boards, 16mo. Frankfurt a.
Main, Barmeier & Nikel, 1958.*

GEFLUSTERTES, die Hitlerei im
volksmund. *paper, 12mo.
Heidelberg, Freiheit, 1948.*

GEGEN ROTE UND BRAUNE
FAUSTE. *buckram, 8vo.
Rorschach, Lopfe-Benz, 1949.*

GELD MUSSTE MAN HABEN.
*boards, 16mo. Frankfurt a.
Main, Barmeier & Nikel, 1959.*

GERLACH, RICHARD. Ich lache
daruber; kleine philosophie des
lachens. *paper, 12mo. Zurich,
Classen, 1960.*

_____ Was uns freut; wahr-
heiten zue lebenskunst. *paper,
12mo. Zurich, Classen, 1959.*

GESCHAFT IS GESCHAFT. *boards,
8vo. Zurich, Caprice-verlag,
n.d.*

GILBERT, ROBERT. Meckern ist
wichtig - nett sein kann jeder.
*boards, 12mo. Berlin, Blan-
valet, 1950.*

GIOVANNETTI, P.L. Aus meiner
menagerie. *boards, folio.
Rorschach, Lopfe-Benz, 1951.*

GIRSCHNER, OTTO. Musikalische
aphorismen. *paper, 16mo.
Leipzig, Reclam, 1913.*

GLANDER, HERMANN, *hrsg.* Das
heitere buch; scherz, humor,
satire. *buckram, 8vo. Schwerin,
Petermannken-verlag, 1957.*

GLASER, HUGO. Anekdoten um
arzte. *buckram, 12mo. Wien,
Verlag fur Medizinische Wis-
senshaften, 1958.*

GLASHOFF, THEODOR, *und*
RAUCH, KARL. Die kleinen
troster; anekdoten und geschichten um kaffee und tee,
tabak und alkoholica. *boards,
12mo. Munchen, Bechtle, 1960.*

GLASSBRENNERS, ADOLF.
Unsterbliche volkswitz. *2v.
buckram, 8vo. Berlin, Das
Neue Berlin, n.d.*

_____ Unterm brennglas.
Berliner politische satires.
*buckram, 8vo. Berlin, Singer,
1912.*

GLEICHEN-RUSSWURM,
ALEXANDER *von.* Der Karni-
val; ein buchlein zu lustiger.
*boards, 8vo. Munchen,
Holbein, 1922.*

GMUR, HANS. Zurich von A bis
Z; ein luckenhafter fuhrer
durch die stadt. *boards, 16mo.
Zurich, Diogenes, 1956.*

GOEBELER, DOROTHEE. Pots-
damer plaudereien. *boards,
16mo. Potsdam, Hayn, n.d.*

GOERTZ, HARTMANN. Lieder
aus der kuche; perlen ver-
gessener poesie. *boards, 12mo.
Munchen, Ehrenwirth, 1957.*

GOETHE, JOHANN WOLFGANG
*von.* Mit Goethe durch das jahr;
ein kalender fur das jahr 1960.
*paper, 16mo. Zurich, Artemis,
1959.*

GOETZ, WOLFGANG. Ergoetz-
liches. *buckram, 12mo. Berlin,
Frundsberg, 1940.*

GOGO-WITZ, G.-W. Kraftausbrucke,
redensarten anekdoten und witze
der Tubinger Weingartner. *paper,
16mo. Stuttgart, Mahler, n.d.*

GOLDENE BUCH DES HUMORS, DAS. *buckram, 12mo. Hameln, Niemeyer, n.d.*

GOLDSTEIN, ARTHUR. Das lustige buch des bucherkreises. *buckram, 8vo. Berlin, Bucherkreis GMBH, 1929.*

GOTT STRAFE ENGLAND! *paper, 12mo. Munchen, Simplicissimus, n.d.*

GOTTHELF, JEREMIAS. Anekdoten. *boards, 12mo. Bern, Scherz, n.d.*

GRAAS, FRITZ, *hrsg.* Die gulaschkanone; eine lustige sammlung. *paper, 12mo. Potsdam, Bertelsmann Gutersloh, 1937.*

GRAF, KURT. Das fidele Kurt Graf buch:neues humor und vortragsbuch. *paper, 12mo. Munchen, Universal, 1923.*

—————————— Das lachende geschichten lexikon des humors. *paper, 12mo. Munchen, Parcus, n.d.*

—————————— Same. *Munchen, Parcus, 1929. 17th aufl.*

GRIFFEL, RUDOLF. Lachbuch fur kraftfahrer. *boards, 24mo. Frankfurt a. Main, Umschau, 1955.*

—————————— Verkehrsschilderungen. *boards, 8vo. Frankfurt a. Main, Umschau, 1959.*

GRILL, SEBASTIAN. Graf Bobby und Baron Mucki; geschichten aus dem alten Wien. *paper, 12mo. Munchen, Heimeran, 1949.*

GRIMM, HERMAN. Leben Michelangelo's. *2v. buckram, 8vo. Hannover, Rumpler, 1873.*

GROCK *see* WETTACH, ADRIEN.

GRONEMANN, SAMMY. Hawdoloh und Zapfenstreich. *boards, 12mo. Berlin, Judischerverlag, 1924.*

GROSSKREUZ, PETER. Bitte recht freundlich. *boards, wide 16mo. Frankfurt a. Main, Barmeier & Nikel, 1959.*

—————————— Urlaub musste man haben; eine ferienfibel fur fernwehkranke. *boards, 16mo. Frankfurt a. Main, Barmeier & Nikel, 1961.*

GROSZ, GEORGE. "Ade, Witboi". *buckram, 4to. Berlin. Arani, 1955.*

—————————— Der spiesser-spiegel. *buckram, 4to. Berlin, Arani, 1955.*

GRUN, BERNARD. Dur und moll; musiker-anekdoten. *boards, 12mo. Munchen, Langen & Muller, n.d.*

GRUNER, JOSEF. Wie kann das unbegreifliche begreiflich werden? *paper, 12mo. Munchen, Scharl, 1959.*

GRUNINGER, GERHART. Der damenwitz; ein bunter Strauss witze und aphorismen uber Eva - gesammelt fur Adam. *paper, 12mo. Munchen, Gassler, 1959.*

—————————— Gute umgangsformen bringen erfolg. *paper, 12mo. Munchen, Scharl, 1959.*

—————————— Heitere medizin von grossen arzten und ihren patienten mit einleitenden worten "uber den umgang mit arzten" von Sacha Guitry, Balzac, u.a. *boards, 12mo. Zurich, Sanssouci, 1959.*

—————————— Sie und er nicht ganz ernst genommen. *paper, 12mo. Munchen, Gassler, 1959.*

GUGGENHEIM, ERNST. Das
bose weib; alte schwanke und
geschichten. *buckram, 16mo.
Berlin, Bard, 1926.*

GULBRANSSON, OLAF. Ach wus-
stest du --- *buckram, 4to.
Hannover, Fackeltrager, 1956.*

─────────── 50 jahre humor.
*boards, 4to. Hannover, Fackel-
trager, 1955.*

GUMBEL, HERMANN, hrsg. Alte
bauernschwanke. *boards, 8vo.
Jena, Diederichs, 1925.*

HABT ACHT! 244 militarische
anekdoten und witze. *quarter-
buckram, 12mo. Wien, Perles,
1910.*

HACKLANDER, FRIEDRICH
WILHELM. Humoristische
schriften und erzahlungen.
*2v. boards, 4to. Stuttgart,
Krabbe, 1872.*

HADL, RICHARD. Sieben und
hundert Chinesische sprichworter. *boards, 12mo. Zurich,
Rascher, 1960.*

HAEM, HANS de und HERDER,
HANS. I like jazz. *boards,
wide 16mo. Frankfurt a. Main,
Barmier & Nikel, n.d. (Text in
German.)*

HAGBOLDT, PETER, hrsg.
Anekdoten und erzahlungen.
Buch 3. *paper, 12mo. Bost.,
Heath, 1933.*

HAGEMANN, CARL. Aphorismen
zur liebesweisheit. *boards,
16mo. Stuttgart, Deutsche-
Verlag, 1925.*

HALBRITTER, KURT. Disziplin
ist alles. *boards, wide 16mo.
Frankfurt a. Main. Barmeier &
Nikel, 1954.*

─────────── Johannes. *boards,
wide 16mo. Frankfurt a. Main,
Barmeier & Nikel, 1958.*

─────────── The murder brothers.
*boards, wide 16mo. Frankfurt a.
Main, Barmeier & Nikel, 1960.
(Text in German.)*

─────────── Rue de plaisir.
*boards, wide 16mo. Frankfurt
a. Main, Barmeier & Nikel, 1955.*

─────────── Die wacht am Rhein.
*boards, wide 16mo. Frankfurt a.
Main, Barmeier & Nikel, 1957.*

HALBRITTER, KURT und
HERDER, HANS. Heimat deine
zwerge; die kulturgeschichte
des gartenwerges. *boards,
wide 16mo. Frankfurt a. Main,
Barmeier & Nikel, 1959.*

HAMANN, EDITH. Die klappe;
heiteres von film. *boards,
12mo. Esslingen, Bechtle,
1957.*

HANEL, WALTER. Privat! indi-
vidualisten idyllen. *boards,
wide 16mo. Frankfurt a. Main,
Barmeier & Nikel, 1960.*

HANFSTAENGL, ERNEST. Hitler
in der karikatur der welt; tat
gegen tine. *buckram, 4to.
Berlin, Braune Bucher, 1933.*

HAGELSTANGE, R. Viel ver-
gnugen ... *boards, wide 24mo.
Hannover, Fackeltrager, 1960.*

HANSCHEN KLEIN. *boards,
12mo. Berlin, Metzner, 1943.*

HARTMANN, ALFRED GORG.
Der kunstlerspiegel. *half-
boards, 12mo. Munchen,
Bruckmann, 1920.*

HASEK, JAROSLAV. Schule des
humors. *buckram, 8vo. Berlin,
Eulenspiegel, 1957.*

HAUFFE, HANS GUNTER. Vereins-
brevier. *buckram, 8vo. Augsburg, Heimeran, 1956.*

HAUG, J.C.F. Spiele der laune und des witzes in epigrammen und versifizirten anekdoten. *boards, 16mo. Tubingen, Ofstander, 1826.*

HEIDEMANN, ERNST. Kultur von der stange; zeichnungen zur zeit. *boards, 16mo. Frankfurt a. Main, Barmeier & Nikel, 1954.*

HEIMERAN, ERNST. Alter witz; neu herausgegeben. *boards, 12mo. Munchen, Meindldruck, 1953.*

——————— Buchermachen; geschichte eines verlegers von ihm selbat erzahlt. *boards, 16mo. Munchen, Huber, 1952.*

——————— Lehrer die wir hatten. *buckram, 12mo. Munchen, Heimeran, 1954.*

——————— Die lieben verwandten. *boards, 12mo. Munchen, Heimeran, 1936.*

——————— Der vater und sein erstes kind. *buckram, 12mo. Munchen, Heimeran, 1956.*

HEINE, THOMAS THEODOR. Der zeichner Th.Th. Heine. *boards, 4to. Freiburg, Klemm, 1955.*

HEINEMANN, KLAUS ROBERT. 700 Japanische sprichworter. *boards, 12mo. Zurich, Rascher, 1959.*

HEINSE, WILHELM. Aphorismen. *boards, 12mo. Leipzig, Inselverlag, n.d.*

HEINZ, BOB. Lachen is die beste medizin. *paper, 8vo. Hamburg, Meteor-verlag, n.d.*

HEITER, FRITZ. Die witzkiste; gefullt mit heiteren sachen zum kirchern und zum lachen. *paper, 16mo. Berlin, Moller, 1957.*

HELLWAG, FRITZ. Die polizei in der karikatur. *boards, 4to. Berlin, Gersbach, 1926.*

HENCKELS, PAUL. Ich war kein musterknabe. *buckram, 12mo. Berlin, Blanvalet, 1956.*

HENKEN, GOTTFRIED. Volk erzahlt; Munsterlandische sagen, marchen und schwanke. *paper, 8vo. Munster, Aschendorff, 1935.*

HENRY, MAURICE. Kopfkissenbuch; ein buch fur traumer, nachtwandler und siebenschlafer. *boards, 16mo. Zurich, Diogenes, 1956.*

HENSSEN, GOTTFREID, *hrsg.* In de uhlenflucht; plattdeutsche schwanke und marchen aus Westfallen. *paper, 8vo. Munster, Aschendorff, n.d.*

HERCHENRODER, JAN *und* KUMM, WILHELM, *hrsg.* Die humor box. *buckram, 8vo. Offenbach a. Main, Kumm, 1959.*

HERDER, JOHANN GOTTFRIED. Gedanken und aphorismen. *buckram, 12mo. Bern, Scherz, n.d.*

HERING, GERHARD F. Sottisen; galantes, mokantes, pikantes. *buckram, 16mo. Koln, Kiepenheuer & Witsch, 1960.*

HERMANN, GUSTAV. Lache mit! *boards, 12mo. Dresden, Rudolph's che Verlagsbuchhandlung, 1940. 2. auflage.*

HERMANN, LEONARD. Das bier im volksmund; alte sprichworter und redensarten. *boards, 8vo. Berlin, Reimar Hobbing, n.d.*

HERTSLET, WILLIAM LEWIS. Der treppenwitz der weltgeschichte. *buckram, 12mo. Berlin, Haude & Spener, n.d. 5te auflage.*

HERZFELD, FRIEDRICH. Adagio
und scherzo; kleine geschichten um grosse meister. *boards,
16mo. Wien, Frick, 1941.*

HEUSLER, ANDREAS. Einfalle
und bekenntnisse. *boards,
8vo. Basel, Frobenius, 1935.*

HEUTE; eine neue illustrierte
zeitschrift, fur Deutschland.
*paper, folio. Information
Control Division, U.S.
Forces, European Theater,
APO 757, U.S. Army.*

HEVESI, LUDWIG. Die funfte
dimension; humore der zeit,
des lebens, der kunst. *buckram, 8vo. Wien, Konegen,
1906.*

HILDESHEIMER, WOLFGANG.
Ich trage eine eule nach
Athen. *boards, 16mo. Zurich,
Diogenes, 1956.*

HIRSCH, WOLFGANG. Des wesen
des komischen. *paper, 12mo.
Amsterdam, Veen, n.d.*

HOCHGREVE, WILHELM. Da
kichert Diana. *paper, 12mo.
Berlin, Paren, n.d. 3te
auflage.*

——————— Jagerpaprika;
uber 300 der besten jager-und
fischerwitze. *paper, 12mo.
Berlin, Paren, n.d.*

HOCHSTETTER, GUSTAV *und*
ZEHDEN, GEORG. Mit horrohr
und spritze. *buckram, 8vo.
Berlin, Lustigen Blatter, 1910.*

HOFF, E.O., *hrsg.* Anekdoten und
episoden aus der Deutschen
geschichte. *buckram, 16mo.
Berlin, Pfeilstucker, 1891.*

——————— Geistlicher humor.
*buckram, 16mo. Berlin, Pfeil-
stucker, n.d.*

——————— Juristischer humor.
*boards, 16mo. Berlin, Pfeil-
stucker, n.d.*

——————— Lehrer und schuler.
*boards, 16mo. Berlin, Pfeil-
stucker, n.d.*

HOFFDING, HARALD. Humor als
lebensgefuhl. (Der grosse
humor.) Eine psychologische
studie. *buckram, 8vo. Leipzig, Teubner, 1918.*

——————— *Same. Leipzig,
Reisland, 1930. 2te auflage.*

HOFFMANN, HEINRICH. Der
Struwwelpeter, oder, Lustige
geschichten und drollige bil-
der. *boards, 4to. Frankfurt a.
Main, Literarische Anstalt
Rutten & Loening, 1871?*

HOFFMANN, WALTER. Humor
aus der kinder-und schules-
tube. *quarter-buckram, 16mo.
Leipzig, Arnoldische Buchhandlung, 1872.*

HOFFMEISTER, HERBERT.
Anekdotenschatz von der
antike bis auf unsere tage.
*boards, 8vo. Berlin, Prakti-
sches Wissen, 1957.*

HOFMANN, FRITZ. Humor-cock-
tail aus witz und lebens-
freude. *paper, 12mo. Munchen,
Gassler, 1959.*

HOFMANN, WERNER. Die karikatur von Leonardo bis Picasso. *buckram, 4to. Wien,
Verlag Bruders Rosenbaum,
1956.*

HOHOFF, CURT. Komik und
humor bie Heinrich von Kleist.
*paper, 4to. Berlin, Ebering,
1937.*

HOLLEROP, HANS. Musiker-
anekdoten. *boards, 12mo.
Stuttgart, Engelhorns Nachf,
1922.*

HOLTHAUS, HELLMUT. Justus
und Angelo; taten, untaten
und wiesheiten diese bruder,
getreulich beschrieben und
philosophisch betrachet.
*buckram, 12mo. Frankfurt a.
Main, Knecht, 1956.*

HOMONCULUS. Die rose und der
ziegelstein; anekdoten. *boards,
8vo. Berlin, Deutsche Buch-
Gemeinschaft, 1938.*

HOPP, FRIEDRICH. Magazin fur
lachlustige. Erster band.
*boards, 8vo. Wien, Benko,
1840.*

HORODISCH, A. Buchwesen und
bibliophilie in der modernen
Amerikanischen karikatur.
*paper, 4to. (Sonderabdruck aus
"Stultifera Navis" 1951-1952)*

HOURSCH, A. Kolsche kratzcher.
*boards, 4to. Koln, Hoursch &
Bechstedt, n.d.*

HUFF, DARRELL. Wie lugt man
mit statistik. *boards, 12mo.
Zurich, Sanssouci, 1956.*

HUHNHAUFER, ALFRED.
Kleines anekdotenbuch. *paper,
8vo. Oslo, Deutsche Zeitung
in Norwegen, 1944.*

HUMOR AUS OSTPREUSSEN.
*paper, 12mo. Munchen, Grafe &
Unzer, 1952.*

HUMOR IM BUCHHANDEL; ein
vademecum fur lustiger und
traurige buchhandler. *buckram,
12mo. Augsburg, Schmid'sche
Buchhandlung, 1887.*

HUMOR IN ZEICHNUNGEN VON
GESTERN UND HEUTE; ein
wochenkalender fur das jahr
1958. *paper, 8vo. Heidelberg,
Richters, 1958.*

HUMORISTISCH-SATIRISCH
VOLKS-KALENDAR DES
KLADDER-ADATSCH FUR
1866. *paper, 12mo. Berlin,
Hofmann, 1866.*

HUNDERT LUSTIGE BOCK-
SPRUNGE, oder, Possen uber
possen. *boards, 16mo. Prag,
Buchler,1801.*

HUTHER, WALDEMAR. Das
lustige kegeln; 25 beliebte
kegelspiele. *paper, 24mo.
Munchen, Gassler, 1958.*

IHRINGER, BERNHARD.
Deutsches schwankbuch.
*boards, 12mo. Stuttgart, Lutz,
n.d.*

ILLUSTRIRTER ANEKDOTEN-
SCHATZ. *buckram, 24mo.
Leipzig, Steinacher, 1862?*

INTERESSANTA UNTERHAL-
TUNGS-LECTURE FUR
JAGER UND JAGERFREUNDE
IN ERZAHLUNGEN, ABEN-
TEUREN, ANEKDOTEN. *2v.
paper, 16mo. Ulm, Ebnerschen
Buchhandlung, 1840.*

IRONIMUS, *pseud.* Julius, ein
kanzler in der karikatur. *buckram, 12mo. Wien-Munchen,
Wedl, 1958.*

....IST EINE HIMMELSMACHT,
mit zeichnungen, von Istvan
Hegedus, Tibor Kajan, Laszlo
Reber und Anna Vasvari.
*boards, 16mo. Berlin, Eulen-
spiegel, 1959.*

JACOBSOHN, EGON. "A propos
jungfrau" eine neues witze-
lexikon. *paper, 8vo. Berlin,
Eysler, 1927.*

JACOBSSON, O. Adamson; lieder
ohne worte. *boards, 12mo.
Berlin, Selle-Eysler, 1927.*

JAGER, OKKE. Die Bibel hat
humor-und wir? *boards, 12mo.
Zurich, Zwingli, 1956.*

JAMESON, EGON *und* LORIOT.
Wie gewinnt man eine wahl?
Ein erschopfender leitfaden
fur wahler und politiker aller
parteien...*boards, 16mo.*
*Frankfurt a. Main, Barmeier*
*und Nikel, 1957.*

JAMESON, EGON, FORD, COREY
*und* LORIOT. Wie wird mann
reich, schlank und prominent?
Ein reich bebildertes lehrbuch.
*boards, 16mo. Frankfurt a.*
*Main, Barmeier & Nikel, 1956.*

JASPERT, WILLEM. Olle kamel-
len; 200 anekdoten. *boards,*
*16mo. Berlin, Siegismund, 1940.*

JELUSICH, MIRKO. Geschichten
aus dem Wiener Wald. *buck-*
*ram, 12mo. Wien, Speidelsche*
*Buchhandlung, 1939.*

JOKUS DES HYPOCHONDERS
FEIND. *paper, 12mo. Nurnberg,*
*Zeh, 1826.*

JOST, LOLA. Liebe unterm
Petersturm. *paper, 12mo.*
*Munchen, Gassler, n.d.*

JUNCUS, GUILELMUS. Des anti-
quars und bucher-freundes
palmen-gartlein. *paper, 12mo.*
*1726. (Neudruck) Darmstadt,*
*Hohmann, 1926.*

JUSTIZ-KURIOSITATEN: allerlei
sachelchen und sachen aus dem
rechtsleben. *paper, 12mo.*
*Munchen, Scharl, 1959.*

KAHN, GUSTAVE. Das weib in
der karikatur Frankreichs.
*buckram, 4to. Stuttgart,*
*Schmidts, 1907.*

KAISER, BRUNO, *hrsg.* Der
gefalschte Don Quijote; literarische missetaten aus drei
jahrhunderten. *boards, 8vo.*
*(Germany) Feldafing, 1957.*

KALKSCHMIDT, EUGEN.
Deutsche freiheit und deutscher
witz; ein kapital revolutions-
satire aus der zeit von 1830-
1850. *buckram, 4to. Hamburg,*
*Hanseatische Verlagsanstalt,*
*1928.*

KANAPEEBUCH, DAS: beschaul-
iches, ergotzliches, galantes.
*buckram, 12mo. Zurich, Clas-*
*sen, 1954.*

KASPER, HANS. 100 Kasperiolen.
*paper, 8vo. Berlin, Grunewald,*
*n.d.*

———————— Hans Kasper, 1946-
1948. *paper, 16mo. Berlin,*
*Verlag der Kurier, 1948.*

KASTNER, ERICH. Grosse zeiten
- kleine auswahl. *boards, 24mo.*
*Hannover, Schmidt, 1959.*

KELLEN, TONY, *hrsg.*
Schauspieler-anekdoten.
*buckram, 12mo. Stuttgart,*
*Lutz, n.d. 2te auflage.*

KELLER, ALBRECHT. Die hand-
werker im volkshumor. *buck-*
*ram, 8vo. Leipzig, Heims,*
*1912.*

KELLER, PAUL ANTON. Die
freiherrlichen hosen; alstei-
rische anekdoten. *boards,*
*12mo. Graz, Leykam, 1942.*

KERNECK, HEINZ. Hort! Hort!
300 ebenso lustige wie uber-
wiegend wahre anekdoten und
geschichten aus der Deut-
schennachkriegspolitik.
*buckram, 12mo. Berlin, Arani,*
*1957.*

KIMMIG, HEINZ. Die besten juris-
tenwitze. *paper, 8vo. Konstanz,*
*Terra-verlag, 1955.*

KIPPE, HUGO. Achtung, witze;
eine sammlung heil-kraftiger
witze, loffelweise ein zuneh-
men. *paper, 12mo. Lindau,*
*Rudolph, n.d.*

———————Kennst du den?
witze am laufenden band.
*paper, 12mo. Lindau, Rudolph,
n.d.*

———————Liebe, ehe und andere argernisse. *paper, 12mo.
Lindau, Rudolph, n.d.*

———————Nichts fur kinder; die
noch nicht lesen konnen. *paper,
12mo. Lindau, Rudolph, n.d.*

KIRN, RICHARD. Der lachende
fussball; anekdoten und geschichten um das runde leder.
*paper, 12mo. Nurnberg,
Willmy, 1944.*

KIWITZ, HEINZ. Enaks ges-
chichten. *boards, 12mo. Berlin,
Rowohlt, 1936.*

KLAUSSMANN, A. OSKAR. Der
humor in Deutschen heere.
*quarter-calf, 12mo. Berlin,
Schorer, n.d.*

KLEINE MODEBUCH, DAS,
plaudereien uber ein uner-
schopfliches thema. *boards,
16mo. Stuttgart, Seifert, 1924.*

KLEINE SPOTVOGEL, DIE.
*paper, 24mo. Amsterdam,
Peypers & Lintvelt, 1854.*

KLEINECKE, RUDOLF. Musiker-
humor; anekdoten und ges-
chichten. *paper, 8vo. Wien,
Perles, 1916.*

KLEINEN SCHMUNZELBUCHER
*see also* FUNFZEHN KLEINE
SCHMUNZELBUCHER.

KLEINEN SCHMUNZELBUCHER,
DIE. 20 booklets. *paper, 24mo.
Frankfurt a. Main Barmeier &
Nikel, 1959-1960.*
*Contents.*-Alles gute!-Amors
pfeile.-Die arche und die tiere.-
Blende auf.-Blucklich auf den
leim gegangen.-Brevier der
zarlichkeit.-Helden.-Ein
katzchen in ehren.-Ein kleiner
tick.-Lasst blumen sprechen.-
Maskottchen am steuer.-Shock-
ing.-Suleika.-Taktik des ehe-
krieges.-Der teufel ist los.-
Trautes heim.-Unentbehrlicher
ratgeber.-Verliebte zeiten.-
Verzauberte welt.-Wie komme
ich zum film?

KLINSKY, E.J. *und* REICH,
HANNS. Lachende kamera.
*boards, 8vo. Munchen, Reich,
1959.*

KLOOKSNUUT, PETER. Ham-
burg wie es est - trink und
schlaft. Scenen aus dem
Hamburger volksleben. *boards,
12mo. Hamburg, Berendsohn,
1835.*

KLOTZ, WILLEM. Pauker, penne
und pennaler; aus der schule
geplaudert. *paper, 12mo.
Berlin, Collignon, 1940.*

KNAP, HENRI. O ihr frauen!
*boards, 12mo. Zurich, Sans-
souci, 1957.*

———————Trostbuchlein fur
vater. *boards, 12mo. Zurich,
Sanssouci, 1958.*

KNAURS LACHENDE WELT.
*buckram, 4to. Zurich, Knauf,
1955.*

KOCH, WILHELM. Ommerjoon-
cher; lustige kolsche ver-
zallcher. *paper, 8vo. Bachem,
1946.*

KOCH-GOTHA, FRITZ. Koch-
Gotha album. *boards, folio.
Berlin, Ullstein, 1914.*

KOHLER, H.E. *und* SUSKIND, W.E. Wer hatte das von uns gedacht; zehn jahre Bundesrepublik Deutshland. *buckram, 8vo. Boppard a. Rhein, Boldt, 1959.*

KOHN, C.M. Wer lachelt mit? eine sammlung deutschen humors. *boards, 4to. Berlin, Deutsche Buch-Gemeinschaft, 1939.*

KOHN, P.J. Rabbinischer humor aus alter und neuer zeit; eine sammlung von anekdoten und "guten wortchen". *boards, 12mo. Berlin, Lamm, 1915.*

KOHUF, ADOLPH. Ernestes und heiteres von beruhmten aerzten, apothekern und naturforschern. *buckram, 12mo. Berlin, Berlinische Verlaganstalt, n.d.*

——————— Furst Bismarck als humorist. *paper, 12mo. Dusseldorf, Bagel, n.d.*

KOLLATZ——————— Na bitte! auf die schippe genomen. *boards, 12mo. Berlin, Blanvalet, 1955.*

KOMISCHE SCENEN AUS DER AKADEMISCHEN WELT ZUR ERINNERUNG FOR ALLE FIDELEN BRUDER. *half-calf, 12mo. Leipzig, Nauck, 1832.*

KONIGSBERGER WEISHEITEN. *boards, 16mo. Konigsberg, Grafe & Unzer, n.d.*

KONIGSWARTER, W. Der witz als waffe. *paper, 16mo. Hannover, Goedel, 1955.*

KOVARY, FERDINAND. Lustiges Osterreich zwischen Bombay und New York. *paper, 8vo. Wien, Selbstverlag, 1947.*

KRAIS, ULRICH, *hrgs.* Kleine geschichten aus dem alten Rom. *buckram, 16mo. Stuttgart, Klett, 1949.*

——————— Kleine geschichten aus Hellas. *buckram, 16mo. Stuttgart, Klett, 1949.*

——————— Kleine geschichten aus Osterreich. *buckram, 16mo. Stuttgart, Klett, n.d.*

KRAMER, KARL HEINZ. Lob der trane; ein moritatenbuch. *buckram, 16mo. Koln, Kippenheuer & Witsch, 1955.*

KRAMER, WOLFGANG. Aus kindermund; vergnugliche fragen und antworten unserer kleinen. *2v. paper, 12mo. Munchen, Gassler, 1959.*

——————— Heiteres allerle! anekdoten, bonmots, scherze, schnurren, zeitungshumor. *paper, 12mo. Munchen, Scherl, 1960.*

——————— Kurtrierische hexenprozelle im 16. und 17. jahrhundert. *paper, 8vo. Munchen, Scherl, 1959.*

——————— Lukasburger stilbluten; aus den aufsatzen der kleinen fur den stammtisch der grossen. *2v. paper, 12mo. Munchen, Gassler, 1958.*

KRAUS, KRISTIAN. Hans Clauert der markische Eulenspiegel... *buckram, 12mo. Berlin, Scherl, n.d.*

KRAUSE, CONRAD. Humor der antike. *boards, 12mo. Bonn, Dummlers, 1948.*

KRAUSS, FRIEDRICH. Zigeunerhumor. *paper, 12mo. Leipzig, Deutsche Verlagsactiengesellschaft, 1907.*

KREIN, DANIELA, *hrsg.* Anekdoten um Konrad Adenauer. *buckram, 12mo. Heidelberg, Kemper, 1959.*

KUBLER, ARNOLD. Velodyssee; ein sportliches epos. *boards, 32mo. Zurich, Diogenes, n.d.*

KUCHENMEISTER VOM EULEN-
SPIEGEL VERLAG, DER,
Berlin empfiehlt Paprika,
zurzige schoten von Ungari-
schen zeichnern. *boards, 12mo.
Berlin, Eulenspiegel, 1959.*

KUKELHAUS, HUGO. Geschichten vom traumling. *boards,
12mo. Frankfurt a. Main.
Barmeier & Nikel, 1960.*

KUNSTLER, DER: kulturbilder
aus dem Simplicissmus. *boards,
16mo. Munchen, Langen, 1906.*

KUNTSWERK, DIE. Heft 5, 1953.
*paper, 4to. Baden-Baden,
Klein, 1953.*

KUNTZE, C. Napoleon anekdoten.
v.2. *buckram, 12mo. Stuttgart,
Lutz, 1908. 2te auflage.*

KURZWEILIG LESEN VOM TILL
ULENSPIEGEL, EIN. *boards,
12mo. Leipzig, Insel-verlag,
n.d.*

KUSENBERG, KURT. Lob der
faulheit. *boards, 16mo. Frankfurt a. Main, Barmeier & Nikel,
1955.*

LAATHS, ERWIN. Heitere meister-
erzahlungen der deutschen lit-
eratur. *buckram, 12mo. Dusseldorf, Droste, 1956.*

LACHE DICH GESUND. 1-8 band-
chen. *paper, 16mo. Berlin,
Hesse, 1955-1956.*

LACHEN IS DIE BESTE MEDIZIN.
*paper, 8vo. Hamburg, Meteor,
1958.*

LACHENDE HAUSBUCH, DAS.
*buckram, 12mo. Berlin, Franke,
n.d.*

LACKAS, N. Witze und spasse vom
"Fischers Maathes". *paper,
16mo. Saarbrucker Druckerei,
1930.*

LALENBUCH, DAS. *boards, 16mo.
Halle, n.p., n.d.*

LANDMAN, SALCIA. Der judische
witz. *buckram, 12mo. Olten und
Freiburg, Walter, 1960.*

LANGMAACK, HEINRICH. Der
gepfefferte zauberspruch.
*boards, 32mo. Stuttgart, Gun-
ther, 1955.*

_____ Humor im amt. *paper,
8vo. Berlin, Sudau, 1943.*

LAVERRENZ, VICTOR. Die denkmaler Berlins und der volkswitz. *boards, 12mo. Berlin,
Author, 1893. 2te auflage.*

_____ Die denkmaler
Berlins im volksmunde. *paper,
12mo. Berlin, Steinitz, n.d.
2te auflage.*

LEBEN, MEINUNGEN UND
THATEN VON HIERONIMUS
JOBS, DEM KANDIDATEN ...
*half-leather, 16mo. Hamm Und
Crefeld, Wundermann, 1839.*

LEDERER, FRANZ. Berliner
humor; sprache, wesen und
humor des Berliners. *boards,
12mo. Berlin, Germania, n.d.*

_____ Ich lach ma 'n ast;
sprache, wesen und humor des
Berliners. *boards, 12mo. Berlin,
Germania, 1929.*

LEHMANN, ARTHUR-HEINZ *und*
ZEIDLER, PAUL GERHARD.
Blauer dunst macht weltge-
schichte. *boards, 12mo.
Leipzig, Kreisel, 1939.*

LEHNIN, HANNES *von.* Lustige
thaten & ebenteuer des alten
klosterbruders. *boards, 12mo.
Stuttgart, Puttmann, n.d.*

_____ *Same. Bern, Stamp-
fli, n.d. 4te auflage.*

LICHTENBERG, WILHELM. Zu
sich selber gesprochen. *boards,
12mo. Rorschach, Lopfe-Benz,
1952.*

LIEBE GELD, DAS; ein trostbuch
fur jedermann. *paper, 12mo.
Zurich, Classen, 1957.*

LINDEN, HANS-JURGEN. Landser
lachen. *paper, 8vo. Darmstadt,
Teich, 1954.*

LIST, HERMANN. Kleine geschichten aus England. *buckram,
12mo. Stuttgart, Klett, 1949.*

——————— Kleine geschichten
aus Frankreich. *buckram,
12mo. Stuttgart, Klett, 1954.*

LOHR, OTTO, *hrsg.* Kleine geschichten aus Amerika. *buckram, 12mo. Stuttgart, Klett,
1950.*

LOOSLI, C.A. Erlebtes und
erlauschtes. *boards, 12mo.
Rorschach, Lopfe-Benz, 1937.*

LORIOT——————— Auf den hund
gekommen; 44 lieblose zeichnungen. *boards, 32mo. Zurich,
Diogenes, 1954.*

——————— Der gute ton; das
handbuch feiner lebensart in
word und bild. *boards, 16mo.
Zurich, Diogenes, 1957.*

——————— Wahre geschichten.
*boards, 16mo. Zurich, Diogenes,
1959.*

——————— Der weg zum erfolk;
ein erschopfender ratgeber in
wort und bild. *boards, 16mo.
Zurich, Diogene, 1958.*

LUCIANUS SAMOSATENSIS.
Parodien und burlesken. *buckram, 16mo. Zurich, Artemis-
verlag, 1948.*

LUSTIG MUSS DIE HERBERG
SEIN; schweizer humor aus dem
Nebelspalter. *boards, 12mo.
Rorschach, Nebelspalter, 1958.*

LUSTIGE BUECHEL DER LILLER
KRIEGSZEITUNG, DIE. *paper,
16mo. Lille, Liller Kriegszeitung, 1916.*

LUSTIGE JURIST, DER: heiteres
in wort und bild aus dem juri-
sten-leben. Des "Vademecum
fur juristen". *paper, 8vo.
Munchen, Braun & Schneider,
n.d.*

LUSTIGE WILLI BRAUN-BUCH,
DAS. *boards, 12mo. Munchen,
Parcus, 1925.* .

LUSTIGEN VOGEL, DIE; ein
illustrirtes anekdoten-buch.
*buckram, 12mo. Stuttgart,
Dittmarsch, 1940?*

LUSTIGES AUS DEM REICHE
DER STENOGRAPHEN UND
MASCHINENSCHREIBER.
*paper, 12mo. Berlin, Steno-
graphie-verlag Schulze, 1906.*

LUTZ, EDMUND JOHANNES. Die
froliche stunde; ein werkbuch.
*paper, 12mo. Munchen, Buchner,
1956.*

LUTZE, ERNST ARTHUR. Hohen-
zollern anekdotenschatz in
versen. *buckram, 12mo. Berlin,
Verlag fur Nationale Literature,
1905.*

MAAG, OTTO. Wer weiss ob worr
is ... komisches von hohen
schulen, von kindern, dichtern
und narren, anekdoten und
eigene erlebnisse. *paper, 12mo.
Zurich, Kober'sche, 1958.*

MAGNUS, KARL. Kenn' sie den
schon? Die kostlichsten witze
und anekdotchen. *paper, 12mo.
Berlin, Falken-verlag, 1957.*

MANTEL, HUBERTUS, *hrsg.* 1000
witze von A biz Z. *paper, 12mo.
Lindau, Rudolph, n.d.*

MANUEL, BRUNO. Nackte tat-
sachen; anekdoten aus einer
jungen republic. Kleine geschichten von grossen mammern.
*paper, 12mo. Dresden, Sibyllen-
verlag, 1927.*

MARGOLIUS, HANS, *hrsg.*
Deutsche aphorismen. *buckram,
12mo. Bern, Scherz, n.d.*

MARSCHALL, HANNS. Komisches
von grossen leuten. *paper,
12mo. Berlin, Wille, 1928.*

MAUCH, THEODOR, *hrsg.*
Schiller-anekdoten. *buckram,
12mo. Stuttgart, Lutz, 1905.*

MCKIE, ROY. Der hund; ein buch
zur forderung der freund-
schaftlichen beziehungen
zwischen mensch und hund.
*boards, 16mo. Zurich, Dio-
genes, 1956.*

MEMELS, JOH. PETER *de.*
Lustige gesellschaft. *paper,
8vo. Halle, Niemeyer, 1893.*

MENGHLIN, OSWALD. Drei schus-
seln Tiroler knodel. *paper,
12mo. Wien, Holzworth &
Berger, 1942.*

MERKENS, HEINRICH. Deutscher
humor alter zeit. *buckram,
12mo. Wurzburg, Stuber, 1879.*

——————— Was sich das wolk
erzahlt; deutsche volkshumor.
*2v. boards, 12mo. Jena, Coste-
noble, n.d.*

MERZ, CARL *und* QUALTINGER,
HELMUT. Blattl vor'm mund.
*boards, 8vo. Munchen, Langen
& Muller, 1959.*

MEYER, JOSEPH. Das paradies-
gartel; ein altmunchener anekdotenbuch. *paper, 12mo.
Munchen, Parcus, 1925.*

MIKES, GEORGE. A propos ferien.
*boards, 16mo. Zurich, Diogenes,
1955.*

MOHR, HEINRICH. Der narren-
baum; deutsche schwanke vier
jahrhunderten. *buckram, 16mo.
Berlin, Ferdersche Verlagshandlung, 1917.*

MOLDAVAN, KURT. Vom umgang
mit drachen. *boards, 16mo.
Zurich, Diogenes, 1958.*

MOLL, FR. ED. Humoristisches
hundert und eins. *boards,
12mo. Berlin, Rubach, 1842.*

MOLLER, VERA. Klein-Erna;
ganz dumme hamburger ges-
chichten. *paper, 24mo. Hamburg, Hans Christian, 1939.*

MOLNAR, GEORGE. Von umgang
mit statuen. *boards, 16mo.
Zurich, Diogenes, 1956.*

MONCKEBERG, FRANZ TH.
Grabbelbudel. Hamburger
schnurren und denkwurdig-
keiten. *paper, 16mo. Hamburg,
Broschek, 1951.*

MONKEMOLLER, OTTO. Narren
und toren in satire, sprichwort
und humor. *paper, 8vo. Halle,
Marhold, 1912.*

MOSTAR, HERMANN. In diesem
sinn dein onkel Franz. *boards,
12mo. Stuttgart, Scherz &
Goverts, 1956.*

——————— Spiel mit rehen.
*boards, 16mo. Frankfurt a. Main,
Barmeier & Nikel, n.d.*

MOSZKOWSKI, ALEXANDER.
"Auserwahlte volk's witze"
399 juwelen aus dem judischen
kronschatz. *boards, 8vo. Berlin,
"Lustigen Blatter" n.d.*

——————— Die ewigen worte;
kronschatz des geistes. *buckram, 8vo. Berlin, Eysler, 1918.*

——————— Goldenes lachen.
*buckram, folio. Berlin, Neufeld
& Henius, n.d.*

——————— Die judische kiste;
399 juwelen. *paper, 8vo. Berlin,
"Lustigen Blatter" 1911.*

——————— Der judische witz
und seine philosophie. *paper,
8vo. Berlin, Ensler, 1923.*

_____ La lachen die buhner. *buckram, 8vo. Berlin, "Lustigen Blatter"* 1914.

_____ Stuss im jus; ein lustiges buch von juristen und schweren verbrechern. *paper, 8vo. Berlin, "Lustigen Blatter" n.d.*

_____ Unglaublichkeiten! ernste und heitere paradoxe. *boards, 8vo. Berlin, Ensler, n.d.*

_____ Die unsterbliche kiste; die 333 besten witze der weltliteratur. *paper, 8vo. Berlin, "Lustigen Blatter"* 1908.

MOZIN._____*Abbe.* Anecdotes francaises-allemandes zum uebersetzen in bende sprachen. *boards, 12mo. Tubingen, Cotta,* 1810.

MULLER, JOSEF. Das wesen des humors. *paper, 8vo. Munchen, Luneburg,* 1896.

MULLER-KAMP, ERICH. So lacht russland; humor und satire. *buckram, 8vo. Munchen, Bassermann,* 1960.

MULLER-SCHLOSSER, HANS. Tunnes; schwanke und schnurren. *boards, 16mo. Hannover, Steegemann,* 1924.

MULLER-ZURLINDEN, J. Der lachende globus. *buckram, 4to. Hamburg, Thordsan,* 1953.

MUNCHNER BILDERBOGEN: alte und neue munchner geschichten. *buckram, 12mo. Stuttgart, Bibliothek der Unterhaltung und des Wissens, n.d.*

MURAWSKI, ERICH. Papa Wrangel; anekdoten, schnurren und schrullen vom alten feldmarshall. *boards, 12mo. Stettin, Ostsee-verlag,* 1933

MUTHESIUS. Humor in geschaft, anekdoten, schnurren, aphorismen und stilbluten aus dem wirtschafts-leben. *boards, 12mo. Frankfurt a. Main, Knapp,* 1954.

NACHSTUNDENBUCH; galantes, pikantes und anderes. *buckram, 12mo. Zurich, Classen,* 1952.

NETTO C. *und* WAGENER, G. Japanischer humor. *boards, 4to. Leipzig, Brockhaus,* 1901.

NEUBERGER, HEINZ. Das jahr in 365 anekdoten. *paper, 8vo. Leipzig, Scholtze, n.d.*

NEUMANN, OTTO. Kulturscherze aus dem ersten jahrzehnt des zwanzigsten jahrhunderts. *boards, 16mo. Berlin, Weber-Haus,* 1911.

1950-1960: zehn jahre Tarantel-Tarentel-Press. "Heinrich Bar" verlag. *paper, 4to. Berlin, Tarantel,* 1960.

NEUNZEHNTE VERSAMMLUNG DEUTSCHER NATURFOR-SCHER UND VERZTE ZU BRAUNSCHWEIG IM SEPTEMBER 1841, DIE; ein humoristisches album. *halfcalf, 12mo. Leipzig, Kollmann,* 1842.

NICOLSON, HAROLD. Kleines weekendbuch. *boards, 16mo. Zurich, Sanssouci,* 1958.

NORK, F. Der festkalender. *boards, 16mo. Stuttgart, Verlag des Herausgebers,* 1847.

NOTTEBOHM, HORST *und* KIPPE, HUGO. Die witzkiste. *paper, 12mo. Lindau/Bodensee, Rudolph, n.d.*

NOTZOLDT, FRITZ. Buntes lach lexikon. *paper, 16mo. Heidelberg, Kemper,* 1959.

_____ Heidelberger anek-
doten. *buckram, 16mo. Heidelberg, Kemper, 1960.*

NOWAG, HEINZ. Wohnen sie auch
mobliert? *boards, 16mo. Zurich,
Diogenes, 1958.*

NOWOTTNICK, GEORGE, *hrsg.*
Christliche heiterkeit. *boards,
16mo. Heidelberg, Kemper,
1960.*

_____ Deutsche kunstler.
*boards, 12mo. Berlin, Duncker &
Humblot, n.d.*

_____ Humor im Gottesreich.
*boards, 16mo. Heidelberg,
Kemper, 1960.*

NUEL, M. Rabbi lach und seine
geschichten. *buckram, 12mo.
Berlin, Hesperus, 1910. 3te
auflage.*

NUSCHITSCH, BRANISLAW. Der
elefant; eine unglaubliche geschichte. *boards, 16mo. Zurich,
Diogenes, 1955.*

O DIESE DACKEL. allerlei lustiges aus dem leben unserer
kleinen krummbeinigen
freunde. *paper, 8vo. Munchen,
Braun & Schneider, n.d.*

OBEREN ZEHNTAUSEND, DIE:
kulturbilder aus dem Simplicissimus. *boards, 16mo. Munchen,
Langen, 1905.*

OCHSENBEINS, HERMANN.
Kleine hausbar. *boards, 12mo.
Zurich, Sanssouci, 1957.*

ODEMAN, ROBERT T. Frech-
dachsereien eines junggesellen;
lachen und lieben in versen
geschrieben. *boards, 12mo.
Berlin, Blanvalet, 1953.*

_____ Kein blatt vor'm
mund. *boards, 12mo. Berlin,
Blanvalet, 1956.*

_____ Unkraut verseht
nicht. *boards, 12mo. Berlin,
Blanvalet, 1957.*

OH, DIESE EVASTOCHTER.
*paper, 8vo. Hamburg, Meteor-
verlag, 1958.*

OLALA. *boards, 16mo. Zurich,
Diogenes, 1954.*

OLSZEWSKI, KARL EWALD. Der
kriegs-struwelpeter; lustige
bilder und verse. *buckram, 4to.
Munchen, Holbein, 1915.*

OSMIN *see* SIMON, HEINRICH.

OSTWALD, HANS. Frisch, gesund
und meschugge; schnurren und
anekdoten. *buckram, 12mo.
Berlin, Franke, 1928.*

_____ Der lachende koffer.
*buckram, 12mo. Berlin, Franke,
1928.*

_____ Der Urberliner in witz,
humor und anekdote. *buckram,
12mo. Berlin, Franke, 1928.*

_____ Vom goldenen humor
in bild und wort. *boards, folio.
Berlin, Weise, 1941.*

OTTAWA, THEODOR. Der mensch
fangt erst beim auto an. *buckram, 12mo. Wien, Wancura, 1958.*

_____ Wiener spaziergange,
1945/46. *boards, 8vo. Wien,
Humboldt, 1947.*

PARTCH, VIRGIL F.
Gesellschaftsspiele mit damen.
*boards, 16mo. Zurich, Diogenes,
1956.*

_____ Gesellschaftsspiele
mit herren. *boards, 16mo.
Zurich, Diogenes, 1956.*

PESTALOZZI, HEINRICH.
Aphorismen. *buckram, 12mo.
Bern, Scherz, n.d.*

PIRCHAN, EMIL. Buhnenbrevier;
theatergeschichten. *paper, 8vo.
Wien, Frick, 1938.*

_____ Die lachende maske. *buckram, 12mo. Wien, Frick, 1944.*

PLAUEN, E.O. Der vater und seine freunde. *boards, 12mo. Zurich, Sanssouci, 1954.*

PLESSNER, H. Lachen und weinen; eine untersuchung nach den grenzen menschlichen verhaltens. *paper, 4to. Arnhem, Van Logum Slaterus, 1941.*

PLIETZSCH, EDUARD. "...heiter is die kunst". *buckram, 12mo. Detmold, Bertelsmann, 1955.*

PODDEL, PETER. Die besten soldatenwitze. *buckram, 12mo. Munchen, Horning, 1954.*

_____ Flusterwitze aus brauner zeit. *buckram, 12mo. Munchen, Hornung, 1954.*

_____ Die idiotenwiese; die besten idioten witze. *buckram, 12mo. Munchen, Hornung, 1954.*

POGGIO BRACCIOLINI. Die schwanke und schnurren des Florentiners Gian-Francesco Poggio Bracciolini. *half-morocco, 8vo. Leipzig, Deutsche Verlag-sactiengesellschaft, 1905.*

POLIZEI LACHT MIT, DIE. *boards, 8vo. Zurich, Capriceverlag, 1956.*

POSSEN IM TASCHENFORMATE: wird gratis ausgegeben. *boards, 24mo. Leipzig, n.p. 1754.*

POTH, CHLODWIG. Konig Heinrich der Heimliche. *boards, 12mo. Frankfurt a. Main, Barmeier & Nikel, n.d.*

_____ Der herr der grosser weiten welt. *paper, 16mo. Frankfurt a. Main, Barmeier & Nikel, n.d.*

_____ Mach dein hobby selbst. *boards, wide 16mo. Frankfurt a. Main, Barmeier & Nikel, 1959.*

POTZL, ED. Klein-Wiener; skizzen in Wiener art und mundart. *half-calf, 16mo. Wien, Szelinski, 1895.*

_____ Moderner Gschnas und andere Wiener skizzen. *buckram, 24mo. Wien, Mohr, 1901.*

PRAGER, WILLY. Sie werden lachen; nichts erfundenalles erlebt. *paper, 8vo. Berlin, Capriccio-Musikverlag, n.d.*

PRESBER, RUDOLF. Das goldene lachen; ein humoristischer familienschatz in wort und bilder. *buckram, folio. Berlin, Neufeld & Henius, n.d.*

PRICE, ROGER. Des drudels kern. *boards, 16mo. Zurich, Diogenes, 1958.*

_____ Der kleine psychologe; einfuhrung in der drudeltest. *boards, 16mo. Zurich, Diogenes, 1955.*

PURZELBAUM, PETER. Greist nur hinein ins tolle menschenleben. *boards, 12mo. Berlin, Franke, n.d.*

_____ "Lusten sie mal". *boards, 12mo. Leipzig, Bergwald-verlag, 1940.*

_____ Neuer witz vom alten fritz. *buckram, 12mo. Berlin, Brunnen-verlag, 1934.*

_____ Starker Toback und anderer tagdhumor. *paper, 12mo. Muhlhausen, Bergwaldverlag, 1939.*

_____ Vom kommist, Kaczmarek und den maikafern. *buckram, 12mo. Berlin, Brunnen-verlag, 1926.*

———— Was ware, wenn? *boards, 12mo. Berlin, Lippa, 1942.*

RAAB, HEINRICH. Dichteranek-doten. *cloth, 12mo. Zurich, Clavis-verlag, 1943.*

RADDATZ, FRITZ, *hrsg.* ... mit uns lachen? *boards, 8vo. Berlin, Verlag Volk u.Welt, 1957.*

RADECKI, SIGISMUND *von.* Das ABC des lachens. *paper, 12mo. Hamburg, Rowohlt, 1953.*

RADNER, SIEGFRIED. Kaffe und humor. *buckram, 12mo. Munchen, Lehmann, 1930.*

RAJOWER, AUSOR. Masses und chochmes; judische humor. *boards, 12mo. Zurich, Scheffel-verlag, 1959.*

RAMSEGER, GEORG. Duell mit der geschichte. *boards, 4to. Oldenburg, Stalling, 1955.*

———— Ohne putz und tunche; deutsche karikaturisten und die kultur. *boards, 4to. Oldenburg, Stalling, 1956.*

RARITATEN UBER RARITATEN, oder, Allerneuste sammlung von allerhand kurzweiligen reden. *paper, 16mo. Ulrich, n.p., 1768.*

RASPE, RUDOLPH. Die galanten abenteuer Munchausen. *boards, 24mo. Berlin, Feldafing, n.d.*

RAUCH, KARL. Die anekdot; heiteres aus der welt des buches. *boards, 12mo. Esslin-gen, Bechtle, 1953.*

———— Die beste arzenei; heiteres von arzten und pati-enten. *boards, 12mo. Esslingen, Bechtle, 1956.*

———— Heilige heiterkeit; anekdoten und geschichten... *boards, 12mo. Esslingen, Bechtle, 1955.*

———— Die palette; heiteres von malern und anderen kunst-lern. *boards, 12mo. Esslingen, Bechtle, 1954.*

RAUCH, OTTO. Humor unsere kleinen; eine tausenfaltige blutenauslese. *paper, 12mo. Munchen, Gassler, n.d.*

RAUCHENEGGER, BENNO. Noch was! *buckram, 12mo. Munchen, Munchner Neuesten Nachrichten, 1894.*

RAWNEZKY, J. CH. Yiddische witzen. *boards, 8vo. Berlin, 1923.*

RECHERT, EMIL, *hrsg.* Humor im grauen hause. *paper, 12mo. Wien, Perles, 1912.*

REHM, HERMANN SIEGFRIED, *hrsg.* Deutches lachen; sie-benhundert jahre deutscher humor. *buckram, folio. Leipzig, Fikentscher, 1950.*

———— Das lachen der volker; dreitausend jahre welt-humor. *half-morocco, folio. Leipzig, Fikentscher, 1927.*

REICHERT, WILLY. Lerne lachen ohne zu klagen. *cloth, 12mo. Stuttgart, Union Deutsche Verlagsgesellschaft, 1938.*

REIMANN, HANS. Mein blaues wunder; lebensmosaik eines humoristen. *buckram, 8vo. Munchen, List, 1959.*

———— Das bunte lachbuch; heitere deutsche prosa. *buck-ram, 8vo. Stuttgart, Gunther, 1958.*

———— Die dritte literazzia. *paper, 12mo. Munchen, Pohl, 1954.*

———— Mit 100 jahren noch ein kind ... *buckram, 12mo. Berlin, Schutzen-verlag, 1939.*

REISNER, BOB und KAPPLOW, HAL. Das frivole museum; oder, Die kunst, in drei stunden ein kunst-kenner zu werden. *boards, 16mo. Frankfurt a. Main, Barmeier & Nikel, 1961.*

RESL, FRANZ. Humor im alltag; heitere kurzgeschichten. *buckram, 12mo. Wien, Frau & Mutterverlag, 1936.*

REUTTER-VORTRAGE, OTTO. Unsterbliche. *3v. paper, 12mo. Koln, Burgwald, n.d.*

REZZORI, GREGOR von. Maghrebinische geschichten. *buckram, 8vo. Hamburg, Rowholt, 1953.*

RICHARDS, P. Amerika durch die lupe der karikatur. *buckram, 4to. Leipzig, Reflektor-verlag, 1913.*

RICHTER, HERMANN ALFRED. Eulenspiegel in Schilda. *buckram, 8vo. Reutlingen, Ensslin & Laiblin, 1949.*

RIDDELL, MARJORIE. Liebe mutter, vom umgang mit tochtern von heute. *boards, 12mo. Zurich, Sanssouci, 1956.*

RIESS, RICHARD. Der grundliche Adolf; und andere grotesken und schnurren. *buckram, 12mo. Munchen, Rosl, 1921.*

RINGELNATZ, JOACHIM. Es zwitschert eine lerche im Kamim. *boards, 12mo. Berlin, Henssel, 1957.*

RINN, HERMANN, *hrsg.* Deutsches anekdotenbuch; eine sammlung von kurzgeschichten aus vier jahrhundert. *buckram, 12mo. Munchen, Callwey, 1927.*

RITZEL, JORG. Der lachende Rhein. *buckram, folio. Koln, Hoursch & Bechstedt, 1930.*

ROBITSCHEK, KURT. Konige in unterhose; das buch der anekdoten. *paper, 12mo. Berlin, Drei Masken Verlag, 1925.*

RODA RODA, ALEXANDER. Donner und Doria. *buckram, 12mo. Berlin, Eysler, 1927.*

_____ Das lachende Deutschland. *boards, 8vo. Berlin, Schuster & Loeffler, 1910.*

_____ Morgensonne morgenland; schildereien. *boards, 32mo. Berlin, Volksverband der Bucherfreunde Wegweiserverlag, 1922.*

_____ Der pascha lacht; morgenlandische schwanke eigenes und echtes. *boards, 16mo. Berlin, Schuster & Loeffler, 1909.*

_____ Schenck ein, Roda! aus slavischen quellen. *buckram, 12mo. Berlin, Zsolnay, 1934.*

_____ Schummler, bummler, rossetummler; sudslavische geschichten. *buckram, 12mo. Berlin, Ensler, 1924.*

_____ Der witz des auslandes. *boards, 8vo. Berlin, Schuster & Loeffler, 1911.*

ROEWER, HANNS CLAUS. Hamburger grog. *paper, 16mo. Hamburg, Schulz, 1952.*

ROMISCH-JURISTISCHE DRE-HORGEL mit 160 strassenliedern uber die corpulentesten kapitel des heiligen corpus juris... *leather, 16mo. Leipzig, Kesselring, n.d.*

ROQUES, K.R. von. Noch ein paar tropfen neue medizin. *boards, 12mo. Frankfurt, Societats-verlag, 1942.*

ROSIE, O. 150 jahre Berliner
humor. *buckram, 4to. Berlin,
Das Neue Berlin, n.d.*

ROSLER, JO HANNS. Das
schonste madchen der welt;
ein lustiges geschichten-
buch. *paper, 12mo. Berlin,
Stephenson, 1940. 5te
auflage.*

ROTH, EUGEN. Die frau in der
weltgeschichte. *paper, 12mo.
Munchen, Hanser, 1956.*

—————— Gute reise! heitere
verse. *paper, 12mo. Munchen,
Hanser, 1954.*

—————— Heitere kneipp-fibel.
*boards, 12mo. Munchen, Ehren-
wirth, 1954.*

—————— Ein hundert jahre
humor in der Deutscher kunst.
*buckram, 8vo. Hannover,
Fackeltrager, 1957.*

—————— Kleines tierleben.
*paper, 12mo. Munchen, Hanser,
1956.*

—————— Ein mensch; heitere
verse. *paper, 16mo. Munchen,
Hanser, 1955.*

—————— Mensch und un-
mensch. *paper, 12mo. Munchen,
Hanser, 1954.*

—————— Neue rezepte vom
wunderdoktor. *buckram, 12mo.
Munchen, Hanser, 1959.*

—————— Sammelsurium;
freud und leid eines kunstsamm-
lers. *boards, 8vo. Munchen,
Hanser, 1955.*

—————— Simplicissimus; ein
ruckblick aus die satirische
zeitschrift. *buckram, 8vo. Hannover, Fackeltrager, 1954.*

—————— Unter brudern.
*boards, 12mo. Munchen, Hanser,
1958.*

—————— Der wunderdoktor;
heitere verse. *paper, 12mo.
Munchen, Hanser, 1954.*

ROTHENHAUSLER, PAUL. Das
kleine partybuch. *boards,
12mo. Zurich, Sanssouci,
1957.*

RUDELSBERGER, HANS.
Chinesische schwanke.
*boards, 8vo. Wien, Schroll,
1920.*

RUHLMANN, WILHELM. Witz und
humor; streifzuge in das gebiet
des komischen. *paper, 12mo.
Berlin, Fleischel, 1910. 2te
auflage.*

RUPPEL, HEINRICH. Der schelm
im volk; kurhessisches anekdotenbuch. *paper, 12mo.
Kassel, Barenreiter, n.d.*

RYSSEL, FRITZ HEINRICH.
Meine lieblingstochter. *paper,
12mo. Zurich, Classen, 1957.*

—————— Rezeptbuch gegen
die manager-krankheit. *boards,
12mo. Zurich, Classen, 1960.*

SAAFNLOB, *pseud.* Das lustige
buch der erzgebirger. *buckram,
8vo. Leipzig, Hofmeister, 1954.*

SAAGER, ADOLF, *hrsg.* Luther-
anekdoten; lebensbilder, anekdoten, kernspruche. *buckram,
12mo. Stuttgart, Lutz, n.d. 5te.
auflage.*

SAFTIGE WITZE AUS ALLER
WELT. *paper, 16mo. Hamburg,
Nolting, 1931.*

SALZER, MARCELL. Das lustige
Salzer-buch; heitere lekture-
und vortrags-stucke. *buckram,
12mo. Hamburg, Benjamin, 1917.*

SAMMLUNG HISTORISCHER
SCHILDERUNGEN UND ANEK-
DOTEN BERUHMTER MAN-
NER. *calf, 12mo. Leipzig,
Junius, 1770.*

SAPHIR, MORITZ GOTTLIEB.
Humoristische schriften in
zwei banden. 2v. in 1. *buckram, 16mo. Berlin, Biblio-
graphische Anstalt, n.d.*

——————— Humoristischer
volks-kalender nach vor und
ruckwarts, fur das jahr 1851.
*boards, 16mo. Wien, Jasper,
Hugel & Manz, 1851.*

SAUERS, DON. Madchen in sicht!
*boards, 16mo. Zurich, Diogenes,
1957.*

SCARPI, N. O. Alle achtung bei-
sseite; eine anekdoten sammlung. *boards, 8vo. Zurich,
Buchergilde Gutenberg, 1950.*

——————— Anekdoten-cocktail;
ein neues handbuch des lach-
elns. *buckram, 8vo. Zurich,
Classen, 1960.*

——————— Don Juan's familie;
geschichten und amouresken.
*boards, 12mo. Zurich,
Classen, 1951.*

——————— Gestohlen bei ...
von anekdoten, bonmots allerlei
spielen und gar keinem ernst.
*buckram, 8vo. Zurich, Classen,
1956.*

——————— Guten appetit. *paper,
12mo. Zurich, Classen, 1954.*

——————— Handbuch des lach-
elns. *buckram, 8vo. Zurich,
Classen, 1954.*

——————— Die herren von do-
re-mi; musiker-anekdoten.
*buckram, 24mo. Zuirch,
Classen, 1952.*

——————— Neues handbuch
des lachens. *paper, 8vo.
Zurich, Villiger, n.d.*

——————— Nicht trommeln
noch trompeten; anekdoten
bonmots und einiges daruber.
*boards, 12mo. St. Gallen,
Zollikofer, 1948.*

——————— Nichts fur ungut.
*paper, 12mo. Zurich, Classen,
1956.*

——————— Ein rollchen ewig-
keit, und anderes vergang-
liche. *paper, 12mo. Zurich,
Classen, n.d.*

——————— 1001 anekdote.
*cloth, small 8vo. Zurich,
Classen, 1951.*

——————— Theater ist immer
schon. *paper, 12mo. Zurich,
Classen, 1957.*

SCENEN, SCHWANKE UND ORI-
GINALITATEN AUS DEM
LEBEN. *paper, 16mo. Nurnberg, Lotzbeck, n.d. 2te
auflage.*

SCHAEFFER-AST ———————
Lustig und listig. *boards, 4to.
Hamburg, Rowohlt, 1957.*

SCHAEFFLER, JULIUS. Der
lachende volksmund. *buckram,
12mo. Berlin, Dummlers, 1931.*

SCHAFER, WILHELM. Die anekdoten. *buckram, 12mo. Stuttgart,
Cotta'sche Buchhandlung Nachfolger, 1949.*

——————— Das fremde fraulein,
und andere anekdoten. *paper,
16mo. Stuttgart, Reclam, 1953.*

——————— Hundert historchen.
*buckram, 12mo. Munchen,
Langen, 1940.*

SCHALDACH, K. Das zersprung-
ene chamaleon; eine revue des
humors der gegenwart. *boards,
16mo. Berlin, Hesse, 1926.*

SCHALK UND KAUZ; blatter fur
deutschen humor. *half-morocco,
folio. Leipzig, 1887.*

SCHEFFLER, KARL. Das
lachende atelier; kunstler-
anekdoten des 19. jahr-
hunderts. *boards, 8vo. Wien,
Gallus, 1943.*

SCHELLENBERG, PAUL.
Lachschach; ausgewahlte
schachhumoresken. *boards,
12mo. Berlin.. Vereinigung
Wissenschaflicher Verlege,
1921.*

SCHER, PETER. Anekdotenbuch.
*buckram, 12mo. Berlin, Volks-
verband der Bucherfreunde
Wegweiser Verlag, 1925.*

SCHERZBURGER ACTENSTUCKE.
Nro.III. Enthaltend einige
rotabene aus der brieftasche
des abgeneordneten Nepomuk
v. Zwicklheim. *paper, Nurnberg, Riegel & Wiessner,
1828.*

SCHILDERUNGEN UND BEGEB-
NISSE EINES VIELGEREI-
STEN DER AUSRUHT. 3v. in
1. *tree calf, 16mo. Leipzig,
Verlags Expedition, 1833.*

SCHLEIZHER, IRENE. Lachende
medizin. *paper, small 4to.
Leipzig, Thieme, 1941.*

SCHLOEMP, FELIX. Der gekit-
zelte Aeskulap; die besten
witze und schnurren von
aerzerten, patienten und
lustigen studenten. *boards,
12mo. Munchen, Muller,
1910.*

———————— Im tingeltangel des
humors; grosse gala-elite-witz-
vorstellung. *paper, 16mo.
Berlin, Henschel, n.d.*

———————— Der lachende erd-
ball; eine lustige reise im
witzug durch aller herren
lander. *boards, 12mo. Munchen, Muller, 1912.*

———————— Die meschuggene
ente. *boards, 12mo. Munchen,
Muller, 1909.*

———————— Der tolle koffer.
*paper, 12mo. Munchen, Muller,
1910.*

———————— Die uber-ente; ein
lustigtoller rekordflug. *boards,
12mo. Munchen, Muller, 1910.*

SCHMIDKUNZ, WALTER. Grosse
berge, kleine menschen; ein
alpines anekdotenbuch. *buckram, 12mo. Zurich, Schweizer
Druck-und Verlagshaus, n.d.*

SCHMIDT-HENNIGKER, FRIED-
RICH. Bismarck-anekdoten.
*buckram, 12mo. Stuttgart, Lutz,
1905.*

———————— Humor Friedrichs
des Grossen. *buckram, 12mo.
Stuttgart, Lutz, n.d.*

SCHMIDT-HIDDING, WOLFGANG.
Sieben meister des literaris-
chen humors in England und
Amerika. *buckram, 8vo. Heidelberg, Queele & Meyer, 1959.*

SCHNACK, ANTON. Brevier der
zartlichkeit. *boards, 16mo.
Frankfurt a. Main, Barmeier &
Nikel, 1957.*

———————— Flirt mit dem alltag.
*boards, 16mo. Frankfurt a.
Main, Barmeier & Nikel, 1956.*

SCHNURRE, WOLFDIETRICH.
Die blumen des Herrn Albin.
*buckram, 8vo. Frankfurt a.
Main, Barmeier & Nikel, 1955.*

SCHOFFLER, HERBERT. Kleine
geographie des deutschen
witzes. *paper, 8vo. Gottingen,
Vandenhoeck & Ruprecht, 1958.*

SCHOLZ, WILHELM von. Das buch
des lachens; schnurren,
schwanke und anekdoten. *buckram, 12mo. Stuttgart, Deutsche
Volksbucher, 1953.*

SCHOPENHAUER, ARTHUR.
Aphorismen zur lebensweisheit.
buckram, 12mo. Bern, Scherz,
n.d.

SCHRANK, JOSEPH und BACH-
EM, BELE. Prinzessin sucht
prinzen. boards, 12mo. Frankfurt a. Main, Barmeier & Nikel,
1958.

SCHRANKA, EDUARD MARIA.
Tabak-anekdoten; ein histori-
sches braunbuch. paper, 4to.
Coln, Neubner, 1914.

SCHREIBER, HERMANN. Die welt
in der anekdote. buckram, 8vo.
Wien, Paul Neff, 1961.

SCHRODER, WILHELM. Jan Peik
de noordutsche spassmaker.
Samlung plattdeutscher humoresken, schnurren, gedichte,
spruchworter. boards, 16mo.
Berlin, Otto Janke, n.d.

SCHROEDER, HANS von. Kleine
geschichten aus den baltischen
landen. buckram, 12mo. Stuttgart,
Klett, 1954.

SCHULERINNERUNGEN: ein
lustiges pennalerbrevier. buckram, 12mo. Koln, Privatdruck,
1925.

SCHULZ, ERNST. Die englischen
schwankbucher bis herab zu
"Dobson's drie bobs" (1607).
pamphlet, Berlin, Mayer &
Muller, 1912.

SCHULZ, JO., hrsg. Lachen und
lachen lassen; ein heiteres
vortragsbuch. buckram, 12mo.
Berlin, Eulenspiegel, 1957.

SCHULZ, ROBERT. Ostpreuss-
ische lachpillen; drastische
vortrage, schwanke und humoresken in ostpreussischer mundart. paper, 8vo. Insterburg,
Blunschein, 1902.

SCHULZ-BESSER, ERNST. Die
karikatur im weltkriege. paper,
8vo. Leipzig, Seemann, n.d.

SCHUMANN, WERNER. Ohne
tritt - marsch! Das militar in
der karikature. buckram, 8vo.
Hannover, Fackeltrager,
1956.

SCHURIG, ARTHUR. Der voll-
kommene spiessburger.
buckram, 24mo. Nurnberg,
Schrag, 1928.

SCHWARZ, GEORG. Pfeffer
Stetten; ein schwabisches
schelmenbuch. buckram,
12mo. Salzburg, Muller, 1939.

SCHWARZ, HANS. Humor hinter
dem rostigen vorhang. paper,
16mo. Bern, "Demokratie im
Angriff" 1951-1952.

SCHWEIZER, BARBARA. Gut
gelaunt — mit ausnahmen.
boards, 16mo. Zurich,
Schwizer Spiegel Verlag,
1955.

SCHWIND, ANTON. Bayern und
Rheinlander; im spiegel des
pressehumors von Munchen
und Koln. buckram, 8vo.
Munchen, Reinhardt, 1958.

SEARLE, RONALD und WIEMANN,
HEINRICH. Mein herz drangt in
der ferne. boards, 16mo.
Zurich, Sanssouci, 1955.

————————— Weil noch das lamp-
chen gluht. boards, 8vo.
Zurich, Diogenes, 1955.

SEELIG, CARL. Nachtgeschich-
ten. boards, 16mo. Winterthur,
Mondial, 1947.

SEELIGER, EWGER. Siebe mit
humor; funf historien. boards,
12mo. Berlin, Siegismund, 1940.

SEIBERT, CURT. Das anekdotenbuch. paper, 8vo. Berlin, Weiss,
n.d.

_____ Ich bin erkannt;
lustige geschichten. *boards,*
*12mo. Berlin, Molich, n.d.*

SEIBOLD, KARL. Deutschland
lacht; volkhafter humor. *buck-*
*ram, 8vo. Munchen, Deutsches*
*Volksverlag, 1940.*

SEILING, JOSEF, *hrsg.* Musikal-
isch-historisches anekdoten
buchlein. *paper, 16mo. Munchen,*
*Huber, 1913.*

SEINE MAJESTAT DAS AUTO;
von menschen und ihren vehik-
eln. *paper, 12mo. Zurich,*
*Classen, 1956.*

SEMPE_____ Wie sag ich's
meinen kindern? *boards, wide*
*32mo. Zurich, Diogenes, 1960.*

SETZ, KARL. Dodeldum; komische
geschichten um eine schwabi-
schen oberamtsrichter. *buck-*
*ram, 12mo. Heidenheim, Hof-*
*fmann, 1956.*

SEUNIG, WALDEMAR. Frauen,
pferde, bucher. *plush, 12mo.*
*Heidenheim, Hoffman, 1955.*

SEYPPEL, KARL MARIA. Er sie
es? II^te aegyptische humor-
esche nach der natur abgemalt
und niedergeschrieben 1302
jahr vor Christi geburt. *burlap,*
*4to. Dusseldorf, Bagel, 1883.*

_____ Schlau, schlauer,
am schlausten, Aegyptische
humoreske. Niedergeschrieben
und abgemalt 1315 jahre vor
Christi geburt. *boards, 4to.*
*Dusseldorf, Bagel, 1882.*

SICHTERMANN, S., *hrsg.* Bank-
humor. *boards, 12mo. Frank-*
*furt a. Main, Knapp, 1955.*

SIEBEN NARREN AUF EINMAHL,
oder, Knau's, Gonella's, Barlac-
chia's. Brusquet's, Morgen-
stern's, Junker Peter's und
Frolich's leben und schwanke.
*boards, 12mo. Brannschweig,*
*Reichard, 1800.*

SIECZYNSKI, RUDOLF. Sitten
geschichte mit humor. *boards,*
*12mo. Wien, Wiener verlag,*
*1946.*

SILBERGLEIT, R. Wahres,
absurdes, paradoxes. *paper,*
*8vo. Berlin, Nauck, 1914.*

SIMMEL, PAUL. Neues Paul
Simmel album. *buckram, 4to.*
*Hannover, Schmidt-Kuster,*
*1955.*

_____ Das war Paul
Simmel, 1887-1933. *buckram,*
*4to. Berlin, Verlag das Neue*
*Berlin, 1957.*

SIMON, ERNST. Zum problem des
judischen witzes. *paper, 12mo.*
*Berlin, Soncio Gesellschaft,*
*1929.*

SIMON, HENRICH. Professor
Kalauer's ausgewahlte musikalische schriften. *buckram,*
*12mo. Munchen, Heimeran,*
*1956.*

_____ Professor Kalauers
musiklexikon und anderer
muskalische schnurren, von
Osmin, *pseud. paper, 16mo.*
*Leipzig, Steingraber, 1921.*

SMEKAL, RICHARD, *hrsg.* Die
schonsten Mozart-anekdoten.
*boards, 16mo. Munchen,*
*Recht, 1921.*

SMITH, ELINOR GOULDING. Die
perfekte hausfrau. *boards,*
*16mo. Zurich, Diogenes, 1957.*

SOLOVJOV, LEONID. Die schel-
menstreiche des Nasreddin.
*buckram, 12mo. Berlin, Verlag,*
*Kultur und Fortschritt, 1959.*

SONNENSCHEIN, HUGO.
Narrisches buchel. *boards,*
*16mo. Paris, Utopia, 1910.*

SORGE, ERNST, *hrsg.* Gespielte
witze aus aller welt. *4v. paper,*
*12mo. Darmstadt, Teich, n.d.*

SOYTER, GUSTAV. Griechischer
humor von Homers zeiten bis
heute. *buckram, 8vo. Berlin,*
*Akademie-verlag, 1959.*

SPASSVOGEL, DER, oder, Witz
uber witz in wort und bild.
*paper, 12mo. Mulheim a.d.*
*Ruhr, Bagel, n.d.*

SPOERL, ALEXANDER. Fische
fangen. *buckram, 8vo. Munchen,*
*Piper, 1960.*

_____ Ich vergass zu sagen.
*buckram, 12mo. Munchen, Piper,*
*1956.*

SPOHR, WILHELM. Garten des
vergnugens ... *cloth, 12mo.*
*Berlin, Scherl, 1936.*

_____ Die narrenschaukel.
*buckram, 8vo. Berlin, Scherl,*
*1937.*

SPRINGENSCHMID, KARL. Da
lacht Tirol; geschichten aus
dem Tiroler volksleben. *buck-*
*ram, 8vo. Stuttgart, Franckh'-*
*sche verlagshandlung, 1935.*

STAUBER, JOSEF, *hrsg.* Es
brummt im karton; schwanke
und schnurren von der front.
*boards, 16mo. Stuttgart, n.d.*

STEGER, H.U. Meine grossen
tiere. *boards, 12mo. Zurich,*
*Diogenes, 1956.*

STEINBOCK, NILS. Filmstars in
karikatur und anekdote. *boards,*
*8vo. Berlin, Frommhagen, 1941.*

STEMMLE, R.A. Aus heiterm him-
mel; theater und filmanekdoten.
*boards, 12mo. Berlin, Herbig,*
*1942.*

_____ Ja, ja, ja, ach ja, 's
ist traurig aber wahr. *paper,*
*12mo. Berlin, Weiss, 1938.*

_____ Die zuflotetheater-
und filmanekdoten. *boards,*
*12mo. Berlin, Herbig, 1940.*

STEMPLINGER, EDUARD. Die
alte truhe; baierns geistes-
kultur in anekdoten. *boards,*
*12mo. Donauworth, Auer, n.d.*

_____ Antiker humor.
*buckram, 12mo. Munchen,*
*Piper, 1939.*

_____ Ernte aus altbayern.
*buckram, 8vo. Munchen, Knorr*
*& Hirth, 1936.*

_____ Sachan gibts!
schnacksen aus baiern. *paper,*
*16mo. Erfurt, Richter, 1943.*

_____ Von berumten
artzen; 202 anekdoten aus
authentischen quellen gesammelt. *buckram, 12mo. Munchen,*
*Piper, 1938.*

_____ Vom jus und von
juristen; anekdoten aus
memoiren und briefen ... *boards,*
*12mo. Munchen, Piper, 1954.*

_____ Von beruhmten
arzten; 187 anekdoten aus
memoiren und briefen ...
*boards, 12mo. Munchen,*
*Piper, 1954.*

_____ Von beruhmten
schauspielern. *boards, 12mo.*
*Munchen, Piper, 1939.*

STERNE UND STERNCHEN:
anekdoten aus der welt des
films. *paper, 12mo. Zurich,*
*Classen, 1957.*

STEUR, A. Der pharisaer; 50
ausgewahlte aphorismen.
*boards, 24mo. Limburg an der*
*Lahn, Steffen, 1916.*

STIGLER-FUCHS, MARGARETE
*von.* Der unsterbliche hans-
wurst; wiener theateranekdoten.
*paper, 12mo. Wien, Bischoff,
1944.*

STINDE, JULIUS. Humoresken und
gedichte. Buchholzens in Italien, etc. *buckram, 12mo. Chic.,
Schick, 1887.*

—————————Humoresken und gedichte. Die familie Buchholz,
etc. *buckram, 12mo. Chic.,
Schick, 1886.*

STOLLE, FERDINAND. Na da
lacht zu! oder. Der dorfbarbier
in seiner besten laune. *boards,
8vo. Plauen & Leipzig,
Schroter, 1848.*

STORM PETERSEN, ROBERT.
Das auto. *boards, 12mo. Munchen, Langen & Muller, 1961.*

STUDENT, DER: kulturbilder aus
dem Simplicissimus. *boards,
16mo. Munchen, Langen, 1905.*

SVENNINGSEN, PAUL. Was kom-
mt denn ja? *boards, 12mo.
Zurich, Sanssouci, 1954.*

SYBEN, FRIEDRICH. Offiziere;
anekdoten aus vier jahrhundert-
en. *boards, 8vo. Berlin,
Bernard & Graefe, 1942.*

—————————Preussische anekdoten nach memoiren und bi-
ographien. *buckram, 8vo.
Berlin, Bernard & Graese, 1939.*

TABORI, PAUL. Bei whisky und
zigarre; anekdoten um Winston
Churchill. *boards, 32mo.
Zurich, Diogenes, 1956.*

TAYLOR, ARCHER. Das ei im
europaischen volksratsel.
*paper, 8vo. (Extract from
Schweiz. Archiv fur Volkskunde. band 53, 1957.)*

TEGETHOFF, ERNST. Marchen,
schwanke und fabeln. *buckram,
8vo. Munchen, Bruckmann,
1925.*

THELWELL————— Ross und
reiter und so weiter. *boards,
32mo. Zurich, Diogenes, 1959.*

THIERRY, ULRICH HERBST. Die
stachelschweine. *boards,
12mo. Berlin, Blanvalet, 1956.*

THIES, HANS ARTHUR. Der
deutsche soldat in der anekdote. *boards, 12mo. Munchen,
Braun & Schneider, 1936.*

—————————Liebs-lach-und lock-
lieder. *buckram, 12mo. Munchen,
Braun & Schneider, 1953.*

THONY, ED. Der leutnant. *buckram, folio. Munchen, Langen,
n.d.*

—————————Kokotten, bauern, und
soldaten. *buckram, 4to. Hannover, Fackeltrager, 1957.*

THUMMET, HANS *von.* Aphorismen
aus den ersahrungen eines
sieben und siezugjahrigen.
*paper, 16mo. Altenburg, Hahn,
1821.*

THURBER, JAMES. Thurbers
gastebuch; ein leitfaden fur
gaste und gastgeber mit zahl-
riechen bildtafeln. *boards,
2mo. Zurich, Sanssouci, 1956.*

TILLMANN, HANS. Die lustige
blatterwiese vom humor in der
presse. *buckram, 12mo. Dusseldorf, Droste, 1956.*

TOBLER, ALFRED. Der appen-
zeller witz. *paper, 8vo.
Rorschach, Lopfe-Benz, 1948.*

TOBSIADE, DIE: ein grotesck-
komisches heldengedicht in
drei theilen. *boards, 12mo.
Hamburg, Schultz & Wundermann, 1823.*

TODDI, SILVIO. Gultig zehn tage. *boards, 12mo. Zurich, Diogenes, 1955.*

TONGER, P.J. Unserleben. *boards, 16mo. Koln, Tonger, n.d.*

TONNIES, NORBERT. Sie konnen auch lachen; humor im bundestag. *buckram, 12mo. Frankfurt a. Main, Wochenschau, 1954.*

TOTTER, ROLF. Heitere Olympiade. *boards, 16mo. Frankfurt a. Main, Barmeier & Nikel, 1960.*

TRAMPLER, KURT. Lebennerneurung durch den geist. *buckram, 8vo. Munchen, Herold, 1959.*

TREBILLIUS (FLORENTINE) *pseud.* Die politische narrenkappe. *half-vellum, 24mo. Franckfurt, Weidmannen, 1683.*

TREICHLINGER, W.M. Wohl ist ihr und auch mir. *boards, 16mo. Zurich, Sanssouci, 1955.*

TRIER, WALTER. Kleines tier paradies. *boards, 16mo. Zurich, Sanssouci, 1955.*

TROLL, THADDAUS. Lesebuch fur verliebte. *boards, 15mo. Zurich, Sanssouci, 1958.*

TSCHUDI, FRIDOLIN. Guter mond .. ein lyrischer kalender. *boards, 12mo. Zurich, Sanssouci, 1957.*

———————— Sie liebt mich, sie liebt mich nicht. *boards, 16mo. Zurich, Sanssouci, 1955.*

TUDYKA, KLAUS, *hrsg.* Theateranekdtoen, von Ekhof bis Reinhardt. *buckram, 12mo. Berlin, Henschel, 1956.*

TUNGERS, AUGUSTIN. Facetiae. *quarter-buckram, 8vo. Stuttgart, Fur den Litterarischen Verein, 1874.*

TWAIN, MARK. Tagebuch von Adam und Eva. *boards, 16mo. Zurich, Sanssouci, 1953.*

———————— Vom ungang mit engeln. *boards, 16mo. Zurich, Sanssouci, 1954.*

TYPISCH EVA. *paper, 8vo. Hamburg, Meteor Verlag, 1958.*

UBERHORST, KARL. Das komische; eine untersuchung. *2v. buckram, 8vo. Leipzig, Wigand, 1900.*

UBERZWERCH, WENDELIN, 100 pumplin; ein heiteres buch. *paper, 12mo. Berlin, Stephenson, 1940. 4te auflage.*

UNFREIWILLIGER HUMOR. *paper, 16mo. Munchen, Meinbildruck-Munchen-Pasing, 1949.*

UNGER, JOSEPH. Bunte betrachtungen und bemerkungen. *paper, 8vo. Wien, Herrmann, 1906.*

———————— Nachzugler. *paper, 8vo. Wien, Herrmann, 1909.*

VADEMECUM FUR LUSTIGE UND TRAURIGE JURISTEN. *buckram, 8vo. Munchen, Braun & Schneider, n.d.*

VETH, CORNELIS. Der advokat in der karikatur. *buckram, 4to. Berlin, Stollberg, 1927.*

VIERLINGER, EMIL. Das 1—2—3—4linger-buch; unter dem motto "Lach dich gsund". *buckram, 8vo. Munchen, Lama-verlag, 1961.*

VOGEL, HANS. Valjewo; erin-
nerungen eines Schweizer
arztes an den serbisch-
turkischen krieg. *buckram,
12mo. Rorschach, Lopfe-Benz,
n.d.*

VOGEL, JOHANNES. Deutsche
frauen; anekdoten, briefe,
curiosa aus funf jahrhunderten.
*boards, 8vo. Leipzig, Boreas-
verlag, 1940.*

VOIGT, C.F.T. Triumph des
deutschen witzes. *boards,
24mo. Leipzig, Baumgartner,
1800.*

VOLKSWITZ DER DEUTSCHEN
UBER DEN GESTURZTEN
BONAPARTE, SEINE FAMILIE
UN SEINE ANHANGER, DER.
12v. in 3. *boards, 24mo. Stut-
tgart, Scheible, 1849.*

VOMENT, JOSEF. Das weissblaue
maul. *boards, 16mo. Seebruch,
Heering, 1949.*

VORSTADT: kulturbilder aus dem
Simplicissimus. *boards, 16mo.
Munchen, Langen, 1905.*

WAGGERL, KARL HEINRICH.
Liebe dinge; miniaturen. *buckram, 12mo. Salzburg, Muller,
1956.*

WAHRBACH, C.O., hrsg. Schnurren. *boards, 12mo. Leipzig,
Wigand, n.d.*

WALTER, GUSTAV. Der unsterbliche witze. *paper, 12mo.
Munchen, Bergmann, 1956.*

WALTER, ROBERT. Das wunder-
liche herz. *boards, 12mo.
Leipzig, Struach, 1939.*

WALTI——————— Walti und seine
figuren aus dem Nebelspalter.
*boards, folio. Rorschach,
Nebelspalter, 1951.*

WARLITZ, ERNST. Bluhender
blodsinn; 1000 witze. *boards,
16mo. Berlin, Hesses, 1925.*

——————— Gesalzenes und ge-
pfeffertes. 1000 witze. *boards,
16mo. Berlin, Hesses, 1926.*

——————— Lacht euch laune;
1000 witze. *boards, 16mo.
Berlin, Hesses, 1925.*

WARREN, GEORGE M. Der parodies von Friedrich Scholtz.
*paper, 16mo. Buffalo, Baker,
Jones, 1881.*

WASCHER, ARIBERT. Das ist
das schone an den frauen.
*buckram, 8vo. Berlin, Blan-
valet, 1954.*

——————— Gedanken nach zwei
uhr nachts. *boards, 12mo.
Berlin, Blanvalet, 1953.*

WEBER, A.O. Der gefesselte
spotter! *paper, 8vo. Saalfeld,
Wiedemann, 1918.*

——————— Das salz der erde,
und andere satiren. *paper,
16mo. Leipzig, Rothbarth,
1906.*

WEBER, A. PAUL. Mit allen
wassern; neue gedichten von
alten fuchs. *boards, 16mo.
Frankfurt a. Main, Barmeier &
Nikel, 1960.*

WEBER, KARL JULIUS. Das
lachen; aus "Demokritos, oder
hinterlassene papiere eines
lachenden philosophen."
*buckram, 24mo. Leipzig,
Reclam, n.d.*

——————— Der humor und die
humoristen. *boards, 8vo. Stuttgart, Scheible, Rieger &
Sattler, 1842.*

——————— Das lachen, das
lacherliche und der witz.
*quarter-calf, 12mo. Stuttgart,
Scheible, Rieger & Stattler,
1842.*

——————— Die leidenschaften.
*2v. quarter-calf, 12mo. Stut-
tgart, Brodhag, 1842.*

_____ Menschliche liehaber-
eien. *quarter-calf, 12mo. Stut-*
*tgart, Scheible, Rieger &*
*Sattler, 1842.*

_____ Menschliche tem-
peramente. *quarter-calf, 12mo.*
*Stuttgart, Scheible, Rieger &*
*Sattler, 1842.*

_____ Satire, komik und
der roman. *quarter-calf, 12mo.*
*Stuttgart, Scheible, Rieger &*
*Sattler, 1842.*

_____ Staat, religion und
sitte. *quarter-calf, 12mo.*
*Stuttgart, Scheible, Rieger &*
*Sattler, 1842.*

**WEBER-BRAUNS, WILHELM.**
Satiren aphorismen nachdenk-
liches. *boards, 12mo. Hann-*
*over-Kirchrode, Author, 1919.*
2te auflage.

**WEIBERFEIND, DER:** liebens-
wurdige bosheiten von der
antike bis zur gegenwart.
*paper, 12mo. Zurich, Classen,*
*1954.*

**WEIDNER, JOHANN LEONARD.**
Teutscher nation apoph-
thegmatum, das ist deren in
den teutschen landen. *vellum,*
*24mo. Zeyden, Hegern, 1644.*

**WEIKERT, FELIX.** Neues narrenschiff in freud und leid zu
lustiger kurzweil. *boards,*
*16mo. Stuttgart, Scheible,*
*1840.*

**WEIS, HANS.** Die laterne des
Diogenes; anekdoten aus dem
altertum. *boards, 16mo.*
*Munchen-Berlin, Oldenbourg,*
*1941.*

**WEISS, OTTO.** So seid ihr!
aphorismen. *buckram, 12mo.*
*Stuttgart, Deutsche Verlags-*
*Anstalt, 1913.*

**WEISSER** _____ Marchen;
erzahlungen und anekdoten.
*boards, 12mo. Wien, Harter-*
*shen, 1816.*

**WELLER, OTTO.** Humor in der
schulstube. *paper, 12mo.*
*Munchen, Gassler, n.d.*

**WELLMANN, FRITZ.** Leidige
liebe; funfzig jahre am rechen-
schieber. *buckram, 8vo. Essen,*
*Vulkan-verlag, 1953.*

**WENDEL, FRIEDRICH.** Geschichte in anekdoten. *buckram,*
*12mo. Berlin, Nachfolger, 1924.*

_____ Wilhelm II in der
karikatur. *buckram, 4to.*
*Dresden, Artemis-verlag, 1928.*

**WENGER, ERICH K.** Kleiner
rauchertrost. *boards, 12mo.*
*Zurich, Sanssouci, 1959.*

**WER ZUERST LACHT..** der
Nebelspalter erzahlt anekdoten.
*boards, 8vo. Rorschach,*
*Nebelspalter, 1955.*

**WESCHER, PAUL,** *hrsg.* Schweizer
kunstler-anekdoten aus zwei
jahrhunderten. *boards, 8vo.*
*Basel, Holbein, 1942.*

**WESSELSKI, ALBERT,** *hrsg.* Die
begebenheiten der beiden Gon-
nella. *boards, 8vo. Weimar,*
*Duncker, 1920.*

_____ Der Hodscha Nas-
reddin; turkische, arabische,
berberische, maltesische, sizi-
lianische, kalabrische, kroat-
ische, serbische und
griechische; marlein und
schwanke. *2v. quarter-calf,*
*12mo. Weimar, Duncker, 1911.*

_____ Narren, gaukler und
volkslielinge. *see* Arlotto,
Alessandro.

WESTENDORP, FIEP. Viel kinder,
viel segen! Ein buch von kinder
ihrer entwicklung von schrei-
hals zum flegel. *boards, 32mo.
Zurich, Diogenes, 1958.*

WETTACH, ADRIEN. Grock nit
m-o-o-o-glich; die memoiren des
konigs der clowns. *buckram,
8vo. Stuttgart, Mundus-verlag,
1957.*

WICKRAM, JORG. Das kollwagen-
buchlein. *buckram, 8vo. Berlin,
Eulenspiegel, 1957.*

WIDMER, WALTER. Die abenteuer
des Guru Paramarta. *boards,
8vo. Frauenfeld, Huber, 1946.*

WIELAND, ERNEST. Welscher
witz; ein franzosenspiegel in
anekdoten. *boards, 8vo. Stuttgart, Strecker & Schroder,
1914.*

WIEN WEHRT SICH MIT WITZ!
Fluesterwitze aus den jahren
1938-1945. *paper, 12mo.
Wien, Weltweiten Verlag,
1946.*

WIESER, EDWIN. Unsterbliche
redner-typen. *buckram, 8vo.
Rorschach, Nebelspalter,
1950.*

WILDE, OSCAR. Aphorismen.
*buckram, 12mo. Bern, Scherz,
n.d.*

WILL, HELMUT. Aber- aber-
Herr Minister; heiteres aus der
politik. *boards, 12mo. Essling-
ern, Bechtle, 1957.*

WINCKLER, JOSEF. De olle
Fritz. *buckram, 12mo. Bremen,
Schunemann, n.d.*

WIT VON DORRING, FERDINAND
JOHANNES. Der lebensroman.
*boards, 12mo. Leipzig, Insel-
verlag, 1912.*

WITNAUER, ALFRED, *hrsg.*
Lachendes allgau; allerei
lustige sachen. *boards, 16mo.
Lindau, Stettner, 1941.*

WITZ UND KARIKATUREN, von
Bren, Ironimus, Mac, Totter aus
einer ausstellung der osterreich-
ischen staatsdruckerei. *boards,
4to. Wien, n.p. 1958.*

WITZ UND LAUNE, oder, Sammlung schershafter anekdoten
frolicher und sonderbarer geschichten. *paper, 12mo. Ulm,
Ebner, 1835.*

WITZBUCHSE DER MUNCHNER
"JUGEND", DIE. *paper, 12mo.
Munchen, Verlag der "Jugend"
1912.*

WITZENHAUSEN, TRIPLEX,
*freiherr von, pseud.* Das buch
hum; oder, Die III besten witze
aller fakultaten. *paper, 8vo.
Freiburg, Heinemann, 1930.*

WITZKOMMODE, DIE. *paper, 8vo.
Hamburg, Meteor-verlag, 1948.*

WOLF, FRITZ. Das lustige atom.
*boards, 12mo. Essen, Vulkan-
verlag, n.d.*

WOLFF, D.L.B. Album heiterer
und komischer deutscher dicht-
ungen. *paper, 24mo. Leipzig,
Haendel, 1850.*

WOLFF, LION. Humoresken aus
dem judischen volksleben.
*paper, 16mo. Rostock, Meyer,
1881.*

WOLFF, OSKAR LUDWIG
BERNARD. Der markische
Eulenspiegel; das ist; salt-
same und kurzweilige ges-
chichten von Hans Clauert in
Trebbin. *paper, 12mo. Leipzig,
Wigand, 1850.*

WOLL, KARL AUGUST.
Pfalzische gedichte. *paper,
12mo. Munchen, Scharl, 1959.*

WOLZOGEN, ERNST *von*. Das gut
alt teutsch schankbuch. *boards,
8vo. Wolfenbuttel, Verlag der
Freude, 1922.*

WORTELMANN, FRITZ, *hrsg.*
Alte landsknechtsschwanke.
*boards, 8vo. Jena, Diderichs,
1925.*

WORTIG, KURT. Die flimmer-
kiste; anekdoten und kuriosa
vom kino und film. *paper, 12mo.
Weimar, Duncker, n.d.*

WURTH, LEOPOLD. Das wort-
spiel bei Shakespeare. *buckram, 8vo. Wien, Braumuller,
1895.*

WURZKASTLEIN, gefullt mit pro-
baten universalmitteln zur
erweckung von frohsinn und
heitere laune. *boards, 12mo.
Mainz, Kunze, 1855.*

ZIEGER, WILHELM PAUL. Der
anekdoterich; in welchen
heitere und besinnliche anekdoten. *boards, 16mo. Wolf-
benbuttel, Verlag der Freude,
1923.*

ZIMMERMANN, KARL. Munch-
ausen; eine geschichte in
Arabesken. *2v. buckram, 16mo.
Berlin, Hofmann, 1864. 2te
auflage.*

ZIMMERMANN, MAC. Traume.
accordion pleated boards.
*Frankfurt a. Main, Barmeier &
Nikel, 1960.*

ZIMNIK, REINER. Die trommler
fur eine bessere zeit; eine
bildergeschichte. *boards, 4to.
Berlin, Dressler, 1958.*

ZOFF, OTTO. Das anekdoten
buch. *boards, 16mo. Munchen,
Hyperion, 1920.*

ZUR ERHEITERUNG: vademecum
lustige und traurige juristen.
Zweiter theil. *paper, 8vo.
Munchen, Braun & Schneider,
n.d. 5te auflage.*

ZUR GENESUNG! ein lustiges
handbuch fur arzte und patienten
beiderlei geschlechtes und
sonst jedermann. *buckram, 8vo.
Munchen, Braun & Schneider,
n.d. 9te unveranderte auflage.*

ZWANZIGPFUNDER AUS SCHIL-
DAS ARTILLERIE. *paper,
24mo. Zerbst, Kummer, 1834.*

## GREEK, CLASSIC

MUSAEUS. Hero and Leander, the
Greek text with introductory
note, by E. H. Blakeney. *buckram, 8vo. Lond., Blackwell,
1935.*

## GREEK, MODERN

ATTICOS, VASSILI. 22 euthema
diegemata. *paper, 8vo. Athens,
1953.*

MOLLA, ANTONIOU. Ena lampro
mathema toy Karagkiozi. *paper,
4to. Athens, 1953.*

PHIOUMORISTIKE ANTHOLOGIA.
*buckram, 12mo. Athens, 1958.*

POTAMIANOU, THEMIS. Euthumos
kosmos to Doukoumi, kai alles
istories. *boards, 8vo. Athens,
1954.*

PSATHA, DEMETRIUS. Gelia kai
dakrua mias spohis. *paper,
12mo. Athens, n.d.*

——————— I themis ehei kephia.
*paper, 12mo. Athens, 1944.*

——————— I themis ehei teura.
*paper, 8vo. Athens, 1941.*

## HEBREW

RABBAH BAR-BAR HANA. The tales of Rabbah bar-bar Hannah; the Aramaic text with Hebrew translation. *buckram, 8vo. N.Y., Behrman's Jewish Book House, 1937.*

SEFER HABEDIHAH VEHAHIDUD, 3170-2084. *3v. buckram, 16mo. Palestine, 1954.*

## HUNGARIAN

DVORZSAK, J.B.M. Anekdoten-lexicon. *buckram, 16mo. Budapest, Kapuziner-Kloster, n.d.*

## INDIA — PAKISTAN
## (Bengali — Hindi — Urdu)

ACBARYA SHRIRAMLOCHAN SHARAN. Balak Vinodamk. *paper, 8vo. Patna, Pustak-Bhamdar, 1954.*

AGA, WAIZU. Urdu adab men tanz-o-Mazah. *buckram, 4to. Khana, Kuma, 1954.*

ARUN. Gappon ka khazana. *boards, 8vo.*

"ASHAK". Pakka gana. *boards, 12mo. Patna, Mandri, 1943.*

ASUN. Sachitra grih vinod. *boards, 8vo. Patna, Kallu, 1948.*

——————— Sachitra vyang vinod. *boards, 12mo. Patna, University Pub., 1941.*

BAJEPEYI, BHAGAWATI PRASAD. Unse na kahna. *boards, 32mo. Patna, Shami, 1953.*

BANARSI, BEDHEB. Bedhab ni Bahak. *boards, 12mo.*

BANARSI, BESHAVA. Dhanyabad. *boards, 12mo. Patna, Kas Press, 1948.*

CANT' MUGE KARHANTI. *buckram, 8vo. Karachi, London Pub., 1949.*

CHAGTAI, MIRZA AZIMBEG. Ful boot. *paper, 12mo.*

——————— Khurpa Bahadur. *boards, 12mo. Patna, Mondri Press, 1948.*

——————— Lieutenant. *paper, 12mo.*

CHATURVEDI, D. Nomk-Jhomk. *paper, 4to. Agra, 1954.*

CHATURVEDI, HSISHIKAGH. Cherachara. *boards, 12mo. Patna, Kala, 1950.*

FOLK TALES AND JOKES WITH A KASHMIRI FAMILY. *paper, 4to. Srinigar, Kashmir.*

GAUR, SARJU PANDA. Char Chandool. *boards, 12mo. Patna, Manchuri, 1950.*

——————— Kahkaha. *boards, 12mo. Patna, Mandri, 1950.*

——————— Luknow wali. *paper, 12mo.*

——————— Murkha Maha Samme-lan. *paper, 12mo.*

GUPTA, MOHAWLAL. Makhamali zooti. *boards, 12mo. Patna, Flower, 1951.*

HARISCHANDRA, SRI P. Hamso Khelo. *paper, 12mo. Ambala, Khrisna Book Depot.*

HASHANATHA. Raja Ripu Mardan. *boards, 12mo. Patna, Shamuri, 1951.*

HUMOROUS LOVE STORY OF TRAYER AND CHOTUR. *paper, 4to. Srinigar, Kashmir, n.d.*

HUMOROUS STORY OF HATIM
TAY. *paper, 8vo. Srinigar,
Kashmir, n.d.*

HUMOROUS WORKS. Story of Lila
and Mudjumun. *paper, 4to.
Srinigar, Kashmir, n.d.*

JHUTTOAN KA BADSHAH. *paper,
12mo. Delhi, Kari, 1956.*

KARA'N MU STINE. *boards, 12mo.
Karachi? Cara, n.d.*

KASHMIRI BOOLCHAL WITH
JOKES. *paper, 12mo. Srinigar,
Kashmir.*

KASHMIRI SONGS AND JOKES.
*paper, 12mo. Srinigar, Kashmir,
n.d.*

KASHMIRI SONGS, PRAYERS
AND HUMOR. *paper, 12mo.
Srinigar, Kashmir, n.d.*

KRISHNACHANDRA. Bavah Pat-
teya. *buckram, 8vo. Patna,
Kari, 1948.*

_____ Ek daghe ki atma-
katha. *boards, 12mo. Patna,
Kala, 1946.*

KUMA DUNP KARATALA.
*boards, 12mo. Karachi, News
Press, 1949.*

MORE FOLK TALES AND JOKES
OF A KASHMIRI FAMILY.
*paper, 4to. Srinigar, Kashmir.*

MUNSHI, K.M. Bah re mai bah.
*boards, 12mo. Patna, Kan-
churi, 1950.*

_____ Do fakkara. *paper,
12mo. Patna, Humhi, n.d.*

_____ Parde ki ara men.
*boards, 12mo. Patna, Kanchuri,
1942.*

NAMKDAN-E-ZARAFAT. *paper,
12mo. Calcutta, Han House,
1959.*

PAL, PRANKRISHNA. Gopal
Bhand. *paper, 16mo. Calcutta,
Tarachand Das.*

PANDEY, KANTANAH. Mahakavi
Sanyha. *boards, 12mo.*

_____ Pani Pandey. *boards,
12mo.*

PANDEY, RAM LAGAN. Ghagh
aur Bhaddari. *paper, 12mo.*

RAGHAVA, RANGIYA. Pakshi ava
akash. *boards, 12mo. Patna,
Shamu, 1950.*

_____ Rah na ruki. *boards,
12mo. Patna, Shamu, 1953.*

RAHMAN, SHAJIKURA. Shaitan.
*boards, 12mo. Patna, Shamuri,
1938.*

RAMAUTAR GUPTA. Akbar Birbal
ke Latiphe: Birbal Vinod.
*paper, 12mo. Delhi, Laksmi
Pustakalaya.*

SEMO PILOU KA. *paper, 12mo.
Karachi, Kristari Press, 1947.*

SHRIVASTAVA, G.P. Bhaiya akil
bahadur. *boards, 12mo.*

_____ Mar markar hakim.
*boards, 12mo.*

_____ Nakdam. *boards,
12mo.*

_____ Nonk jhonk. *boards,
12mo.*

_____ Saheb bahadur.
*boards, 12mo.*

_____ Ulat-pher. *boards,
12mo.*

SHKULA BADRI NARAYAN.
Shastri Saheb. *boards, 12mo.*

SINGH, RAMESHWER "KASH-
YAP". Loha Singh. *boards,
12mo. Patna, Mandri Press,
1950.*

SRINATH PRASAD. Hamso-
Hamsao. *paper, 12mo. Benares,
Bharatiya Prakashan Mendol.*

STORIES AND JOKES OF KING
AKBAR AND PRIME MINISTER
BIRBAL. *paper, 4to. Srinigar,
Kashmir.*

"TAY" INITYAI ALI. Chacha
Chakkan. *boards, 12mo. Patna,
Kahuni, 1941.*

THA, HARI MOHAN. Khattab
Kakak Tarang. *boards, 12mo.*

THANBI, SHANKAT. Bakbas.
*boards, 12mo. Patna, Mandri,
1950.*

——————— Char so bees.
*boards, 12mo. Patna, Mandri,
1950.*

——————— Inshahallah.
*boards, 12mo. Patna, Kanteri,
1948.*

——————— Kutiya. *boards,
12mo. Patna, Mandri, 1942.*

——————— Maulana. *boards,
12mo. Patna, Mauna, 1948.*

——————— Sasural. *boards,
12mo. Patna, Kari, 1948.*

TRIPATHI, RAM NARESH.
Ghagh aur Bhaddari. *paper,
12mo.*

TRIVEDI, SUDARSHAN LAL.
Akbar Birhal. *paper, 12mo.*

VERMA, KESHAVA CHANDRA.
Ras ki Sirka. *paper, 12mo.*

——————— Katha ka ullu aur
kaboo tar. *boards, 8vo. Patna,
Kas, 1948.*

VYAS, GOPAL PRASAD. Aji
suno. *boards, 8vo. Patna,
Mandri, 1945.*

——————— Mainen Kaha.
*boards, 8vo. Patna, Mandri,
1946.*

# INDONESIAN DIALECT

KAM SANG KIEW. Hong Sin (Pel-
antikan Dewa-Dewa). *3v.
paper, 16mo. Serarang, Toko
Buku "Liong" 1954?*

# ITALIAN

ABRAMI, GIÖRGIO. Le facezie
dei secoli d'oro. *paper, 12mo.
Firenze, Castellaccio, 1944.*

AFORISMEN. *quarter-calf, 32mo.
Padua, Tarone, n.d.*

ALLEGRI, GIOCONDO. Un milione
di frottole; raccolta di aneddoti, facezie ... *boards, 24mo.
Milano, Rossi, 1865.*

ARIOSTO, LODOVICO. Satira.
*paper, 16mo. Venezia, Antonio
Zattae, 1787. (Bound with:
Berni, Francesco. Burlesche.)*

ARLETTO, PIOVANO. Il cherico
del Piovano Arlotto; antichi e
moderni. *half-leather, 16mo.
Firenze, Tipografia della
Gazetta d'Italia, 1878.*

——————— Motti i facezie.
*paper, 4to. Milano, Riccardo
Ricciardi, 1953.*

BARATTA, ANTONIO. Epigrammi
editi e inediti. *paper, 16mo.
Torino, Scioldo, 1881.*

BELTRAME, BENEDETTO. Per
ben digerire. *paper, 12mo.
Udine, Autore, 1931.*

BERNADINI, FRANCESCO.
Perche ridiamo? Comicita -
satira - umorismo. *paper, 12mo.
Milano, Hoepli, 1934.*

BERNI, FRANCESCO. Dell'
opere burlesche, del Berni, del
Casa, del Varchi, del Mauro,
del Bino, del Molza, del Dolce,
del Firenzuola. *3v. calf, 16mo.
Firenze, Broedelet, 1760.*

——————— Burlesche. *(Bound
with Ariosto, Ludovico. Satira.)*

BERTARELLI, ERNESTO.
Exculapio ride ... medicina e
medici nell' anneddotica, nell'
ironia e nella satira. *paper,
12mo. Milano, Hoepli, 1950.*

BERTINETTI, GIOVANNI, ed.
L'allegro cacciatore; storielle,
aneddoti, panzane idiozie di
caccia ... paper, 12mo. Torino,
Lattes, 1935.

BRUSONI, GIROLAMO. Nvova
scelta di sentenze, motti, e
burle d'huomini. vellum, 24mo.
Venetia, Steffano Curti, 1678.

CAMPANILE, ACHILLE. Codici
dei fidanzati. paper, 12mo.
Milano, Elmo, 1959.

CAZZAMINI MUSSI, FRANCESCO.
Lo spirito meneghino attra-
verso i tempi. paper, 12mo.
Milano, Ceschina, 1950.

CIRIBRISCOLE, FABIO, comp.
Almanacco delle facezie per
l'anno 1863. paper, 16mo.
Torino, Della Gazzetta del
Popolo, 1863.

CONTI, GIUSEPPE. Firenze
vecchia; storia - cronaca -
aneddotica - costumi (1799-
1859). buckram, 8vo. Firenze,
Bemporad, 1899.

CORNAZANO, ANTONIO. Pro-
verbii ... in facetie. paper,
12mo. Catania, Guaitolini,
1929.

CROCE, GUILIO CESARE.
Bertoldo e Bertoldino, in
appendice dialogo di Salomone
e Marcolfo. paper, 16mo.
Firenze, Felice le Monnier,
1951.

_____ Le piacevoli e
ridice ... semplicita di Bertoldino, figliuolo del gia astuto,
ed accòrto Bertoldo. paper
(boxed) 16mo. Milano, Maz-
zucchelli, 1758.

DA GIUNTA, MELCHIORRE.
Antologia epigrammatica
Italiana. buckram, 16mo.
Firenze, Felice le Monnier,
1857.

DANINOS, PIERRE. Vacanze a
tutti i costi. paper, 12mo.
Milano, Elmo, 1959.

DELL'ARCO, MARIO. Pasquino e
le pasquinate. buckram, 8vo.
Milano, Martello, n.d.

DOMENICHI, LODOVICO. Facetie,
motti, e burle, di diversi sig-
nori et persone private. vellum,
16mo. Venetia, Muschio, 1571.

_____ Same. Venetia,
Giovanni Griffio, 1576.

DOPO IL CAFFE. paper, 12mo.
Roma, Societa Editrice Laziale,
n.d.

FANCIULLI, GIUSEPPE.
L'umorismo; note di estetica
psicologica. paper, 12mo.
Firenze, "La Cultura Filoso-
fica" 1913.

FERRIGNI, MARIO. Uomo allegro
... "Yorick"; aneddoti. paper,
8vo. Roma, Formiggini, 1930.

‹FISIOLOGIA DEL RIDICOLO.
O Corso di osservazioni di una
societa di persona ridicole. 2v.
paper, 16mo. Milano, Truffi,
1834.

FRISONI, GAETANO. Dizionario
moderno genovese-italiano e
italiano-genovese. paper,
12mo. Genova, Donath, 1910.

FUMAGALLI, GIUSEPPE. Aneddoti bibliografici. paper, 8vo.
Milano, Bietti, 1939.

_____ Chi l'ha detto?
Tesoro di citazione Italiane e
straniere, di origine letteraria e
storica, ordinate e annotate ...
buckram, 12mo. Milano, Hoepli,
1958.

GALIANI, FERDINANDO. F.
Galiani e il suo secolo; aneddoti. paper, 8vo. Roma, Formiggini, 1930.

GIANERI, ENRICO. Storia della caricatura. *buckram, 8vo. Milano. Editrice Omina, 1959.*

GUERRINI, OLINDO. Bibliografia per ridere. *paper, 16mo. Roma, Sommaruga, 1883.*

GUIDICI, CESARE. Le pazzie per far cervello, consigli politici, e morali. *paper, 16mo. Milano, Malatesta, 1709.*

GUICHARD, L., *ed.* Aneddoti, novelle e racconti. *buckram, 12mo. Paris, Librairie Vuibert, 1928. 2da edizione.*

HOEPLI, MANUALI. L'ape latina. Dizionarietto di 2948. *buckram, 16mo. Milano, Hoepli, 1955.*

———————— Cinque cento i sedici proverbi sul cavallo. *buckram, 16mo. Milano, Hoepli, 1896.*

JANDOLO, AUGUSTO. Aneddotica. *buckram, 12mo. Milano, Cescnina, 1949.*

JARRO *see* PICCINI, G.

LEVI, GUILIO A. Il comico. *paper, 8vo. Genova, Formiggini, 1913.*

LIBRO DIVERTENTE, IL; aneddoti, amenita storielle, raccolti da Nica e Zica. *paper, 8vo. n.p., n.d.*

LOZZI, CARLO. Vecchia Russia; aneddoti. *paper, 8vo. Roma, Formiggini, 1934.*

MANETTI, DANTE. Aneddoti Carducciani. *paper, 8vo. Milano, Bietti, 1939.*

MANI, GIUSEPPE. Si morira e non s'intendera nulla; ossia ultimi firzzi e facezie. *paper, 16mo. Firenze, Tipografia Rebagli, 1865.*

MARC' AURELIO I ALMANACCO DE I 4 ELEMENTI. *paper, 4to. Milano, Arti Grafichi Pizzi & Pizio, n.d.*

MARFORIO———————— Storiella antifasciste; barzellette fiorite in un ventennio di regime fascista. *paper, 24mo. Catania, "Etna" 1944.*

MASSARANI, TULLO. Storia e fisiologia dell' arte de ridere. Favola - fiaba - commedia - satira - novella, prosa e poesia umoristica. *3v. paper, 12mo. Milano, Hoepli, 1900-1902.*

MAURI, L. *de, pseud. see* SARASINO, ERNESTO.

MORANDO, F. ERNESTO. Aneddoti genovesi. *paper, 8vo. Roma, Formiggini, 1932.*

MUSSI, FRANCESCO CAZZAMINI. Aneddoti mizanesi. *paper, 8vo. Roma, Formiggini, 1932.*

———————— Meneghino ride ... (Ma non sempre) nuovi aneddoti milanesi. *paper, 8vo. Roma, Formiggini, 1937.*

NUOVISSIMA ENCICLOPEDIA DEGLI ANEDDOTI. *paper, 8vo. Milano, S.A.C.S.E., 1941.*

PALAZZI, FERNANDO. Enciclopedia degli aneddoti. *3v. boards, 8vo. Milan, Ceschina, 1946, 1950.*

———————— Il libro dei mille savi; massime, pensieri - aforismi - paradossi. *paper, 12mo. Milano, Hoepli, 1955.*

PALMAROCCHI, R. Voltaire; aneddoti. *paper, 8vo. Roma, Formiggini, 1930.*

PASQUALIGO, CRISTOFORO. Paccolta di proverbi veneti. *3v. in 1. half-calf, 16mo. Venetia, Pipografia del Commercio, 1857.*

PATRAI, GIUSEPPE. Roma sparita; figure e figurine. *paper, 8vo. Roma, Formiggini, 1932.*

PICCINI, G. Firenze umoristica;
macchiette, bizzarrie, aneddoti
fantasie, di Jarro. *boards,
12mo. Firenze, Bemporad, n.d.
Seconda edizione.*

PICCOLI GENOVESE, ALBERTO.
Il comico, l'umore e la fan-
tasia, o, Teoria del riso. *paper,
8vo. Torino, Bocca, 1926.*

PITIGRILLI, *pseud. see* SEGRE,
DINO.

PIUMATI, ALESSANDRO. Figaro
(aneddoti). *paper, 8vo. Roma,
Formiggini, 1933.*

PLEBE, ARMANDO. La teoria del
comico da Aristotele a Plut-
arco. *paper, 8vo. Torino,
Universita di Torino.*

POLIZIANO, ANGELO. Angelo
Polizianos tagebuch, 1477-
1479. *buckram, 8vo. Jena,
Diederichs, 1929. (Italian &
German.)*

PROVENZAL, DINO. Dizionario
umoristico. *paper, 12mo. Milano,
Hoepli, 1950. Terza edizione.*

PROVENZANI, ALDO. La
casermo; aneddoti. *paper, 8vo.
Roma, Formiggini, 1929.*

—————— Il cofolare domesti-
co; aneddoti. *paper, 8vo. Roma,
Formiggini, 1929.*

—————— Esculapio; aneddoti.
*paper, 8vo. Roma, Formiggini,
1929.*

—————— Il vile metallo; aneddoti. *paper, 8vo. Roma, Formiggini, 1929.*

RADICIOTTI, GIUSEPPE. Aneddoti Rossiniana autentici.
*paper, 8vo. Roma, Formiggini,
1929.*

RAGUSA, ENRICO. Filosofia
umoristica (saggi). *paper, 8vo.
Palermo "La Voce sul Mondo"
1935.*

RIDENTI, LUCIO. Vere e bene
inventate; raccolta da ridenti.
*paper, 12mo. Torino, Mulaterce
& Perrero, n.d. Seconda edizione.*

RONCATI, EMILIO. Le voci;
aforismi. *paper, 8vo. Torino,
Bocca, 1923.*

ROSA, SALVATOR. Satire. *vellum, 24mo. Amsterdam, n.p.,
1790. Terza edizione.*

SAGREDO———— Aneddotica
delle scienze. *paper, 12mo.
Milano, Hoepli, 1948.*

SALUCCI, ARTURO. Gandolin;
aneddoti. *paper, 8vo. Roma,
Formiggini, 1929.*

SALUSTRI, CARLO ALBERTO.
Pulviscolo; aneddoti Trilussi-
ani, di Trilussa. *pseud. paper,
8vo. Milan, Bietti, 1939.*

SANDRO, ALFONSO. Nuovi aneddoti teatrali. *paper, 8vo.
Roma, Formiggini, 1931.*

SARASINO, ERNESTO. L'epi-
gramma italiano del risorga-
mento delle lettere au tenpi
moderni, di L. de Mauri,
*pseud. buckram, 12mo.
Milano, Hoepli, 1908.*

—————— Flores sententiarum;
raccolta di 5000 sentenze, proverbi e motti latini. *paper,
16mo. Milano, Hoepli, 1949.*

SEGRE, DINO. Dizionaria anti-
ballistico, di Pitigrilli, *pseud.
paper, 8vo. Milano, Sonzogno,
1953.*

SHEPHERD, WILLIAM. Vita di
Poggio Bracciolini. *2v. half-
calf, 8vo. Firenze, Ricci,
1825.*

SPELTA, ANTONIO MARIA. La
saggia pazzia fonte d'alle-
grezze, madre de' piaceri,
regina de' belli homori. *vellum,
16mo. Venetia, Somasco, 1608.*

TESTONI, ALFREDO, e TREBBI, ORESTE. Aneddoti bolognesi. *paper, 8vo. Roma, Formiggini.*

TREBBI, ORESTE. Aneddoti teatrali. *paper, 8vo. Roma, Formiggini, 1929.*

TRILUSSA, *pseud. see* SALUSTRI, CARLO ALBERTO.

UGHETTI, G.B. L'umorismo e la donna. *paper, 8vo. Torino, Bocca, 1926.*

VACCARO, GENNARO. Nuovissima enciclopedia degli aneddoti. *buckram, 8vo. Roma, Curcio, n.d.*

VALIGIA DELLE PIU RECENTI CORBELLERIE. *paper, 16mo. Roma, Perino, 1884.*

VINASSA, PAOLO. Aneddoti universitari. *paper, 8vo. Roma, Formiggini, 1930.*


## JAPANESE

"BIRDS AND BEASTS". Painted by Priest Toba. Originals in Kozanji Temple, at Taganoo, Kyoto. *2 scrolls in wooden box.*

BOMPU KUSE MONOGARI. *paper, 12mo. Edo, 1848.*

BUNBUKU CHAGAMA. *paper, 12mo. Edo, 1928. (Reproduced in 1928 from the original edition published ca. 1716.)*

DOBASHITEI-RYUMA. Huakumenso shikatabanashi. *2v. paper, 12mo. Edo, 1842.*

DOKE YOBUN. *paper, 12mo. n.p., n.d.*

EISEI KYOIKU GAWA. *paper, 12mo. Tokyo, 1896.*

ENGLISH WITHOUT TEARS. *buckram, 12mo. Tokyo, n.d. Japanese and English.*

FURAI SANKIN, *pseud. see* HIRAGO GENNAI.

GAHON KOCHO ZUKAI. *paper, 8vo. Osaka, 1805.*

GAKUYO. Genpei Moji-E. *paper, Japanese binding. (1929 reproduction of an 18th century book.)*

HAGIWARA, FUNKHIKO. Burondi, no eigo. *buckram, 12mo. Tokyo, 1960.*

HAKUENSAI-BAIKO. Kyoka ehon otsu miyage. *paper, Japanese binding, n.p. 1919.*

HANAKURABE. Shikan hanashi sakura no maki. Rikan hanashi no maki. *2v. paper, Japanese binding. Kyoto, Soshiro Sasaki.*

HIRAGO GENNAI. Furai rokubu shi, *by* Furai Sanjin, *pseud. 4v. paper, Japanese binding, 1780.*

HOZO UKIGO LOGO. *paper, Japanese binding. Tokogo Press, 1876.*

HUMOUR BOOK. *paper, Japanese binding.*

IBARA SAIKAKU. Nippon eitaigura. *buckram, 12mo. Tokyo, Kokuseido, 1955.*

IKEBE TOEN. Tosei fuzoku gojuban uta-awase. *2v. paper, Japanese binding, 1907.*

IKKADO-HANSUI. Anasagashi kokoro no uchisoto. *paper, folding scroll. Osaka, 1830.*

ISOBE, YAICHIRO, *tr.* Musings of a Chinese vegetarian. *buckram, 16mo. Tokyo, Kanda, 1926. Japanese and English.*

JICHOSAI. Saiji Meppokai. *paper, 4to. 1903.*

JUPPENSHA-IKKU. Hito no kuse tokuse chogen. *paper, Japanese binding. 1820.*

——————— Hizakurige. *43v. paper, Japanese binding. Edo, 1810, 1814. 1st and 2d series.*

——————— Mune no karakuri. *paper, Japanese binding. 1853.*

——————— Oou dochu hiza-kurige. *15v. paper, Japanese binding. Edto, 1848-1850.*

——————— Seiyo diche hiza-kurige. *30v. paper, Japanese binding. Tokyo, Bankykaku & Wanya, 1870-1874.*

——————— Zatsudan kami-kuzukago. *2v. paper, Japanese binding, 1820, 1822.*

KAKUCHU ENPU. *paper, Japanese binding. 1910-1915.*

KANWATEI-ONITAKE. Ykiyo monomane kyukancho nihen. *3v. paper, Japanese binding. Osaka, 1809.*

KAZO BON LUKI MOZI. *6v. paper, Japanese binding.*

KEIHITSU TOBAGURAMA. *3v. paper, Japanese binding. Osaka. (Reprint of 1720 edition.)*

KINJUDO. Kokkei suizoku-kan. *paper, Japanese binding. Tokyo, 1900.*

KITAZARA, RAKUTEN. Deko chame mang shu. *cloth, in slip case. 4to. Tokyo, 1931.*

——————— Kingen keiku senryu manga shu. *cloth, in slip case. 4to. Tokyo, 1931.*

——————— Meiji taisho showa shakai manga shu. *cloth, in slip case, 4to. Tokyo, 1931.*

——————— Onna hyakutai ero guro manga shu. *cloth, in slip case, 4to. Tokyo, 1931.*

——————— Sekai buru puro manga shu. *cloth, in slip case, 4to. Tokyo, Atoriesha, 1930.*

——————— Sekai gaikosen manga shu. *cloth, in slip case. 4to. Tokyo, Atoriesha, 1930.*

——————— Setai Jinshin fuzoku manga shu. *cloth, in slip case. 4to. Tokyo, 1930.*

KOSHIGAYA-SANJIN. Doke hya-kunin isshu, yamiyo no tsubute. *paper, Japanese binding. Edo, 1833.*

KYOKA EHON OTSU MIYAGE. *paper, Japanese binding. Otsu, 1919. (Reprinted from original edition of 1780, issued in Osaka by Naniwa Shorin.)*

KYOKUNTEI-SHUJIN. Daigaku shoku. *paper, Japanese binding. n.p. n.d.*

KYOSAI. Kyosai gafu. *paper, Japanese binding. (Reprint of the original edition of 1860).*

MOKOKO LUMA HYSHESH. *paper, Japanese binding. Takogo Press, 1876.*

MORI, MASANAO. Hyoroku mono-gatari. *paper, Japanese binding. 1914.*

MORI, YASOTARO. Joku shushei. *buckram, 12mo. Tokyo, 1957. (Japanese and English)*

NAZO ZUKUSHI. *paper, Japanese binding. n.p. n.d.*

SANGETSUAN SHUJIN. Ikakyaku shoshin. *2v. paper, Japanese binding. 1835.*

SHIKITEI SAMBA. Meitei katagi. *3v. paper, Japanese binding. 1806.*

SHINJI ANDON. *5v. paper,*
*Japanese binding (in slip case)*
*1900-1910. (Reproduction of the*
*original edition of 1823-1829)*

TAKAYAMA, SUNPO. Eiri koku-
yaku hyakuyu kyo. *paper,*
*Japanese binding. Tokyo, 1922.*

TOBA EHON. *paper, Japanese*
*binding. n.p. n.d.*

TOBA MEIHITSU-FU. *paper,*
*Japanese binding. n.p., n.d.*

TOBAE. *paper, Japanese binding.*
*1739.*

TOBAE FUDE HYOSHI. *paper,*
*Japanese binding. 1772.*

TOBAE OOGI NO MATO. *3v.*
*paper, Japanese binding.*
*Osaka, Terada. (Reprint of the*
*1720 edition)*

TOTO JUNIKEI KYOKA SHU.
*paper, Japanese binding. 1820.*

YOSHITOSHI. Kokke chushingura.
*paper, accordion binding.*
*Tokyo, Hatsutaro Fukuda, 1897.*

YOUNG, CHIC. The English of
Blondie. *buckram, 12mo.*
*Tokyo. (In Japanese and*
*English.)*

ZOMO CAPUZE TO. *paper,*
*Japanese binding. Takogo*
*Press, 1876.*


# LATIN

AESOPUS. Fabularum Aesopi-
carum delectus. *calf, 12mo.*
*Oxioniae, E Theatro Shel-*
*doniano, 1698.*

AMPHITEATRUM SAPIENTIAE
SOCRATICAE JOCO-SERIAE,
hoc est, Encomia et commen-
taria avtorvm, qua vetervm.
*2v. in 1. calf, folio. Hanover,*
*Typis Wechelianis, Impensis*
*Denielis ac Dauidis, 1619.*

ANTIDOTUM MELANCHOLIAE
JOCO SERIUM INSPICE
VOLVE VALE. *calf, 24mo.*
*Francofurti, Joann. Bencard,*
*1668.*

ARNAUDUS, ANDREAS. Joci
And. Arnaudi, hae sterata editione mendae prioris
fablatas multa adieta plura
abiecta. *calf, 24mo. Avenioni,*
*Bramereav, 1605.*

——————— Joci. G. du V. Sena-
tus Aquensis principi. *calf,*
*24mo. Avenioni, Bramereav,*
*1600.*

AURELIUS ANTONINUS, MAR-
CUS. Vita, gesti, costumi,
discorsi, et lettere di Marco
Aurelio, imperatore, sapientis-
simo, filosofo, & oratore
eloquentissimo. *calf, 24mo.*
*Venetia, Lucio Spineda, 1619.*

BEBELIUS, HENRICUS. Facetiarum Heinrici Bebelii, poetae
ad Maximiliano laureati,
libritres a mendis repurgati &
in lucem rursus redditi.
*vellum, 16mo. Tubingae, 1570.*
*Bound with: Poggio Bracciolini.*
*Sales sev facetiae multum*
*iucundae selectae ex libro*
*Poggii Florentini.*

BRUSONIUS, LUCIUS DOMITIUS.
Facetiarum exemplorvmque,
Libri VII. *vellum, 12mo.*
*Lugduni, Antoniŭm Vicentium,*
*1560.*

——————— Same. *Lugduni,*
*Antonium Vincentium, 1562.*

CICERO, MARCUS TULLIUS.
Libri De officiis. De senectute
et De Amicitia. *buckram, 48mo.*
*Lond., Corrall, 1831.*

COMICORVM GRAECORVM
SENTENTIAE, ID EST...
*vellum, 24mo. (Paris) Henry*
*·Stevens, 1569.*

CREPUNDA POETICA SOMNIATA, a somniculosissimo omnium somniatorum somniatore nunquam somniante ... *vellum, 24mo. n.p., 1642.*

DEMOCRITUS RIDENS. sive, Campus recreationum honestarum exorcismo melancholiae. *leather, 24mo. Amsterdam, Jansonium, 1649.*

DEMOCRITUS RIDENS: sive, Narrationum riducularum centuria ... *calf, 24mo. Ulmae, Balthasar Ruhnen, 1567.*

EPIGRAMMATUM DELECTUS EX OMNIBUS TUM VETERIBUS TUM RECENTIORIBUS POETIS ACCURATE DECERPTUS... *calf, 16mo. Lond., Smith & Walford, 1689. Quarta editione.*

FACETIAE FACETIARUM, hoc est Joci-Seriorum. *vellum, 32mo. Pathopoli, Gelastinum Severum, 1645.*

FACETIARVM EPIGRAMMATICARVM CENTVRUAE SEX. *vellum, 32mo. Antverpiae, Typis Jacob Mesij, 1672.*

HADAMARIO, IOAN. Aenigma tvm libri III. Recens conscripti recognitti & aucti. *paper, 16mo. Francoforti, Christianum Egenolphum, 1545.*

HIPPOCRATIS. Aphorisimi; ad optimorum librorum fidem accurate editi. *boards, 24mo. Paris, Barolini, 1822.* (Greek and Latin on opposite pages.)

LANGIUS, JOHANN PETRUS. Democritus ridens; sive narrationum ridicularum centuria... *calf, 24mo. Ulmae, Balthasar Ruhnen, 1567.*

NUGAE VENALIS, sive, Thesaurus rideni & jocandi ad gravissimos severissimosque viros, patres melancholicorum conscriptos. *calf, 24mo. Veique, Prostant apud Neminen, 1648.*

PHAEDRUS. Phaedri Augusti Liberti Fabulae... editionem emendavit Steph. And. Phillippe. *tree calf, 16mo. Lutetiae Parisiorum, Typis Josephi Barbou, 1754.*

——————— Phaedri. Aug. Liberti Fabularum Aesioparum, Libri V. Notis doctorum selectibus novisque passim ... Tho. Johnson. *calf, 16mo. Londini, Harper, 1701.*

——————— Same. Interpretatione & notis illustravit Petrus Danet. *calf, 12mo. Londini, Nicholson & Sprint, 1707.*

——————— Same. Cum novo commentario Petri Burmanni. *calf, 4to. Leidae, S. Luchtmans, 1727.*

PINCIER, JOHANN. Aenigmatvm libri tres, com solutionibus. *calf, 24mo. Hague, A. Vlacq, 1655.*

POGGIO-BRACCIOLINI. Facetiarum liber. *calf, 24mo. Cracoviae, 1612.*

——————— Facetiarum libellus unicus... *2v. paper, 24mo. Londini, 1798.*

——————— Sales sev facetiae multum iucundae selectae .. *(Bound with: Bebelius, Henricus. Facetiarum... q.v.)*

PRAXIS IOCANDI, hoc est iocorvm, sive, Facetiarvm in conversationibvs hominvm... *calf, 16mo. Fancofurti, J. Spiessij, 1602.*

REGIUS, HENRICUS. Philosophia
naturalis. *calf, 8vo. Amster-
dami, Elzevir, 1661.*

RHETORVM COLLEGII S.
ADRIANI oppidi gerardimonti
in Flandria; poesis anagram-
matica sub Quintino Ovretir
insvlensi monasterii eivsdem
S. Adriani. *calf, 16mo. Antverpiae, Petrum Bellerum,
1651.*

SCHREGER, ODILO. Studiosus
jovialis, seu auxilia ad
jocose, & honeste discurrendum.
.. *calf, 12mo. Pedeponti, J.
Gastl, 1766.*

SELECTA EPIGRAMMATA EX
FLORILEGIO ET ALIA
QVAEDAM EX VETERIBVS
POETIS COMICIS POTISSI-
MUM. *vellum, 24mo. Romae,
B.Zannettum, 1608.*

SWEERTIUS, FRANCISCUS.
Epitaphia joc-seria, Latina,
Gallica, Italica, Hispanica,
Lusitanica, Belgica. *vellum,
16mo. Coloniae, Bernadum
Gualtheri, 1623.*

——————— *Same. Coloniae,
Iodocum Kalcoven, 1625.*

THESES NEC NON DISPUTATIO
EX UNIVERSA VINOSOPHIA,
quas in antiquissima ac cer-
reberrima Vinoversitate Wein-
Bieriensi humoribus ... *paper,
24mo. Tricnkhausen, 1860.*

## LATVIAN

SMITS, P. Anekdotu izlase; latvju
tautas anekdoti. *paper, 8vo.
Jana Liepina Apgads
Eslingena.*

## NORWEGIAN

AAS, EINAR K., *og* ZAPFEE,
PETER WESSEL. Vett og
uvett; stubber fra troms og
Nordland. *paper, 12mo.
Trondheim, Bruns, 1957.*

ADRESSEAVISENS TRONDER-
SKRONER. *boards, 8vo.
Trondheim, Bruns, 1956.*

BENGTSSON, GEORGE V.
Litteraere funker; aforismer,
*paper, 12mo. Ringkjobing,
Norske Landes Bogforlag,
1944.*

BENNECHE, STEEN. Glade
Sorlandhistorier. *paper,
12mo. Oslo, Erichsen, 1958.*

BO, FINN. Forbuden frukt.
*boards, 8vo. Oslo, Aschehoug,
1946.*

DAHL, THEODOR. Humor fra hav
til hei. *paper, 8vo. Stavanger,
Stabenfeldt, 1944.*

EIDEM, PAUL LORICK. Juridisk
billedbok. *paper, folio. Oslo,
Aschehoug, 1934.*

GLADE OSTFOLDHISTORIER.
*paper, 12mo. Oslo, Erichsen,
1957.*

GUDE, INGEBORG. Gamle norske
ordtak. *boards, 8vo. Oslo,
Aschehoug, 1941.*

HOLST-JENSEN, JOACHIM. Glade
Bergenhistorier. *paper, 12mo.
Oslo, Erichsen, 1957.*

KVAENNAVIKAS, MARTIN.
Kvaennavikas beste. *half-calf,
8vo. Trondheim, Bruns, 1940.*

——————— *Same. boards, 8vo.
Trondheim, Bruns, 1951.* (Not
the same as the 1940 edition.)

PROYSEN, ALF. Glade historier
fra Hedemarken og Osterdalen.
*paper, 12mo. Oslo, Erichsen,
1957.*

SELAND, HANS. Moro-stubbar.
*paper, 12mo. Oslo, Fonna
Forlag, 1950.*

# PERSIAN

CHELTUTI. *paper, 16mo. Ter-
heran, n.d.*

HAIM, S. Persian-English proverbs. *buckram, 8vo. Teheran,
1956.* (Persian and English)

HEKAYAT SHIRI ABAS DAOS.
*paper, 16mo. Teheran, n.d.*

HIDAYAT, SADIK. Vagh vagh
sahab. *buckram, 8vo.
Teheran, 1956.*

ISMAEL DAR NEW YORK. *3v.
paper, Teheran, n.d.*

JOUHA, HIS SON AND HIS
DONKEY; jokes. *paper, 8vo.
Teheran, 1948.*

KETADEH MULLAR NASR
UDIN. *paper, 8vo. Teheran,
n.d.*

KHAYAM SOHELI. *buckram,
16mo. Teheran, n.d.*

LATOYEF. *paper, 8vo. Teheran,
n.d.*

MULLAH (Mullah Naar Vadin).
*paper, 12mo. Teheran, 1954.*

NAMAGH PASH. *paper, 8vo.
Teheran, n.d.*

PLEASANTRIES OF MULLA
NASR-UD-DIN, THE. *paper,
8vo.*

PLEASANTRIES OF UBAYD
ZAKANI, THE. *boards, 24mo.
Teheran, n.d.*

UABYD ZAKANI. *boards, 8vo.
Teheran, 1955.*

VALEJEH AGA MUSTAFA.
*paper, 8vo. Teheran, 1947.*

# POLISH

NOWAK, ZDZISLAW. Humor z
wojskowego kotla. *paper,
16mo. Warszawa. Wydawnictwo
Ministerstwa Obrony Naro-
dowej, 1959.*

———————— Napoleon nosil
rapier. *paper, 16mo. Warszawa,
Wydawnictwo Ministerstwa
Obrony Narodowej, 1958.*

SAMOZWANIEC, MAGDALENA.
Tylko dla mezczyzn! *paper,
8vo. Katowice, Wydawnictwo
"Slask" 1958.*

WALENTYNOWICZ, M. Przygody
walentego pompki. *paper,
wider 12mo. Windsor, Ontario,
1941.*

WIECH————Wariackie papiery.
*paper, 8vo. Warszawa,
Spoldzielnia Wydawnicza
Czytelnik, 1957.*

———————— Wysoka eksmisjo;
50 felietonow Wiecha. *paper,
12mo. Lond., Sklad Glowny,
1945.*

# PORTUGUESE

ABREU E SOUSA, MANUEL
GUSTAVO *de.* Boas
maneiras (tratado comico de
civilidade). *paper, 12mo.
Porto, Livraria Progredior,
n.d.*

———————— Cinco a zero.
*paper, 12mo. Porto, Livraria
Progredior, n.d.*

———————— D. Payo de Ar-
raiolos. *paper, 12mo. Porto,
Livraria Progredior, n.d.*

———————— Juizo a arder (prosa
malucas). *paper, 12mo. Porto,
Livraria Progredior, n.d.*

——————— Larachomicina (bon humor injactavel). *paper, 12mo. Porto, Livraria Progredior, n.d.*

——————— Manual do perfeito cinefilo. *paper, 12mo. Porto, Livraria Progredior, n.d.*

——————— O moita calado (historia alege dum novo rico). *paper, 12mo. Porto, Livraria Progredior, n.d.*

——————— Pintado de fresco. *paper, 12mo. Porto, Livraria Progredior, n.d.*

——————— Rua da elegria (prosas bem humoradas). *paper, 12mo. Porto, Livraria Progredior, n.d.*

ARRIAGA, NOEL *de.* A menina gramofone. *paper, 32mo. Lisboa, Livraria Classica Editora, 1954.*

BAER, RENE. O homen que encontrou a felicidade. *paper, 12mo. Porto, Livraria Progredior, n.d.*

CARDOSO, NUNO CATHARINO. Cancioneiro popular portugues e brasileiro. *paper, 12mo. Lisbao, Portugal-Brasil, 1921.*

CRUZ, JORGE *da.* Henrique, o, Coxinbo. *paper, 32mo. Lisboa, Livraria Clessica Editora, 1953.*

FONTALVA, JOAO. Anedotas, e ditos de espirito de toda a gente. *paper, 12mo. Porto Lopes, n.d.*

FREITAS, IVAN. Anedotas. *paper, 16mo. Rio de Janeiro, Carneiro, n.d.*

LEAL, MORAES. Biblia da vida; thesoiro do pensamento humano. *buckram, 12mo. Lisboa, Portugal-Brasil, 1922.*

MADUREIRA, JOAQUIM. Impressoes de theatro, 1903-1904. *buckram, 8vo. Lisboa, Ferreira & Oliveria, 1905.*

NAZARE, ANIBAL e BARROS, NELSON *de.* Aventuras do Casal Inocencio. *paper, 12mo. Porto, Livraria Progredior, n.d.*

——————— Lele e Zequinha. *paper, 12mo. Porto, Livraria Progredior, n.d.*

NUNES DA PONTE, C. Salada de frutas. *paper, 12mo. Porto, Livraria Progredior, n.d.*

OLIVERIA COSME, JOSE *de.* As licoes do tonecas; dialogos humoristicos. *paper, 12mo. Lisboa, Ricardo Falcao, n.d.*

PEREIRA DE VASCONCELOS, ROBERTO. Anedotas sobre policia e justica. *paper, 4to. Rio de Janeiro, Editor Borsoi, 1953.*

ROXO, ALICE. El-rei "Tiro-Liro". *paper, 32mo. Lisboa, Livraria Classica, 1954.*

SAGUNTO, PEDRO *de.* Feira popular (prosas originals e adaptadas. *paper, 12mo. Porto, Livraria Progredior, n.d.*

VALLE, CARLOS. As miserias do fortuna (novela humoristica). *paper, 12mo. Porto, Livraria Progredior, n.d.*

——————— O noivo da Costa Rica (romance humoristico). *paper, 12mo. Porto, Livraria Progredior, n.d.*

## RUMANIAN

**SPERANTIA, TH. D.** Anecdote proaspete. *paper, 12mo. Bucuresti, Editura "Cartea Romaneasca", n.d.*

―――――― Alte anecdote populare. *paper, 12mo. Bucuresti, Editura "Cartea Romaneasca" n.d.*

―――――― Anecdote noua. *paper, 12mo. Bucuresti, Editura "Cartea Romaneasca", n.d.*

―――――― Calatorille lui enache cocolos. *paper, 12mo. Bucuresti, Editura "Cartea Romaneasca, 1924.*

―――――― Tot anecdote populare. *paper, 12mo. Bucuresti, Editura "Cartea Romeasca" n.d.*

## RUSSIAN

**NOVIEISHIE ANEKDOTY PRO NIKOLAIA II.** *paper, 12mo. Berlin, Steinitz, 1907.*

**PRIVOLENKO, M.E.** Kurskie chastushki. *boards, 8vo. Moskva, Kurskoe Knixhnoe Izdatea'stvo, 1960.*

**SOLOVJEV, LEONID.** Povest o Khodzhe Nasreddine. *boards, 8vo. Moskva, 1957.*

**TEVFIK, MECKMED.** Bu Adam. *paper, 12mo. Moskva, 1960.*

**TORDLEVSKOGO, V.A.** Anekdoty o khodzhe Nasreddyne. *buckram, 8vo. Moskva, Vostochnoy Literaturii, 1957.*

**ZOLOTAIA ZEMLIA;** skazkii, legendyi, poslovetsky, pogovorke Afeopee. *paper, 16mo. Moskva, Izdatelstvo Vostochnoy Literaturii, 1960.*

## SPANISH
### (including Catalonian)

**ACEVEDO, EVARISTO.** Enciclopedia del despiste nacional. *paper, 12mo. Madrid, Taurus, 1957.*

**AESOPUS.** Fabulas escogidas. *paper, 12mo. Barcelona, Aymami, n.d.*

**ALARCON, PEDRO ANTONIO** de. Poesias serias y humoristicas. *quarter-calf, 12mo. Madrid, Estrada, 1870.*

**ALBILLO Y MOSCATEL――――,** ed. Almanaque politicosatirico de La Filoxera para 1880. *buckram, 8vo. Madrid, Administracion, 1879.*

**ALMANAQUE ILUSTRATO HISPANO-AMERICANO,** para 1931. *paper, 12mo. Barcelona, Maucci, 1931.*

**ALMANAQUE 1958;** aunque el Bisonte se vista de seda. *paper, 12mo. Madrid, Taurus, 1957.*

**ANGELES CABALLERO, CESAR A.** Bibliografia del folklore peruano. Tomo 1. *paper, 4to. Lima, Universidad Nacional Mayor de San Carlos, 1958.*

**ANTIGUEDAD, ALFREDO.** Anecdotario. *paper, 12mo. Madrid, Libreria y Editorial Madrid, 1926.*

**ANTOLOGIA DEL HUMOR.** (1951-1952, 1953-1954-1960-1961.) *boards, 12mo. Madrid, Aguilar, 1951, 1953-1960.*

**ANTOLOGIA DEL HUMOR ESPANOL.** *paper, 12mo. Madrid, Taurus, 1957.*

**ANTOLOGIA DEL HUMOR RUSO.** *paper, 12mo. Madrid, Taurus, 1957.*

ARNAL CAVERO, PEDRO. Refranes, dichos, mazadas... en el somontano y montana oscense. *paper, 4to. Zaragoza, "Fernando el Catolico" 1953.*

AYQUALS DE IZCO, WENDESLAO. La carcajada; coleccion de lo mas selecto que en el genero jocoso han escrito nuestros antiquos poetas. *halfbuckram, 4to. Madrid, Sociedad Literaria, 1844.*

AZCONA, RAFAEL. Chistes del repelente nino Vicente. *boards, 12mo. Madrid, Taurus, 1957.*

——————— El pisito; novela de amor e inquilinato. *paper, 12mo. Madrid, Taurus, 1957.*

BARRANCO, JUAN. La gracia del pueblo; coleccion de cuentos humoristicos. *paper, 12mo. Barcelona, Maucci, 1910.*

BARREDA, JOSEPH. Barrediana erudita. *leather, 24mo. Luis de Luque Leyva y Lopez, 1749.*

BARRIOBERO Y HERRAN, E. Los viejos cuentos espanoles. *paper, 16mo. Madrid, Mundo Latino, 1930.*

BARROS, BERNARDO G. La caricatura contemporanea. *2v. paper, 12mo. Madrid, Editorial-America, n.d.*

BELDA, JOAQUIN y DEL OLMET, LUIS ANTON. Narraciones picarescas (Cuentos para adultos). *paper, 12mo. n.p., n.d.*

BERMUDEZ FRANCO, A. Album de caricaturas. *paper, 4to. Talleres, n.d.*

BIBLIOTECA DE LA RISA, por una Sociedad de Literators de Buen Humor. *2v. in 1. buckram, 12mo. Madrid, Ortigosa, 1859.*

BORRAS, JOSE., *comp.* Diccionario citador. *quarter-calf, 8vo. Barcelona, Imprenta de Indar, 1856.*

BUEN SANCHO DE ESPANA, EL; coleccion metodica. *paper, 16mo. Madrid, Villaverde, 1862.*

CAJAL, S.R. Chacharas de cafe; pensamientos, anecdotas y confidencias. *paper, 8vo. Madrid, Moya, 1920.*

CAMBA, JULIO. Ni fuh ni fah. *paper, 12mo. Madrid, Taurus, 1957.*

CAMINO CALDERON, CARLOS. Diccionario folklorico del Peru. *paper, 8vo. Lima, Compania de Impresiones y Publicidad, 1945.*

CARRASCO, CASTULO. A bordo de un telefono. *paper, 12mo. Madrid, Taurus, 1958.*

CASAL, JESUS. El chiste tecnica y analisis. *paper, 12mo. Madrid, Instituto Editorial Reus, 1950.*

CASANAL SHAKERY, ALBERTO. Baturradas; coleccion de cuentos baturros. *paper, 16mo. Zaragoza, Allur, 1901.*

CASTANYS, VALENTIN. El mundo en zapatillas. *buckram, 8vo. Barcelona, Destino, 1958.*

CASTILLO, JOSE VICENTE. La risa en Bogota. *paper, 12mo. Bogota, Talleres de Ediciones Colombia, 1919.*

CENTON, O, MISCELANEA DE HECHOS INTERESANTES, ANECDOTAS ... *paper, 24mo. Cadiz, Libreria de Feros, 1835.*

CERTAMEN HUMORISTICH-
LITERARI DE LA SOCIETAT
L'ARANYA celebrat en lo
teatro de Novetats de Barcelona, lo mati del diumenje
dia 23 de Juny del any 1878.
*buckram, 12mo. Barcelona,
Folleti de "Lo Gay Saber"
1878.*

CERVANTES SAAVEDRA,
MIGUEL. El alma de Cer-
vantes. *paper, 12mo. Caracas,
P. de H. de los Cuerpos de
Intendencia e Intervencion
Militares, 1929.*

CHISTES DE TODOS COLORES:
para quitar el mal humor a los
enojados. *4v. paper, 12mo.
Mexico, El Libro Espanol,
1960.*

CHISTES MULTICOLORES. *paper,
16mo. Mexico, "Buen Humor"
n.d.*

CHISTES PARA TODOS: los
mejores chistes de los tiempos
modernos. *paper, 12mo. Mexico,
Editorial "Olimpo" 1954.*

CHUMEZ, CHUMY. El manzano de
tres patas. *paper, 12mo. Madrid,
Taurus, 1956.*

CLARASO, NOEL. Diccionario
humoristico. *paper, 12mo. Barcelona, Jose Janes, 1951.*

——————— Enciclopedia del
humor y de la risa. *buckram,
12mo. Barcelona, Gasso, 1956.*

——————— Iconografia del
chiste. *boards, 12mo. Madrid,
Aguilar, 1956.*

CLAVE, T.A. y TORRES, J.M.
El carnaval de Barcelona en
1860. *buckram, 8vo. Barcelona,
Libreria Espanola, 1860.*

COLUCCIO, FELIZ. Diccionario
del folklore Americano. Tomo
I. A-D. *paper, 8vo. Buenos
Aies, "El Ateneo" n.d.*

——————— Folkloristas e
instituciones folkloricas del
mundo. *paper, 8vo. Buenos
Aires, "El Ateneo" n.d.*

CONFERENCIAS DESARROLL-
ADES CON MOTIVO DEL IV
CENTENARIO DEL NACIMI-
ENTO DE MIGUEL DE CER-
VANTES, 1547-1947. 5 parts.
*paper, 4to. Barcelona, Biblio-
teca Central, 1949.*

CORDOBA, ALBERTO. Burlas
veras. *paper, 12mo. Buenos
Aires, Compania Impresora
Argentina, 1935.*

COWARD, NOEL. Un espiritu
burlon; una farsa improbable in
tres actos. *paper, 12mo. Barcelona, Monigote de Papel,
1948.*

CROCE, GUILIO CESARE.
Historia de la vida, hechos y
astucias sutilismas del
rustico Bertolde. Traducida al
Castellano, por Juan Bartolome.
*buckram, 16mo. Barcelona,
Bastinos, 1877.*

CURIOSIDADES, CUENTOS,
BUFONADAS, el Quijote en
laminas, pasatiempos y con-
ocimientos utiles. *paper, 8vo.
Astorga, Fidalgo, 1907.*

DANINOS, PIERRE. La vuelta al
mundo de la risa. *boards,
small 8vo. Madrid, Taurus,
1956.*

DE LAS HERAS, DIONISIO.
Comicos y comiquillos; sem-
blanzas en verso. *boards,
12mo. Madrid, "La Propaganda"
1896.*

DEL CAMPO, JOSE LUIS F. El
humor ingles. *paper, 32mo.
Madrid, Koel, 1941.*

DIAZ DE ESCOVAR, NARCISO.
Nuevas coplas; nueva
coleccion. *paper, 12mo.
Barcelona, Bauza, n.d.*

DIAZ DEL AGUILA. Folklore Amazonico. *paper, 8vo. Lima, Libreria Juan M. Baca, 1959.*

DOCTEUR, CARLOS. Historia anecdotica de la musica y de los grandes musicos. *buckram, 8vo. Paris, Bouret, 1901.*

DUTOURD, JEAN. Pan amor y mantequilla (a la buena mantequilla). *buckram, 12mo. Madrid, Taurus, n.d.*

ENSALADILLA: ouentos, chistes, historietas, epigramas, agudezas y chascarrillos de todos los colores, olores y sabores. *paper, 12mo. Barcelona, "Eros" n.d.*

EPIGRAMAS CLASICOS. *boards, 24mo. Madrid, Hernando, 1926.*

ESCALANTE, GIL de. Nuevo diccionario. *paper, 16mo. Madrid, Compania Ibero-Americana, 1931.*

ESQUELLA DE LA TORRATXA, LA. *buckram, 4to. Barcelona, 1907.*

ESTESO, LUIS. Tonterias y chistes. *paper, 16mo. Madrid, Puerto del Sol, 1926.*

FERNANDEZ FLOREZ, WENCESLAO. De porteria a partieria. *paper, 12mo. Madrid, Taurus, 1957.*

——————— Antologia del humorismo en la literatura universal. *buckram, 8vo. Barcelona, Editorial Labor, 1957.*

FORASTER y RUIZ, RICARDO, *comp.* Fabulas famosas de todos los tiempos. *boards, 12mo. Barcelona, Mateu, n.d.*

FRANQUELO, RAMON. Risa y llanto. Tomo 1. *leather, 8vo. Malaga, Francisco Gil de Montes, 1850.*

FRIAS Y FONTANILLES, ISIDOR. Poesias, serias, festivas, humoristicas y satiricas. *quarter-calf, 12mo. Reus, Navas, 1889.*

FRIOLERA, SIMPLICIO. Colecciono, invento y arreglo estos chistes y cuentos verdosos. *paper, 12mo. Paris "El Libro Alegre" n.d.*

FRONTAURA, CARLOS. Las tiendas; dialogos humoristicos. *2v. paper, 12mo. Madrid, Fernando Fe, n.d.*

——————— Viaje comico a la exposicion de Paris. *quarter-calf, 12mo. Madrid, Administracion de el Cascabel, 1867.*

FUCHS, EDUARDO. La mujer en la caricatura. *boards, 4to. Barcelona, Graficas Delriu, n.d.*

G., A.Z. Gran floresta joco-seria. *half-buckram, 8vo. Madrid, Verges, 1836.*

GARCES DE MARCILLA, F. Fabulas, cuentos y epigramas; morales. *quarter-calf, 8vo. Madrid, Rivadeneyra, 1853.*

GARCIA ARRIETA, AGUSTIN. El espiritu de Miguel de Cervantes Saavedra, de este grande ingenio. *paper, 24mo. Madrid, Del Ojo y Gomez, 1885.*

GARCIA MERCADAL, JOSE. Antologia de humoristas espanoles del siglo I al XX. *leather, 12mo. Madrid, Aguilar, 1957.*

GASQUEZ, MANOLITO. Vulgaridades; diccionario comicosatirico. *paper, 16mo. Granada, Alveria, 1901.*

GILA, MIGUEL. Gila y sus gentes. *boards, 12mo. Madrid, Taurus, 1957.*

GOMEZ DE LA SERNA, RAMON.
El incongruente. *paper, 12mo.
Madrid, Taurus, 1957.*

GUMA, C. Mil y un pensaments.
*quarter-calf, 12mo. Barcelona,
Lopez, 1885.*

GUTIERREZ-RAVE, JOSE.
Alfonso XIII; anecdotario.
*paper, 16mo. Madrid, Graficas
Osca, 1957.*

HERCE, FELIX. Humor en com-
primidos. *paper, 12mo. Mexico,
Imprenta Europa, 1947.*

HIPPOCRATES. Aforismos de
Hypocrates, traducidos del
Griego al Latin, y de este al
Castellano. *calf, 16mo.
Madrid, Gonzalez, 1789.*

———————Aforismos de
Hipocrates. Traducidos por
Manuel Casal y Aguado.
*boards, 24mo. Madrid, Imprenta
de Repulles, 1818.*

IRABARREN, JOSE MARIA.
Retablo de curiosidades. *paper,
16mo. Pamplona, Editorial
Gomez, 1948.*

JACINTO SALA, FELIPE.
Nuevas fabulas morales e
instructivas. *quarter-calf, 8vo.
Barcelona, Bastinos, 1896.*

JARDIEL PONCELA, ENRIQUE.
Para leer mientras sube el
ascensor. *leather, 32mo.
Madrid, Aguilar, 1951.*

LACROIX, JEAN-PAUL. El
hombre que no queria ser
gangster. *paper, 12mo.
Madrid, Taurus, 1956.*

LAIGLESIA, ALVARO *de.* Un
naufrago en la sopa. *paper,
12mo. Barcelona, Planeta,
1955.*

———————Solo se mueren los
tontos. *paper, 12mo. Barcelona,
Planeta, 1955.*

LAJO, R.E., *comp.* Cuentos de
salon y de alcoba (solo para
mayores). *paper, 16mo. Mexico,
Albatros, 1950.*

———————Dichos mexicanos,
y otros. *paper, 16mo. Mexico,
Albatros, 1950.*

LARA, ANTONIO *de.* Conchito,
por Tono. *paper, 12mo. Madrid,
Taurus, 1957.*

———————Diario de un nino
tonto. *buckram, 12mo. Barcelona, Janes, 1948.*

LIACHO, LAZARO, *ed.* Anecdotario judio (folklore, humorismo y ehistes. *paper, 12mo.
Buenes Aires, Gleizer, 1939.*

LLATES, BOSSEND. Llibre de
l'humour catala; antologia
literaria i anecdotica. *buckram,
24mo. Barcelona, Editorial
Selecta, 1953.*

LLOPIS, JORGE. Las mil peores
poesias de la lengua castell-
ana. *paper, 12mo. Madrid,
Taurus, 1957.*

———————? Quiere usted ser
tonat en diez dias ? (Manuel de
la mujer moderna.) *paper,
12mo. Madrid, Taurus, 1957.*

LOPEZ HIPKISS, GUILLERMO.
200 pasatiempos, jeroglificos y
crucigramas. *paper, 12mo.
Mexico "Helios" 1953.*

LOPEZ-VALDEMORO Y DE
QUESEDA, JUAN GUILBERTO.
El chascarrillo andaluz. *paper,
4to. Madrid, Conferencias
Dadas en el Centro de Inter-
cambio Intelectual Germano-
Espanol.*

LOREN, SANTIAGO. Dialogos
con mi enfermera. *paper, 12mo.
Madrid, Taurus, 1958.*

LULL, RAMON. Proverbis de
Ramon; mil proverbis, proverbis
densenyament. *quarter-morocco,
8vo. Palma de Mallorca, Amen-
gual i Muntaner, 1928.*

MARINO, VICTOR, ed. Sia para
todo el ano. *paper, 12mo.
Mexico, "Olimpio" 1957. 6ta
edicion.*

MARTINEZ VILLERGAS, JUAN
y SATORRES, RAMOND. El
tesoro de los chistes. *quarter-
leather, 8vo. Madrid, La
Ilustracion, 1847.*

MASRIERA, ARTURO. Los
buenos Barceloneses; hombres,
costumbres y anecdotas de la
Barcelona ochocentista (1850-
1870). *buckram, 12mo. Barcelona, Poliglota, 1924.*

MELCHOR DE SANTA CRUZ.
Floresta espanola, de
apotgemas, o sentencias ...
*vellum, 24mo. Madrid, Ibarra,
1779.*

MESTRES, APELES. Cuentos
vivos. *buckram, 12mo. Barcelona, Industrias Graficas,
1918.*

_____ Epigradas. *buckram,
12mo. Barcelona, De Salvat,
1901.*

MIHURA, MIGUEL. Mis memorias.
*paper, 12mo. Madrid, Taurus,
1957.*

MIL Y UN EPIGRAMAS CATA-
LANS. *buckram, 8vo. Barcelona,
Martinez, 1878.*

MINGOTE, ANGELO ANTONIO.
Doscientos chistes. *paper, 8vo.
Madrid, Prensa Espanola, 1957.*

_____ Chistes III. *paper,
4to. Madrid, Prensa Espanola,
1958.*

_____ Historia de la gente.
*boards, folio, Madrid, Taurus,
1950.*

_____ Humor 1953-55.
*paper, 8vo. Madrid, Prensa
Espanola, 1956.*

MIQUEL Y PLANAS, R. Els cent
aforismes del bibliofil. *paper,
24mo. Barcelona, Author, 1924.*

MOLINE Y ROCA, MIGUEL.
Chistes, anecdotas y chascarr-
illos, taurinos. *paper, 12mo.
Recreao del Viajero, n.d.*

MUSEO EPIGRAMATICO, o,
Coleccion de los mas festivos
epigramas. *buckram, 4to. Barcelona, Establecimiento Tipo-
Litografico Editorial de
Easpas y Co., n.d. Nueva
edicion.*

NAT DEL SANTA CRUZ. El
tiburon. *paper, 32mo. Mexico
City, Nat del Santa Cruz, 1952.*

NEVILLE, EDGAR. Don Clorato
de potasa. *paper, 12mo. Madrid,
Taurus, 1957.*

_____ La piedrecita
angular. *paper, 12mo. Madrid,
Taurus, 1957.*

_____ Producciones Garca,
S.A. *paper, 12mo. Madrid,
Taurus, 1956.*

NUEVOS CHASCARRILLOS.
(title-page missing. n.p. n.d.)

OESTERLE, GORDON, ! Animao,
doctor ! *paper, 12mo. Madrid,
Taurus, 1957.*

_____ El doctor en el mar.
*paper, 12mo. Madrid, Taurus,
1956.*

_____ Un medico en la
famila (El doctor en su casa).
*paper, 12mo. Madrid, Taurus,
1958.*

ORAD, REMEDIOS. Matar a una
mujer no es nada facil. *paper,*
*12mo. Madrid, Taurus, 1956.*

ORTIZ DOYS, DANIEL. Chirigotas
y epigramas. *buckram, 16mo.*
*Barcelona, Lopez, 1902.*

OTEYZA, LUIS *de.* Anecdotas
picantes. *paper, 16mo. Madrid,*
*Mundo Latino, n.d.*

PAREMOLOGIA O TRATDO
EXPOSITIVO DE LOS APOT-
EGMAS PROVERBIALES.
*buckram, 12mo. Valladolid, De*
*la Viuda de Cuesta, 1889.*

PELAYO DEL CASTILLO. Eh!
Eh! riase usted. Libro comico
de chistes con algunos epigramas. *paper, 12mo. Madrid,*
*Montoya, 1883.*

PERATONER, AMANCIO. Museu
epigrammatico, o, Coleccion
de los mas festivos eipgramas.
*tree calf, 4to. Barcelona,*
*Espasa, n.d.*
——————— *Same. Madrid,*
*Duran, 1865. Nueva edicion.*

PEREZ CAPO, FELIPE. ! Ja, Ja,
Ja ! chistes, chascarrillos,
monologos, entremses, y ainda
mais. *paper, 12mo. Barcelona,*
*Maucci, n.d.*

PIN, OSCAR. El pobre de pedir
millones. *paper, 12mo. Madrid,*
*Taurus, 1956.*

POGGIO-BRACCIOLINI. Faceies
llepoles. *half-calf, 24mo.*
*Barcelona, Giro, 1910.*

PUNADITOS DE SAL. *paper,*
*12mo. Barcelona, Victor, n.d.*

QUEVEDO Y VILLEGAS,
FRANCISCO GOMEZ *de.* El
gran tacno. Visita de los
chistes. Cuento de cuentos.
Casa de los locos de amor.
*buckram, 12mo. Barcelona,*
*Biblioteca Clasica Espanola,*
*1884.*

QUIJADA JARA, SERGIO.
Canciones del ganado y
pastores. *paper, 8vo. Huancayo,*
*Talleres, 1957.*

RAMON Y CAJAL, S. Charlas de
cafe; pensamientos, anecdotas
y confidencias. *buckram, 12mo.*
*Madrid, Espasa-Calpe, 1941.*

REYES, ALBERTO. Chascarrillos
escogidos. *paper, 24mo.*
*Mexico, Herrero, 1925.*

RISA PARA TODO EL ANO 1892;
almanaque util y curioso. *paper,*
*8vo. Madrid, Eguilaz, 1891.*

ROGLAN, A. M., *ed.* El libro de la
sabiduria. *boards, 12mo. Bar-*
*celona, Seneca, 1935.*

ROURE, CONRADO. Recuerdos de
mi larga vida; costumbres,
anecdotas, acontecimientos y
sucesos acaecidos en la ciudad
de Barcelona, desde el 1850
hasta el 1900. *3v. buckram,*
*12mo. Barcelona, Garrofe, 1925.*

SAILLAND, MAURICE EDMOND.
Bromas y chistes franceses,
por Curnonsky y Bienstok.
*paper, 16mo. Mexico, "Buen*
*Humor" 1952.*

SALAS, FRANCISCO GREGORIO
*de.* Coleccion de los epigramas, y otras poesias criti-
cas, satiricas y jocosas. *calf,*
*24mo. Madrid, Repulles, 1816.*
*3ta edicion.*

SALES COMICAS, AGUDEZAS, Y
RASGOS DE IMAGINACION DE
AUTORES ESPANOLES Y
EXTRANGEROS. *paper, 32mo.*
*Valencia, Cabrerizo, 1831.*

SANCHEZ SOMOANA, JOSE.
Modismos; locuciones y
terminos mexicanos. *paper,*
*12mo. Madrid, Minuesa de los*
*Rios, 1892.*

SANCHEZ Y RUEDA, ENRIQUE.
Acertijos, enigmas, adivinas y
adivinanzas infantiles. *boards*,
*16mo. Madrid, Espinosa, 1922.*

SANDECES MINUSCULAS Y
SANDECES MAYUSCULAS,
*paper, 8vo. Toledo, Palaex,
1902.*

SANTA CRUZ DE DUENAS, MEL-
CHORDE. Floresta espanola de
apotegmas, o, Sentencias,
sabia y graciosamente dichas
de alguno espanoles. *vellum,
24mo. Madrid, Imprenta Real,
1657.*

SEPULVEDA, RICARDO.
Almanaque de el mundo comico,
para 1875. *paper, 8vo. Madrid,
Administracion, 1875.*

SILENO——————Caricaturas.
*paper, 12mo. Madrid, Calleja,
1918.*

SINTES PROS, JORGE. Diccion-
aro de maximas, pensamientos
y sentencias. *buckram, 16mo.
Barcelona, Sintes, 1954. 3ta
edicion.*

TALLANDER, ANTONI. Aforismes
& proverbis historichs &
tradicionals. *paper, 12mo.
Barcelona, Torres, n.d.*

TOMEY, JULIO VICTOR. Nuevas
cosas baturras. *paper, 12mo.
Barcelona, Maucci, n.d. 3ta
edicion.*

——————Prosica baturra.
*paper, 16mo. Barcelona,
Torrella, n.d.*

TONO *see* LARA, ANTONIO DE.

1000 REFRANES, PROVERBOS Y
ADAGIOS: sabiduria popular.
*paper, 16mo. Mexjco, "Nueva
Xochitl" 1958.*

VADORREY, VICTOR.! Que venga
la bruja ! *paper, 12mo. Madrid,
Taurus, 1957.*

VEGA, VICENTE. Diccionario
illustrado de anecdotas. *buckram, 12mo. Barcelona, Gili,
1957.*

VIADA y LLUCH, L.C. Libro de
oro de la vida. *buckram, 8vo.
Barcelona, Montaner y Simon,
1905.*

VIDA DE UN MERTO. Revista
comico-funebre de 1865... por
Cuatro Ciudadanos Importantes.
*paper, 8vo. Madrid, Duran,
1866.*

VIVAS, GONZALO. Todos los
timidos visten de gris. *paper,
12mo. Madrid, Taurus, 1956.*

WODEHOUSE, PELHAM GREN-
VILLE. El hombre con dos
pies izquierdos. *buckram,
12mo. Barcelona, Janes, 1952.*

XAUDARO, T. Chistes. 1951-
1952. *paper, 8vo. Madrid,
Prensa Espanola.*

ZAPATA, ESMERALDO GIJON.
El humor en Tirso de Molina.
*paper, 8vo. Madrid, Artes
Graficas H. de la Guardia
Civil, 1958.*


# SWEDISH

ADAMS BASTA. Andra samlingen.
*paper, folio. Stockholm, Adams
Forlag Aktiebolag, 1945.*

ANDERSEN, OSCAR. En resa
jorden runt, och andra teck-
ningar. *boards, 4to. Stockholm,
Natur och Kultur, 1955.*

ANEKDOTER OM FURST
POTEMKIN, TAURIERN.
*buckram, 16mo. Stockholm,
Haeggstrom, 1822.*

BENGTSSON, SIXTEN. "Vastgota-
Bengtssons" vastgotahistorier.
*paper, 8vo. Stockholm, Wahl-
strom & Widstrand, 1956.*

_____ Vastgota-Bengtsson
berattar; historier om urvast-
gotar. *paper, 8vo. Stockholm,
Wahlstrom & Widstrand, 1957.*

BERETNING OM DE VIDTBEK-
IENDTE MOLBOERS VISE
GIERNINGER OG TAPPRE
BEDRIVTER. *paper, 12mo.
Trikt, n.p., 1807.*

BOOK, FREDRIK. Nasreddin
Hodscha; Turkiska sager och
skamthistorier. *boards, 8vo.
Stockholm, Norsted & Soners,
1928.*

BRODER LUSTIG. Skrattkalender
innehallande, ofver tre hundra
lustiga anekdoter ... *paper,
12mo. Stockholm, Flodins,
1857.*

CAY, A.M. Menneskevennen Wilson
et moderene aeventyr. *paper,
folio. n.p., n.d.*

ENGSTROM, ALBERT. Bland
Kolingar, bonder och herreman.
*paper, 12mo. Stockholm,
Bonniers, 1948.*

_____ Fralse och ofralse.
*paper, 12mo. Stockholm,
Bonniers, 1944.*

_____ Extra tilldelning.
*paper, 12mo. Stockholm,
Bonniers, 1944.*

_____ Glad och god.
*paper, 12mo. Stockholm,
Bonniers, 1942.*

_____ Grandet och bjalken.
*paper, 12mo. Stockholm,
Bonniers, 1944.*

_____ Handlingarna i
malet. *paper, 12mo. Stockholm,
Bonniers, 1944.*

_____ Hjarterdam och
svartpetter. *paper, 12mo.
Stockholm, Bonniers, 1941.*

_____ Hundra gubbar.
*paper, 12mo. Stockholm,
Bonniers, 1948.*

_____ Kann dig sjalv!
*paper, 12mo. Stockholm,
Bonniers, 1937.*

_____ Kolingen dess
slakt och vanner; ett famil-
jealbum. *boards, folio.
Stockholm, Bonniers, 1958.*

_____ Kolingens moder
och andra medmanniskor. *paper,
12mo. Stockholm, Bonniers,
1944.*

_____ Kritiska situationer.
*paper, 12mo. Stockholm,
Bonniers, 1944.*

_____ Lasebok for svenska
folket. *paper, 12mo. Stockholm,
Bonniers, 1952.*

_____ Pampar och stack-
are. *paper, 12mo. Stockholm,
Bonniers, 1926.*

_____ Sjalv-deklaration.
*paper, 8vo. Stockholm, Bon-
niers, 1944.*

_____ Sjofolk och land-
krabbor. *paper, 12mo. Stockholm, Bonniers, 1944.*

_____ Sotblomster och
brannasslor. *paper, 12mo.
Stockholm, Bonniers, 1948.*

_____ Det starka och det
skona. *paper, 12mo. Stockholm,
Bonniers, 1944.*

_____ Svensk horisont.
*paper, 12mo. Stockholm,
Bonniers, 1941.*

_____ Svenska folket.
*paper, 12mo. Stockholm,
Bonniers, 1942.*

——————— Tokar, kloka o som
folk ar mest. *paper, 12mo.
Stockholm, Bonniers, 1947.*

——————— Trakmansar och
gyckelbockar. *paper, 12mo.
Stockholm, Bonniers, 1944.*

——————— Vettigt och ovettigt
folk. *paper, 12mo. Stockholm,
Bonniers, 1944.*

ERICSSON, GUNNAR. Jartecken
over svitjed. *paper, 8vo.
Stockholm, LT'S Forlag, 1958.*

——————— Sa var det i svitjod.
*paper, 8vo. Stockholm. LT'S
Forlag, 1958.*

——————— Stora tvetalans ar.
*paper, 8vo. Stockholm, LT'S
Forlag, 1957.*

FALSTAFF FAKIRS VITTER-
LEK. *boards, 4to. Uppsala,
Geber, 1957.*

FLODH, ELIS. Ett glas for
mycket, bachihistorier och
godtemplarkarikatyee upp-
tecknade och berattade. *paper,
8vo. Stockholm, Wahlstrom &
Widstrand, 1951.*

FOGELSTROM, P.A. Fyra ars
varldspolitik i karikatyrer,
1939-1943. *boards, 8vo. Stockholm, Varldspressens, 1943.*

GRIP, MARTIN. Glada vastgotahistorier. *paper, 8vo. Stockholm, Wahlstrom & Widstrand,
1954.*

GULLBERG, HJALMAR.
Ensamtaende bildad herre;
tragikomisk vers. *paper, 4to.
Stockholm, Nordstedt & Soners,
1942. Tredje upplagen.*

HENTZEL, ROLAND. Crazy; i
techningar och text fran OA
till Hin. *boards, small 4to.
Stockholm, Natur och Kultur,
1957.*

HUMOR DET HANDLAR OM
BILAR. *boards, 16mo. Zurich,
Diogenes, 1959.*

HUMOR DET HANDLAR OM
FISKE. *boards, 16mo. Zurich,
Diogenes, n.d.*

HUMOR DET HANDLAR OM
HUNDAR. *boards, 16mo.
Zurich, Diogenes, n.d.*

HUMOR FRAN SKANE; det basta
av de skanska humoristerna -
en kavalkad i ord och bild.
*buckram, 4to. Malmo, Bernce,
1958.*

HUMOR FRAN SMALAND: det
basta av de smalandska humoristerna - en kavalkad i ord och
bild. *buckram, 4to. Malmo,
Bernce, 1958.*

JONSSON, GABRIEL. Skane-
historier. *paper, 8vo. Stockholm, Wahlstrom & Widstrand,
1955.*

KARLSON, EWERT. Fallfrukt,
eller, Adams ode kort skapel-
seberattelse samt vorldhistoria
intill nyaste tid i ny version.
*paper, 8vo. Stockholm, LT'S
Forlag, 1955.*

LARSON, GUNNAR. Humorns
Uppsala. *paper, 12mo. Stockholm, Bonniers, 1958.*

LINDORM, PER-ERIK. Svensk
humor under 100 ar. *boards,
4to. Stockholm, Hokerberg,
1951.*

——————— Utlandsk humor i
text och bild. *boards, 4to.
Stockholm, Hokerberg, 1951.*

LOJLIGA BOKEN, DEN, en
samling af berattelser och
anekdoter. *boards, 12mo.
Stockholm, Norman, 1844.*

LUSTIGHETER, eller utwald
samling af historietter, anekdoter och infall. *paper, 16mo.*
*Norrkoping, 1818.*

MINNEN FRAN POJK-AREN,
skolan och kathedern &c, &c,
Nya original-anekdoter.
*paper, 12mo. Stockholm,*
*Nordstromska Boktryckeriet,*
*1840.*

NORDEEN, JOHN. Genom.
Skrallboms glasogon. *paper,*
*12mo. Seattle, Publications*
*Press, 1946.*

NYA GOTLANDSHISTORIER.
*paper, 8vo. Stockholm,*
*Wahlstrom & Widstrand, 1951.*

PLATEN, MAGNUS *von.* Svenska
aforismer; ett husapotek
sammanstallt. *paper, 12mo.*
*Stockholm, Wahlstrom & Wid-*
*strand, 1951.*

POLIS-ANEKDOTER. *boards,*
*24mo. Stockholm, Wallden,*
*1848.*

POLIS-ANEKDOTER. *boards,*
*24mo. Stockholm, Petersson,*
*1886.*

SKRATTPILLER OCH HUMOR-
INJEKTIONER. *paper, 8vo.*
*Goteborg, Simonson, 1960.*

SONDAGS-NISSES KRIGSALBUM,
1914-1915. *paper, folio.*
*Stockholm, Bonniers, 1915.*

STRINDBERG, AUGUST.
Anvisning att pa 60 minuter
bliva konstkannaer. "Over-
sattning". *paper, 24mo. Stock-*
*holm, Konstvarldens Forlag,*
*1943.*

SVENSK ANEKDOT-KALENDER
FOR 1882. *paper, 16mo.*
*Stockholm, Marcus, 1881.*

SVENKST SKAMTLYNNE UNDER
ETT HALVT SEKEL. *10v.*
*paper, 12mo. Stockholm,*
*Nordiska Forlaget, 1903-1916.*

TEGNER, HANS. Hans Tegner
album. *boards, 4to. Stockholm,*
*Seeling, n.d.*

WILDE, OSCAR. Mest om livet;
aforismer. *boards, 8vo. Stock-*
*holm, Nordisk Rotogravyr, 1957.*

# THAI

KUKRIT PRAMOJ. Thok-kamen,
*buckram, 8vo.*

──────── Pai Dang. *buckram,*
*12mo.*

──────── Jo Cho. *buckram,*
*12mo.*

OR-ROR-DOR. (Inside Pra Abhai
Mani.) *buckram, 12mo.*

SRI TANONCHOI. *buckram, 12mo.*

# TURKISH

BALE, MAHMUT. Baldan dam-
lalar. *boards, 8vo. Istanbul,*
*Kenan Matbaasi, 1944.*

BUYUK NASREDDIN HOCA.
*boards, 8vo. Istanbul, Maarif*
*Kitaphanesi ve Matbaasi, 1958.*

GUNEY, EFLATUN CEM. Nas-
rettin Hoca; fikralari. *paper,*
*16mo. Istanbul, Yeditepe*
*Yayinlari, 1957.*

GUR, A. REFIK. Nasreddin
Hocanin nukte mensurundan
isiklar. *paper, 8vo. Istanbul,*
*Celtut Matbaasi, 1959.*

KANIK, ORHAN VELI. Nasrettin
Hoca; hikayeleri. *paper, 12mo.*
*Istanbul, Dogan Kardes Yayin-*
*lari A.S. Basimevi, n.d.*

NASREDDIN HOCA. *paper, 8vo.*
*Istanbul, Istikbal Matbaasi,*
*1959.*

NASREDDIN HOCA, hikayeleri.
*paper, 8vo. Istanbul, Maarif
Kitaphanesi ve Matbaasi, 1958.*

SAKIR, ZIYA. Nasreddin Hoca
(senema romani). *paper, 8vo.
Istanbul, Maarif Kitaphenesi,
1956.*

UYKUSUZ, MIM. Nasreddin Hoca.
*boards, 8vo. Istanbul, Selek
Yayinevi, n.d.*

YURDATAP, S.M. Resimli Nasreddin Hoca; fikralari. *paper,
8vo. Istanbul, Ercan Matbaasi,
1958.*

## UKRAINIAN

SHCHERDUNA, A.A. Sushchiost' i
iskusstvo slovesnoii ostroty
(Kalambura). *paper, 12mo.
Kiev, Isdatel'stvo Akademii
Nayk Ukrainskoi SSR, 1958.*

## YIDDISH

AYALTI, HAHAN J. Yiddish proverbs. *buckram, 12mo. N.Y.,
Schocken, 1949. (In Yiddish
and English)*

KLEIN, MORRIS. Shabes noch'n
kugl. *buckram, 8vo. Baltimore,
Farlar "Yiddish Humor" 1947.*

OLSVANGER, IMMANUEL, *ed.*
L'Chayim! *buckram, 8vo. N.Y.,
Schocken, 1949.*

—————————— Rejte pomeranzen,
ostjudische schwanke und
erzahlungen. *buckram, 12mo.
Berlin, Schocken, 1936.*

—————————— Rosinkess mit
mandlen. Aus der volksliterature
der Ostjuden; schwanke,
erzahlungen, sprichworter und
ratsel. *paper, 8vo. Basel,
Schwizerischen Gesellschaft
fur Volkskunde, 1931.*

OSTROEPOLER, HERSCH.
Jewish jests. *buckram, 12mo.
N.Y., Star Hebrew Books, n.d.*